THE CRUELLEST OF TESTS

THE CRUELLEST OF TESTS

Roy Close

The Book Guild Ltd
Sussex, England

First published in Great Britain in 2005 by
The Book Guild Ltd
25 High Street
Lewes, East Sussex
BN7 2LU

Typesetting in Baskerville by
SetSystems Ltd, Saffron Walden, Essex

Printed in Great Britain by
Antony Rowe Ltd, Chippenham, Wiltshire

A catalogue record for this book is
available from the British Library

ISBN 1 85776 879 5

Chapter 1

1944

He relaxed a little as he felt the small aircraft straighten out at the top of its climb, and in the dim light of the interior he smiled across at his companions. The noise of the engines prevented any other form of communication. They were all seated on the floor in the narrow fuselage, the parachutes on their backs on top of their equipment, pushing them forward slightly. Between their legs lay the kitbags containing weapons, explosives and rations. They were headed, for the second time (the first having been aborted the day before just short of the target because of cloud and high winds), for their designated dropping zone in the centre of occupied France.

Major Tony Beckett, MC, of the 1st Special Air Service Regiment was in charge of a Special Forces mission charged with seeking out, arming and training two French Maquis groups which had established themselves in the centre of France amid a number of enemy installations and close to lines of communication between the north and south of the country. His mission was to organise the Maquis groups in a campaign of disruptive attacks on both and to interrupt the movement of reinforcements from the south when — and wherever — the Allied invasion of Europe occurred. They had been told that they would be parachuted into France

1

before the attack to ensure that the Maquis were supplied with the weapons and explosives they needed, to train them and prepare a coordinated plan of operations to be launched when they were given the signal.

The SAS, having returned from activity in the Western Desert, Sicily and Italy, credited by Army Command with many successful, audacious operations, were training in Scotland when one day in May he had been sent for by the Commander of Special Forces, Colonel 'Pat' Manley, DSO and bar, who 'invited' him to take charge of the AMCA mission: AMCA – Arm Maquis, Coordinate and Attack. Tony had served with Major Manley in the desert, and each had a high opinion of the other's abilities. The Strategic Operations Executive (SOE) agent in the region had been informed about AMCA and he had warned of possible friction between Maquis groups arising from their different political backgrounds and objectives, especially between the left-wing (often Communist-led) Francs-Tireurs et Partisans (FTP) and the more right-wing Armée Secrète (AS) of the Free French forces under General de Gaulle, both of whom were expected to operate after the invasion of Europe began, under the 'unifying' command of the Forces Françaises de L'Intérieur (FFI). In an emergency, SOE could be contacted under conditions of strict secrecy.

Tony Beckett was one of that generation whose early years had been dominated by the threats posed by the aggressive, expansionist policies and 'master race' pretensions of Nazi Germany and Fascist Italy. It had seemed to him and his friends at school and his colleagues in his first job that war was inevitable. They realised that the peace cobbled together after World War I had come apart and that German plans for expansion in Europe would be halted only by force. In their youthful single-mindedness they saw Neville Chamberlain's attempts to appease the dictator's demands as futile and feared that the country was being betrayed by its lack of preparedness. His reaction to it, like that of so many others, was to join one of the armed forces' reserves and get some training 'before the balloon goes up'.

At the end of 1938 he joined the Territorial Army. He had not known which arm to choose, but the recruiting sergeant insisted it should be something near his home. It was essential to attend drills regularly if he was to be properly trained. Not far from home was an RASC company in the 44th Division. A year of Friday-night training and a summer camp later, the inevitable mobilisation order came on 31st August 1939. Armed with First World War rifles and equipped with a variety of commandeered civilian lorries and trucks they began to practise their operational role with some relief, almost enthusiasm, now that the die was cast. Relief was mixed with frustration at the evidence of military unpreparedness. As the proper equipment slowly arrived they became operationally proficient.

Early in 1940 the division was ordered to France as part of the British Expeditionary Force. On the eve of their departure Tony found himself elevated to the rank of Lance Corporal and put in charge of a light-machine-gun team comprising himself and two comrades. Their role was to defend their supply column from attack by Messerschmitt fighters and Stuka bombers. For this they were issued with a 1914 Lewis gun.

His baptism of fire occurred on the 23rd May after the division had moved into Belgium following the brutal blitz-krieg by German Panzers through Holland. It was their first direct experience of the swiftly changing situation. Their rendezvous point had already been overrun and they were turned back by heavy shelling. He remembered it because he had been surprised that he felt so cool – almost cold – and found that he saw the events with great clarity unfolding on a slower-than-normal timescale – almost in slow motion.

From then on it had been a continuous but unequal and ultimately losing fight against strafing and dive bombing as the army fell back. Movement on the roads became almost impossible as crowds of terrified refugees barred the way and made easy targets for attacking aircraft. Uncertainty, rumour and continual change of rendezvous was the environment in which they worked as the division, in common with the rest of the Expeditionary Force, was day by day beaten back. After one fierce attack on their convoy when they had been brought to a standstill they heard that the Panzers had broken through. They were told to wreck their vehicles and 'make for Dunkirk'. Picking their way across country, avoiding a section of enemy tanks on the way, they reached Dunkirk a couple of days later, and then spent three days under repeated aerial assault on the vulnerable beach. Finally they had been taken off by a minesweeper under shell-fire and aerial bombing, from the port's damaged mole.

Although he had been part of it he had not understood the enormity of the rout and evacuation until later. When he had, he shared the anger and feeling of shame at having taken part in the biggest defeat the British Army had ever suffered. After the depleted division had been re-formed, he had been commissioned and joined a unit that was sent to the Middle East. There he had heard the call for volunteers to carry out raids behind the German lines in the Western Desert. He had joined the unit that became the 1st Special Air Service, just after the first disastrous parachuted raid in force on Rommel's lines of communication. Lessons were being learned and the new tactic of raids in depth by small groups guided by the Long Range Desert Group was being developed.

The dispatcher, who looked as if he had fallen asleep, looked at his watch and went forward to speak to the pilot. Returning, he shouted above the noise of the engines, "Over the other side. Flak and enemy-aircraft territory. Hold on to everything in case we have to take evasive action." He settled back in his corner and put on a safety strap. Tony looked across at 'Larry' Lawrence and 'Ginger' Turner and raised his eyebrows. They nodded their reply. Yes, they had heard.

It was a small but experienced team he was leading. At the second briefing by Pat Manley he had been told that he could choose his colleagues himself. The only proviso was that they had to be experienced, resourceful and able to work as a team. Notices asking for volunteers for 'Special Duties' had appeared on unit noticeboards. Tony Beckett had spent several days interviewing hopeful candidates, whose motives for volunteering were often mixed, before he saw Sergeant Air Gunner Gordon Lawrence. Before the war he had worked in a bar in Paris and he had seen with growing concern, behind the curtain of fun and gaiety, the insidious desire to appease Hitler whose threats seemed dangerously close. As soon as he heard of the RAF's short-term-commission scheme to expand the air force he had returned to England and joined up. He had hoped to become a pilot, but his unexpected facility in handling the new drum-fed twin Vickers guns marked him out as an air gunner. He became a highly successful 'tail-end Charlie', the envy of other crews on his station. But in 1943 his plane was shot down over central France. He had parachuted safely into a wooded region to the north-west of the Morvan region. Carefully following the procedure recommended 'in the event of landing in enemy-occupied territory', he folded his 'chute, buried it, checked his emergency rations, and moved quickly but quietly away from the area where he landed, which had been some miles from where the Stirling had crashed. He easily found a concealed position from which he could take stock of his surroundings before making another move.

He had found himself looking down on a narrow track through the woods and after a period of observation concluded that a short way up the track on the other side a group of Frenchmen were hiding in the woods. Next morning as he watched he saw someone walk up the track, make a sign to a concealed figure and turn into a gap in the trees. The one hidden by the track was armed and appeared to be on guard. He waited and watched, and when he saw the guard leaning against a tree he approached him with arms raised shouting, "*Ne tirez pas. Ne tirez pas. Je suis aviateur anglais. Aviateur anglais.*" Taken to where the group were hiding, he showed his identity discs and endured a couple of hours keen interrogation by the leader before his story was accepted. The leader was a fiercely patriotic young postman from Orléans, as were his fellow resisters. They were poorly armed but desperate to carry out sabotage against railway lines and installations. Could Larry help them? It was while staying with them that Larry saw the potential for similar small – but better-equipped and properly trained – clandestine groups to harass the enemy's lines of communication.

He had spent about three weeks with that embryonic Maquis before deciding to try to contact the 'escape chain'.

The postman knew someone in Nevers who he thought might help. Promising to see if he could get some supplies sent to them from London, Larry made contact with the chain, who after checking his identity passed him on. Within two months he was back in England – via Switzerland.

All of this, Tony learned, was the real story behind the terse official record of Sergeant Air Gunner Gordon Lawrence: 'Volunteered air crew September 1939: basic training followed by air-crew training; qualified as air gunner; operational missions in Whitleys and Wellingtons;' (My God, thought Tony, remembering his first parachute jumps though the steel 'dustbins' in the Whitleys described by the instructor as 'thousands of rivets in flight formation'.) 'promoted sergeant gunner February 1941; shot down over France 1943; French Resistance group assisted his return to active service in UK same year. Linguistic ability, almost fluent French; has some knowledge of part of occupied central France.' A typical Whitehall warrior's report, Tony thought at the time.

Suddenly the aircraft began to pitch and roll. The dispatcher wearily extricated himself from his straps and staggered forward to the cockpit again. "Patch of bad weather," he shouted as he returned. "Heavy cloud." Then he added, "Hope we can see the DZ." That last aside struck a chord of frustration in Tony's and his colleagues' minds. Not again! Surely not aborted two nights running! He got up and pulled himself forward. Tapping the pilot on the shoulder, he yelled, "You must let us out when we get there. We cannot be aborted again. Operational necessity." The pilot turned his head. "I understand, Major," he said quite calmly. "We'll do our best. But my instructions are quite clear: if the

DZ is not clearly visible, I have to return. We get into trouble if we drop you in thick forest, into rivers or into the waiting arms of the enemy. All you have to do then is get shot or become a prisoner of war. I have to face my CO. Anyway, there seems to be an open patch ahead. When we're there I'll call you up and we can look at the situation together."

Tony Beckett returned to his place on the floor of the fuselage, a grim smile of understanding hidden behind his set features. This squadron, whose duty was to fly SOE, Jedburgh and SAS troops into enemy territory, and pick up those who had to come out, had an unassailable reputation. They were well aware of the operational imperatives and courageous in their efforts to fulfil them. His thoughts of reassurance were violently interrupted. A bright flash lit up the interior as the aicraft lurched to starboard and went into a steep climb, which but for their safety straps would have sent them all sprawling. "Flak," yelled the dispatcher. "Hold on." Which, of course, was all they could do. Outside the plane, bright beams swept the sky as the searchlights tried to find them. Inside they rolled from side to side as the pilot weaved and dodged his way through the bursting flashes and puffs of smoke. "Clouds, clouds. Where are you when I want you?" they heard him shout. "Hold tight, everyone. I see some." He put the plane into a steep dive which had them all sprawling towards the nose, holding on to their safety straps and their rogue kitbags. They were like that for one of those age-long periods of seconds before the plane levelled out and the flashes outside gave way to swirling greyness and darkness. They pulled themselves up to their seated positions and exchanged nods of reassurance. The dispatcher staggered over to check safety straps and positions. "Everyone OK?" he yelled, and got his share of nods in reply. "Won't be too long now," he shouted in what he obviously thought was a comforting way.

As he looked across at his companions Tony could see that Ginger Turner, rolling his eyes up to the higher sky, didn't see it that way. Good old no-nonsense Ginger. When Colonel Manley had told him he could choose his own team, he knew immediately that if he wanted the 'chemistry' of the group to be right, one member would have to be Ginger. They had served together before and they trusted each other. He was sure that the chirpy, irrepressible East Ender would not want to pass up the opportunity to be 'in on this one'. But he did not decide to send for him until he had made the other selections – Larry Lawrence and Roddy Holmes, and the then-unknown radio operator. The 'mix' had to be right. In a small team anything short of complete understanding and trust could be disastrous. Once he had decided on Larry and Roddy he was sure that Ginger would fit in and be accepted. If he was wrong their training sessions would show up any potential flaws. They did not.

Ginger had been born on the Isle of Dogs. He was ten and his sister eight when their devoted, hard-working, luckless mother died of TB. Tony recalled from the conversations with him lying under their camouflaged Jeep, sheltering from the Libyan sun, that Ginger could not think of her without a tear rolling down his toughened cockney cheek. His father had been a sailor in the First World War and a docker afterwards, working mostly in the West Indian docks when work was available under the infamous casual-employment system of those days – but enjoying with his mates in his gang the liberal quantities of 'dockers' perks'. Young

Ginger had watched with growing disapproval, but with much filial understanding and sympathy, his father's disintegration under the strain of the loss of the only woman he had loved, and his entrapment in the trade unions' control of his working prospects in the narrow dockland life, which he could not handle and which so accelerated his decline through the effects of increasing quantities of pilfered rum.

When he was sixteen he went to Stockwell to find an aunt, his mother's sister, whom he had met but once, to persuade her to take him and his sister 'in' on the understanding that he would pay something towards their keep. He decided he could do this by 'acquiring' a barrow and selling fruit and vegetables from it. He knew in his young mind that they had to get away from the dockland and its destructive atmosphere. The following Saturday afternoon when his father returned from his dinner-time session in the Black Boy and slumped in a chair by the kitchen table, Ginger and his sister came into the room with their few clothes and toys packed in a brown-paper parcel. Quietly he said, "We're leaving, Dad." His father pulled up his lolling head and tried to focus his bloodshot eyes. He had not heard. "We're leaving, Dad. We have to get away." The man, made too old too soon by an uncaring world, frowned and screwed up his eyes as he tried to comprehend. Slowly he did, and his eyes filled with tears as he nodded his understanding. He reached out a trembling hand which Ginger grasped. "Thanks, Dad." Instead of the speech which was beyond him the old man just kept nodding. It said all that was necessary. Tony's sister nervously hurried to kiss his prickly, unshaven cheek and whisper, "Bye, Dad." They turned and left hand in hand.

Tony was touched by Ginger's willingness to confide these and other things about his background, bit by bit, sometimes out on an observation patrol in the desert, sometimes back at the operational base at Kufra. But he recognised that Ginger had had no one to listen to him – probably since his mother had died. He also recognised, in a more personal way, that life only existed between one raid and the next. The relief that one had returned from the last one, together with the inevitable uncertainty about the outcome of the next, evoked a willingness to confide: a kind of need to leave with someone some kind of recognition of some kind of life. So it was with Tony, a commissioned section leader and Ginger, ex-gunner, his patrol sergeant in the Western Desert. Ginger had paid his aunt for his and his sister's upkeep – 'well, almost paid for it', as he put it – out of the earnings from his barrow, becoming in the process a very astute costermonger.

In September 1939 he gave part of what he had to his sister and the rest to his aunt and joined the army. Put into the Royal Artillery, his division was sent to the Middle East in 1941, where he experienced the thrills and frustrations of the see-saw Desert Campaign. In 1942 he had also answered David Stirling's appeal for volunteers for his 'L' Detachment. As the new tactic was being developed, Ginger was assigned to Tony's Section. They took part in numerous raids on Rommel's airfields, deep in enemy territory, and on his convoys. Developing great confidence in each other they went on to fight together in Sicily and Italy.

The two other members of the AMCA team were not in the plane. They would, Tony hoped, be on the DZ waiting to receive them. They had dropped in three nights ago to recce the area and make initial contact with the Maquis groups. One was Roddy Holmes; the other was a French officer who had escaped from France in 1940 and who in order to protect his family had been given the *nom de guerre*

Jacques. From GHQ Liaison – the Phantoms – he was their radio link with HQ back in England. He had taken the name Jacques in honour of Colonel 'Jackie' Astor, the commanding officer of the Phantoms. Tony knew little about his background – kept from him for security reasons – other than he had been a member of a Resistance group and had escaped to England when his work for the Resistance had been compromised. But Tony had been impressed by his knowledge of resistance work – and by his firm belief that Germans occupying France could and would be driven out.

The somnolent dispatcher roused himself, looked at his watch and heaved himself up to the cockpit. Coming back he held up both hands. "About ten minutes to run-in. Ten," he repeated, shaking his outstretched hands at them. Larry and Ginger nodded. Tony waved his hand in acknowledgement. He was praying that the clouds would let them see the DZ, and that Larry Holmes and Jacques were there without trouble ready to light the lamps that would mark it.

The noise of the engines, which in such a small aircraft had at first seemed intolerable, had as he got used to them become a loud, almost comforting throbbing which suited his mood of recalling how it had all begun.

Colonel Manley made only one intervention when Tony was interviewing hopeful volunteers. He had asked Tony to interview Lieutenant Roderick Holmes from the Commandos, handing him a copy of his official record. The details were brief. Roddy was 22 at the time. 'Minor public school (boarder); parents in East Africa; father a district commissioner. Read modern history at Oxford; gave it up after first year (1939) to join army as a ranker in the Royal Engineers. Shipped into Dunkirk in mid-May 1940 with unit to prepare defences and dismantle installations. Evacuated under heavy fire, 1st June. Commissioned 1942, and transferred to Commandos. Took part in several cross-Channel raids in 1943, gathering information about the coastline and the beaches. Mentioned in dispatches for landing a French agent in Brittany by canoe from a submarine, and, when enemy patrol appeared, created a diversion at personal risk to ensure safety of agent.' It was pretty impressive. A few days later Lieutenant Roderick Holmes had arrived in Scotland. He was not as Tony had visualised him. Of medium height, slender in build and slightly stooped, he was not a commanding military figure. But his record spoke for him. Whatever he may have lacked in physique, he was well endowed with in courage and initiative. Tony was surprised also by his relaxed, unassuming attitude. It was clear that he regarded the war as a necessary evil that interrupted his education and delayed the career – teaching – he had set his mind on. But it was a deeply held conviction that Nazism and Fascism had to be defeated that persuaded him to leave Oxford before completing his degree, so as to join the army. He talked of these things quite quietly when Tony questioned him. The only emotion he displayed was when he was asked if he had enjoyed his parachute training. No, he bloody well hadn't. He thought that throwing yourself out of an aircraft in flight and relying on a bit of rayon, and the competence of some anonymous person who had folded it up, to get you down safely – never without some pain, it seemed – was the most ridiculous military activity, among many, ever invented.

Tony recalled how he had laughed at Roddy's fierce indignation at being required by the army to do such a mad thing and had immediately decided that this calm and realistic man would be a first-rate member of his team. And it was Roddy, the enthusiastic amateur photographer, who, once he had comprehended the nature of the mission, persuaded Tony to let him take his camera and a bag of films with him. 'A chance in a lifetime to get some authentic operational pictures,' he had said.

It was what Tony had assessed as a quiet determination to do, without fuss, whatever he was required to do – even the disagreeable business of jumping out of airplanes – to get the damn war over that persuaded him to send Roddy ahead to find a suitable area for them in the proximity of the Maquis groups they were required to arm and train. He sent Jacques with him in order to provide the essential communications link. The last message they had received, in code, at HQ provided the map reference of a suitable DZ and of a campsite a sufficient distance away. Now, as they were approaching their destination, he would soon know whether his judgement had been sound.

The dispatcher crawled his way over to Tony and shouted into his ear, "Better go and have a word with the driver. We're almost running in." Tony pulled himself up and made his way to where the pilot was easing the plane down into a bank of clouds. Looking over his shoulder he shouted, "Not too good, Major, but we may find a gap."

"You've got to. You must."

"I know, I know, but I can't *make* gaps. I have to find them if they're there."

The navigator, who was poring over his map and his instruments, spoke into his intercom. "Two degrees star-

14

board, boss." The pilot eased the plane over and put it into another gentle dive. Clouds swirled round them.

"Bugger, bugger." muttered Tony.

"Patience, Major. We still have a few miles to go," the pilot said. He eased it lower and they flew in silence.

"Four miles," called the navigator.

The pilot nodded. Then suddenly he yelled, "Look, a break. You may be lucky."

Peering ahead, Tony saw through the clouds the dark shape of countryside in the light of a three-quarter moon, and farther to the port side a circle of flickering fires marking the DZ. "Look, there," he yelled.

"You are in luck. I'll bring her round and make another run. Probably the only one. So be quick – and good luck."

The pilot put the plane into a steep bank that threw Tony against the fuselage as he made his way back. "Quickly. We're on. One chance." The dispatcher was unlocking the door as he shouted, "Running in. Hook up", and pointed up to where the red light, which would soon be replaced by the green, had come on. Cold air rushed into the aircraft. Tony strapped his kitbag on to his leg and hobbled to the door. He clipped the static line to the cable above his head. Larry and Ginger came behind him and did the same. Tony took a quick look out into the night and saw broken cloud swirling past and below, and from above an occasional glimpse of the moon. There were no DZ fires. They would be ahead if the pilot had got the run-in right. He turned his attention to the lights by the dispatcher's head. The green suddenly replaced the red, and at the same time the dispatcher clapped him on the back and yelled, "Go. Go", in his ear. Tony leapt into the night.

The night air struck him in the face and he felt a slight

tug on his shoulders as the static line drew the pilot 'chute clear; a shudder told him that his main 'chute was being pulled from the pack. But he was still in free fall – those dread seconds before you knew for sure whether the canopy would open. Then he felt a sharp jerk as it filled and spread. He found himself almost horizontal, gazing at the cloud-filled sky as the slipstream filled his parachute. Then he swung down until he could see the dark spread of the ground below him. Relief was tempered by the need to stop the oscillation. He was swinging like a pendulum. He lowered the kitbag on its rope as far as it would go, providing a counterweight, and pulled on the rigging lines as he peered down. The circle of fires, with thick woods on either side, was moving rapidly towards him. He prayed that Roddy and Jacques had not been compromised and that these were friendly fires. He threw a quick glance over his shoulder and was reassured by the sight of two parachutes swinging down behind him.

Suddenly the moonlit ground came rushing up to him. He pulled again on the rigging to stop the swing and to straighten up. The wind was stronger than they had thought. He saw he was going to land past the middle of the DZ area. OK for him, but it did not leave much room for the others. He felt the kitbag hit the ground in the split second he had to clap his legs together, bend his knees, put his arms either side of his head and roll onto his right side as soon as his feet hit the earth.

After a couple of near somersaults he managed to get to his feet and, hanging on to the rigging lines, ran round so that the wind would collapse the canopy. He had not seen or heard anyone, but at least no one was firing at him, so presumably Roddy and Jacques were in control somewhere. He had seen Ginger land as he was trying to control his 'chute, and now he saw Larry swooping over him and going beyond the limit of the DZ. Larry's choice expletives were drowned by the sound of tree branches breaking. He cursed silently and hoped that Larry had not been hurt and hoped also that the noise had not aroused suspicion. He had punched the release catch on his harness and had started to roll up his 'chute in the required fashion when he was conscious of two dark figures running towards him. One of them spoke softly.

"Skipper, this is Roddy . . ."

"I'm glad to see you, Roddy."

"Don't worry to bury the 'chute. We'll take them up to the camp. They'll be useful. Henri here will take you to the edge of the DZ. I left Jacques up in the camp guarding the radio – and standing by it in case anything went wrong. Wait there under the trees. Fernand will collect the lanterns and put the fires out. We have to be quick. I'd better go and look for the other. Who was it?"

"Larry."

"Won't be long . . . I hope."

Another figure emerged from the shadows, pulling the inevitable beret from his head. He also spoke softly. "*Bonsoir, Commandant. Je suis Henri. Suivez moi, s'il vous plaît.*" Moving quickly, he led Tony towards Ginger. "*Portez le parachute, monsieur*," he said, and moved off towards the woods. All around, the fires and the lanterns were being extinguished. Four other figures were waiting by the edge of the woods. "*Mes camarades, Commandant; ils portent vos sacs et vos parachutes.*"

"*Bonsoir et merci,*" said Tony, nodding towards them.

The ten minutes they then had to wait, apprehensively, seemed like an hour. "*Dépêchez-vous, Lieutenant. Dépêchez. Nous avons fait trop de bruit,*" Henri muttered and then, "*Ah,*

17

voilà", and Tony saw two figures loping along the line of the trees.

"Sorry about that," said Roddy. "We had to untangle the 'chute from the trees and tidy the fallen branches."

"You hurt Larry?" asked Tony.

"No. Just a few scratches . . ."

Roddy Holmes interrupted. "Come on. We've a long way to go. Fernand?"

"*Ici, Lieutenant,*" said a hushed voice from behind Henri. Tony saw an unrecognisable figure carrying hurricane-style lamps in each hand.

Roddy turned. "You OK? Keep close – it's a bit tortuous and very dark through the woods."

Tony was momentarily worried. "Half a minute, Roddy, I don't want to lose sight of those kitbags. You know what they contain. We have to keep them securely in our charge until we know how and to whom they should be distributed."

"Sorry, Tony. Yes I do know what they contain," he said, and, turning, he called in a stage whisper, "*Henri, demandez que les soldats avec les sacs viennent ici.*"

There was a shuffling in the dark and the young Maquisards with the kitbags full of weapons and explosives came up to where Roddy and Tony were standing. "*Suivez-vous le commandant,*" said Roddy. Tony turned to Ginger and Larry. "Keep an eye on them."

With that they plunged into the trees. If they were following a track, Tony could not discern it in the dark. And they were climbing all the time. After a while they crossed a narrow road into more woods, still climbing. Tony pitied those who were carrying the 'chutes and the kitbags. It was a tough climb. He could not tell how long it was before he detected by the change in the night light that they might have emerged into a bit of a clearing. He was right. Ahead

18

of Roddy two figures armed with what looked in the dark like shotguns emerged from the trees and demanded softly, "*Qui va là?*"

"Roderick."

"*Bonsoir, Lieutenant. Tout va bien.*"

Roddy led them into the woods the other side of the clearing.

"Mind the slope," said Roddy Holmes over his shoulder. Even in the darkness Tony Beckett could see in a hollow a small area with signs of habitation. Two parachutes hung from the boughs of two trees, making two reasonably sized tents. A figure came forward from the trees, slipping his .45 into its holster. "*Bienvenue, Commandant. Ici Jacques.*"

"*Bonsoir, Jacques. Comment ça va?*"

"*Ça va bien, merci.* Shall I send the 'arrived safely' signal now?"

"Yes, there's no time restriction on that kind of message. Go ahead."

Roddy relieved himself of the pack he was carrying. Turning to Henri, he told him they should pile the kitbags and the parachutes between the two 'tents' before he and his comrades could return to their camp.

"This is home, Tony until you decide otherwise. As you instructed we have kept clear of the Maquis camps, at least until we can assess their security. We are about midway between Maquis François and Maquis Léon. They provide me with guards for this hideout, as you saw. They're not very well trained, but like them all they are enthusiastic, and we do need that kind of help. I told François and Léon that I would take you over to see them tomorrow morning. It's a double journey for you, and there was the alternative of calling them here for a meeting. But I decided against it for two reasons. It's unwise to have too many people tramping

19

their way to this hideout. And I thought you should take an early opportunity to see their locations. Is that OK? If not, there's time to do it differently."

Tony smiled, partly in appreciation of Roddy Holmes's thoughtfulness and efficiency, but also in appreciation of Colonel Manley's judgement in recommending Roddy to him. Sound judgement. "That's fine, Roddy. We'll visit them in the morning. Meanwhile let's fix up our 'chutes. I don't know what you've organised for nosh. There are a few choices in the kitbags if you are stuck, but more important you'll find some booze. Let's toast the arrival of the AMCA team."

"Good idea, skipper." said Ginger extracting a bottle of Scotch and a couple of mugs from one of the bags. They sat on the ground, leaning on the bags.

"Roddy, tell me about your contact with the Maquis groups."

"Well, we are about the same distance from each of their camps. About a mile either way. The covered approach to each takes longer. Maquis François is north-west of us; Maquis Léon, to the south-east. They are both in good wooded locations on hills. From our perimeter on either side we can see where they are. To my untrained eye Maquis Léon has the slightly better position. They have a more commanding view and a good escape hatch down a wooded gulley. The François camp is not bad, but on a lower slope and a less-well-covered escape hatch. I have not had much time to talk to them except to confirm that we have come to help arm and train them in order to carry out some special operations. As arranged, François and a few of his men met Jacques and me when we dropped in. When I mentioned that we came to work with two Maquis groups, François

20

confessed that he and Léon had made little contact with each other. Léon was already *in situ* when François and his core group moved in from the north, but for a few days he did not know they were there . . ."

"Which probably means that Maquis Léon are good at concealment and very cautious. That's good. What sort of chaps are they, the two commanders?"

"Very different. Almost opposites. Léon is taciturn – reserved, secretive. When I told him what he had come for he said, 'That's good. We need good weapons and explosives to do our work.' From the little I've seen of them, they seem very disciplined, but when I said we would be working with another group, he just, well . . . sort of grunted. François is by comparison an extrovert. He talks well and is enthusiastic. He wants to get on and attack the 'Boche'. As you know he and his core men are not local. He tells me he is still, cautiously, recruiting. Léon and his crew are more local – they probably know the country better, and seem suspicious of intruders."

"Thanks, Roddy. All you've said shows that our briefing was fairly accurate. We were told quite a lot about the two, but until we meet them we cannot know them. You'll remember that intelligence gleaned – with difficulty – from the Free French and amended by the Regiment's SOE contacts – who seem to have quite a file on Resistance leaders – said that François – Georges François Lebrun – was an architect from Chartres who moved to Orléans when he witnessed with alarm the tightening of Occupation by the Germans, the increasing repression and the demoralisation of his countrymen. He had tried teaching there but realised that teachers were coming under close observation, with classes monitored for any teaching that smacked of criticism

21

of the Occupation or the glorification of France's history. With a few friends he made his way south to set up a Maquis group."

"And remember, too, we were told that Léon – Jean Léon Boulanger – had been a motor mechanic in Bourges and then in Nevers. He had been a member of the Communist Party since his youth, and was promoted to lead the cell in Nevers. Like Communists everywhere in France, they were the first to resist and, having been an illegal party, were well organised for the task. Léon and his group carried out minor acts of sabotage against Pétain's government in southern France. When the Germans occupied southern France in late 1942, he took his men to the woods and carried on his war against the hated enemy from there."

"Do you think Léon might be touchy that we used, on HQ advice, François to see us in?"

"That's a bloody shrewd question. Yes, I do – based on my very limited observations."

"Then I think tomorrow we shall visit Léon first. Larry, I'd like you and Ginger to come with me to Maquis Léon – Roddy will have to guide us – because I want you to be our liaison with them and be responsible for arming and training them. Ginger, it will be an opportunity for you and Léon to meet. Let's start early. Roddy, I want you to be our liaison with Maquis François and similarly to be responsible for arming and training. I'll see that you, Ginger, meet both Maquis commanders. In addition I'll get you and Jacques to organise the DZs – it may not be wise to use the same one each time, because careful as we are there are always a few telltale marks in the grass – for when we get further deliveries, and organise bringing the merchandise in, checking it and distributing it to our friends. Well, I guess that's all we can do tonight. I'll have another nip and then turn in."

"Just one thing, Tony." said Roddy. "I refused François' offer of guards for our camp once you arrived. I didn't want a stream of people coming here. Until you decide what we want and where, I thought that Larry, Ginger, Jacques and I could handle the watch . . ."

"Good of you!" said Larry.

"Who is this man? said Ginger.

Tony smiled. Things felt good. "Night, all," he said teasingly.

Next morning, Tony, Larry and Roddy set off for the Maquis Léon camp. They followed a line of trees down into a gulley and then climbed up into the camp. It was as Roddy had said – well sited. At the entrance to the wood two guards halted them. They accepted Larry's name as a password and led them into a clearing. A tall lean man came forward to meet them. "*Enchanté, Commandant,*" he said politely when Larry introduced Tony and Ginger. "*Ici, s'il vous plaît,*" he said, indicating two rough benches on the grass between which was a bottle of wine. As they sat down, Tony said, "I would like to think of this as a circle rather than two benches facing each other." Léon's half smile showed that he took the point. "*D'accord, Commandant. Maintenant, prenez-vous un verre?*"

"*Avec plaisir, Capitaine.*"

Following the brief exchange of pleasantries, which from Léon's side were formal rather than warm, Tony initiated a discussion on the perils facing France following the German Occupation and the need to concentrate all Allied effort on liberating the country before invading Germany. This evoked a fierce condemnation from Léon of the pre-war French governments and of the traitors now collaborating with the enemy. The discussion, interesting in itself, enabled Tony to measure his man. He was, he judged, a sincere, disciplined, unwavering adherent to his ideology and an implacable enemy of Nazism and Fascism. He would be, probably was, a brave fighter for his cause.

Tony then got down to explaining that he and his comrades were there to help organise a coordinated campaign of attacks on German communications, and to prevent reinforcements reaching the Normandy invasion area. For this they would provide up-to-date weapons and explosives. And they would help with training. Léon listened carefully, but displayed no reaction until Tony explained that their operations would be coordinated with Maquis François within a campaign planned by himself. At this Léon showed his irritation. "*Pourquoi?*" he said. "*Ils sont les nouveaus. Les amateurs.*"

Tony responded firmly. "They will be armed and trained by us. We will not allow them to compromise these operations so vital to the Allied cause, any more than we will allow you to compromise them. Is that understood?" Léon, the realist, understood. They understood each other.

As they parted Tony said, "I will leave Lieutenant Lawrence with you to make an assessment with you of your present compliment of weapons and your requirements. He will be my liaison officer with you. You can rely on him to help you in whatever way he can and you will know he carries my full authority. You will be seeing Sergeant Turner from time to time. He will organise the airdrops and distribute the arms, and help with the training. I would be glad if you could come to our camp tomorrow morning – about eight – so that together with François we can assess the current situation and plan future operations." Léon nodded his agreement. They shook hands and Tony left the camp convinced that the dour Léon, however ideologically single-minded, was honest and could be relied on.

They moved on, past their own camp, to the other Maquis. There the reception they received was quite different. Captain François greeted them effusively. In contrast with Léon, he immediately displayed an extrovert charm. Tony and Ginger received the warm Gallic hug, while Roddy, whom he had already met, received a warm double handshake. Tony had noticed that the approach to the camp was not so well covered as Maquis Léon. The poorly armed guards were too easily seen, and the members of the Maquis were more casual. Roddy would have to put in a lot of training time quickly. But whatever the Maquis lacked in the essential disciplines of arms and security, they gained in sharing the enthusiasm of François himself and their obvious willingness to learn and to fight the enemy. It was the aggressive keenness of both Maquis that Tony later realised was his outstanding impression of his first contacts with them.

It was over the inevitable, and welcoming, *verres* that he found himself warming to this ex-architect whose office was in the shadow of the magnificent Chartres Cathedral, a patriot who so loved his country that he could not hide the shame he felt deeply over its pre-war cynicism, its defeat by the Germans, the collaboration of many of his countrymen; nor hide his determination to fight for its liberation. Tony repeated what he had told Léon about the objective of the mission; the need to arm, train properly and plan a coordinated campaign ready to support the invasion when it came. He described again the role he had given Ginger, and appointed Roddy Holmes as his liaison officer with Maquis François. The planning would begin next morning. Agreed.

As they made their way back, Tony felt confident that he had in 'Captain' François a trustworthy and enthusiastic, but untried, supporter of their cause. "You'll need to get them to tighten their discipline, Roddy, make better use of their cover and generally learn the constraints imposed when leading a clandestine life. They're keen, but green. I don't want them finishing up dead keen."

Next morning Tony greeted the two Maquis commanders amiably and then briskly conducted this first mini council of war. They sat in a circle round a makeshift table formed by the kitbags they had brought with them. He emphasised the need for greater security, especially in moving to, from and between their camps. To the obvious dislike of Captain Léon he insisted there should be no sabotage or ambush operations until they had word of the impending invasion. Meanwhile he would arrange for the delivery of weapons and explosives, and his liaison officers would assist in training. They made a mental note of numbers and skills in each of the Maquis, and assessed their requirements. They should carry out discreet reconnaissance to locate installations and critical rail and road junctions. All information would be shared at regular meetings. Each commander would appoint a second in command. It was essential that they set up reliable and secure local sources of information so that they could be aware of enemy movement and rumour in the area. Informants must be absolutely reliable. To a large extent the safety of operations – and lives – would be in their hands. It was agreed that François would establish contacts to the west, and Léon to the east because he already had informants in Nevers.

Much later Tony reflected on how well served they were in this respect by a postman, a curé, a chemist, a baker, and a midwife; all voluntarily risking torture and death for the Allied cause.

At the end of their meeting Tony obtained their reluctant agreement to provide alternately four sound, well-trained

26

men for twenty-four hours for guard duties in his camp. He then pacified their objections by distributing the Sten guns, ammunition, plastic explosive and time pencils, together with cartons of soup and reconstituted meat they had brought with them. There must be no fires; food would be cooked only by using the solidified paraffin tablets he also handed out. It was vital that commanders regularly inspected the approaches to and from their camps. There should be no sign that the woods were visited from time to time. Especially no sign from the air. Once their activity began, enemy patrols and aircraft would begin searching the area.

In the end, all these agreements were reached amicably, though not always easily or quickly. Tony was too sensitive of the hurt feelings and patriotic pride of his new colleagues to rush his fences. He was patient and sympathetic to their points of view, to which he wanted them to give full expression. But, finally, Tony believed he had, in an atmosphere of mutual understanding, managed a business-like briefing which set a disciplined approach to their task and a recognised chain of command The firm handshakes and Leon's "*C'est tout compris, Commandant. Tout compris*" justified his belief in the outcome.

A week later they received their first parachute drops of weapons in response to Jacques' coded transmissions. They were disappointed in the amount sent. They were promised more in the next available drop. But what they had gave the mission the opportunity to demonstrate, albeit without the luxury of a shooting range, the Bren gun, the Sten gun, the new .303 rifle and the anti-tank bazooka. And they demonstrated the manufacture of time bombs by putting the appropriate time pencil into plastic explosive. Their enthusiastic Maquis comrades learnt quickly and were impatient for the opportunity to go into action. Their frustration might, if unrelieved, threaten the structure of the mission and its objectives. Tony put his faith – for the time being – in getting the two commanders to organise plenty of training activity, practising their techniques of concealment and movement, and extending the range of their reconnaissance, with Roddy photographing routes and locations in order to provide better briefing material. But he prayed for early news of an invasion, which would release them from their enforced inactivity.

Two days later Jacques, who was keeping his usual dawn radio watch, woke Tony and showed him a scribbled piece of paper on which the received nonsense had been decoded: 'Allied invasion of Europe began this a.m. Commence operations immediately.' It was the 6th of June 1944.

As Allied troops and tanks stormed ashore in Normandy fighting desperately to overcome the determined resistance of the defenders and establish the essential beachheads, groups of resistance fighters and Maquis throughout regional France met, as did the AMCA mission, to finalise their assault plans.

As soon as Tony heard the news he dispatched Roddy and Larry to their Maquis groups with instructions to contact their informants immediately for any news of German troop movements, and to meet him as soon as possible. He was satisfied that his groups were now somewhat better armed – though they needed more – better trained, and eager to hit the enemy. They were ready. Now they needed targets.

Captain François and Captain Léon arrived almost together, excited and full of Gallic emotion. "*C'est vrai, Commandant? C'est sûre? Aujourd'hui?*" Tony assured them it was true. Fervent murmurs of "*Vive la France. Vivent les Alliés À la victoire*" were followed by warm handshakes all round. Tony tolerated the display with some amusement and a lot of impatience. "Good, my friends. It's good news. It is the day we've waited and prepared for, but now let us start winning the war. What news have you?"

"Yes, yes, I have news," Georges Lebrun, 'Captain François', responded excitedly. "Just yesterday evening a German convoy of about six trucks carrying what might be radar equipment, with a number of *Wehrmacht* troops – perhaps twenty – and an armoured car at front and rear, arrived in Autun. They appeared to have parked up for the night, but they asked about the road west to Nevers and to Orléans. Early this morning they were still there."

"That sounds like an ambush opportunity. Get me the maps, Ginger. We don't have much time if we're going to catch them."

They bent over the maps. "Have you done any recce along there, Roddy?"

"Not in great detail, I'm afraid, but I did take a shot of a wooded section between two bends on the Nevers–Château Chinon road. The print is in my kit. I'll fetch it."

Tony, Captain François and Roddy passed the photograph amongst themselves.

"Looks good. There's cover for our troops behind the bank on the north side . . . on the south side the ground falls away to a stream – no cover there."

"You'll have to position your bazooka man to take out the front armoured car and get him to run to the rear to take out the one there. Then, François, it's up to your men to deal with the rest. What fighting strength are you?"

"Eighteen."

"Sounds like a fair fight . . ."

"Commandant." It was 'Captain' Léon, Jean Boulanger who interrupted. "Perhaps, Commandant, remembering Maquis Léon's experience it would be better if . . ."

Tony knew what he was going to suggest. "Thank you, Léon, but this one is for François. His information; his side of our territory." Leon looked aggrieved, but nodded his acceptance of the situation.

"Roddy, François, go and brief your men. We have to be quick. Roddy, you'll have to lead us to the location. I'll meet you at the exit from the François camp."

As Roddy Holmes and Georges François Lebrun turned to go down the tree-lined exit they turned as they heard a shout. "*Bon chance, François. Bon Chance.*" François raised an arm in salute to Léon. And as Tony picked up the .300 carbine he had brought with him, to follow them, he nodded his head in approval to Léon.

At the exit to camp François, the group, led by Roddy, ran alongside the bushes at the edge of the field nearest to the road. Quickly posting lookouts, they crossed the road and again followed the edge of the fields until by a zigzag route they reached the Nevers–Château Chinon road. They ran beside it under the edge of a wood until they reached, as in the photo, the double bend with a bank on one side and a slope running down to a stream on the other. A line of trees and bushes running from the concealing bank on the north side provided the withdrawal cover away from their camp. Always a good idea in the event of pursuit, even if it meant a long detour back.

François put a lookout on the bend in the direction of Autun, then ran along the bank, placing his men in their firing positions, and positioned himself by the second bend with the man carrying the all-important armoured-car-stopping bazooka. Roddy took a position behind the bank close to where they would all have to scramble up to the 'safe' withdrawal line.

They had scarcely settled into position before Tony heard

the distinctive sound of German motorcycles and the deeper sound of moving vehicles. There were outriders in the van of the column; would the Maquis let them through so that they could concentrate on the main convoy, thought Tony? As he watched, the lookout by the bend, in the shelter of the trees, was pumping his rifle up and down above his head before dropping low in the undergrowth.

Two German outriders came sedately into sight and proceeded past the concealed Maquisards. It seemed an age before they disappeared round the far bend, by which time the leading armoured car, followed by a lorry full of *Wehrmacht* soldiers and other covered lorries, had entered the ambush zone. Timing, thought Tony, is now vital. They had to stop the armoured car before it too disappeared.

As it got nearer to the bend Tony became anxious. Then the muzzle of the bazooka and the head of the young Maquisard in charge, with François beside him, appeared above the bank. Tony uttered a sigh of relief as he saw Francois tap the man on the shoulder. A flash from behind the gun was followed by a bright flame from the front of the armoured car as the projectile smashed into the engine, sending the vehicle out of control off the road and down towards the stream. The hatch and the back door were flung open as the occupants leapt out and after a quick look round scrambled up the slope to the road.

At the same time the vehicle behind stopped and German infantry jumped down, shouting, gesticulating and pointing in different directions. The half who had sat facing the stream did not see what had happened; the other half did. Those helpful minutes of confusion allowed François and his gunner to run, bending low behind the bank, towards the tail of the convoy. The troops in the penultimate vehicle were already leaping out and gazing forward to see what had happened, by which time François had reloaded the bazooka and with a flash and a roar the armour-piercing shell smashed into the body of the vehicle, swinging it across the road. He could hear cries and screams from inside, but no one emerged.

By this time the well-drilled German soldiers, now certain from which direction they were threatened, threw themselves flat under their vehicles and began firing towards the bank on the north side of the road. But they were exposed, and the fire of the Maquis, at first too rapid and indiscriminate but gradually more disciplined, took its toll.

One or two of the soldiers, obviously well trained and probably experienced, crawled out from their cover and tried to charge the bank. Their courage did them and their comrades no good at all. They were cut down as they ran. François, guiding the all-important bazooka operator, was moving from one vantage point to the other in the shelter of the bank to fire at the covered vehicles, disabling them one by one.

It was a relatively short but critical battle. For the Maquis, the shorter the better, before the sound of battle alerted German forces elsewhere. Thanks to the choice of ambush site, the Germans were fatally exposed; if they fell back to the stream they were even more in the open. Their dead and wounded lay right across the road and beneath their trucks.

Tony saw Roddy signal to François, who shouted an order. Two by two the Maquis ran along the back of the bank to the cut in the trees that formed their withdrawal route. They had performed as a well-disciplined force. As they withdrew, Roddy kept up covering fire with his Bren. Then, to Tony's surprise, before joining the withdrawal he stood up and took two or three pictures of the destruction and carnage which in a short space of time the poorly armed, inexperienced volunteer resisters had wrought on the enemy. His relief at the successful outcome was elevated by his feelings of pride in them.

As the opposition fire ceased, the remaining able-bodied Germans cautiously looked round then hauled themselves to their feet and turned their attention to their fallen comrades. Some they turned over were beyond assistance, but others needed medical help. There was no question of pursuing their attackers. Before he left his observation point, Tony took a tally of the damage. It was a good result from a quickly arranged ambush. He had been confident of the professionalism of Maquis Léon under the command of Jean Boulanger, but apprehensive about the new, untried Maquis François. Their first showing promised well for the future.

When he arrived at the AMCA camp, having taken a very roundabout route so as not to compromise the withdrawal, François had just arrived, having led his elated comrades back to their own camp. Larry, Ginger and Léon were already there and anxious to know how it had gone. Ginger, impulsively, said, "Sounded like a good party, skip. Was it?"

Tony stretched out his hand to 'Captain' François. "Well done, Captain" he said, and, turning to the others, added "Maquis François and Roddy have just done a good one: two armoured cars destroyed, four vehicles out of action, about ten enemy dead or wounded. No home casualties."

"Great."

"Well done."

"*Felicitations, Capitaine*," said Léon more reservedly, but his eyes as he grasped François' hand were warm with some kind of Boulanger admiration.

"Good," said Tony, anxious to break the mood of self-satisfaction when there was so much more to be done. "Have we any news that could give us another target?"

"Yes," replied Léon quietly. "We have news that the petrol dump in the Forêt de Montreuillon is being added to almost daily, presumably as a source of supply to other dumps on the way to Normandy. And there is news of a rather mysterious, large, protected road convoy being prepared in Bordeaux for a route directly to Germany."

"That's important information, Léon. You are satisfied it's reliable?" Tony knew that Léon's sources were special and trustworthy, but for the sake of the others the question had to be asked.

"Quite sure, *Commandant.*"

"Good. Then there's much work to be done and we shall all be involved. Maps, please."

Chapter 2

1965

Tony Beckett, freshly back in the UK, stood looking out of the large bay window of the ground-floor flat in Gloucester Road he had borrowed from Jimmy Hardaker for his return. He watched the continuous stream of cars, buses, taxis, and the steady procession of worried-looking pedestrians unsmilingly intent on what they were about. London hasn't changed much, he thought – just busier, more traffic, more people, and – looking up to the clouds just visible above the roofs opposite – probably greyer. Of course he was prejudiced. For the last five years he had lived under clear blue skies, a round golden sun and in almost continuous heat in the measured tempo of the tropics.

With a sigh he turned away and settled back in the chair surrounded by copies of *The Times* and *Daily Telegraph* he had been searching for appointments and accommodation ads. He needed a flat. He needed a job. Should he try for a flat before trying for a job? He hadn't long to find one. Jimmy had been adamant. All Tony need do was to keep the flat clean, make a contribution to heating and lighting, and pay for his own telephone calls; but he needed it back when he returned from Hong Kong in about a month. So there was no time to lose. Perhaps he should try for the job first in case the best opportunity was out of London? A dilemma.

The trouble was, he had not made any decisions for years on where or how he should live. As security and community affairs manager for a group of large sugar estates in South America that formed a local subsidiary company of an American conglomerate, he had occupied a house on one of the estates and been looked after by a cook, a housemaid and a gardener-handyman. He had got the job on the strength of his experiences as a member of the World War II Special Forces (now some twenty years ago) and a powerful recommendation from his former commanding officer. And he had enjoyed every minute of his time there. He had been charmed by the happy disposition and friendliness of the estate workers at every level, and their keenness to learn skills and do well for their families. All he had been told about the untrustworthiness and laziness of the local population by the head-office senior executives in New York had been wrong, But as he had learnt later, the head-office knowledge of local affairs, social conditions and the shifting political landscape was scant and biased.

He had been sorry to leave and he knew that the people he had worked with – who had seen how he had made them more secure at work and much safer in their nearby villages from raids by outlawed extremists operating out of the rainforest – had been sorry to see him go. But his departure was unavoidable once he had directly opposed the policy judgement of the distant board sitting in a skyscraper on Wall Street. His contacts with local politicians, and the knowledge he had gained of the needs and hopes of the people he worked with, had convinced him of the basic sincerity of the newly elected very left-wing government. This was not the view of the company's head-office proprietors, who saw the proposals for land reform and taxation as direct threats to their existence there – and to the existence of the other expatriate companies.

He had pleaded for understanding of the necessity for

land reform and suggested that the company's position could be better safeguarded by cooperating with it. He had proposed that they set up peasant farms, with land title, on areas of the estates which, because of improving productivity, were no longer essential to them. And he had argued that by helping the government to succeed in that vital part of its programme, they would be helping to deny the extremist opposition the support they would get if it failed. But this was too radical for Wall Street, who regarded it as betrayal and sedition. He had flown to New York to argue his case, but his fate had been sealed before he arrived. They did not want to discuss 'this nonsense': he must arrange to remove his belongings and leave the country before the month's end. They were still 'negotiating' about the compensation he should get for having his contract terminated.

Though it was no good dwelling on the past, he could not easily forget his unfulfilled hopes. But the hard truth was, he now faced an uncertain future, and he turned again to the papers. He scanned the news as he searched for the ads. The balance of payments was a cause of concern. Another study of productivity in British factories showed how the country was falling behind its international competitors. Well, there were a couple of items that made him feel at home again! He paused to read more thoroughly the reports from Paris. Following the recent demonstrations and general strike, there was talk of a reorganisation of the Gaullist Party by the astute and haughty General, ahead of a possible general election.

Poor France, a country and a people with whom he had developed a kind of exasperated love affair through his wartime experiences, and through the years he had spent in Paris afterwards as an enthusiastic but unskilled news correspondent. Fighting with the Maquis, he had grown to admire the courage of those who took the dangerous path of resistance. And he respected the deeply injured pride they bore from the shame of their defeat in 1940, and of the actions of the collaborators which they were determined to avenge. Often during those years he had reflected on the luck of the British in not being occupied by an enemy, and not having to chose between collaborating and fighting. How many would have had the strength to resist a betrayal if their loved ones were threatened with torture? How many would have taken the easier path of collaboration? He had also seen how in France the imperative of liberating their country had bridged the gulf between political beliefs and religious doctrine. Although the Communists, with their deep hatred of Nazism and Fascism and an underground organisation already in existence, were first in the field of resistance, Maquisards of the centre right, once organised, fought as determinedly and died as bravely as did the left-wingers. But the tragedy, he had observed later as a sympathetic reporter, was the speed with which the political divisions, set aside by those who fought but never forgotten by those in authority, re-emerged afterwards, often with bitter recriminations fuelled by deep anger over high-level collaboration and the activities of the Vichy Government.

With a sigh he turned the page. Halfway down a heading suddenly gripped his attention – 'Hit and Run Kills War Hero' – and the name in the opening paragraph stared up at him. 'Mr Roderick Holmes, who won the MC for his part in raids behind enemy lines as a member of Britain's Special Forces during the war, was struck down while out jogging yesterday morning by a vehicle which did not stop. This tragic end to one of . . .'

He dropped the paper. Good God! Roddy Holmes, one of the team of four he had taken on that special mission into central France. A key member with previous experience behind the lines – the 'quiet one' . . . Tony got up and stood staring out of the window again, this time blind to the traffic and the people. His mind went back to the tense and fraught days when those of his generation had grown in a few years from headstrong, careless – but not thoughtless – youths to mature, hardened and fairly skilled warriors. From September 1939 it had taken just nine months – including a month under continuous attack and a dreadful retreat to bombed and strafed beaches at Dunkirk – to transform them from that raw state into battle-tried soldiers wise beyond their years in the ways of war, though in little else. That and subsequent experiences in North Africa, France, Holland and Germany, involving several periods of intensive action between the boredom, had forged him into . . . into what? A mature, skilled guerilla fighter? Useful only in special and now rare circumstances! Perhaps. But it had also left him with the indelible experience of an unforgettable and undying comradeship.

Tony Beckett grunted as he freed himself from this introspection, picked up the paper again and read on. 'Mr Holmes's widow, Jennifer, was distraught and unable to explain how the accident could have happened. "Roddy was always so careful," she said, sobbing. "He has jogged at about that time for ages. He always wore a luminous belt and jogged facing the oncoming traffic, yet he was run down from the back. How could that be?" The police are pursuing their inquiries.'

Jennifer, poor Jenny. He remembered meeting her for the first time in 1943. He and Roddy had travelled down to London together from Scotland, where they and their other comrades had completed part of the training for that special mission behind the lines in France. The bonds of mutual respect and friendship already in the forge, they were due for another stage somewhere in Lincolnshire after a bit of leave. Jenny, looking so young, smart and eager in her Fany uniform, had been there to meet Roddy at King's Cross. They had found a pub and lowered, a few drinks before going their separate ways. He remembered coming to the conclusion that Jenny was an alert and exceedingly understanding young lady who obviously adored Roddy, so different in temperament from Celia, whom he had met when on leave from North Africa in 1943 and whose vivacious and unsettled charm must have been a great asset on the RAF fighter stations where she served as a member of the Women's Auxiliary Air Force, and which had haunted him ever since.

He must speak to Jenny. His address book was on the desk. Communication between them all had lapsed into the uninformative summary of news scribbled round the edges of Christmas cards. This was going to be very different. Nervously, he dialled. A soft voice answered, repeating the number.

"Er . . . Mrs Holmes? Jenny?"

"Yes. Yes. Who is that?"

"Jenny, it's Tony, Tony Beckett."

"Tony? Tony, what on earth . . .? Where are you?"

"I got back from South America last week. I was looking through the paper and saw the dreadful news about poor Roddy. Jenny, I'm so sorry . . . such a terrible, tragic accident . . ." He heard a choked sigh. "Are the police anywhere near catching the bastard that did it? I wish I could catch him . . . Roddy was such a fine man. Sincere, deeply thoughtful and caring, and he played such a key part on the old mission . . ."

"I know. He often spoke about you and the others, and

some of the things you all did – when I could force it from him – not much about himself, of course. You know what he was like. You have all remained such good friends, even though regular contact has not been possible. But Tony, I just don't understand it. He was always so careful. He always wore a luminous belt and ran facing the oncoming traffic, but he was . . ." – another strangled sob – "he was hit from behind. The police are inclined to blame it on a drunk. I suppose it's the only explanation, but there must be a trace of . . . of . . . it . . . on . . . a car somewhere . . ."

Her voice faded. Tony could feel her agony. He paused. Then, "Jenny," he said. "Have you heard from any of the others?"

"Oh yes, Ginger and Larry both phoned earlier. Larry thought you were on the way back, but didn't know when. They are both coming to the funeral. It will be next Tuesday at twelve noon at St Mary's in the village here. Oh, and Marguerite, the CO's widow – you remember – was kind enough to phone. Wonderful that she should remember and think to do that. I don't suppose . . .?"

"No, not surprising really. She was a good commanding officer's wife. It's a special breed, you know . . . and Jenny . . . of course I'll be there. It will be nice to see you and the others again – though not in these circumstances."

They chatted for a few minutes longer. She had wanted to know about his time in South America, but he sensed it was – understandably in the circumstances – a polite rather than an interested enquiry. So, after a few general comments he promised more news at a later time and rang off.

For a while he sat staring at the wall opposite. "It will be nice to see you and the others again," he had said. Roddy, Larry, Ginger and Jacques had been a team he had been proud to fight with; of course it would be wonderful to see

41

them again, even though the circumstances would be sad. And there were two others he would dearly like to see again: the two Maquis commanders: Georges Lebrun, 'Captain François', and Jean Boulanger, 'Captain Léon'. In retrospect it had always surprised him how quickly the two groups, so different in background and political philosophy, had welded together under the guidance of his team into a very enthusiastic and effective fighting force.

He thought of them frequently but had not been able to keep in close touch. He knew Georges Lebrun had returned to Chartres and architecture. During the time he was in Paris reporting on the stresses of post-liberation France, the political tensions and the frustrations of former Resistance groups at the delay in bringing collaborators to justice, they had met on a few occasions. Tony had found Georges' views on the turbulence that lay under the surface of post-war euphoria a helpful reflection of French opinion. The war may be over, he had said, but the conflict within the soul of proud France continues and will influence her actions sometimes for good, sometimes for bad, for a long time to come. Marianne, he said, has been deeply hurt. Jean Boulanger, on the other hand, had disappeared from his view. He recalled his surprise when shortly after it became clear that the mission's task was virtually finished, Jean had come to him to announce that he was withdrawing his Maquis "to another part, some way from here".

Once the Allied invasion had begun the two Maquis groups, better armed and trained, embarked on the coordinated strategy required by Allied Command and concentrated their attention on German formations which might have reinforced hard-pressed comrades in Normandy. They had ambushed German convoys, sabotaged installations, provided the Allied Command with information about troop dispositions and identified targets for the attention of the RAF. Their job was not done until Paris and Brussels were liberated following the breakout from the Normandy bocage country and General Patten had delivered his 'right hook' to the south. The remnants of the German Army from the centre and south of France – capable still – fled, harassed by the Maquis, north-east through the Belfort Gap into the Fatherland. Tony and his team were awaiting orders as to how they and the Maquis groups were to be deployed when Jean Boulanger had sprung his surprise. He would have to withdraw his Maquis to another location "some way away". He would not say where, nor would he explain the reason for the sudden decision. Clearly it was not an instruction from the Free French Forces command in London.

Tony could not forbid the move, but he pleaded with Jean not to cause a problem after their successful collaboration in fighting the common enemy, the comradeship they had forged, and the hardship and losses they had shared. "What about the hospital?" he had asked. Earlier, Jean had been wounded in the chest and the leg. He had been treated by the Maquis doctor operating in the woods in makeshift circumstances, and it had always been the intention to get him to a proper hospital as soon as they could. But Jean was adamant. "We must go. *Il faut.*" The more they argued about it, the more Tony felt that Jean was embarrassed and would have liked to apologise. He could press him no further.

In the end they parted amicably as comrades who had done much together in a common cause should. Without rancour and with shared memories they shook hands and embraced warmly. They admired each other and had established a good mutual understanding. Tony now realised that Jean's instructions had come from another source, and were a discomforting hint of France's future political difficulties.

When early the following morning he walked the five kilo-metres through the woods and across the valley, enjoying the half-forgotten tranquillity of the scenery and his own lack of tension, to thank the members of Jean's group and bid them farewell, he found the camp deserted. The area was clean and as much restored as possible, but quiet and empty.

Over the weekend Tony tried to resume his search for a home and work, but could not concentrate. The shock of Roddy's death in such tragic circumstances left him angry and frustrated that he could not avenge his brave and selfless friend on the careless bastard who had killed him. And more memories of those adventurous weeks behind the enemy's lines in 1944, stirred up by the tragedy, now began to haunt him. He was looking forward to seeing the other members of the mission so unexpectedly, though hating the circumstances. He felt he should contact them before the funeral.

Both 'Larry' Lawrence and 'Ginger' Turner, not knowing where he was staying, were delighted to hear from him and had been as devastated as he was on reading of the tragic accident that had killed Roddy Holmes. Larry was now a senior marketing manager with a group of engineering companies, and Ginger had left the Metropolitan Police to join a security company specialising in personal security for executives travelling to 'unreliable' countries in the Middle East, Africa and South America. Both were sincerely sad for Jenny, and spoke of their memories of Roddy's quiet humour and 'unflappability' during the many crucial moments on AMCA. They agreed that after the funeral on Tuesday, and after spending time with Jenny, they would hold a private wake to bid their own farewell to a loved and admired comrade-in-arms.

Tony moved away from the telephone. The thought haunted him. On the right-hand side of a straight road . . . struck from behind . . . How the hell?!

Chapter 3

A grey sky reflected his sombre mood as he drove out of London in the middle, it seemed, of an endless column of traffic – delivery vans, private cars and bunches of omnibuses – that proceeded slowly between frequent stops. Post-war reconstruction seemed to have done little to improve the roads or relieve the congestion he remembered from five years earlier. Bromley brought some hope of a freer run and, as he settled back to enjoy the route to Sevenoaks, his mind went back to adolescent weekend pub crawls with new-found friends from the TA, revelling brashly in their growing confidence as part-time soldiers, unaware then how immature they really were. And so on into the undulating Kent and Sussex countryside of hedgerow-lined fields and woods showing signs of the new season's greenery. This same garden-like countryside had looked so beautiful and calm under the summer sun of 1940 when, after being discharged from hospital, he had returned to his unit in Kent to take part in its defence against the expected German invasion.

Across the channel, that strip of water, the first line of defence, the *Wehrmacht* and *Luftwaffe* were rampant with their successes. True, hundreds of thousands of British Allied troops had escaped, but they had had to abandon their equipment, leaving them a poorly armed and besieged garrison. Tony's unit, part of the re-formed 44th Division which had been so badly mauled in France, were stationed in Nissen huts under trees between an orchard and a hop field. Signposts had been removed from the roads, poles had been set across open fields to deter glider landings, and they busied themselves digging slit trenches in concealed positions commanding good fields of fire. They discussed defensive plans with the keen and devoted local Home Guard, and they rehearsed moving quickly to other areas where a breakthrough might occur.

Rifles, Lewis guns and ammunition began arriving from the factories, replacing those they had handed to the heroic guardsmen manning the perimeter defences of Dunkirk as he and others went through to the crowded, strafed and bombed beaches. When tommy guns and Bren guns arrived they had felt capable of repulsing any onslaught. But in the warmth of that late summer they could do nothing but watch the defence of the nation, and what they truly believed was the defence of Western civilisation, taking place tens of thousands of feet above their heads. The twisting and weaving of Hurricanes, Spitfires and Messerschmitts around formations of Heinkels, Dorniers and Stukas left patterns of thin white tracery in the blue sky, and fuselages flashed reflections of the summer sun. But the constant rattle of machine-gun fire in the heavens, the plunging, spinning, smoking aircraft – which they had cheered hoping they were 'theirs' and not 'ours' – and the occasional gently swaying, floating white parachutes marked the deadly seriousness of the duel they were powerless to enter. And every evening they huddled round the radio sets in their huts to hear the score of 'enemy aircraft destroyed', 'our planes missing' and 'our pilots safe'. It seemed impossible that it could continue with such intensity in the face of such losses. And of course it could not. Suddenly it stopped. 'Their' failure to turn up that morning signalled the failure also of Hitler's invasion strategy. His invasion force and the barges were dispersed from the French and Belgian channel ports. The belief that a muddled democracy was better than an arrogant tyranny prevailed, and the matchless beauty of the countryside through which he was driving had been preserved by matchless deeds of heroism in the air above it.

But as everyone knew, the Battle of Britain was not over then. Having failed to destroy RAF's Fighter Command and the airfields from which they operated, the *Luftwaffe* turned its attention to London and the country's other main cities in an unprecedented campaign of sustained bombing of civilian communities that had begun in Poland, Holland and Belgium. He recalled thinking that once again the armed services who were supposed to be protecting the nation from invasion were relatively safely away from the focus of the conflict. He remembered returning to his parents' house on a period of leave and being surprised at the way they, who were not combatants, had adapted their daily – and nightly – lives without fuss or complaint to the discipline of self-preservation.

"We have to have dinner early dear because we have to be down in the shelter by 6.30 p.m. 'He' generally gets here about that time. We take the kettle and some cocoa and a few biscuits so that we can have a nightcap later on. We have a wireless set down there: Tommy Handley is on tonight in ITMA. He's usually very funny. Do you hear him at your camp? I think you'll find the bunks quite comfortable. I've put lots of blankets on top of the little mattresses to soften them a bit. And if you get bored with reading or listening in we could have a game of cards or something."

It was all so wonderfully, admirably, matter of fact. His mother, normally a rather highly strung person, had said all this in the same even tone of voice and in the same manner as if she were showing him to his room upstairs on a Friday evening. Of course, what she had described as dinner was a snack, but presented properly with something of a sense of pride. Pride perhaps that though rations were pitifully small, at least they could keep standards up. His 'unexpired portion' of the day's rations which he was entitled to carry had helped a little, and next day she would be able to make use of the coupons he was able to bring. "Have plenty of potatoes and beans," she had said. "You won't be depriving us. We're lucky. We've had a good crop of both this year." He had noticed that the front lawn and the one at the back – his father's pride and joy – had been turned into vegetable gardens. "They're so nice straight from the ground, so to speak." He also noticed that the raiding *Luftwaffe* squadrons were always referred to as 'Him' or 'He', meaning, of course, Hitler.

Later – following the air-raid warning – they were 'settled' on camp stools in between the bunks in the brick-and-concrete shelter his father had had built in what had been the rose garden just outside the back door so that they could get into it quickly. When they heard the heavy drone of the approaching bombers, his father had looked up from the six-page newspaper he was reading, put his head on one side as if listening to a bird song and said authoritatively, "He's going for the docks again." "Poor devils," said his mother. "That's on our route. I expect we'll get a few again. They're not very accurate and they're not particular, you know. They'll drop them anywhere to get home quickly." He marvelled again at her shrewd calmness and returned to reading the thin, rationed newspaper. They did 'get a few'. Tony recalled with a grin that he had spent half the night outside the shelter putting out incendiary bombs with a dustbin lid and buckets of sand. Next morning as soon as the all-clear sounded his mother put on her dressing gown and took the kettle with her out of the shelter, saying, "Time for a nice cup of tea now, dear."

As he got nearer to Hawksworth he shook these memories from his mind and turned his thoughts to Jenny and the misery she must be suffering. Presumably her daughter – Claudia, wasn't it? Now in her twenties? – would have been with her, helping her with the distressing formalities that have to be performed on such occasions. Was there more family? He remembered that Roddy had mentioned a younger stepbrother, too young to be in the services when they had first met. Tony guessed that the relationship was not a close one, and that Roddy had not approved his father's remarriage, so the subject was never referred to again.

He slowed down as he entered Hawksworth. It was a small village, with all the charming characteristics of this part of Sussex not far from Lamberhurst. Wooden, thatched cottages side by side with later brick and tile-hung houses and bow-fronted shops along the wide main street. The Red Lion was on the left and the Regency-style Stanhope Hotel on the right. He could see the church just round the bend, set back behind a small green. Cars were already parked beside the green and he drove slowly round looking for a place. Ahead he saw a space just as someone emerged from it holding up a hand to stop him. He stopped, stared at the well-built figure with receding red hair as it moved, arms swinging, towards his window and started laughing.

"I'm afraid this space is reserved for the commanding officer, sah!"

"Ginger, you silly bugger. How are you? Good to see you," he said, and as he got out of the car he added, "How did you know it was me?"

"Lookout man in concealed position by road bend, communicating by way of secret signal, namely jumping up and down waving, sah!"

"Oh, shut up, you fool, Ginger. Where is he?"

Turning round he saw 'Larry' Lawrence striding up the road, grinning broadly. He quickly put his car in the space kept for him. Then they embraced, shook hands and embraced again, happily indulging themselves in the warmth of their reunion and forgetting momentarily the reason they were there. Then, quietly expressing to each other their bewilderment at the circumstances of Roddy Holmes's death, they walked through the lychgate, up the path and into the cool dimness of St Mary's Church. Conscious of the whispering respectfulness of those around him who had also at some time been part of Roddy's life, Tony gazed at the stained-glass window beyond the altar and the small chapel to the left of the choir. A movement in the congregation behind them brought them to their feet as the coffin was carried down the nave. Jenny, dignified, in half-mourning, walked with her daughter behind it. When it came to the address, the headmaster of the school where Roddy had taught spoke of his easy rapport with the young and his concern that their education should provide an opportunity for exploring ideas and beliefs as well as providing learning. The vicar referred to Roddy's and Jenny's life in the local community and to Roddy's quiet and modest manner which concealed a background that included "a war record of bravery in dangerous circumstances". Tony, Larry and Ginger looked at each other with identical thoughts in mind – 'If only he knew . . . if only he knew . . '

As the coffin was borne slowly back to the west door for the 'private interment in the churchyard to be attended only by family and close friends', Jenny paused at their pew: "You will join us at the graveside, won't you? He would want that." So they stood beside Jenny and her daughter, passive participants in the ritual of burial devised by Church and undertakers, yet honouring in their own silent way the memory of a much-loved and respected husband and father and comrade in arms.

Invited also to go back to the house for refreshments, Tony and his companions stood talking on the village green while Jenny accepted the many condolences expressed personally by departing friends, before inspecting the long line of floral tributes by the church porch. That done, they climbed into their cars and followed her out of the village for about a mile, turning through an open gateway up a gravel drive to the front of a white wooden-walled, thatched cottage. Jenny got out of her car and walked towards the front door. Tony waited beside his car for the others to join him. He saw Jenny pause by the door, looking at an open ground-floor window swinging gently in the breeze. As they walked forward together Jenny came running out of the house.

"Tony, Tony, it's awful . . . We've been broken into . . . Everything's all over the place . . . It's awful . . . How could anyone . . . on such a day. Oh, Tony, what shall we do . . .?"

He caught her in his arms and tried to calm her as he called out, "Larry, Ginger, go and have a look, and one of you go round the back . . ." Over Jenny's shoulder he saw Claudia come running towards them. "Oh, Mummy, how rotten . . . disgusting . . . Who would . . .? Please don't upset yourself . . . You've had more than enough . . ." Jenny pulled away from him. "Yes, I'm sorry. I'm all right. It was the shock. It was the last thing . . ." She took Claudia's arm. "I'm fine now . . . really."

Tony smiled at her. "Course you are, Jenny," he said as he

started towards the house. "The first thing is to get the police, and, if you can, Jenny, have a look around to see if anything is obviously missing – you know, jewels, money, cheque book, radios. That's the first thing the police will ask."

Tony made the 999 call and stood in the lounge looking around. Most of the furniture seemed to him to be in place. A couple of table lamps were on the floor, as were all the books from the bookshelves, and also the drawers and contents from the bureau and from a beautiful mahogany chest. Ginger and Larry came in through the passage to the kitchen.

"Whoever it was got in through a kitchen window," said Ginger. "One's broken, glass on the inside, and forced open. It's fairly sheltered out there. Trees all round the lawn. Difficult for anyone to have seen them."

"Yes, but if they got in at the back I think they left through that lounge window. There's a set of footprints in the flowerbed to the right of the window going in the direction of the perimeter hedge, and to judge from the prints and the gap made in the shrubs 'they' were a 'him'," added Larry.

"Jenny, would you mind taking a look upstairs," said Tony. "Would you like me to come up with you?" She nodded.

Upstairs the scene was much the same. In the main bedroom and the guest room, the drawers had been pulled out and emptied. Shelves in the wardrobes were cleared, and stored luggage had been opened and left on the floor. In the study it was worse. Contents from the desk drawers and the filing cabinets, photographs from photo albums, and books from the shelves were all scattered on the floor, including, Tony noticed, Roddy's wartime medals – suggesting a hasty search.

The police had arrived and Tony and Jenny heard their heavy tread on the stairs. A sergeant and a constable entered. The sergeant looked at Jenny.

"Mrs Holmes?"

"Yes, that's right."

"And you, sir?"

"Tony Beckett. I was a friend of the late Mr Holmes, and Mrs Holmes, and I came with other friends to attend Mr Holmes's funeral."

"Ah, the funeral. Yes, I'm very sorry, madam, this must be very difficult for you. And your friends, sir, will be the two gentlemen downstairs, I take it." Tony nodded. The constable standing behind the sergeant was taking notes.

"Sergeant Thompson and Constable Blake answering your call, madam. I'm afraid we must ask you some questions." Jenny nodded. "Can you tell yet what has been taken, madam?"

"Well, no, I can't, I'm afraid. Strangely enough, from a quick look around I can't see that anything is actually missing."

"Aha," said the sergeant meaningfully. "Jewellery?"

"My jewellery was untouched. The jewel box had not even been opened."

"Cheque book?"

"On the floor with the papers from the bureau."

"Hmm. Young tearaways, or vandals, I expect. They're everywhere today."

"Do you think so, Sergeant?" said Tony. "Wouldn't vandals do some wilful damage, and wouldn't tearaways take something – radios, cutlery, something easy to conceal? In any case it looks like one person, not two or more." The sergeant gave Tony a withering look.

"They don't always, sir. Devilment, you know. But what, if I may ask, makes you think this is the work of one person?"

"Well, there's a single set of footprints in the flowerbed by the open lounge window, suggesting the way the villain left – though it's possible that one could have left by the window and others by the broken window at the back, but I can't think why."

"No, neither can I, sir, but thank you for your observations." Dismissively he turned away from Tony to Jenny. "I take it that everything was locked up, madam, when you left for the . . . when you left the house."

Jenny nodded. "Oh yes. Claudia – my daughter – helped me do that."

Well, the constable and I will have a good look round and I will arrange for someone to come and dust the place for fingerprints. Perhaps you would take another look round to see if anything at all has been taken, but I must ask you not to put things back in order until we've finished testing for prints. Thank you."

It was a good three hours before the police left. Jenny went round the house again with Claudia, checking through her scattered belongings. Tony and his friends, unable to help in that depressing task, sat in the garden puzzling over the bizarre turn of events.

"There's something very odd about all this," said Larry. "The place has been done over but nothing's been taken – unless Jenny discovers something now." He nodded towards the house. "But if anything has gone it couldn't have been very important, otherwise she would have been able to tell straightaway . . . more or less."

Tony frowned. "You're right, Larry. It looks very much as though they – he – was searching for something in particular, and that suggests something more worrying than plain burglary – a different sort of villain; a different sort of motive. But what on earth could a sincere and socially aware chap like Roddy have that would be of interest to such a villain? The more I think about it the less I like it. I was angry at the killing of Roddy, and at the thought of a bloody burglary on such an occasion. I'm now also suspicious about a break-in the purpose of which was to find something – we don't know what – that was, is, of great importance to the perpetrator. For Jenny's sake, I hope it turns out to be a straightforward burglary – if there is such a thing."

The discussion went round in circles, seeking an explanation. Inevitably it turned to their earlier days together. Ginger started it.

"Roddy always seemed so calm on ops, didn't he, skip?" he said, reverting to the informal mode of address used when sharing the dangers of operations behind the enemy's lines. "I used to wonder whether he really was or whether it was simply better self-control than the rest of us had. But you don't ask that sort of question at the time, do you?"

Tony thought for a minute. "Yes, he was pretty cool under stress. But then you had no place in our kind of work unless you were. I don't know how you two would describe it. I've never thought of asking you. I just knew you had it. You, Ginger, because we had fought together with the SAS in the Western Desert and in Italy. I guessed – correctly – that you had it, Larry, because you would never have escaped capture after you were shot down and found your way to that embryonic Maquis group, and then back to this country, unless you had made lots of calm judgements. For me it was a strange change in my senses. When in action I think my body temperature dropped, I felt cold and could see things in clearer, sharper focus, and there was more time in a second than there is normally: more time to observe and more time to act. Of course, I never analysed it like that at the time; it was only later, thinking back on an action as one does afterwards, that it seemed to me that was what was happening to me."

"Christ, that's a bloody good description, Tony. Spot on."

"Bearing in mind what he did, I'm sure Roddy felt much the same. Somehow he gave the impression of being more relaxed than the rest of us." Then almost to himself he added, "Roddy, the quiet unflappable one."

"He was certainly that." Larry nodded his agreement. "You remember when we dropped in that night I overshot the DZ." The others did not conceal their grins. "All right, all right. Pilot error, I call it. Anyway, I extricated myself from the branches of the tree and was trying to get the 'chute down, swearing like the proverbial trooper, when I felt an arm round my throat and a commando knife in front of my eyes. A voice whispered in my ear, 'Quiet is best, Larry.' It was him, of course, and he was reminding me of something I should not have forgotten. Then he said, 'Come on, we have to tidy up the mess.' "

"I didn't know that. At the time I was relieved to see you both. But it was because of his assured manner – and his record – that I had sent him ahead with Jacques to organise our arrival – make the initial contact and organise the DZ. And later he took on the training of the less-experienced 'François' Maquis group. It seemed to me the two pro-fessional men, Georges Lebrun, the architect, and Roddy Holmes, the teacher, would get on well together. And they did. You will remember that, immediately after we got that fateful signal that the invasion was on, he organised Maquis François' first ambush of a German convoy, and on another occasion they unexpectedly ran into an enemy patrol in strength. He was a teacher, with a cool head in a crisis. Curiously, I think it was his sense of history that caused him to plead with me to let him bring his camera and some films. At first I was reluctant. It seemed to me to be an unnecessary distraction. But it turned out to be more useful than I thought . . ."

"I agree." said Larry Lawrence, as Ginger Turner nodded his assent.

"His shots of possible ambush sites were so useful in briefing the troops."

"Yes, and those of the results of raids and ambushes were invaluable in our own debriefing, and when we were eventually debriefed. And, of course, as a result we all have a bit of a visual record of those times in the set of photos he sent us all, including the Maquis commanders."

"Yes, and thanks are also due to the brave pharmacist who worked at night in his kitchen to develop the films. I wonder, what happened to him?

"Yes, we owed him – André Phillipe, I think – a great deal. And do you recall the apt message which Roddy sent us with the set of photographs? It said so much about Roddy himself: 'Mementos of our successful collaboration, and of friendships forged in the best of causes.'"

"'The best of causes'. It was, wasn't it? I wonder how long it will take before people forget why it was . . ." Ginger, whose survival of a hard life had made him a cheerful optimist, was for a moment the sad cynic.

"I know what you mean, Ginger, but let's stay with the man who delivered that message. He was so proud when Maquis François successfully carried out their first convoy ambush. It was a good one too. It was at short notice we learned that the convoy in Autun was headed for Orléans. And it was fortunate that Roddy had done a bit of a recce of the Château Chinon road. As it happened the site was almost perfect. They didn't often come like that.

"As you know, I watched the whole operation. It was vital for the success of the AMCA mission that Maquis François did well. And they did. Best of all, they stood firm when the Boche inevitably fought back. I felt then that my main doubt had been removed. And I witnessed not only the value of Roddy's camera but his brave dedication in recording our operations."

"Yes, that success was a great relief to us all," said Larry. "I remember your words when you came back. All you said was, 'Roddy's and the François' lot have just done a good one: two armoured cars hit, four vehicles out of action and about ten enemy dead or wounded. No home casualties.'"

Ginger agreed. "That's right, and I remember Boulanger was quite impressed, in spite of his earlier doubts. And when next day he saw Roddy's photos of the damage they had done, he was convinced."

"Yes, I remember his comment," said Tony. "'*Ils apprennent, ils apprennent*' – they're learning, they're learning. And that was the beginning of a true comradeship between them. What is more, from that moment AMCA operated as a united force. Different people, different backgrounds, different political motives, united in the common objective of freeing France from German occupation. It was a vital turning point."

So deep were they in their memories that none of them had seen Jenny approach from the house. Her voice refocused them. "You were talking about Roddy and the mission, weren't you?"

Tony looked round. "Oh, hello, Jenny. Yes, we were. Do you mind? It seemed natural – especially today."

"Of course I don't mind, but I want to have some of it.

Claudia and I have more or less straightened up the lounge and the bedroom. Still nothing missing, as far as we can see. It's weird. But I'm not going to tackle Roddy's study until tomorrow. There are his papers, his medals and photos and I can't face going through those now." She paused. "The good news is, the alcohol's still there. Come on in, have a drink and tell me what you've been talking about. I'm sure you can tell me much more about his life in those times than he ever did. Claudia is making sandwiches."

As they followed her into the house, Tony reached for Jenny's hand. "Did you notice anything unusual – anything at all – in the days before Roddy's accident, or the days before the funeral?"

She looked at him searchingly, puzzled. "No. Everything was beautifully normal. Why?"

"Oh, I just wondered. But there was nothing?"

"No. Well, only a few wrong-number calls on the telephone."

"What do you mean, 'wrong-number calls'?"

"When we answered and gave our number the caller just said, 'Sorry, wrong number'. It sometimes happens, as you know, but there were several at about that time, and of course after the accident the phone was in use a lot."

"Before the accident as well as after? And was it the same voice, could you tell?"

"Yes, for two or three days before as well as after. Roddy answered most of them before and he was getting irritated by them, saying, 'Some damn fool doesn't know how to dial.' I can't really say whether it was the same voice. The ones I answered were of a man's voice – but, as I say, the phone was in use a lot and I'm afraid I wasn't in a very discerning frame of mind. Why? Is it important?"

"Oh no, I don't think so." said Tony, casting a surreptitious glance at Ginger and Larry as he blandly lied.

They entered the reordered lounge and settled down with a very welcome drink and a sandwich. Hesitantly at first, they related to Jenny what they had been recalling among themselves – with the added detail of aspects they had taken for granted, as Jenny, calmly enthralled, avid for the full story, interrupted with probing questions. They went on to describe the importance to them of Roddy's reconnaissance expeditions, so fearlessly undertaken, and the importance of the photographs he took in planning their raids.

And they described how, when they received a tip about possible air-raid targets – like the railway junctions, depots and fuel dumps – Roddy would take shots of the locations so that the team could decide whether it was worth passing on the 'target', coded, to London. Often these 'photo-reconnaissance trips', as they called them, involved fairly long cross-country journeys, accompanied by perhaps half a dozen of the Maquis whose job it was to protect Roddy and his camera and get it and its contents back to base if anything happened to him. It was tricky stuff done calmly in the Roddy manner, and Jenny's wonder and pride was visible for all of them to see.

It was Larry who recalled that it was on one photo-recce that the group "fell into trouble" and might have been wiped out had it not been for Roddy's coolness and swift action. Larry continued, "We had had word that a new fuel dump was being established in the Forêt de Montreuillon . . ."

"But wasn't that dangerous, contacting people outside for information?" Jenny interjected.

"Well, yes, it could be." Tony replied. "The point was we

had to have ears and eyes that could tell us what was going on, or what was thought to be going on. At the same time we had to protect ourselves and the mission as best we could. So each Maquis commander nominated trusted local men in his group to maintain an 'old friendship' contact in some of the local villages or towns. Sometimes we used Jacquie in his dungarees, shirt and beret to make contacts. He loved doing it, but it was a misuse of his real expertise, so we relied more on the Maquis contacts. Those individuals were not allowed to discuss the Maquis or its location, though I'm sure that after a time that became known. The great thing was, it worked. Not like the poor devils on the CABAL mission." The others nodded their agreement.

"What was the CABAL mission and what happened to it?"

Tony smiled sadly at Jenny. "I think that's another story. It was a mission some way to the west of us, and one night the Hun walked through their camp all guns blazing. Only six men survived; two of them reached us by sheer luck. They did not know we were there. We managed to get them picked up by Lysander and taken home to tell their story. Four were taken prisoner, tortured and shot. It was a chilling reminder of the need for constant care and vigilance. We think there could have been some error of judgement at CABAL. Another story, another time I think, Jenny." She nodded a sympathetic understanding.

"Anyway," continued Larry, "We heard that this dump was being put down in the Forêt de Montreuillon to supply the convoys being sent to up Normandy. It was said to be very large, but these reports were sometimes exaggerated and had to be checked out. It was about twenty kilometres from our camp – more when you have to proceed undercover and keep well clear of towns and villages. Apart from which the party would have to cross two main roads going and returning. It was never a good idea to move in large numbers unless a major fight was in prospect, but it was a fairly long trip and the level of activity round the dump was unpredictable. So Roddy decided to take a section of nine men, partly for protection, but also to safeguard an escape route if necessary. They were to carry rations against the likelihood of having to lie up on the way back, and they were to be lightly armed – Sten guns and grenades – since they had to avoid trouble, not look for it. Unfortunately it was not to be.

"They set off before dawn and made good progress for the first three hours. Then with increased movement around them they had to slow down. They did not reach the edge of the forest until mid-afternoon. Searching for signs of the fuel dump in the forest was then very slow and hazardous because they did not know from which entry to the forest the dump was being formed, nor how well guarded it was. After about an hour they found it. Mounds of jerrycans well concealed under camouflage nets and widely dispersed. A wall of layers of coiled barbed wire surrounded the area, the extent of which was hard to judge accurately. There was little point in taking many photos inside the forest. The more important task was to take a landmark or two outside the perimeter of the forest to identify the part of it in which the dump was located. So Roddy crawled around until he got what he wanted, then returned to his waiting companions. It was getting late; they agreed that they would have to lie up for the night, but needed to put some distance between themselves and the dump – a likely focus of activity – before doing so. They crossed one main road quite safely, but became conscious of traffic on the other as they approached it. They pulled back, found a suitable wood on a rise and lay up.

"Early next morning they set off again. The point where they came to the second road was about twenty-five or thirty yards from a double bend. The cover up to the road was quite good, but on the other side there was a deep ditch and some exposed ground. Not ideal, but as it was early Roddy decided to cross if it was all clear round the bend. He sent one of the men round the edge of the wood to have a look round the corner. As he came running back, he gave an 'all clear' sign. Whether he had only been able to see a part of the road round the bend, or whether it took him too long to return to the waiting group, we do not know. He was killed in the fighting that followed. But as they began to cross, a German patrol – two motorcyclists and an open personnel truck with a Spandau mounted at the front and containing about a dozen armed troops, came round the bend."

Larry paused as he saw Jenny's questioning frown. "A Spandau was a very nasty, effective German machine gun." Jenny nodded.

"Roddy and one man had almost reached the ditch on the other side, but the others were caught on the road. They hesitated, and as the motorcyclists came to a stop and dismounted, and the troops tumbled out of their carrier, they turned and ran for the cover they had just left. Roddy yelled, 'Find cover! Open fire!' and dived into the ditch. The Germans ignored Roddy and his companion, their attention probably taken by the sight of the others scrambling back into the woods. The Maquisards were outnumbered and outgunned, but they had one early advantage. By the time the enemy had fanned out across the road and the deadly Spandau opened up they had found themselves broad trees and fallen trunks to give them cover, while the *Wehrmacht* patrol were in the open. The first volley from the woods knocked three of them over. The others went to ground – behind the fallen motorcycles, the back of the truck, or flat on the road. When the Spandau opened up Roddy knew it would prevent his friends in the woods taking good firing positions. He saw that one of the Germans had picked off the wretched man who had gone to check the road round the bend – he had not got back into the woods – and the others were beginning to inch forward undercover of the Spandau's fire. It was obvious that unless something was done quickly the whole party would be wiped out.

"With his companion Pierre, a close friend of François from Chartres, Roddy ran along the ditch in the direction of where the Germans were deploying. They risked exposing themselves, but speed was essential. They got behind them and then quickly disposed of the two Germans behind their bicycles and the one behind the corner of the truck. Then Roddy lobbed a grenade into the truck carrying the Spandau crew, which dealt with them. Then he rolled another under the truck, from where the other soldiers were edging their way towards the woods. The Maquisards in the woods were then able to engage the survivors now caught between them and Roddy and Pierre. It was all over. It was brilliant."

"Yes, it was brilliant." said Tony. "In those few minutes Roddy not only saved all his men except one, he destroyed the enemy patrol, brought back his filmed evidence of the dumps location, but also brought back a Spandau and some rifles and ammunition. He and his colleagues also brought back the body of their one unfortunate casualty, who was buried with such military honours as we could provide in the woods close to their camp. And for good measure we were able to pass back home information about the fuel dump, providing – with the help of Roddy's photos of the landmarks – the map coordinates of the location. Three nights later the dump was raided. The whole sky was lit up; it was such a sight.

"We pieced together the account of the engagement from – as you would expect, Jenny – Roddy's inadequate report and the stories of Pierre and the others. Between them there was enough corroboration for me to be able to put in my citation for his gong." He paused. "You said it was still there, Jenny?"

"Yes, all his medals are there still. After hearing that – and I never knew it was like that – I am so grateful that they are, and . . . and . . ." She looked down, and when she looked up again her eyes were moist. "And I feel so proud of him."

"So you should, Jenny, so you should. And so are we."

The mood became subdued as the tension relaxed and they chatted mostly about some of the light-hearted times together. There was no room for serious recollection after the account of the fuel-dump expedition, and it was soon time for them to leave Jenny and Claudia on their own. As the three of them walked to their cars, they reflected again on the tragic and unexplained mystery of Roddy's death. They agreed that the matter could not be left as it was. They could not leave their suspicions unexplored, but they needed more to go on. Perhaps the police inquiries would yield something in the next day or two, though they were not sure what to do. It was left to Tony to contact Sergeant Thompson and then arrange for them to meet again.

Chapter 4

It was nearly lunch time the following morning when Jenny telephoned. "Tony, I've come across something rather odd. At least I think it is." There was a tone of puzzled excitement in her voice.

"Oh, what's that?"

"Well, Claudia and I set to early this morning to put Roddy's study back together. You remember that papers and books were all over the place, as well as photographs that had been torn from their albums. And you remember how Roddy made up a set of photos from all those taken on the mission which he had copied for you and the Maquis leaders as a memento?" she went on without waiting for a reply. "Well, I think there's one missing from Roddy's set."

"One? Are you sure?"

"Yes, I am. You see, when he was sorting them out, he wrote 'war album' on the back of those he selected and after copying them made slots in the album to put them in. I found all those marked in that way and put them back in the album, but I have one space left. That *is* odd, isn't it?"

"Are you sure it hasn't got mislaid or else hidden somewhere in the room?"

"Quite certain. That was the first thing we thought of, but Claudia and I checked carefully. It's definitely not in the room. Isn't it peculiar that the only thing that was taken in that burglary was one wartime photo? Not the set, just one photo?"

"Very peculiar. Of course, you wouldn't know which one, would you Jenny?"

"Fraid not. I wasn't all that familiar with them. I wondered if you could compare what's left with your set?"

"I'd like to, Jenny, but mine are packed away with all my stuff awaiting shipment in New York. But what I'll do, if it's all the same to you, I'll come over tomorrow and look them through to see if I can identify the 'missing link' – though it's some years since I looked at mine."

"Oh, I shall be glad if you would. I'm intrigued. If we can identify it we may be able to tell why it was taken. But, Tony, I don't really understand it. Why would someone go to all that trouble just to get an old photo?"

"Heaven knows, Jenny. But don't worry about it. I'll come across tomorrow morning and have a look."

"Thanks, Tony. See you tomorrow."

As he rang off Tony hoped he had concealed his own anxiety. There was something rather odd, even a bit sinister, about a risky break-in perpetrated in daylight, with not much time to search for one article. And it occurred shortly after Roddy had been mown down in suspicious cirumstances. Coincidence? Perhaps. But he did not like it. Not at all.

That night Tony's sleep was disturbed by a dream that had not bothered him since the immediate post-war years. Almost a nightmare, but not quite. A dream that evoked deep fear but not panic. Its cause, he knew, was the dread he had nursed during those weeks in occupied territory of what he called the CABAL experience. The dread of waking in the night to the sound of a line of German troops striding through the woods where they camped, firing and stabbing with their bayonets into the undergrowth where they lay hidden. He had no idea how many hours sleep he lost during those clandestine weeks, lying awake in his shelter under a bush listening to every forest noise, wondering . . . What was it that had recalled that dream from the depths of his mind into which he had thrust it? Perhaps it was the uneasy feeling that he and his friends were facing a threat?

Before leaving for Hawksworth he telephoned Ginger and Larry to tell them of Jenny's belief that her burglar had stolen only one thing: one of Roddy's wartime photographs. Ginger found it incredible that anyone should go to that trouble, take that risk, for a single photograph. At the same time he was intrigued by the possibility. However, he could not help to identify the missing one, as his set, along with a lot of his furniture and other belongings, was at his sister's farm in Devon. In the light of his many absences abroad on security work he had decided to keep only a small pied-à-terre in London. He promised to go down to Devon when he could and dig out his set. The trouble was his sister and her husband were visiting one of his relations in Canada and would not be back for a couple of weeks.

"Sorry I can't do more at present, skip. Perhaps you'll have better luck with Larry. Let me know please what you find out. I must say I don't believe it could be a robbery of just one snap – but if it is, it will be of concern to us all. Won't it?"

But Tony did not have better luck with Larry. His elderly housekeeper, Edith, whose service since his wife had died suddenly Larry had once described as fussing him like an old Dutch aunt, told him that he was away on business and would not be back for a couple of days. The day after tomorrow perhaps, but he always arrived late in the evening. Tony asked her to leave a note saying he wanted to speak to him about his wartime album. The Dutch aunt took a note of the message, read it back with great precision, and promised to put it on the desk in his study. "He always goes there first, no matter what time, to look for messages."

He arrived at Jenny's house just before one o'clock. She had got everything back in place, cleaned and polished. With its country-cottage theme the lounge looked comfortable and relaxing. In the dining room mahogany and rosewood blended. Some sandwiches stood on the sideboard between plates and a bottle of white Burgundy, and glasses bottoms up. However, they were both keen to look at the photographs first. In the study the album was open on the desk. The pictures, neatly slotted into position on the pages marked at the top with the simple title 'AMCA May–September 1944.'

"If I remember correctly, Roddy wrote a reference to the incidents on the backs of the prints so that we could put our own headings in our own albums, so there's nothing here to identify the missing one."

"That's right." she paused and, ever perceptive and concerned, continued, "This must be a pretty emotional experience for you, Tony. Do you mind?"

"No, I don't. Strangely, I'm rather enjoying it. That evening when we were reminiscing, we were – or I was – reaching back, remembering Roddy as a comrade, and also his unique contribution to all we did on the mission. It was an act of respect ... of homage ... of ... of ... love. Looking at these photographs – and I haven't seen them for some years, there just was not time out there in South America – looking at them now, sharp reminders of a whole sequence of events, almost literally takes me back there. That's not as uncomfortable as it may sound. It's almost a therapy. The strain, the enduring nervous tension – one was wound up the whole time – have gone. One can look at what happened to friends – and to oneself – less emotionally. I think it's something we should do from time to time to prove that the demons that then roused fear and questioned one's resolve are now dead."

In the silence that followed Jenny stared blankly at the album's pages with a smile of understanding, perhaps more for Roddy than for Tony. It was he who broke the moment by stabbing a finger at the pages.

"Look, there's the shot of the results of the confrontation with the patrol that we were talking about, where Roddy earned his gong. And here the landmarks identifying the petrol dump, and there the railway junction at Autun after the RAF had paid a visit." He pointed to another, a picture of a tall man wearing a beret, dressed in an open-necked shirt and dark trousers, pointing a Sten gun at a German soldier slumped against the wheel of a burning truck, with a younger man similarly armed at his side.

"That's Captain Léon, the Maquis commander, isn't it?" enquired Jenny. "Roddy pointed him out to me. He and his men were Communists, weren't they?"

"Yes, that's Jean Boulanger, and the young man beside him was – presumably is – his nephew Henri. He joined us about halfway through the mission. He was clever to find Léon. His father, Léon's brother, had been in the Resistance in Brest, but was captured and sent to Paris for questioning. He was a quiet lad, did not say very much. I asked him about his underground work with his father in Brest, but he simply said it was passing information. And when I asked how he found Maquis Léon he said he had friends who helped him. It must have been a great strain to have gone through so much at such a young age. He became Léon's shadow. Léon

71

said he owed it to his brother to ensure Henri came through the war safely, and he told us Henri had left a younger brother behind."

"Did he? Come through?"

"Oh yes. He came through, but his father didn't. He was tortured. His friends in Brest who survived said he must have kept silent through all the excruciating pain until the end. After four days he was executed. A couple of other young lads who played only a minor part, and who had been taken with him, were questioned and then sent to work as forced labour in German factories."

"Oh, how awful, especially for Henri's father – and Henri."

"Yes, we did not know all this had happened until later. All Henri knew when he joined us was that his father and one or two others had been arrested, and he had gone into hiding until he judged it was safe to find his uncle. We heard the details when Léon went into Nevers to get information and came back with the whole tragic story he had learned through the Resistance network. Henri was inconsolable when he heard what had happened to his father. For a while Léon would not let him go on any operations. He said he was too emotionally upset, and would be unreliable.

"Yes, Henri's father was a hero, and there were many like him. Real heroes. Unsung. And, yes, some were Communists. A very disciplined lot, very good fighters and very brave. I admired them a lot and had a great respect for Léon. It really didn't matter then that they were Communists. We knew their background, just as we were aware of François' allegiance to the Armée Secrète, but we let that knowledge stay where it belonged – in the background. Léon and François were together fighting a common enemy.

72

Our job was to make a coordinated force of them and focus their actions on the overall tactical objective of obstructing the movement of troops in reserve, sabotaging and attacking at every opportunity. Politics didn't come into it. Although at first Léon – Jean Boulanger – and his men were reserved and reluctant to collaborate and accept our overall command, once they recognised us as competent professionals and saw that François – Georges Lebrun – and his men were an effective Maquis devoted to the cause of defeating the Germans, there was no difficulty. I imagine also, though I have no proof, that Léon needed to get confirmation in his own way that all Maquis groups were to come under the strategic command of the FFI in accordance with the copy of the letter from General Koenig, the Commander-in-Chief of the Free French, which I had given him and François just after we arrived. After that initial hesitation I neither saw nor felt any of the friction the SOE had warned me of – at least not until Léon came to me after the fighting was over to say he was removing his Maquis from my command."

"Good heavens. What was that about?"

Tony explained briefly how, while they were awaiting dispersal instructions, Jean Boulanger had announced, with some discomfort, that he was taking his men to another location. It was clear that he was responding to orders from another authority and disliked breaking the alliance of comradeship and trust they had established in fighting together. And he told Jenny of his suspicion that it was connected with the later reported attempt by the Communist Party to march on Paris. It was the first sad indication Tony had had of the re-emergence of France's deep and destructive political divisions. Whether or not Jean was involved in any attempted coup, the possibility of which was discounted by many, Tony retained a great respect and affection for him whose life and beliefs had been moulded by a culture and an environment he could never know.

And so with Jenny at his side, and through Roddy's photographs, he revisited those areas of conflict from the days when the issues were uncomplicated. The choice then between right and wrong had been simple. Our cause was right, theirs was wrong. What we could do to help defeat the enemy was good; their regime, their conquests, their treatment of occupied territory and peoples, was bad. Fighting the Germans (and the Italians and the Japanese) and helping those who fought the enemy were noble duties, but helping the enemy was treachery which should be punished – though circumstances such as torture and abuse of family raised difficult and inconvenient questions of judgement. But by and large you knew where you stood. By ignoring the consequences of error or failure, yet remembering the precautions that had to be taken to avoid mistakes, and by putting your trust in the elements of surprise and audacity, you knew you could win.

Occasionally, Tony would pause as he gazed at particular photos and comment to Jenny. There was a series showing bent and tangled railway lines with deep holes in the track. "Those were all separate occasions." he said. "You can see how many times we had to blow that rail link. It was used frequently to transport material, and men, northwards. We used to lie in wait where we expected the wreck to happen and attack the troops as they jumped out of the trucks. Unfortunately, sabotaged railway lines are fairly easy to repair, so we had to keep at it. There was a long stretch we could work on, but of course after we had done it a couple of times they patrolled it, which meant we had to deal with the guards as well as lay the explosive.

"There, that was a big one." He pointed to a series of three pictures showing the results of an ambushed convoy. One showed burning trucks with bodies on the ground; a shot of himself and Léon standing by a wrecked personnel carrier with a German officer and two *Milice* in the background with their hands up; and one of Léon talking to Larry and Ginger in front of fallen German motorcycles.

"We had news about a convoy coming up from Bordeaux. The information was that it was headed for Germany, not Normandy. It did not appear to be a movement of troops in reserve. Yet to judge from its size and the way it was protected it was a movement of some importance. I remember, it was said to include five or six covered lorries with machine guns mounted on the cabin roofs, two personnel trucks of *Wehrmacht* troops and French *Milice*, all protected by an armoured car front and rear with half a dozen motorcycle troops as outriders."

"The *Milice* were French troops fighting with the Germans, weren't they?"

"Yes. At their head was a man called Joseph Darnand, who was a loyal supporter of Marshal Pétain, the head of the Vichy Government, and who was later accused of the deportation of French Jews. The Maquis detested the *Milice* as much as they hated the Germans, because they regarded them as traitors.

"The convoy was going to be a difficult one to deal with and the expected route was some way from us. Fortunately, by this time we had armoured jeeps dropped to us by parachute. Two dropped straight into a lake a short way back from the DZ; one broke an axle on landing and was unusable until we could repair it; and two – the two we used here – were operational straightaway. They were a great boon. Together with the civilian cars each Maquis had

75

'rescued' from known or suspected collaborators, they gave us much greater and safer mobility. And with the weapons they carried – twin Vickers K0.33 calibre front and rear; perhaps that doesn't mean much to you, but believe me they gave us much greater firepower."

"Roddy had told me how important the jeeps were. There's a picture of one in the background in this set. But I thought you had more than two or three."

"Yes, later we did. As soon as the invasion force had set up an advance flying field in Normandy they flew in a half-dozen more and we sent Ginger back via a Lysander pickup to guide a convoy of armoured jeeps through the German lines to us. That is quite a story in itself.

"Anyway, for this job we knew we would have to use almost the entire manpower of the two Maquis. And we needed a damn good ambush site. As soon as we heard that the convoy was staging at Digoin, travelling north, we surmised – correctly, thank heavens – that it would make for Autun, where there was a strong garrison, and then Dijon on the way to Germany. So Roddy and Ginger set off to look for a site on the Gueugnon to Autun road. They found a good one. The road passed through a tree-lined stretch where there was a shallow gully. We positioned Ginger with a small group so that they could bring a tree down across the motorcyclists and in front of the leading armoured car, and another behind it so it was isolated from the main part of the convoy. We had to engage the *Wehrmacht* and *Milice* troops from both sides of the gully, while the rear armoured vehicle came under fire from Larry in one jeep and a group with a bazooka. I was with François and his men on one side of the gully with the other jeep. Léon and his men were on the other with Roddy.

"It was a good plan and worked well at first, some of us concentrating on the machine-gunners on the cabin roofs while others concentrated on the *Wehrmacht* troops and *Milice* as they leapt clear of their carriers to take up firing positions. What we had not realised was that the middle truck was a Q-truck, rather like the Q-ships in the First World War. As soon as the convoy came to a halt the cover was flung off and there were three manned Spandaus in action immediately. My jeep wasn't in a position to engage them straightaway and in any case I was trying to prevent some of the *Wehrmacht* deploying themselves along the gully, but I could see that much of the fire from the Q-truck was directed on Léon's group at the point where the bank flattened out. They were in trouble and losing men. Larry saw the danger too and immediately turned his jeep and went tearing up the grass verge on Léon's side and put himself into the Spandau line of fire. It was brilliant, and dangerous, but his cannon soon dealt with the spandaus. Léon was able to move his wounded and regroup.

"On our side of the road it was a bit of a long battle. The *Wehrmacht* do not give up; some had got into good firing positions. We had to move out of our position to get behind them, and the rear armoured car was still firing in support of them. I had to leave my jeep to get to the back of the car and deal with it with a couple of hand grenades. The members of the *Milice* were not so well disciplined and as soon as some of them saw they were beaten they managed to get aboard an undamaged personnel truck and edge it past the armoured vehicle we had just put out of action, to make a getaway. Their discretion was certainly the better part of valour. They did not relish falling into the hands of the Maquis. However, I caught them up in the jeep and the twin Vickers soon stopped them. The three that didn't get killed quickly gave themselves up. Unfortunately, those prisoners caused us some difficulty."

"Oh, how was that?"

"Well, I wanted to question them away from the Maquis camps. Spirits were running high against the *Milice* and I knew I would be under considerable pressure to hand them over to one of the Maquis' so-called field courts martial, where they would have got pretty rough justice. Especially as these *Milice* apparently came from Bordeaux, where a prominent and hated collaborator was working with Pétain. They realised it too. They were very frightened. So I arranged for Léon and one of his men to blindfold them and the German officer – who I wanted to question about the purpose of the convoy, which was obviously not sent to support the German Army in Normandy – and take them in one of the captured FFI Citroëns back to our camp, not theirs, by a roundabout route. After an action we always dispersed in smaller groups in different directions before homing in on our camps. There was always a chance that the noise of an ambush would cause patrols to be sent out. That way we did not leave clues as to the whereabouts of our camps, and only part of our force risked getting compromised by a German patrol. And that is what happened – but it was Léon and his prisoners who ran into trouble."

"What happened, for heaven's sake?"

"After they left we were in a hurry to 'tidy up' at the ambush site. It was bad to hang around after a shoot-up. We were busy destroying the equipment in the trucks – radio transmitters and what appeared to be aircraft spares – with hand grenades, regrettably, making more noise. Then we discovered that one truck contained not equipment but paintings – oil paintings in classical gilt frames, jade statuettes and porcelain. As far as I could tell from a quick inspection, pretty valuable stuff. Someone was using the convoy to get loot from Bordeaux back to Germany! I then had an additional special reason for questioning the prisoners. But the urgent problem was what to do with the loot. I had no intention of leaving it to the enemy again. We had to get it well away from the scene and carefully concealed until I could decide how to dispose of it. I thought – I fervently hoped – that as there was only one truckload it was likely to be someone's piece of private enterprise rather 'official' looting. If Higher Command knew nothing of it there was unlikely to be a great search. So I got one of Léon's men who knew the area fairly well to take one of the serviceable motorcycles and lead Pierre driving the truck to a hiding place deep in a wood somewhere, eliminate any sign of their entry, and bring Larry back.

"It was while we were sorting all this out that we heard distant firing. It seemed to be a short but sharp exchange of small-arms fire. I immediately feared for Léon, but there was nothing I could do about it. However, the sound put speed into what the rest of us were doing. We finished up, collected our dead and wounded and dispersed quickly. I led one group, with Roddy, in one jeep; Ginger, with François, led the other."

"But Léon was all right, wasn't he?"

"Yes and no. When I got back to our camp there was no sign of him or the prisoners. As it got later I became more apprehensive. Ginger had arrived with François and came over to tell me that the wounded were being taken care of and that there would be a burial party in the woods later that night. Pierre had returned on the back of the motorcycle. It was then that Léon came limping up the track carrying a Sten gun and a rifle, and helping himself along on a roughly cut stick. He had been shot through the leg; he had tied a tourniquet round his right thigh near the crotch. The leg of his dungarees was wet with his blood. We got him over to the 'sickbay' in his own camp. Typically, he had come first to me to report in!

"It appeared that he had run across a German motorcycle-sidecar patrol a few miles from the ambush site. The German officer whom Léon had ordered to drive was killed in the first exchange and the car ran into a ditch. The rest of them tumbled out. He and one of the *Milice* were on one side, the other two on the other side. He saw one of the *Milice* killed and another hit just before he was hit in the leg. He had to crawl back undercover of the car into a wood. He was fairly sure he had hit the two motorcyclists, but he thought one of the *Milice* had escaped. Fortunately, his wound wasn't serious: the bullet had passed through the thigh muscle, and after being patched up by our nurse and a few days rest he was soon back in action. Needless to say he took it all very calmly."

"He was lucky, wasn't he? I think Roddy said he was wounded again."

"Yes, that was in a later episode, and then more seriously, in the chest. That time he was really lucky. He had to be operated on by our doctor in the woods. For a few days he was very poorly. It was agreed that he should go to a proper hospital for more expert attention as soon as we could safely get him there. When he left us suddenly, I reminded him that he should do this, but whether or not he did I do not know."

"A brave man."

"Yes, a brave and strange man. Strong in his beliefs, focused on a distant objective, and very determined. I have thought of him often and wondered what happened to him.

Ginger wrote to me in South America to tell me he had heard he was in hospital in the South of France somewhere."

"And François, Georges Lebrun?"

"He returned to his profession, architecture, and eventually became a partner in the practice in Chartres where he trained. While I was trying to be a foreign news correspondent in Paris I saw him from time to time. He was very good at commenting on my amateur interpretation of the French scene. He taught me a lot about France and probably saved me from many gaffes. We still exchange Christmas cards with scribbled greetings."

They fell silent and Tony slowly turned the remaining pages of the album, pausing occasionally to study a picture more closely, but without further comment, until he came to the last page with its blank rectangular space between corner slits where the missing photograph should have been.

"Jenny, I really can't tell what's missing. It's so long since I looked at mine that I would not have remembered half of these. Many came quite freshly to me. And of course the sequence is no guide. The missing one could have come from any part of the series. You did not know one was missing until you got to the end, did you?"

"No, that's right. But it is strange, isn't it Tony?"

"Yes, but there are negatives, aren't there?"

"Negatives?" She frowned for a moment. "Film negatives of this set? No, there aren't." She noticed the surprise on Tony's face. "You see, Roddy spent a school holiday sorting out his wartime memorabilia – he had his Sam Browne, his revolver holster, some maps, photos from lots of different times besides these of the mission – an Easter hol in 1947 I think it was. He was trying to reorientate himself towards a teaching career. As you know, he felt strongly about the sort of education young people should get in the post-war world.

He said he had to make a conscious effort to shed his military skin, as he called it, forget the soldier's way of thinking he had adopted during the previous six years, if he was going to be able to develop the right mental framework for teaching."

"I know exactly what he meant. I decided I had to do the same in order to concentrate on earning a living. It was an extremely difficult transition to make. It may sound strange now, but it was hard to settle back to the routines and social customs of civilian life after the excitements and stresses and basically brutal objectives of our sort of soldiering. And of course some could not make it."

"What do you mean?"

"Well some brave men turned to crime and finished up in prison. Some turned to drink. Some committed suicide. All casualties of the war. And there may be casualties we don't know about or may never recognise. We don't really know what those stresses have done to our personalities."

"I see. How tragic for those who could convert to militarism but could not change back again. But it was this need to change that was in Roddy's mind during that break from school when he decided to keep just a few things; to make up sets of photos for you all, and discard the rest – including, I'm afraid, the negatives. He said the important people concerned had got their copies and no more would be needed."

"I can certainly understand what poor Roddy was getting at. And of course he made his conversion brilliantly. Sadly it has cut off one of the ways we might have found out what the missing photo was about. Now our best bet is to wait until Larry comes back from wherever he is, and compare his set with this."

"I suppose so. I hope it won't be long. It's nagging at me."

"I'm sure it is. And me too. We can only be patient."

"Of course." Jenny stood up. "Let's forget it for a bit. Come and have a drink and a sandwich. By the way, what did you do with the loot?"

"I considered the situation merited seeking the advice of the SOE agent. I put the request to London in code through Jacquie, explaining the reason. After a little delay they sent back map coordinates for a rendezvous with appropriate passwords. We met one afternoon 'after school hours' – he was operating as a schoolmaster. He was charming and helpful and, I judged, very skilled. He arranged for us to drive the vehicle to a small chateau not far from Nevers, occupied by a friendly, anglophile marquis. He hid the loot in his cellars, concealed the lorries at the back of a barn, and sent back some damn good claret! I understand the loot was handed to the authorities after Paris was liberated. Until now it has never occurred to me to wonder exactly how that was done. Strangely, we got very little feedback concerning the ambush or the episode with the patrol afterwards. Apparently, the *Wehrmacht* came and took away the wrecked trucks – and their dead – and scout planes flew around for a couple of days. That was all. Usually they made much more fuss. We assumed 'they' were embarrassed that the convoy was used to conceal some looting by one of their number."

"Do you think these happenings have some connection with that loot?"

"I really don't know. They might."

"After all this time?"

"Well, something is badly worrying someone after all this time."

They retired to the lounge and chatted inconsequentially as they ate and drank. When it was time to go Tony tried again to calm Jenny's concern by insisting – with an assumed assurance – that there would probably be a quite harmless explanation for the burglary.

On the way back through the village he called on the local constabulary. Sergeant Thompson was in and agreed to see him. Tony reintroduced himself.

"Ah yes. The burglary at Mrs Holmes's. You were one of the friends at the house at the time."

"That's right, Sergeant. I was wondering if you have been able to find out who ran down Mr Holmes that morning, and if you have any information about the break-in and burglary?"

"I take it that you are making these enquiries on behalf of Mrs Holmes, sir?"

"Of course I am," said Tony, feeling irritated. "You appreciate that Mrs Holmes is under a lot of strain, having suffered these two tragic events within a short time."

"Quite so, sir. I understand. I am sorry to say there's no real progress on either incident. There has been no trace of the vehicle that struck Mr Holmes. We have put out an all-regions inquiry without result. Unfortunately, no one saw a car on that road that morning. It was quite early. And there's no information about any repairs that might have been needed. Whoever did it is lying very low. But they often do – for quite a time.

"As to the burglary, there is no real clue as to who the intruder might have been. One possible development came to nothing. Someone on the way to the funeral remembered seeing a motorcycle leaning against the hedge at an opening to a field not far from Mrs Holmes's house. It might have been the intruder's but they did not remember the registration number, so we have no means of tracing it. The footprints – we found another set – " he added in triumphant tone, "were of the sole of a common plimsoll of the kind sold in shops everywhere. As you know, I believe it was the work of a petty thief who may have been interrupted before deciding what to take and fled with the last thing in his hand.

"I'm sorry there is nothing more. I believe you think there is a connection between the the two incidents, sir. But I have to say there is no evidence to support that view. But I can assure you we will investigate any new information anyone can give us. But experience tells me that in these cases the simple answer is usually the correct one."

Tony could not argue against the sergeant's reasoning, though he still had serious doubts. He thanked him and gave him his card. "If you do come across anything, perhaps you would be good enough to let me know. I am trying to help Mrs Holmes cope with her difficulties. She's been thrust into widowhood in tragic circumstances and become the victim of a sordid burglary at the same time. I'm sure you will want to help ease her pain by providing satisfactory answers to the questions that are troubling her."

The sergeant stared at the floor a moment. He had received Tony's message. He looked up, and in softer tone said. "Yes, of course, sir. We're not treating either event lightly. We're doing our best. Thank you."

As he drove off, heading for London and the Gloucester Road, Tony turned over in his mind the tragic and puzzling events of the past few days, questioning himself about why he, Larry and Ginger thought they could see in them something – but what? – more sinister than could the police. There was no doubt that logic was on the side of the forces of law and order, but . . .

First there were the circumstances of Roddy Holmes's death: struck from behind while running wearing a luminous belt on the right-hand side of the road; in daylight; in the morning; on a straight clear road he used regularly; not a glancing blow as if the driver had inadvertently swerved, but a savage direct blow from the back which threw him several yards; no witnesses. Was it merely an sheer accident? Possible, of course, but what would make a driver veer to the wrong side of the road on a straight stretch at the precise point where Roddy was running? A drunk? At that time of the day? Unlikely, but possible. But, again, if the driver was not in full control, why had he not hit something before or after on the road? Why at that precise point? And where was the car? Someone involved in an accident, drunk or sober, would want to hide the evidence. But if the vehicle was in everyday use – for business, school runs, shopping – it could not be concealed for long and would, presumably, have to be repaired or at least 'touched up'. Someone would get to know about it. This vehicle was being very carefully concealed. No, with the best – fairest – will in the world, he could not accept that this was an ordinary hit-and-run accident – if there was such a thing. It was more like murder.

Secondly, the burglary. Plainly it was not a 'normal' burglary. Nothing had been taken except, it seemed, one wartime photo. One selected from many. Without a doubt that was very odd – perhaps sinister. But the answer to the question 'why' lay in being able to identify the scene of that photo. That must wait for Larry's return. Were the two incidents connected? There was no real evidence that they were. The burglary could have been a quite separate – but still highly questionable – occurrence. Yet the more he felt that Roddy's death was not the result of an ordinary accident, the higher the odds were on a connection between the two. But why? Could there be any reason at all to murder for a single photograph? Perhaps, in a criminal mind, if the stake was high enough. What was the stake here?

Chapter 5

It was early evening when Tony arrived back at the flat. He was tired but feeling unsettled and frustrated. There was nothing more he could do until Larry returned. Tony rang his flat, but he was still not back. "No, not yet sir," said the Dutch aunt. "But I have your message and it's on top of the pile on his desk . . . as I told you, sir." The last was in a firm voice, the nearest she could get to forthright asperity.

He returned to the hall and picked up the mail from the mat. He scanned the envelopes then turned back to the one with the New York postmark. The back of the envelope told him it was from Strachan Estate Enterprises Inc., his former employers. Inside the message was brief and to the point, unencumbered by any personal warmth. 'Following your recent departure' – nice touch that, he thought – 'from your employment with the corporation, we are now in a position to discuss a final settlement of your contract. Would you please arrange to visit these offices any morning in the week commencing the 24th June, when Jim Karensky, VP Operations, and Oscar Patterson, Treasurer, will be available to see you. Please let us know . . .'

Week of the 24th? That's not much notice, surely. He went to the desk and picked up his diary. Today was Thursday 20th. Next Monday! Hell! He certainly could not go before contacting Larry – tomorrow or Saturday. Contact Jenny again – Saturday or Sunday. Have another discussion with Larry and Ginger about it all, whatever it is . . . Sunday or Monday. Leave out Tuesday in case something develops concerning Roddy's 'accident'. So he could fly on Wednesday or Thursday and meet the steel-eyed colleagues that afternoon. Then they would be anxious to reach agreement so that it would not interfere with their flights to the country at the weekend. Not that he would feel much pity for them if it did. In fact Friday would be better. They would be very anxious to settle then. That was a tight timetable, but he wanted a settlement. He had no income, no job! No, the quicker the better, so long as he did not leave the mystery of the missing photograph hanging in the air. Larry was the key to making sense out of it. So, go Thursday and fight the good fight on Friday the 28th. He walked over to the telephone and sent his cabled reply.

Switching his attention unexpectedly to that half-forgotten but urgent issue made him even more restless. Looking at his diary he noticed a pencilled entry for Friday: 'Cels; dinner???'. Glamorous, extrovert, entertaining, selfish, hugely insecure Celia. How they had loved, argued and parted – because Celia had thought, when in a petulant mood, that differences in their temperaments were an obstacle to any kind of serious relationship – though their mutual understanding grew with every meeting. "But let's keep in touch," she had said, rather too casually. That had not been easy during the war, nor recently with thousands of miles between them. That distance had reduced contact to a long-distance telephone call once a year around the time of her birthday. Naturally, it was he who rang her. Each time it was clear that she had been expecting him to telephone and was cross if the call missed the day. Their brief conversations usually centred on what she had been doing; whether she was still with the same advertising agency; what exciting

88

account she was working on; and what interesting people she was working with. And they often ended on a petulant note with her wondering, "What on earth you are doing over there in that godforsaken place – wherever it is – when all the important things are happening here!" He had not tried to explain over the telephone. It would only have provoked an argument. Just once he had said, "Its my job, Cels. Its here. One day I'll explain why I think it's important." To which her parting shot was, "If I'm still around!"

Why the attraction they felt, each for the other, had persisted in spite of the carping arguments and the long absences still intrigued him. Perhaps his love of adventure was stimulated by her unpredictability and her insecurity, which he had so quickly recognised. Perhaps she saw in him someone who could cope with uncertainty and did not need an ordered life. Someone who not only accepted but irritatingly comprehended her irrationality. Certainly he had some understanding of her broken and unhappy home life as a child which, he guessed, could be the cause of her unsettled lifestyle – a cause she vehemently denied whenever he had tried to get her to face up to the damage of those early years. Nonetheless she realised, but would not admit, that he was the only person she knew who had shown her some sympathetic understanding. Most of her admirers in wartime days – and in the arrogant, self-interested circles in which she now moved – were more interested in her bedroom than her background. She never forgot her surprise that he had managed to get her to talk about herself the first evening they had met.

Tony remembered that first meeting well. It was in 1943, when he was on leave from the Middle East. That part of the war there was being won handsomely, after a series of defeats inflicted by the legendary Rommel. He and Johnny

Burton, one of his light-machine-gun team in 1940 who had gone with the division to the Western Desert, had taken part in the defence of and then breakout from El Alamein. Johnny had been able to borrow his parents' flat in Barons Court for a 'bit of a binge-up'. Tony had been late arriving and the party was in full swing. The long hall and the large Victorian lounge and dining room were full of happy toping young members of the armed forces. Some were old hands, like Tony, Johnny and friends, but there were also a lot of younger, newer representatives of His Majesty's Army, Navy and Air Force – friends of Johnny's younger brother – all at an early stage of war experience, including growing numbers of ATS, WRNS and WAAFs. The noise of laughter and chat was deafening. This was no time for seriousness. The new, liberal wartime morality, shaped and justified by the increasing proximity of danger and death, had dawned.

He had stood with his first drink just inside the lounge door, surveying the scene, searching through the hot smokey haze for faces he recognised. A great shout of laughter from the far corner drew his attention, as it did many other guests. The sight of the blonde WAAF, glass in hand, tunic undone, tie loosened, shapely breasts prominent under the shirt, standing in the midst of a circle of admirers from all services, was a picture he never forgot. She was laughing and chatting animatedly with them all. As he watched he smiled to himself, thinking, 'She's got them all – poor suckers – completely under her control'. At that moment she had stopped talking and looked up over their heads inexplicably straight at him, straight at the amused look on his face. He recalled giving a slight nod, a tribute as he thought to her obvious magnetic charm, turning away and struggling slowly through the crowd round the edge of the room looking for chums.

He was halfway along the wall, trying to get by another

large and noisy group, when he had felt the fairly heavy slap on his shoulder. He turned and there she was. Clear blue eyes shining brightly, a curl from her short blonde hair falling evocatively over one eye; and aggressive.

"Why were you laughing at me just now?"

"Sorry?"

"You were laughing to yourself – about me. Why?"

"I certainly was not laughing at you. If you must know – it seems to be worrying you for some reason – I noticed you and your friends because of the shrieks of mirth. You were obviously enjoying yourselves and it amused me to see that you had them all eating, so to speak, out of your hand. I wondered if they realised it."

A softer tone – "Oh, I see." Then the aggression again. "Does it matter if they were? Are you a wet blanket or something?"

He had stared at her for a moment without speaking. What a lovely little vixen she was, but there was a problem deep in there somewhere. He grinned at her. "No, I'm not a wet blanket. I enjoy parties, and I came to enjoy this one since you never know when the next one will be – or where. I certainly did not come *here* for a fight. Why do *you* want to fight?" He paused and then added quietly, "Why are you so touchy? What are you frightened of?"

She looked up at him, eyes blazing, breasts heaving – so enticingly, he had thought. "I'm not touchy. How dare you," she snapped. Then he had watched the anger ebb from her and the eyes soften. "Oh, damn you."

For a moment her defences were down and he saw fleetingly the real woman – beautiful, almost radiant, but unstable and vulnerable. He was fascinated. Before she raised her guard again he said gently, "My name's Tony Beckett, what's yours?"

She had looked down at her glass and frowned, as if undecided whether to argue or reveal her name. Then, "Celia Southwood".

"Well, Celia Southwood, I need another drink. Let me get you one, then let us find somewhere less crushed where we can argue in quieter surroundings." She gave him an angry look and seemed ready to throw him a spirited response, but then said nothing. When he returned with the drinks she followed him almost meekly out into the hall, where they climbed the stairs and sat on the top step, above the clamour.

He had often reflected how it was that, after the initial clash when he had so quickly and surprisingly pierced her armour, they had talked openly and unreservedly of themselves. He had learnt how a happy childhood on a fruit farm in Kent had been shattered when her father had been killed by a fall from an apple tree, and her mother had remarried too rapidly, she had thought, to a man she immediately intensely disliked. Her mother had claimed it was to provide a stable home life again. Celia declared it was damned unfair to Daddy's memory and felt the family idyll had been dealt a further blow, not restored. Going away to school had simply fed her restlessness. The war and the need for recruits to the womens' services had been a welcome opportunity to lead a different life away from home. She had volunteered for the WAAFs as soon as she left school – barely seventeen but looking older, she had lied about her age as so many others had done. She had rung her mother to tell her once she had been accepted.

When they talked about the war he had confessed to her that although he and his friends were convinced of the war's serious and utterly just objective – the defeat of Nazism and Fascism – he had also been secretly attracted by a sense of adventure. He had been somewhat ashamed of this feeling because he knew the war would bring much anguish and pain, and he had seen this in the columns of frightened refugees, mostly women and children crying and bewildered, that clogged the roads of France in 1940. It had happened also in the terrible air raids on London and the other cities. It was total war on a scale never before experienced. Yet there was in personal action a thrill he could not hide – a thrill first felt on the road to Dunkirk and again in the Western Desert with the SAS, taking part in some audacious raids on German airfields deep behind the lines. He remembered with surprise how he had explained to her then, as he had more recently to Larry and Ginger, that when the adrenaline flowed everything became clear and sharp, he became icy cold, and every second became a minute. He could not explain it; he was not proud of it; it was simply the way it was. On reflection he had been astonished that he had confessed all this to a young girl he had just met.

She had looked straight at him and quietly said, "Thank you for telling me that. It was very personal." There was a pause, then in a different mood again she said, "Well, what are you going to do to win this war for us?"

He smiled and acknowledged the tease. "Well, in 1940 I tried to do something with a bloody ancient Lewis gun. But now we can do more. At Alamein we were no longer outgunned. We had the equipment, the initiative and the spirit. Now we have the chance for a more mobile, more audacious form of action. Small parties, well armed, raiding the enemy back where he least expects it. I'll tell you more sometime." She could not then draw him further.

They had discussed home life, school, parents, service life as they knew it so far, ambition and politics over several drinks. Suddenly she had said, "I want to go. Will you take me back?" She was using a flat, not far from the Albert Hall, belonging to a friend. He had needed no persuading to go in 'for a coffee'. But the coffee never materialised. Once inside she had turned and kissed him, holding him close to her, then turned and taking his hand led him to the bedroom. With a complete lack of shyness she had stripped and hurriedly helped him out of his clothes. There had been no enticing, anticipatory caressing. She pulled him down on top of her on the bed and they satisfied each other urgently, almost desperately. She had clung to him next morning, but when it was time to go she had pushed him away. "Go on, then. Go." She was manning the ramparts again.

So began a strange romance that had lasted (if that was the word) on and off for years. Not long after his return to the desert, he discovered that her squadron had been posted to the Middle East. They had met when he had a few days in Cairo. For those few days they enjoyed an almost rapturous relationship. Later, after he had joined the Special Air Service, they were able to meet between raids. Life for him then was tense but exciting, and when they met she sensed his need for a deep relationship that required no preliminary development but an intense instant togetherness. At the same time their outward relationship had grown calmer, though it was never placid. She was always ready to hear whatever he chose to tell her about life behind the lines in the Western Desert or about the landings in Italy. Often she pressed him for detail he was not prepared to give. In a strange way she liked sharing the feeling of danger. Her fear of "being tied down" required that they never questioned each other about other friendships. So their mutual understanding grew the more they were together, and with a new

94

tenderness came a more mature excitement and contentment in their lovemaking. But still, whenever Tony tried to get her to face her fears she resisted. Once he had said, "You know, there is nothing frightening about normal happiness." "There's no such thing, Tony. No such thing," she had retorted angrily.

He found her telephone number and went to the phone. He waited, as always, a little apprehensively for her to answer. When he heard her repeat her number, he said, "Hello, Cels, this is Tony, Tony Beckett."

"Oh, I know who it is. You are the only one I allow to call me Cels. How are you? I was wondering when you would ring. I heard some time ago you were on your way back from that tropical hellhole."

"Well, I can tell you're in good form. First, the Ciudad Guayana region of Venezuela isn't a hellhole. Secondly, I shall not be going back. And thirdly, a number of things have happened since I arrived which delayed this call. I would like to explain it all to you, but not over the phone. Over dinner would be nicer."

"Not going back! That's interesting. What have you got in mind? Er . . . are you all right, Tony?"

He laughed at the afterthought. "Yes, I'm fine, but Roddy Holmes has been killed and then his house robbed. Larry, Ginger and I were at the funeral with Jennifer and her family when the burglary took place."

"Oh, how gruesome. How was he killed?"

"By a hit-and-run driver in rather strange circumstances which I will explain later."

"Oh, OK. How awful for Jenny. How is she? It's years since I saw her. She was a pretty steady type, wasn't she?"

Again he grinned to himself. "Jenny's taken it all pretty well, but she's still shocked and a bit worried about what it all might mean. Yes, steadiness is one of her enduring qualities."

"Ouch. I'll let that go, you bastard. I don't understand what you mean by 'what it might mean'."

"No, you won't, but that is among the things I want to talk about. I wonder if you are free for dinner tomorrow evening when I could tell you all."

"God, you've got a nerve, Tony Beckett. I don't hear from you for months and you expect me to be sitting here waiting for you to take me to dinner at short notice. Well, I'm not, and I'm not short of dinner dates, thank you."

"'Twas ever thus with us, Cels. I'm quite sure you've plenty of dates. Just tell me when you can squeeze me into your schedule. I was just hoping we could meet before I fly to New York next week to try to get a settlement on my broken contract."

"Sarcasm is a cheap form of wit. I've told you before it's beneath you." He heard the rustle of turning pages. She cleared her throat. "What time tomorrow, Tony, and where shall we meet?" The mellow tone was back; the petulance gone.

"Thank God you haven't changed, Cels. As difficult as ever. I don't think I could handle you if you were normal."

He heard her giggle. "I don't suppose your handling ability would suffer."

"Oh, Cels!" Mock shock. "I'll pick you up about seven o'clock and we'll go somewhere quiet. And before you say anything, I will choose where we go. I don't want one of your shriekingly smart advertising haunts where everyone is a 'darling'."

It was agreed.

The next day Tony forced himself to concentrate on finding a flat. Time was getting short and he decided to look for something in London. Looking for a job would be even more time-consuming. He gathered together the cuttings he had marked as 'possibles' and went off to visit agents: some in the Gloucester Road, some in South Kensington. It was a tiring, frustating day. One bedroom or two? Kitchen/dining room or lounge/dining room? Facing front or back? Upstairs? Ground floor? Garden flat (read basement)? Buy or rent? Not much to buy except on a lease. In view of the job uncertainty, better to rent on a short-term basis. There was the choice of the bustle of the Gloucester Road or the hubbub of South Kensington, though quieter roads off both localities offered some solace – together with higher rents. He must have looked at eight or nine flats, the agent ferrying him and encouraging him with non-stop chatter about how difficult "things" were these days, "which I expect you've noticed, coming back from abroad, sir". Eight or nine flats and up and down twice that number of flights of stairs, perhaps. He was tired and frustrated. Only one flat had appealed to him, just off Kensington Church Street: first floor, with a lounge/dining room overlooking a garden at the rear. The snag was, it was occupied by a couple who were on holiday. They had told the agent they would be moving on their return. But until they got back nothing was certain. So he asked for first refusal and started back to Gloucester Road. On the way back he spotted a pleasant-looking French restaurant not far from South Kensington Underground station. He read and approved the menu, peered inside, liked what he saw and reserved a table for two. Now he felt a bit better.

The restaurant lived up to his expectations and even pleased Celia. He had given her the address so they could meet there. When he arrived he insisted on a table at the back of the retaurant where he settled, facing the door with

97

an open bottle of chilled Pouilly Fumé in the stand and a glass of it on the table to keep him company during what he feared would be a bit of a wait. He remembered how at one of their rare meetings during the war they had 'discovered' Pouilly Fumé together. It had been a required aperitif ever since. In the event he did not have long to wait. 'Either business life had reformed her, in this respect at least, or she has made a special effort – probably the former,' he thought as he saw her come in and pause to ask for his table. He did not get up until, led by the head waiter, she was only a table away: he wanted to watch her as she approached. This had been a five-year gap – above average even for them – yet after each long interval he had always been amazed how little the years had changed her. Of course, she was no longer the pert, tempting girlish blonde he had first seen in uniform during his leave from North Africa, but increasingly a gracious and self-possessed beauty. As she got nearer he was again surprised – and glad – at the way she had retained such a voluptuous slenderness, which the tight-fitting fawn skirt, honey-coloured blouse and waisted jacket emphasised.

"Cels, how nice. Virtually on time too! Great effort!"

"Just for you, Tony, dear, you sarcastic bastard. And it was a bloody effort. You should be grateful." She offered him both cheeks and sat down. "You look pretty good yourself. You're well, I take it?"

"Yes, I'm fine, though a little depressed. Much better for seeing you."

She was looking around as he replied, as if the question had been but a formality and she was not really hearing the reply. "I like this. Quite a find. Well done. Why are you a bit depressed?" She had listened.

"Because of Roddy," he said, and reminded her she had

met him with Larry and Ginger during one of their wartime leaves. His account of Roddy's death and the burglary shocked her. She mocked Tony's suspicions, but agreed that 'something wasn't right'. With her attention absorbed by this and by Tony's explanation of his row with the 'Wall Street imperialists', she became the woman Tony knew, but rarely saw, as the real Celia. Ravishingly beautiful, enticing, yet intelligent and sympathetically understanding, forgetting her self-imposed need to keep alive her resentment of past unhappiness. It seemed she was a part of his life again as she had been from time to time before. 'If only this mood could last,' thought Tony as they were talking. 'If I were here more often perhaps I could make it last. Like this she's irresistible.'

After dinner they wandered hand in hand up to Hyde Park before catching a taxi to her flat in Paultons Square. They made love beautifully that night. They took their time, sensitive to reactions as they explored each others' bodies anew, each coaxing more feeling and more excitement out of the other. And when he entered her at the peak of the excitement she had caressed, stroked and kissed into him, she was warmly waiting and wanting. Together they plunged and thrust into a deep, lasting and satisfying rhythm.

Next morning they were reluctant to part, lazily drinking coffee and eating toast as they filled in details of things that had happened during their latest absence from each other. But she had to get back to her office and he had to think more about a job. "Choose one carefully, Tony," she said. "Don't frustrate your sense of adventure with a nine-to-five dose of purgatory which", she added teasingly, "would prevent me grumbling about your frequent absences."

"God," he had replied. "That would be a relief. Almost worth it, I should think."

"Get out, lover. Get out."

He got back to his flat at about ten o'clock. The phone was ringing as he opened the door. He made a dash for it. It was Ginger's voice.

"Skip where have you been, for God's sake. I've been trying to get you for a couple of hours."

"Well, I don't know that it's any of your business," he replied testily "but I've been with Cels. Why? What's the panic?"

"Oh, sorry. Have you listened to any news this morning?"

"Are you being funny? No, I haven't. Why?"

"It's awful. Larry's been killed. Murdered. There was a bit on the news about someone living in Fraser Gardens, Primrose Hill having disturbed a burglar late at night. I knew Larry lived somewhere there and I feared the worst. I rang his number. The Dutch aunt answered – sobbing – and confirmed it. The police came on and wanted to know who I was. I told them I was an old friend and Larry and I had recently met. They want me to go and see them to see if I 'can throw any light' et cetera. And you. I told them about us having been with him together . . . And, Tony, his study was turned over and all his personal belongings – papers, diaries, medals, and . . ."

"No, don't tell me . . ."

"Yes, you've guessed it – wartime photographs strewn all over the place."

"What the hell's going on?"

"I wish I knew, Tony. I wish I knew."

"I have a nasty feeling that if we have an opportunity to gather up what's left of Larry's collection we shall find they match what's left of Roddy's – with one missing. We will be no nearer finding out which picture is missing, but we shall know that in some way it's important to the bastards who have cynically taken another heroic life." Tony's voice was loud and bitter. Then, more controlled, "Did the police say when they would like to see us?"

"As soon as possible. We should contact Detective Inspector Richards at Larry's flat if we go today, or Primrose Hill station later. When can you make it?"

"Well, today. Today. Let's get along there now. I want to get to the bottom of this. It really does look as if these events are connected and if they are, there's something very nasty behind it all. The level of brutality shows it. How are you fixed today?"

"I'm free. My man's in London for a few days. Shall we go together?"

"Yes, grab a taxi and come round here as soon as you can. We'll take it on to Larry's place."

Larry's house in Fraser Gardens was cordoned off with the regulation Metropolitan Police tape. Tony and Ginger had to wait while the constable guarding the entrance went off to verify that the 'DI' wanted to see them. They were conducted to the study at the back of the house, where the DI stood by the desk surrounded by books, papers, file covers – and photographs – spread round him on the floor. On the far side of the desk a sheet covered the lifeless body of Gordon Lawrence. No one spoke as Tony and Ginger stared for a few moments at the crumpled form of the friend they had been with only a couple of days before. Tony turned with anger written all over his face and introduced themselves. John Richards was a squarely built, young-looking man, probably in his late thirties, Tony thought, with a wide-eyed open face above which short fair hair failed to settle on either side of a centre parting. He shook their hands and looked into their eyes with evident understanding.

Tony took another glance at the covered body. "How did it happen?"

"He must have interrupted the intruder, sir. It looks as if there was a struggle, but Mr Lawrence received two knife wounds, one of which, according to the doctor, was instantly fatal, I'm afraid."

"Bastards. Cowardly bastards." said Tony explosively.

"Quite so. Quite so." The Inspector paused. "Er . . . thank you for coming to help with these enquiries, gentlemen. I understand from talking to Mr Turner on the phone that your connection with the deceased is that you are friends – ex-comrades from the war, I believe – and that you were with him recently." He was assured and businesslike.

"That's right, Inspector," said Tony, and he went on to explain the circumstances of their last meeting at Roddy Holmes's funeral, the nature of Roddy's fatal 'accident', and the burglary during the funeral service.

"How very unpleasant for the widow."

"Yes, but it was fortunate that we were there. I think it helped. However, it was not until the following day that Mrs Holmes discovered that the only thing taken by the burglar was one wartime photograph. We believe it was of a scene at one of our actions, during our mission in France in the war. But we do not know which action and we do not understand how it can justify burglary and murder. I know there is no proof to support me but I believe those two incidents – Roddy Holmes's death and the burglary – are connected. I also believe the amount of wrong-number telephone calls the Holmes household received just before all this happened had something to do with it."

"What telephone calls?"

Tony explained how, when he had asked Jenny about anything unusual happening before Roddy's accident and

102

before the break-in, she'd remembered the phone calls in which the caller simply said, "Sorry, wrong number" and rang off.

"I have to say, Inspector, that the Hawksworth Police do not accept my theory. Nevertheless I can conceive of no reasonable explanation as to how Mr Holmes could have been *accidentally* run down when running on the right-hand side of a clear road in broad daylight. And the fact that shortly afterwards one of his photographs was stolen on a risky break-in, made me – the three of us when Mr Lawrence was alive – more than a bit suspicious. Now, it seems to me that this brutal killing of Mr Lawrence supports that suspicion."

"Well, I understand your point, sir, and appreciate why you feel strongly about it. Of course, what you have said about Mr Holmes's accident and the burglary at Hawksworth is new to me, and I shall have to contact the Hawksworth Police to get a report from them." He saw Tony's frown and impatient gesture. "It is not that I doubt what you have told me, but in view of what you have said I am obliged to contact them. It may help our investigations here." He made his point emphatically.

"I'm sorry, Inspector. But you will see that what has happened here ..." – he turned and pointed down at Larry's corpse – "suggests, if only because of our wartime connection and the photographs we all possess, that this is part of a pattern of ruthless events."

"We don't know about the photographs here yet, sir."

"That's true, but my guess is that what is left of them here will match those that were left with Mrs Holmes. Would you let me take them to compare the two sets?"

DI Richards thought for a moment. "For the time being we must keep them to test for fingerprints, but if you could borrow Mrs Holmes's set and bring them down to the station I would be happy to sit with you and see if they match."

"That's fair enough. I'll go and get them tomorrow. Now, I wonder if you would be good enough, Inspector, to ask Larry's Dutch aunt . . ."

"Who?"

Tony smiled and explained. "The housekeeper, Edith . . . about any unusual calls?"

The inspector turned to his constable. "Ask the house-keeper to come in."

Edith came in red-eyed, pale and sobbing, holding a very damp handkerchief to her mouth. As soon as she saw Tony and Ginger she ran towards them. "Oh dear, sir, it's terrible. What are we coming to? Burglars who will strike a dear kind man dead. They should be strung up. That's what . . ." – and turning to the Inspector – "that's what you have to do, sir. Catch them and string them up! If only he hadn't gone to the study – but then he always did after being away." Tony put his arm round her and tried to comfort her.

"Yes, it's a terrible shock to us all, but especially to you, Edith – finding him . . ."

He immediately regretted referring to that traumatic moment. Edith wailed and moaned and sank her head into her hands again. They sat her down, fetched water and tried to calm her. Then Tony tried again.

"Could you just answer a couple more questions from the inspector, Edith?"

She sniffed, blew her nose and nodded.

"Well, Edith, the first thing is, I can assure you we will do everything to catch whoever did this awful thing and bring them, or him, to justice." Edith nodded again and looked up at DI Richards with a forced little smile. "It's just that I wondered if you noticed anything unusual in the last few days?"

"Unusual, sir? Where? Here?" she said indignantly. "Everything's been normal here. That's my job. Look after poor Mr Lawrence when he's here, and keep everything going normally when he's away."

"Yes, of course, and I'm sure you do it very well – but just think and see if you can remember anything a bit out of the ordinary. Callers, for instance?"

"No, no callers. Lots of telephone messages, of course. Always is . . . er . . . was . . . when he went away. But I take the messages down with the date and time and leave them on his desk . . . or did. There were two from you, sir," she said, turning to Tony. "Weren't there?"

Tony nodded. Inspector Richards picked up a bundle of paper from the desk. "Yes, I have them here, just as you said. But I see there were two where the caller did not leave his name. One the day before yesterday and one yesterday morning. Could you tell whether they were from the same man?"

"Oh! Oh, well, I think they must have been. The messages were exactly the same, I seem to remember. He just said he wanted to speak to Mr Lawrence on business. Yes, that was it – I remember now his funny voice."

"What do you mean, 'funny voice'?"

"Well, I couldn't understand it properly. I had to keep asking him to repeat what he was saying, though he didn't seem to want to and got a bit cross. Raised his voice to me he did. I didn't like that," she added in an icy tone.

"Can you describe the voice? Or say why you had difficulty understanding it?"

"Well, he wasn't from London, that's for sure. But I don't

105

know where from. A northener, perhaps, or from Scotland, or some other foreign part. I don't know." They all noticed unblinkingly Edith's views of where foreigners began. "Oh, and he said it in a funny way each time. I remember he said, 'No, it is a business matter, isn't it?' when I asked him what it was about. 'Isn't it?' he said as if asking me. I thought that was funny."

The inspector caught Tony's expression of satisfaction as he thanked Edith for her trouble. "You will let me know when I can clear up after poor Mr Lawrence has gone, won't you, sir. He wouldn't like it in such a mess," she said as she stood up to go.

"Of course I will," he said with a smile of sympathy and understanding.

"Well, Inspector, what do you make of that? The unnamed messages could have been the equivalent of the 'wrong number' messages in Roddy Holmes's case, couldn't they? The pattern is the same."

"Perhaps, Mr Beckett. Perhaps. But it's not *quite* the same pattern, is it? Why not just accept the 'wrong number' theory?"

"Mmm. I thought you might say that. But it is a very similar pattern of events so far as the burglary is concerned. Certainly, this murder is different; it was not planned, and the telephone oddities are different, but my guess is – which I know you will not like – that this voice belongs to a different man engaged on the same mission – searching for a certain photograph."

"Maybe, maybe. But you must remember, sir, we don't yet know whether Mr Holmes was murdered. The only evidence we have of a link between these tragedies is the friendship and wartime comradeship between you all . . ."

"And the missing photo . . ." Tony interrupted.

"Again and with respect," DI Richards continued firmly, "we don't know that yet either. I have said I will get a report from Hawksworth, and I will consider your theory about the photographs as soon as you can borrow Mrs Holmes's set. At this stage of our enquiries I can't do more than that, can I?"

"No, that's fair, Inspector. I apologise for my impatience. You'll understand that I'm very concerned and I want some answers."

"We both do, Mr Beckett and it's my job to find them. Now, I must thank you again for coming so promptly. I must get this enquiry launched. Apart from seeing you with the other set of photographs, I take it that you will both be available for further . . . er . . . discussion if necessary?"

They both nodded. As they turned to go Tony suddenly remembered, "By the way, I have to go to the United States for three or four days – on business."

"That will be all right, sir. Let me know when you are back."

Chapter 6

Sad, angry and puzzled, Tony and Ginger left the cordoned-off house and walked along Fraser Road to Prince Albert Road looking for a taxi. The motorcyclist wearing an old pilot's helmet, complete with side flaps, and goggles, who had stopped opposite to make an adjustment to the engine, quickly remounted. He turned round and slowly followed their direction, bending down frequently to look at the engine, which appeared to be causing problems. A short way down Prince Albert Road they found a free taxi. Inside Ginger turned to Tony. "What do you make of it all, skip?"

"With my naturally suspicious mind. I'm even more of the opinion that it's sinister, Ginger. Pretty sinister. As you will have guessed from our conversation with DI Richards I am convinced that Roddy, the two burglaries and Larry are all connected. I know that view can be written off as a hunch. We have to find evidence to support it."

"Bloody motorcyclists," the taxi driver bellowed. "One minute they roar past and cut you up, the next they're right up your exhaust pipe. Look at this silly bugger, right on my tail. If I had to brake suddenly he'd be in real trouble." He pulled into the side, waving the cyclist to pass. Tony and Ginger turned to see the subject of their driver's rage, but were too late: man and machine accelerated past.

"Look, we can't really talk about it here. It's too late for a proper lunch. Why not come up to my flat, open a bottle of wine, see what's in the fridge and do a proper debriefing?"

"OK, Ginger. You're on."

They redirected the driver and settled back with their thoughts. Some ten minutes later the cab pulled up in front of the block of flats in Cranleigh Gardens where Ginger had his pied-à-terre. As the driver put his arm through the open window to open the door for them, he said, "There you are. I told you he didn't know what he was doing. He's over there playing with his bloody engine. Didn't get far, did he? Nor could he with a clapped out bit of machinery like that," he said triumphantly. Tony gave a quick glance across the road without paying the crouched figure any serious attention. His mind was on the events of the last few days.

Inside the flat Ginger went to explore the fridge while Tony moved into the small lounge dining room. It was everything a bachelor's pied-à-terre is expected to be: newspapers on the floor; two used coffee cups and a tumbler on the table; shoulder bag from the last trip abroad with 'his man' open on the floor, socks and shirt still inside; magazines piled on a side table; crumpled cushions on the two easy chairs and the small two-seater settee. But it was a long way from, and much better than, the grubby terraced house on the Isle of Dogs with one room and a kitchen (which doubled as a bathroom) downstairs and two rooms upstairs, and a lavatory outside adjacent to next door's, where he and his sister had spent their early years and which his father cared little for after his wife had died.

Tony shouted to Ginger for writing paper and pen.

"Writing pad in the small bureau in the corner; may be under something. Dig deep, sir, dig deep. Pen in top drawer."

Tony groaned as he tried to catch numerous letters and

papers that fell out when he opened the bureau lid. He burrowed into a lot more. The pad was at the bottom of the pile.

"Don't write to anyone very often, do you?" he asked as Ginger came through the door with a tray bearing a bottle of Julienas, two glasses and the carcass of a chicken that still had half its breast, one wing and a leg.

"Not if I can help it," he replied cheerfully. "It's incriminating." And with a grin he said, "No trouble in finding it, then, I see."

Tony glared. "God knows how you managed to keep your kit in good order."

"Ah! That was different – a matter of life or death. This is a matter of living."

"Ha ha."

Ginger set down his tray, poured some wine, and hacked at the carcass until there were two roughly equal platefuls. "OK. Let debriefing commence."

"Right. Let us assume first a benign scenario. Roddy Holmes, out on his morning run on the right-hand side of the road, gets hit by a car from behind. The driver, who wasn't looking where he was going, is scared because he's obviously done something terribly wrong. He conceals the car. Tells no one. On the day Roddy is buried a petty burglar, who may have come by motorcycle which he left parked up the road, spots an empty house and breaks in. Doesn't want any silver, radios, or other portable loot, so – it seems – pockets one of the wartime photographs ripped from an album. Before Roddy was killed he had a number of 'wrong number' calls on the telephone. Before the funeral, Jenny also gets some 'wrong number' calls. By coincidence, a couple of nights after that burglary Gordon

Lawrence, a friend of Roddy's, returns late from a business trip and disturbs a burglar in his flat. Tackles him and gets knifed. The burglar escapes. Appears to have taken nothing, but may have grabbed a photo from Larry's wartime collection. Edith the housekeeper remembers some calls for Larry from a man with an accent who would not leave his name. Roddy and Larry were wartime comrades on the same mission in France and each had a set of photographs of that mission which Roddy had taken. However, there is nothing to link these incidents together. How does it sound so far?"

"In a word – or two – un-bloody-likely."

"Right, now for the malign scenario. Same chain of events. But Roddy was deliberately run down by someone who wanted him out of the way, perhaps knowing that with schools on half-term he would be around when he wanted to break in to get from his collection a certain photograph of an incident on the AMCA mission. Having got rid of Roddy, a convenient time was while everyone was at the church. The villain – or villains – knows that there is more than one set of photos around, so they need to remove all copies of that certain one. We don't yet know why. Villain with foreign accent – perhaps a Frenchman – finds out that Larry is away on business, so does not have to plan his murder. But Larry returns while the burglary is in progress and tackles intruder. In a straight fight Larry would have nobbled him. Tragically, the villain has a knife and kills Larry and makes off with the photo he came for. That last supposition is valid only if we find by comparing the remains of both sets of photos that both are missing the same one. How does that sound?"

"Unfortunately, that sounds plausible. It means that something that happened on that mission twenty-odd years ago is

111

seriously worrying someone now! Seriously enough to murder. Why now, after so long? Incidentally, why do you think the foreign-sounding voice could have been a French one?"

"The construction of the sentence that the Dutch aunt said she remembered – assuming she remembered it correctly. She said it was 'funny' because he said, 'No, it's a business matter, isn't it?' as if he was asking her. Well, that could have been someone unfamiliar with idiomatic English making an almost literal translation of the way he would have said it, something like, '*Non, c'est une chose d'affaires, n'est-ce pas?*'"

"Ah, I see. In any case a French connection wouldn't be surprising if our suspicions prove right."

"Quite so. But Ginger, there is another implication in our theory which I'm sure you'll have spotted. You and I have sets of those photos. Mine are packed away in New York. Yours are temporarily inaccessible in Devon. But the villains do not know that. We could be future targets. I suggest we keep in close touch. Not long telephone calls, but brief 'checking in' ones. And if either of us gets a wrong number, or any kind of 'funny' call, let the other know straightaway. We do not, repeat not, wait to see if it will be followed by others. Just one of those could be a danger signal, and if it comes we'll plan accordingly. OK, Ginger?"

"Received and understood."

"I will ring Jenny tonight, and ask if we can borrow what is left of Roddy's set of photographs. I hope I don't have to tell her the reason over the phone. I don't want her to start worrying on her own. I'll see if I can pick them up tomorrow and go along to see DI Richards with them. Incidentally, I took a good view of him; broader-minded and more flexible than most. I will ring you after I've seen Richards. But don't forget, anything suspicious judged in the light of our view of events, get in touch immediately. You know my movements tomorrow. Where are you?"

"I shall be here apart from a short shopping expedition down the road. Good luck with Jenny."

"Yes, thanks. I have to get back now. We'll keep in touch."

Back at Gloucester Road he first went through the waiting mail, among which was a cable from New York confirming his visit and appointment, and a couple of letters from estate agents telling him of possible new vacancies. Unable to concentrate on them he put them on the mantelpiece for future attention. After a tour of the apartment, seeing nothing but trying to focus on his forthcoming conversation with Jenny, he walked to the phone and called her. She was delighted to hear from him; yes, she was gradually adjusting to her new circumstances and coping as she knew Roddy would want her to; Claudia was still with her; friends were very good to her, but of course there was a huge gap; she was keeping herself busy. Tony could feel the bravery through the phone. When he asked if he could borrow the album for a couple of days because he thought if he studied it again he might find some clue about the missing print, she agreed immediately. He would arrive about mid-morning, but, no, he would not stay for lunch; there was much to do before going to New York. Coffee? Yes, please, that would be very welcome. He put the phone down, relieved that he had finished the conversation pleasantly without being asked any questions about Larry or Ginger. That had to be faced on the morrow.

Before walking down the road to a small but comfortable restaurant he had discovered, which served good Italian food, he poured himself a drink and, sitting back, afforded himself the luxury of marvelling at life's infinite capacity to surprise. From being forced to leave his job in South America, which he had enjoyed so much, with its mixture of security work, public affairs and community development, and trying to reconcile himself to a tedious 'home' job, he found himself thrust within a few days into a sinister, violent mystery that had taken the lives of two close friends. Unpredictable in the extreme. How would it turn out? If it were not for his need of money for the future, he would forget about the corporate imbeciles in New York and concentrate exclusively on finding the answer to the mystery and in some way avenge his comrades. That was the important objective. However unexpected, what was needed to achieve that was, still, a familiar way of living and he was comfortable with it. While he had thought he had left the necessary skills, thrills and mentality behind, was his future going to be one of unsought action? Or was it in his blood to make choices that led inevitably to that sort of life?

The drive to Hawksworth the next morning was trouble-free. He had successfully missed the early, workbound commuters. The sun was bright between patches of cloud and pleasantly warm. Not yet hot. The year was still young; a spring morning, full of promise, dormant life reviving everywhere along the way; the countryside as he had remembered it over the past few years. The overseas worker always retains an image of everything – scenes, even emotions – that epitomises his love of the home country. This had been his. The only shadow now cast over it was the uneasy feeling that something unpleasant was afoot. Larry's murder may not have been planned, but it showed that whoever wanted copies of that photo would stop at nothing to get them. But, however deep his own concern, he must not allow the news to alarm Jenny. He rehearsed different approaches but concluded there was no nice way of referring to a ruthless killing. He arrived at the house at about eleven.

"It sounded on the phone as if you are in a bit of a hurry.

The coffee's nearly ready. Go and sit in the lounge. The album is on the table in a carrier bag."

"Jenny, you're marvellous."

As he waited for her to come back he pondered on just how marvellous she really was: so thoughtful, so organised, he thought. She and Roddy were so suited to each other that the brutal ending of their relationship must be a massive blow probably not yet fully felt. He was suddenly vividly aware of the immense personal problem Jenny was trying to face up to. For her now the missing photo was a minor issue, even though it could have been an important factor in the tragedy that had struck her. He *had* to find the reason – and the bastards responsible. His anger was heightened by his renewed compassion for Jenny.

She was talking as she re-entered the room carrying a tray with a coffee pot and two cups. 'I think it's a good idea of yours to study the album quietly. Something may remind you of what was there."

"Yes. Incidentally, is Claudia staying with you for long?" He tried to make it sound casual.

"She says she wants to stay a while until she has adjusted to the loss of her father." Clever girl, thought Tony. "She's a dress designer and can do a lot of her work at home. When she has to go up to the studio in London, she can commute from here quite easily."

"That will be good for her, and I'm sure you'll be able to help her." He had no difficulty in concealing the real reason why he was glad.

She poured the coffee. "Will you keep the album for long? I don't mind, but it's even more precious to me now."

"I can understand that, Jenny, and I will let you have it back as soon as I can. But I have to confess I did not give you the real reason why I want it."

"Oh?"

"It's bad news again, Jenny. As if we haven't had enough. You see, Larry has been killed."

"Oh God! Larry? But we were all together only the other day . . . How? . . . When?"

"It was the night before last. He came home late from a business trip and disturbed an intruder in his study. There was a struggle and Larry was stabbed. Apparently, he died immediately."

"Oh, that's dreadful. Poor, poor Larry. Such a nice man. But what on earth is happening to us, Tony? Why should such close friends suddenly be taken from us in these violent ways?" She was bewildered, as he had been, but she could see no answers to her questions. "But what has the album got to do with it? Oh no . . . Don't tell me . . ." Suddenly she saw an explanation she didn't want to accept.

"Yes. I think you've guessed it, Jenny. I'm sorry to say, Larry's papers and wartime photos were gone through and we need to check whether any are missing. I didn't like worrying you, but you had to know. Moreover, we only have your set of photos available at present . . ."

"Of course you had to tell me. I always ask after the others anyway. You think they have taken one of Larry's photos, don't you? And you think it's the same one that was taken from this set?" Tony looking straight at her, nodded slowly. "What does it mean? And who are they?"

"If the same one *has* been taken it probably means there is something in that shot important enough for someone to rob and kill for. And that makes it very important. I don't know who 'they' are. People with some link to something that happened about a quarter of a century ago, which is now worrying them very much. Until we get some idea about the subject of that photo we shan't know who they are."

116

"Obviously important enough to rob for. Twice. Which is bad enough. But you said 'important enough to kill for'. Isn't that carrying suspicion a bit far? After all, Larry's death may have been an accident in the sense that the burglar did not set out to kill him, but killed him to avoid capture. Ghastly and foul, but not premeditated murder. And so far we have no evidence that Roddy's death was anything but a horrid and unnecessary accident that has agonisingly changed our lives. That is difficult enough to cope with, but I don't think I could handle the thought that he was murdered; that someone who probably did not know him – know what a fine man he was – set out to kill him."

This was the very point that he did not want to discuss with Jenny. "I expect you are right. Part of my training left me with a really nasty, suspicious mind. It's a protection in some circumstances, but a handicap in others. I can't really control it, you know," he said with a wry grin, trying to refocus the conversation. "It just clicks in whenever I come across something I don't understand. Of course, it's the photo we must concentrate on. When we compare sets we may know more."

"Could it be anything to do with that lorry full of loot in the German convoy you ambushed? You mentioned it when we went through the album together. Was there anything important in that, do you think? It was stolen art treasures, wasn't it?"

"Yes I have wondered about that too. Unfortunately – well, unfortunate for what we are now considering – we did not have time to examine the contents thoroughly. When I opened the covers at the back of the trucks I saw lots of oil paintings in gilt frames, statuettes in what I thought might be jade, large vases and dishes that looked like porcelain, and a big chest with metal fastenings. The urgency at the time was to get rid of it; to take care of our wounded; to tidy up and remove ourselves from the scene. I closed it up and had it driven away to a temporary hiding place until I could think what I could do with it. It was a burden I did not want at the time. The trouble is that I cannot remember whether Roddy took a picture of it or its contents."

"Might the German commander of the convoy, or whoever was trying to get away with the stuff, be trying to trace it? Or the original owner?"

"Well, the German commander was killed when Léon ran into the patrol after the ambush. But perhaps the intended recipient is still searching for his ill-gotten gains. Or the original owner is looking for his property. But I do not understand why it is happening after so long. Perhaps we should start looking at both those possibilities. It will require a lot of backtrack sleuthing, if you see what I mean. Was the German commander the actual thief? Or someone else? Was the treasure meant for someone high up in the German political hierarchy? If it is the original owner trying to recover it, why should he need to rob to find out about it? After all, I was told the loot had been handed in to the authorities after Paris was liberated. I did not question it. I really was not that interested. Perhaps the Anglophile marquis did not hand it over – that's another possibility. Perhaps he was an art collector. He should be easy to trace. The German commander and the original owner, not so easy. But to all these questions another important one is attached – why now? Why not earlier? I think we shall have to look into this aspect seriously, because at present we have no other possible explanation. It will be a long and involved journey of enquiry.

"Yes, I see."

"Anyway Jenny, one step at a time, and the first one is to

compare the two sets. Thank you for letting me borrow the album. I know how you value it, and I will take great care and return it as soon as I can. Bless you, and please do not worry. It may all be simpler than we think."

He was halfway towards his car in the drive when she shouted, "I bet it *is* to do with that loot lorry. Someone who shouldn't have it has got it and they don't want people to know how they came by it. You'll see."

Tony turned and waved as he reached his car. "Maybe. Maybe. Bye, Jenny."

As he drove back he decided to go straight to Primrose Hill police station in the hope that DI Richards would be able to see him. He could, but would Mr Beckett mind waiting for ten minutes. Tony did not mind, nor did he mind waiting the half-hour it actually took to see him. John Richards advanced to the front desk energetically, in shirt sleeves and looking very fit with tousled hair, a friendly smile, hand outstretched and profusely apologetic. No red tape-bound bullshitter this one, thought Tony. His office was small. On the inadequate desk a tray carrying half a dozen buff-coloured folders, a blotter on which doodles were visible beneath a pile of papers, and two telephones covered most of the space. Two grey filing cabinets with more buff-coloured files on top stood in one corner; a hatstand in the other. The DI pulled the one spare chair to the front of the desk. "Not much room, I'm afraid," he said, stating the obvious with a grin.

"I presume you've brought Mrs Holmes's photograph album," he said, noting instantly the package in Tony's hands.

"Yes. You probably remember the conversation when I told you about Mr Holmes's death and the burglary on the day of his funeral."

"I remember it well. I have been in touch with Sergeant Thompson and am aware of the situation as he sees it." Tony noted the caution and warmed again to the DI's open-minded professionalism. He watched as he went to a filing cabinet, opened a drawer and ran his finger over the contents before extracting a large envelope, from which he took a handful of loose photographs. Tony opened the album and as he turned the pages they matched the prints one by one until they reached the empty used space at the end. But there was nothing left in Larry's set to fit it. In vain hope Richards picked up the corner of the envelope and shook it over the desk. Nothing.

They looked at each other and Tony waited. "Your hunch was right, Mr Beckett. The same photograph has been taken. That seems to have been the motive for the burglary in which Mr Lawrence was murdered. The question is, why? As we went through those pictures, there were so many questions I wanted to ask, all of them about the impressive, brave mission they record. I wish I had time to learn about it from you. But for now we urgently need to know the subject matter of that missing shot. That should tell us why it is worth carrying out dangerous burglaries and killing for. Have you any ideas you can pull from your memory that might tell us what that subject might be?"

"Nothing certain. The only possibility I see at the moment is that it has something to do with a lorry full of expensive-looking objets d'art that was in a German military convoy we shot up in 1944 when we were part of that mission. On the advice of one of our SOE agents in the area we handed them over to a marquis who was described to us as Anglo-phile. He hid the articles in his chateau and concealed the lorries in one of his barns until the war was over. I was told the loot was then handed to the French authorities. Of course, once it had been delivered to the marquis, I had no direct knowledge of what happened thereafter."

"I see. Could it have gone astray? Is someone trying to find out how it went astray and who was responsible for stealing it? Do you know if the SOE man is still around? And the marquis?"

"Well, it could be any of those things, but it might also be something else. I'm afraid I don't know whether the SOE man and the marquis are still alive. I could find out about the SOE man through an association I belong to, and if he is still around he will know the identity of the marquis. It's the only plausible lead we have, though identifying the photo might be quicker."

"Thank you. I understand you all had sets. So you and Mr Turner also have one each. Anyone else?"

"Yes, the two Maquis commanders: Georges Lebrun and Jean Boulanger."

"Do you know where they are?"

"I think I may have Georges Lebrun's address in Chartres. At least the address where he was. I'm not sure about Jean Boulanger. He's somewhere in France, I believe, but when I last heard – you know, I've been abroad for some years – he was not well. Again, I can try to find out."

"Well, it shouldn't be difficult to find the missing subject from one of your . . ."

"Not so easy, unfortunately. Mine are in a packing case in New York. Ginger Turner's are in a farmhouse in Devon and he can't get them until his sister gets back from Canada. It looks as though we shall have to track down Georges Lebrun."

"I now share your suspicions about a possible link between these incidents and that the motive is a secret that the photo contains, but I have to work on evidence. It would be helpful if you could get hold of one of the existing sets. But there is another important point I have to mention – though I'm sure you will have thought of it: if the worst of our suspicions are right you may all be in some danger. I have to say, however, I do not have enough evidence of that potential danger to offer you protection, if you would want it."

Tony smiled. "Thanks for the offer you can't make – I wouldn't accept it if you could. I think Ginger and I would prefer to protect ourselves. I think we can remember enough about the ways and means. But of course we must identify that photo. I think the next step is to find Georges Lebrun."

They shook hands and Tony left the police station. When he got back to the flat, true to his word he rang Ginger. It was nearly six o'clock. When Ginger answered he told him about the meeting with DI Richards and the vain attempt to identify the missing photo, "proving" he said, "that as we suspected the two burglaries had the same objective and were linked in motive." For once Ginger listened quietly. Then when Tony had finished he said, "Tony, I've had a couple of wrong-number calls."

"Christ, Ginger, why didn't you say so?"

"I'm saying so, Tony – the instant I could get a word in."

"OK. OK. When was this?"

"About lunchtime and about half an hour ago."

"How did he sound? I assume it was a male voice."

"Yes it was. And he was a foreigner – but it was too short a conversation to identify the accent. In any case I'm not very good at that."

"Right, Ginger. He must be fairly anxious to get on with whatever he's about to try you twice in one day. He could well try again. How do you think he got on to you?"

"I've been thinking about that. It might have been the motorcyclist that taxi driver was on about when we came back from Larry's. He must have been watching Larry's place and followed us back. If you remember, he stopped outside the flats. Perhaps the same bike seen near Roddy's house that day – perhaps the same swine who . . ."

"Of course. Of course. We should have been more alert. Now then, is there some kind of back way into your block of flats that people would not normally know about?"

"Yes, there is. In fact there are two. There are outside fire-escape stairs on each side of the block with exits from kitchen doors of the flats. But they are partly visible from the first floor upwards from the front. However, at the back there's an entrance to a basement which contains the heating furnaces and there's a staircase up to the main entrance lobby from it. I've had to use it on occasions coming back very late. You don't reach it from Cranleigh Gardens, but down a passage from the road at the back, and the entrance itself is hidden at ground level by the wall round the back of the block."

"Sounds ideal. Here's what we'll do. I'm coming over to spend the night with you . . ."

"Oh, darling . . ."

"Shut up and listen, you fool. You leave your flat in the normal way. I'll meet you in some coffee shop in Kensington High Street, then we'll slip back via the basement and wait – armed with heavy objects."

"Great, Tony. Kardomah coffee shop. One block west of Cranleigh Gardens. What time?"

"What's the food and drink position?"

"Not up to scratch, I'm afraid. I was going to . . ."

"OK. I'll pick up some grub and some wine on the way –

so just before seven. Is that OK with you? If our villain is hoping to try anything tonight I expect it will be much later."

"Fine. See you there."

Tony went to the bedroom and changed into a black roll-neck sweater, grey slacks, an old pair of soft-soled suede shoes, and dark-blue blazer. He felt happy, buoyant. There was a touch of excitement again in life. At the front door he selected a heavy walking stick from Jimmy Hardaker's collection standing in a tall Chinese-style pottery jar, went out and strode up Gloucester Road toward Kensington Gardens using some of the surveillance techniques which though unused for years he had never forgotten. So, stopping suddenly to look at a menu in a restaurant window, crossing the road, and back again, retying his shoe lace, doing a short detour through Canning Place and De Vere Gardens, he satisfied himself he was not being followed. Fifteen minutes of brisk walking took him to Kensington High Street where he bought wine, French bread, frankfurter sausages at an overcharging all-night food store. Farther down the road he found the Kardomah. He chose a table away from the window but from which he could watch the street. Ginger arrived about five minutes later. Over coffee he asked, "Did you come straight here, Ginger?"

Ginger looked at Tony, a grin spreading over his rugged friendly face, light-blue eyes twinkling. "O ye of little faith! We're on operational alert, aren't we?"

Tony smiled back and nodded to acknowledge the light-hearted rebuke. "Yes, we are. Just checking. You forgot your prismatic compass once."

"Not that again! You're like a bloody elephant. Never forget. I wish I could remember the things you've forgotten."

"Don't try. Seriously, now we've proved that the object of

124

Larry's burglary was to get hold of another copy of the same photo, discovering its identity is urgent. Getting to Georges Lebrun's set may be the quickest way. But what we're expecting tonight may not happen. It might be tomorrow – or the next night . . ."

"Or never."

"Quite. If this event is delayed we may have to take a decision to split – against my bettter judgement – and one of us go snooping round Chartres. I'm time-limited because of my appointment in New York, which is pretty crucial."

"Understood. And if it comes to that – and if it comes to me – I may have problems too. I'll have to try to find out my man's travel plans. I can't break the contract."

"Yes, I realise that. Let's pray for action tonight." He looked at his watch. "Come on then. Take us in the back way. Which direction from here?"

"Turn right outside, Tony."

"You leave first. I'll watch from here. Then meet you down the road in a couple of minutes."

When he was satisfied that no one had followed Ginger after he left the cafe, at least on this side of the road, he went out. Outside he turned left, walked a few yards, crossed the road, stood in a doorway for a few minutes then turned round and walked the other way. There was no tail. To judge from the technique of the motorcyclist, who it seemed had followed their taxi, he did not think they were dealing with a sophisticated opponent. He found Ginger in a shop doorway studying cameras. Together they set off and, led by Ginger, were soon walking down a narrow alley between apartment blocks to the back of Broadmere Court – a name with a rural connotation hard to reconcile with the vicinity of Kensington High Street. With the aid of a torch dramatically produced by Ginger with a comment about forward thinking, they made their way round the boilers and up a short flight of stairs to the entrance lobby. In the lift they went to the floor above Ginger's flat and walked down one – a precaution by no means foolproof with three flats on each floor – to leave the indicator in the lobby showing a floor other than Ginger's.

Chapter 7

Once inside the flat they went round drawing all curtains except in the kitchen, where the thin blinds would not have concealed any illumination. They quickly set the French bread, the cheese and the wine on two trays and left them on the kitchen table. In the small lounge Ginger took a table lamp off the bureau and put it on the floor behind a chair, giving them just enough light. From a cupboard in the corner he selected a club from his golf bag. "A number-two wood: should do nicely," he said, grinning at Tony. With this on the floor beside him he settled in one chair, while Tony settled in another with his walking stick on the floor. There was nothing to do but wait.

"A bit like lying up at night shivering with cold in that wadi during those watches on the coast road in Libya, isn't it? Watching the traffic, waiting for a long-enough gap and for the right time when we could get everyone across to get to the airfield a mile or two – we never knew just how far – farther on," said Ginger.

"Yes, or waiting under wet bushes, bitten by mosquitoes on the way to recce an ambush site in central France. God, how it rained there that summer. I think my mind was more on the bloody mosquitoes than the possibility that German patrols could appear unexpectedly on the roads. But I give this marks for superior comfort."

"I'll say. Warmer than a freezing bloody wadi, and fewer

mosquitoes and less rain than those days and nights deep in the French countryside."

That brief exchange roused memories which occupied both of them for a while. There was no need for conversation: each knew the nature of the other's thoughts. Some time later – how long? – Tony returned to the present and consulted his watch. "Might be a good time to get the nosh over and done with, Ginger."

Ginger went into the kitchen, heated the frankfurters and poured the wine. He returned with a tray in each hand.

"Also slightly better rations than the old days, I must say. But only one glass of wine tonight. Got to keep awake."

"Quite right."

"Although they did their best for us in those days with their meat-and-veg cubes, and our home-made nettle soup, it did get boring. Sometimes I would have given anything for a tin of bully – or beans – or both. But you know, it's a funny thing, when I think back I miss some of it – I shouldn't, because it was war, but I do."

Tony was silent for a while, then in a soft and serious tone murmured, "Yes, I know, Ginger. So do I sometimes. I think it was having the focus of a single purpose, the intensity of the comradeship, and the relative independence. Within the task given us we made it or bitched it by our own efforts. And I'm afraid there's no denying the thrill we got from being kept alert by a fearful kind of excitement. I suppose you still get a bit of that from your job as a minder."

"Not the same, Tony. It's harder to stay alert. There's no obvious threat. There's a general kind of danger. We are told by the authorities that there is the possibility of terrorist activity in the context of local politics, or assassination of targeted foreigners with business interests that are resented, or – more likely – threats of kidnap in order to extract a

128

ransom for their war chests. Yet it's all a bit nebulous – you don't know whether your man or his business is a likely target. He may never be, but he could be tomorrow. You devise what you think are suitable precautions that will not be anticipated by the unknown villain, and then wonder if it's all a waste of time. Perhaps no one wants to steal the man's documents – or kidnap him. It can get boring and when it does there's the danger of relaxing on the job. Sometimes I think it would be nice to get home and have a round of golf for a bit of excitement. No, it's not the same."

"I hadn't thought of it like that. Anyway, let us see what tonight brings. It may be as good as a game of golf."

They ate contentedly and silently. When they had finished the glass of wine, Ginger took the trays into the kitchen.

"I left the trays rather precariously perched on the shelf between the window and the door," he said as he returned.

"Good thinking." Tony looked at his watch again. "Nearly eleven. Time to settle into watch-and-wait mode. I suggest we do it in two-hour shifts. Agreed?"

"Yep. I'll take first go if you like, as you've been driving."

"Kind of you. OK."

Ginger got up and went into the bedroom and came back with a pillow. "Put some cushions on the floor, and there's a rug if you need it. We shall have to douse the light, I'm afraid. You can see it in the kitchen."

"That's no problem. We'll keep torches and weapons handy, and I think we could have an inch of light through the curtains on that window, if you don't mind."

Ginger carefully just separated the curtains, admitting a thin sliver of dim light from a street lamp, and went and sat in a chair in the far corner, behind the kitchen door but facing the entrance door. "Can you see where I am, Tony?"

"Yeah, that's fine and . . ."

Whatever he was going to say was interrupted by the jarring ring of the telephone that suddenly filled the flat with a tense expectancy.

"Let it go, Ginger."

"You bet." And they waited until the persistent double rings finally ceased.

"Bloody well making sure, wasn't he?"

"Maybe. If it is our villain and he's in the vicinity, we shall soon know. If he's checking from a distance, we shall have to wait and he will probably try again to make sure. But it may just be your girlfriend."

"Pessimist."

Again they waited, without speaking. They sat with every nerve straining for sounds or signs of a possible intrusion. The noises of a passing car, a distant hooter and a more distant police siren echoed in turn round the room. Then nothing but the silence of the middle of the night. The unmistakable sound of a taxi pulling up outside the flats stretched them to full tension again, but voices shouting their respective 'goodnights' brought a relaxation of disappointment. And relaxation began to turn to a kind of anger that their hope, their readiness, was in vain, until the shrieking telephone bell again shattered the silence and lifted their spirits.

"Bingo!" whispered Tony.

When at last it ceased ringing the sudden silence was almost tangible. Their nerves were coiled as they waited, silently, breathing controlled, ears straining for telltale sounds of stealthy forced entry.

"Give him time. He won't be far away, but he's got to get here, watch, then choose his way of entry and exit. It'll take a little time. I know what he's got to do – I can see him in my mind." Tony was whispering to himself, but Ginger, heard and unseen by Tony, nodded his agreement.

Three, four, five, six hour-long minutes ticked past, then two more, before they heard from the kitchen the just-audible sound of a door handle being gently turned back and forward. A metallic sound followed as if from a key that would not turn. Quietly they stood up, torches, stick and club in hands. For some seconds there was silence in the kitchen, then the sound of wood being crunched followed by metal on metal and a sudden gust of air. A tray fell to the ground with a loud clatter, followed by a muffled excla-mation. The door to the lounge was slowly pushed open and in the dim light from the kitchen window the silhouette of a tallish, stooped figure could be seen momentarily before he pulled the door closed behind him. A thin beam shot out from where he stood and began to search the room as his outline emerged again in the dim light of the fractionally opened curtain. The darting beam swung round towards the corner where Tony knew Ginger stood. In a second their initiative would be lost.

"Now!" he shouted, and he leapt forward, stick raised. But Ginger, alert to the danger and slightly nearer, had started to move. At the sound of his approaching stride the intruder turned swiftly and lunged at him with the instrument which he had used to force the door. It struck Ginger in the stomach. Tony heard the groan of pain as he launched himself at the man's legs in a classic rugger tackle. The charge knocked him against the table and onto the floor. Tony, who had also gone down, scrambled up, one knee bent half in a sprinter's position, ready to throw himself onto the figure who despite his fall was twisting onto his back, head raised and eyes glinting from under his balaclava.

Ginger, bent over, though struggling to get his breath, saw it first.

"Tony . . . careful . . . knife!"

The blade glinted in the light from the curtain opening as the man began pulling himself up and pointed it towards where Tony, now in a crouching position having stopped his forward move, was watching every movement. His stick was on the floor. From the corner of his eye he saw Ginger, still bent double, carefully reach for his fallen golf club. To keep the man's attention he made as if to jump, but swayed to the side to avoid the forward thrust of the knife, giving Ginger the chance to swing his club down on the man's wrist. There was a loud crack as the bone snapped. The knife fell to the floor and the luckless intruder's head went back, mouth open, teeth bared as he uttered a piercing scream of agony.

"*Aaah! Merde! Merde!*"

Tony, now upright, went over to where the man lay and looking down muttered, "*Merde*, eh? As we suspected – a French connection."

He reached down, grabbed the man's left arm and pulled him to his feet. With his other hand he snatched the balaclava from his head and pushed him into a chair. He stared at the curly-black-haired, swarthy-complexioned individual who sat moaning before him, his right arm hanging useless beside him. Everything about him was dark: dark slacks, black roll-neck pullover, blue soft shoes.

"Better give him a drink, Ginger, to help him answer a few questions. In fact make it two – or three!" He stooped and picked up the knife, a folding knife with a long blade and long black handle. "Vicious bloody thing," he muttered as he put it out of reach on the table.

"Certainly three," said Ginger as he went into the kitchen.

132

"The kitchen door was forced with the jemmy he shoved into my guts," he said as he returned with the drinks. "Not very sophisticated – either use of it." He held out one of the glasses of scotch to the captive, whose head was rolling from side to side as he groaned, whispering, "*Mon dieu, mon dieu.*"

"Here, get some of this down you, you miserable bloody villain. You'll feel better."

The head stopped rolling as he saw the glass under his nose. He tried to focus on it then sniffed. "*Non, non. Jamais, jamais,*" he said, and turned his head away.

"Please yourself, you son of a bitch."

"*Vous êtes français? Que cherchez-vous?*" Why have you broken into this apartment? What are you looking for?

The man's head came round as he tried to focus on his questioner. He looked up at Tony then slowly shook his head. "*Rien. Je dis rien.*"

"Come on, man. What are you after. A photograph?"

At the mention of the word photograph he stopped shaking his head and momentarily stared at Tony before closing his eyes again and repeating his mantra, "*Je dis rien. Rien.*"

Tony tried again and again but with the same negative result. The man, whoever he was, whomever he worked for, refused to talk. "I don't think we are going to get anything out of him. Better give him to the police. In any case he needs some repairs. Ring them please, Ginger while I try to put a splint on him. Just tell them that we caught a burglar, there was a fight and the man needs medical attention."

Ginger went to the phone, dialled 999 and delivered his message. "Sending a patrol car and ambulance," he said as he opened the desk and took out two rulers. "Here, these might do," he said, handing them to Tony with his handkerchief. Then he grabbed the man's left arm, gently but firmly sat him up and pulled the arm up behind his back. "No offence, mate, but we don't want you trying anything while Tony plays Dr Kildare with you, do we?"

After much gasping and groaning they managed, with the rulers and two handkerchiefs, to get a crude splint on him by the time the peace of Cranleigh Gardens was broken by police and ambulance sirens. As soon as they heard the lift, they opened the door to two advancing policemen and an ambulance attendant with bag. Ginger confirmed that he had made the call and that he was the owner of the flat. Inside one of the policemen, a sergeant, introduced himself and his colleague.

"Sergeant Watts and Constable Wilkes." He walked over to where the man sat, now looking distinctly scared. "*Gendarmes, gendarmes*," he whispered, eyes staring at the uniforms.

"What's that? What's yer name then."

"I don't think he'll answer that, Sergeant. We've tried to find out who he is. He's French and I'm not sure how much English he understands. But understand or not, he's sticking to the line that he won't talk."

"I see. Well, perhaps you would tell me who you are and exactly what happened here."

"My name is Tony Beckett. I'm a friend of Mr Turner's. I was here when the break-in occurred, but as this is Mr Turner's flat perhaps he should tell you what happened."

"All right, then. Pass the parcel and you tell me, sir."

Ginger recounted how having received some telephone calls that got a 'wrong number' response when he answered, he was convinced they were a prelude to a burglary. So he invited Tony over and they waited to see what might happen. After two more calls the break-in occurred and when they tackled the man he drew a knife. The blow with his golf club was intended to stop him using it on Tony, which it did, though unfortunately it also broke the man's arm.

"Mmm," said the sergeant. "And what made you suspicious of the those earlier wrong-number calls? They happen all the time. Why did you think they signalled a burglary, and why were you so sure of trouble that you armed yourselves, so to speak, with sticks and clubs? It could be called provocative . . ."

"Or a wise precaution . . ." began Ginger.

"Excuse me, Sergeant," It was the ambulance attendant. "This man should go to hospital. Whoever it was put a fairly good makeshift splint on his arm. I've applied a new one, but he needs to have the fracture set by a doctor."

"Very well, then. You take him to hospital, and you, Constable, accompany him and stay with him until we can either fetch him or arrange for him to be charged and questioned in hospital." The two of them supported the wretched man and took him out to the waiting ambulance. "Now," continued the sergeant, "perhaps you will be good enough to answer those questions."

"I'm happy to do that, sergeant. But you know, when a man breaks into an apartment armed with a knife you can hardly claim he was provoked by the people inside. The fact is, we have good reasons to believe that this attempted burglary is linked to two other incidents that not only involved burglary, but also included an unexplained death and a murder." The sergeant's head jerked up, a frown of annoyance on his brow and a mixture of surprise and interest in his eyes as he turned to Tony.

"Oh?"

"It's a bit of a long story, sergeant. Perhaps we can all sit down." They did, and Tony went over the whole sad and puzzling chain of events that seemed to centre on the secret mission behind the enemy's lines in France during the war, which had already resulted in the death of two dear friends and ex-comrades, and which appeared to be a search for a single unidentified photograph of one of their operations.

"Any idea why?" asked the sergeant, who had sat quietly fascinated by the explanation.

"Not really. The only theory we have at present concerns the ownership and whereabouts of a load of valuable loot found in a German vehicle we captured during an ambush." And he went on to describe the possibility that whoever stole it, or whoever now had it, wanted to eliminate evidence of its origin as recorded somewhere in one of Roddy Holmes's photos. "If you don't mind my suggesting it, sergeant, it could be worth your while getting in touch with Detective Inspector Richards of Primrose Hill, who is in charge of Mr Lawrence's murder case and is acquainted also with the circumstances of Mr Holmes's death and the subsequent burglary. It may be that you have there," and he nodded towards the knife on the table, "the weapon that killed Mr Lawrence. And you may have the murderer. Incidentally, my fingerprints are on the knife; I picked it up after he dropped it."

"Er ... um ... thank you, sir. But we can't jump to conclusions. Our enquiries will proceed in the normal way. I don't think there is much more I can do here. We will try to get a statement from the intruder when he is well enough. If you will be good enough to give me your full name and address, I will leave you." Tony went to the bureau, took some paper, wrote his name and address, then planted the fingers and thumb of his hand firmly on the paper. "There you are, sergeant, name, address and identification." Sergeant Watts stared at Tony for a few moments, grunted a kind of approval, then bid them goodnight. As he was going

136

through the door Tony mentioned his forthcoming trip to New York on business. Sergeant Watts turned. "Right, sir. Thank you," he said, and closed the door behind him.

Tony and Ginger looked at each other for a moment. Tony broke the silence. "I think we can have the rest of that wine now." As they finished the wine they reviewed the night's events.

"Does that finish it, I wonder?" said Ginger. "Have we caught the killer? Have we caught the burglar? Will we find out just what he was after and why? It seems to me that although we've caught a villain we're left with a load of unanswered questions."

"We certainly are. I don't know what you thought of him, Ginger, but he seemed to me to be a second- or third-rate villain." Ginger nodded thoughtfully. "Someone you might see in the port area of Marseille – with great respect to the bulk of the Marseillaises. He did not strike me as the person with the real interest – whatever that might be – in the mystery photo, nor someone who might be interested in works of art looted from Bordeaux when he must have been an adolescent – or younger. So, we might have caught a burglar and a murderer, but we may not have caught the principal in the case. We shall have to wait and see what the police get out of him and whether they can say if the knife is the one that killed poor Larry. I think I shall ring DI Richards in the morning to tell him what has occurred and to expect a call from Sergeant Watts of West Kensington." He paused, stretched himself in his chair and yawned. "Now the excitement is over, what about a bit of shut-eye before the night has completely gone."

They slept fitfully – Ginger in his bed, which Tony had refused to take from him, and Tony uncomfortably on the floor in the living room. He was watching a German general being interviewed by a London bobby when he was roused by noises in the kitchen. Ginger appeared with a mug of coffee.

"Here, skip. This will restore your will to live."

"Thanks, Ginger, but I'm not sure even that will do the job. I can't take late nights – at least not very late nights – any more."

"I know, Tony," said Ginger with mock sympathy. "It's a combination of age and the toll of past pleasures that debilitates people of your seniority."

He dodged the cushion that flew in his direction. "Cereal, toast and coffee. That's all there is for breakfast. You know where the shower is," he said, and disappeared into the kitchen. Over breakfast Tony, revived, said, "First I'll ring DI Richards. Then we must settle how we make contact with Georges Lebrun and do a photo check with him."

When he telephoned Primrose Hill station John Richards was in and would speak to him. Tony recounted the events of the last evening, finishing by emphasising that there was a possible murder weapon and a burglar – perhaps a murderer – in custody. Even his calm professional manner did not conceal Richards' surprise.

"Aha. So some of the suspicions are looking more like facts, but . . ."

"Yes, I know what you are going to say, Inspector: 'we still don't know why'. As I said before, our best bet is to see Georges Lebrun. If it had not been for the calls to Ginger one of us might have been on the way now. We are arranging a visit now, but may we take Mr Lawrence's set of photographs, if you have finished with them for the time being? I think it would be unsettling for Mrs Holmes if we used hers again, for which I would have to give another explanation – and I want, if I can, to avoid telling her what happened in Mr Turner's flat. She's not ready to accept that her husband might have been deliberately killed, and as these events are occurring a conspiracy of some kind seems more likely to be behind them.

"I see your point, sir. I think we might let you have Mr Lawrence's photos if you will return them for another period afterwards. They will of course form part of Mr Lawrence's estate. We have actually copied the fingerprints on them, but I don't think they will help us very much – there were so many and they were rather indistinct. Nevertheless, we shall have to see if there are any that might match those of the villain you just caught at Kensington. When will you be leaving for France?"

"We're not sure yet, but I hope it will be later today; early tomorrow at the latest."

"OK. I'll get the villain's prints sent over today. I shall have to see the knife, too. You should be able to collect the photos later. We'll let you know."

"That's very cooperative of you. We appreciate it. Goodbye, Inspector."

Tony walked over to the table, where Ginger waited patiently, and sat opposite him. "Part one achieved. Richards is now in the picture. He will let us borrow Larry's photos when he has checked them for the villain's fingerprints. I wish they were all like him.

"Good," said Ginger. "Now, how do we proceed? I'm free until, say, Friday evening. On Saturday I have to go with my man to Washington, where he has an appointment in the State Department."

"Well, as you know, I have to be in New York on Thursday morning, so I think there's just time for us to make contact with Georges and pay him a quick visit, if we can. Now, I suggest that as you are good at making travel arrangements"

– Ginger groaned – "you get us both an early flight to Paris for tomorrow – to give time for us to get the photos from Richards later today. You'll need a return. I shall want an onward flight to New York for Wednesday evening with an open return to London. Reserve us a car at the airport for our drive to Chartres. If (a) we cannot contact Georges, or (b) we do not get the photos in time, we shall have to cancel and do a rethink."

"Sounds OK."

"Meanwhile, I will search out Georges's number and try to get in touch. I won't go into detail. We can do that when we see him. Right now I'll drive down to Hawksworth to return Jenny's set – I would rather she has them while we are away. It's going to be some rush, but we cannot leave it all until I get back from New York next week. I'll phone you tonight to check where we've got to on travel and so on. But don't forget, emergency procedure is still in force. We get in touch at the least sign of anything suspicious, yes?"

"Agreed."

The drive to Hawksworth was uneventful. Tony was now so familiar with the route that he was bored by it. Bored and irritated. Irritated by the delays in getting out of London. Post-war reconstruction did not seem to have done much to ease the congestion or to improve the quality of road surfaces. The good intentions are probably tightly bound by reams of red tape, he thought. And so like everyone else he took his place with suppressed impatience in the slow-moving queues until he could break free just beyond Bromley. Jenny was surprised and delighted to see him again, and, of course, pleased to have her cherished album back. He did not mention the little adventure of the previous night, but did tell her of the planned visit to Georges Lebrun the following morning to have a look at his collection of photos.

"Oh, that will be good. That may help you to clear up the mystery. And it will be interesting for you to meet again after so long. It's strange, isn't it, that all the things you went through together years ago are coming to the surface again, stirred up by these awful events. The memories are disturbing you, yet pleasing you at the same time."

"Yes," he said quietly. "I sometimes wonder if we will ever be free of the recollection of those times."

"Do let me know what you find out – especially", she added with a mischievous twinkle in her eye, "about who has the loot now."

He promised, pointing out that it would be after he got back from New York. Time was short. He got back to Gloucester Road in record time. He had scarcely entered the flat when the telephone rang. It was Cels.

"Tony, I've been ringing you all afternoon. I want to talk to you urgently. Where have you been?" It was a bit of the old Cels: tetchy and aggressive when things did not work out the way she wanted. Tony slipped into the mode he used for such occasions: quiet in tone, calm, polite and understanding.

"Hello, Cels. What a surprise. It's nice to hear from you. Strange to say, perhaps, but I've had quite a lot to do today. After a busy sort of morning spent with Ginger, I went down . . ."

"Tony!" Her voice was up an octave. "Tony, I hate you when you do this to me. You sound so bloody sanctimonious. I don't want to know all that. I just want . . ." But he didn't stop.

". . . down to Hawksworth to return Jenny's album and I have only just got back . . ."

"Aaaaaaaaah! I could scream!"

"You just did. Now Cels, stop being a spoilt kid. Start

141

again and tell me calmly what's on your mind." There was a moment or two of quiet.

"Sorry. It's just that I have some exciting news and I wanted to . . . to . . . consult you about it. When did you say you have to go to New York?"

"Well, Ginger and I are probably going to France tomorrow to talk to Georges Lebrun, and I shall fly from there to be in New York on Thursday. Why?"

"Three of us from the agency have to be in New York by Monday morning to make a competitive pitch for a big advertising campaign. It's very important to us, and I thought . . . well, I thought that if I could fly out on Friday or Saturday we could perhaps meet over the weekend and do something . . ."

"That's wonderful news, Cels. Of course we can. And I'm very much in favour of the 'doing something'."

"Don't be coarse, Tony. You know what I mean."

"I thought I did know what you mean. Yes, it's a great idea. We can have the weekend together. I shall be staying at Brooklyn Heights, across the East River from Manhattan. I have the use of an apartment on Montague Terrace. It faces the river. You'll love it. It belongs to a retired lawyer who came out to that 'hellhole', as you call it, where I worked to advise us on a land-title problem. He spends most of his time in Florida now."

"It sounds lovely, but, Mr Beckett," she said prudishly, "are you suggesting that we share . . ."

"Of course I am. Such a chance to have my way with a lonely, innocent young thing away from home . . ."

"Oh, good."

"Have you met her, then?"

"Who?"

"The innocent young . . ."

142

"You're a rotter, Tony Beckett."

"I know. Look, I have my end-of-contract negotiations on Friday, so if you can get a mid-morning flight on Saturday it will get to New York early afternoon. Unfortunately, the taxi ride from the airport can take a long time. I will meet you in the lobby of the Plaza Hotel at the top of 5th Avenue near Central Park, mid-afternoon. We can either have a late brunch or tea – or whatever you feel like. If my negotiations drag on and I'm likely to be late, I'll leave a message for you. Ask at the desk. Then we can go across to Brooklyn."

"That's fine. I know where you mean. I shall look forward to it."

"Me too. Cels, I don't want be rude, but I've got a lot to do if we are to get to see Lebrun, so . . ."

"OK, OK . . . I get it. Bugger off. I'll see you in Manhattan."

Dear Cels, he thought to himself as he went to the bureau to search through his address books for Georges Lebrun's telephone number. Although she was more mature and more confident, she still retained some of the old selfish, pugnacious traits, but also – thank heaven – her beauty and alluring charm. Strangely, he sensed that, though older and wiser, she seemed to need him more, yet was unlikely to admit it, even to herself. He found the numbers: office and home. Which? It was just after six in France. Try the home number. The ringing tone sounded faint and continued without response. He was about to hang up when he heard the welcome, but uninformative "*Allo*".

"*Est-ce que c'est Monsieur Georges Lebrun qui parle?*"

"*Oui.*"

"*Bonsoir, mon Capitaine. Ici Tony Beckett.*"

At the ensuing explosion of surprise and pleasure Tony held the telephone away from his ear until he could answer at least some of the questions. Yes, he was well. The others? He had seen most of them recently but he would tell him more later. Well, the reason for phoning was to see if he and Ginger Turner could come and see him tomorrow – sorry about the short notice but they wanted to see him before he had to go to New York. They wanted to consult him about some of the wartime photos taken by Roddy Holmes. They were coming by car from Paris.

Of course, it would be a great pleasure. An exercise in remembering, eh? If they were coming by car it would be better to meet somewhere central. To find his office would be complicated. Too many one-way streets. He suggested the big cafe, the Espérance in the Place Chatelet, near the cathedral. On the main road in from the Paris direction, turn left by the station and you go straight to Place Chatelet. About four-thirty to five o'clock unless he heard differently. Until tomorrow then.

So far so good, Tony said to himself as he put the phone down. No sooner had he done so than it rang.

"Mr Beckett? John Richards here, sir. Just to let you know, as promised, that the photos are waiting for you to collect from the desk here. We got no meaningful fingerprints from them, I'm afraid. Just two more things, sir. The villain who broke into Mr Turner's flat is an Algerian from Marseille – or so he says. He cannot produce a passport but claims his name is Ahmed. Does that mean anything to you?"

"I'm afraid not. No, certainly not. And the other thing?" There was a pause. "Hello . . . Inspector?"

"Sorry, sir." He cleared his throat. "Our doctor is not certain that the knife is the one that killed Mr Lawrence. He thinks that the murder weapon had a much broader blade."

It was Tony's turn to be silent as he tried quickly to consider the implications of what he had just heard. "Could

144

he have had two knives? Or disposed of the murder weapon and obtained another?"

"That's possible, of course. But the one he tried to use on you was made in France, which suggests he brought it with him. But we must also consider another possibility . . ."

"That there are two villains engaged in this little enterprise, assuming all the events are linked, and we have caught only one of them."

"Precisely, sir. Which means a second miscreant is at large and may still be searching for copies of the mystery photograph. You and Mr Turner will have to keep your wits about you – if I may put it that way. When will you be going to France?"

"Tomorrow morning if Ginger – Mr Turner – has managed to get the tickets. And I shall be going on from France on Wednesday evening to New York. I expect to be back after the weekend. Mr Turner has to go to Washington at the same time."

"I see. Well, let us hope your trip to France will tell us what we want to know. Let me know the results, please."

Tony Beckett's next task was to phone Ginger, find out about the flights and, of course, pass on to him the news he had just heard. But he needed a moment to think. He sat at the desk staring at the large bay window at which he had stood looking out onto Gloucester Road barely ten days ago, contemplating the boring but necessary prospect of finding a job and somewhere to live. How that prospect had been changed by the violent intrusion of a ruthless hunt for evidence of something that occurred in the course of a secret mission in time of war more than twenty years earlier. Something that was important enough even now to require felony and the murder of gallant men! Their – his and Ginger's and, indeed, Detective Inspector John Richards' –

hopes that the perpetrator had been caught were now dashed. The stakes were now much higher than they had thought. Yet there was still no firm indication as to what the issue or event was that vicious criminal acts were needed to remove evidence of it. If it was to do with the lorryload of art treasures they captured, why had it taken so long to surface? Many claims concerning looted property were being dealt with by the courts in France. What was different about this one? Something was so vital that two dangerous, but not very skilled, villains had been assigned the task of finding and removing the evidence. But assigned by whom?

Chapter 8

It was 10.30 a.m. local time when Tony Beckett and Ginger Turner stood waiting for their luggage in the baggage-retrieval hall of Orly Airport, the one chosen by them as being on the right side of Paris for the next part of their journey. Tony had not entrusted to the aircraft hold the package of photographs he had collected from Primrose Hill police station the evening before. They were safely in the briefcase he had kept with him throughout the taxi ride to Heathrow and during the flight. They would be safer that way, he had thought. But in all the traffic to the airport just after seven that morning he could not have known that one of the many helmeted motorcyclists travelling two car's-lengths behind had their cab in sight until they had left it at the terminal. Nor with crowd at the checking-in desk for the Paris flight would he have paid attention to the individual behind them in the queue who broke away from the line once Tony's onward flight to New York was confirmed, and walked in the direction of the public telephones. And after they had collected their luggage at Orly and went to the car-hire desk to collect the documents for the car Ginger had reserved, there was no reason to suppose that among the half-dozen or so other people also hiring transport there would be one who noted the directions given them to get from the airport to the road to Chartres. After all, Tony would be the first to agree that the surest way to conceal oneself is to be one of the crowd doing normal things.

Once they had cautiously felt their way through the outer suburbs and emerged into the countryside – the French countryside of tree-lined roads and apparently unpopulated villages – Tony, having devolved driving duties to Ginger, settled back in his seat and absorbed happily again the unique atmosphere of this very French environment. This was the France he loved: calm, amiable, with an acceptable lifestyle of local, friendly shopping, coffee and aperitifs, and long enjoyable meals with animated conversation which wine helped but never blurred. It was the France of the regions, not the France of Paris – enjoyable though that was in a different way. No capital represents the real nation. They travelled south before turning west at Arpajon. At Dourdan on the edge of the forest they stopped for a coffee break at a cafe in a small village. At a table outside they sat as tourists do with folded map and Michelin guide before them. There was nothing much to the village. The main road ran through it. Opposite where they were sitting, on a small, dusty tree-lined square in front of a small church, a group of the local worthies were playing boules. The few necessary shops and another bar-cafe were evident on either side of the road to the left. Fairly typical of villages of this size, Tony was thinking when he became conscious of Ginger drubbing his fingers on the table top.

"Something worrying you, Ginger?"

"Not really. Being unnecessarily suspicious, I expect. But that car which has just pulled up outside the boulangerie was behind us all the way from Arpajon. I hadn't noticed him before that. The driver has just gone into the shop."

Tony shifted his chair enough to bring the parked Mercedes and the baker's shop into view. Almost immediately the door opened and a man emerged carrying two loaves. They heard the cheerful "*Merci. Bonjour, monsieur*" as he closed the door behind him. He got into the car drove off. "Probably nothing, Ginger but let's keep our eyes open for him along the road."

Leaving Dourdan they turned onto a 'D' road through the forest and drove very slowly until they reached Ablis. Their precaution seemed to have been unnecessary. The few cars they saw were travelling in the opposite direction. At Ablis they joined the N10 and drove on into Chartres. Georges Lebrun had been right: turning left by the railway station and going up the hill they easily found Place Chatelet and the Cafe Espérance. They were a little early. They parked the car on the reservation opposite that divided the two roads joining the place from the right. A few of the tables outside the cafe were occupied, but Tony was able to choose one which gave him a good view farther up the hill to where the majestic cathedral stood dominating all around it. As they sat down they were both aware that a table behind them was taken by two men who had approached from the other side of the cafe and now seemed to be deep in conversation.

"We should take note of our surroundings," said Tony quietly.

"I already have," replied Ginger. "I think they may have bought bread en route from Paris."

"I thought it might be them. They parked the Merc over there just after we parked. May be a coincidence, but safer to assume it isn't. We'll act normally but with abnormal vigilance."

Tony ordered two glasses of white wine and they sat silently, taking in the scene around them. Tony let his mind slip back a few years, recalling the first time he had stood in the square in front of that huge Gothic structure with its many lovingly carved figures and its large, breathtaking, richly coloured glass window. It was when he had been struggling to be a good foreign reporter in Paris just after the war. He had on that occasion come to seek Georges's guidance through the political and emotional complexities of post-liberation France. In common with most visitors he had been overawed both by the grandeur of the architecture and the depth of its spiritual influence, felt even by agnostics like him. The bit of national pride he felt in the knowledge that the beautiful glass in the window had come in the Middle Ages from the small Surrey village of Chiddingfold was more than balanced by his recognition of the weight of the cathedral's historical significance.

It was on the occasion of that early visit that Georges had expressed his concern about the political, and personal, consequences of France's injured pride. "Tony," he had said, "you must judge our actions in the context of a deeply felt shame we attempt to hide and feel we must compensate for, and an anger felt by some towards those they feel betrayed their honour. Keep that in mind, my friend, and you will understand us better. You will probably find many reasons to accuse us, but also, I hope, many reasons to excuse us. I hope the Americans will understand and make excuses for us, but I think they will find it more difficult. You see they think it is perverse – and perhaps it is – that we cannot forgive them for liberating us, with your important help and some from us, and for being the decisive force in winning the war against the Axis powers. Your country carries some resentment against the Americans, for their economic success and vast international power, but you are more tolerant and accept the reality. We are not and do not.

150

e call American influence 'Coca-Colonisation', and we are
ncouraged to believe that our contribution to our libera-
on was greater than it was so that we do not have to feel
obligated. I only hope we do not treat you in the same way.
s peoples I think we quite like each other. But do not rely
n a nationalistic French Government to reflect that
eling."

Tony had protested. "But, Georges, you and I and many
thers like us know the importance of the work of the
esistance: the destruction, disruption, and the tying down
f enemy troops. And we know that few single engagements
r battles are decisive. Most are important elements in the
gsaw of an overall strategy. Moreover, Georges, you have
o reason to share any sense of guilt. You were part of the
esistance, which upheld France's honour. You fought
ravely against your country's enemies."

"You are kind to say such things, old comrade, but it is
ecause of those things that I am part of our . . . our . . .
wisted psychology. But make no mistake Tony, France will
ffer her people a policy which will calm anger and conceal
name. A policy of strong national ambition. General de
aulle sees that necessity. The Left do not like that because
ney see in it a right-wing triumph that will include some of
neir bitterest opponents. They will oppose it, but they will
ose because too many people will want it. Perhaps in the
nd they will become part of this nationalism."

He had often recalled that conversation and it had helped
n his understanding of the country he loved second only to
is own, whose spread of people had a way of life so richly
alanced between intellectual and material pleasures and
ho could be, at the same time, so charming and so
nfuriatingly stubborn. Now he wondered what Georges

151

would think of it all, with so much social unrest, and the student riots, in France. Perhaps they would have time to discuss these things, as well as find out about the photo.

The opportunity for both was nearer at hand than he thought. Hearing the cry, "*Tony, mon ami. Et Ginger. Salut. Salut*", he looked up to where the easily recognisable figure of Captain 'François' was striding down the hill from the buildings near the cathedral, waving a hand as he came. As he approached Tony could see he was fit and tanned, perhaps a little plumper and with greying hair. They shook hands and embraced. "I am very happy to see you again, Georges," Tony said warmly, to which Ginger added his "Me too, Georges."

Lebrun responded enthusiastically about the unexpected pleasure of their visit and bombarded them with questions about where they had been and what they had been doing recently. Was Tony finished with South America? What was he going to do? What was Ginger doing now? How were things in England? They answered them all and put their own questions to him about his wife and family, and his architectural practice. It all took time; it was very animated and much wine was drunk in the process. It was only when Georges asked about "our other comrades" that the mood changed. It was inevitable and it fell to Tony to speak.

"Georges, unfortunately I have to tell you that both Roddy and Larry are dead. Roddy was killed in an accident, the circumstances of which we – Ginger and I – think are very suspicious, and Larry was murdered."

"My God! How could such things happpen? Why? Why?"

"Georges, this is why we have come to see you. We think it has something to do with our time with you and Jean Boulanger during the war."

"The mission? How could that be?"

Tony was conscious of the need to avoid a detailed conversation in their present surroundings.

"It's a bit of a long story, Georges. Could we talk about it over dinner tonight. Are you free? I'm sorry we are springing this on you, but I have to go to New York tomorrow evening and Ginger has to be in Washington on Saturday and we wanted to put you in the picture as soon as we could. Would your wife and family spare you? It's rather important."

"Of course, of course. You are right, it is very important. I'm sure Jeanne will understand. Where are you staying? I'm sorry I cannot ... We only have an apartment just big enough for us and the children."

"Georges, we wouldn't dream of imposing on you. We wondered about the hotel across the place there."

"Yes, it's not a great hotel but I think you will be comfortable. We recommend it to clients sometimes. But we should not dine there. You must come to a very nice little restaurant I know close to the cathedral. It's in the rue de L'Abbé to the right of the Place Cathédrale as you go up from here. It is called Maison Madeleine. I shall have to go home to explain to my wife. We could meet there at six-thirty perhaps? That's early for French people, but at least it will be quiet then."

Maison Madeleine was in the old part of the district round the cathedral. Rue de L'Abbé ran from the Place Cathédrale to a park containing the ruins of the old abbey. It was narrow and most of its buildings were medieval in origin; the style had been maintained by the houses, the offices, and the Maison Madeleine. Inside, Tony and Ginger were greeted first by the warmth and the aroma of good French cooking, and secondly by Georges Lebrun's equally warm greeting. He came forward to meet them from a table in a corner at the front of the restaurant, informing the head waiter as he did so that "These are my good friends from England, Pierre". Pierre Rambert welcomed them to Maison Madeleine and conducted them all to their table.

As they took their places Georges confided to them that Pierre had reserved a table in the middle of the restaurant, but Georges had thought this one in the corner would be more suitable as they would be doing a lot of talking. Tony looked round approvingly. The beamed ceiling, raw brick walls, red-and-white checked cloths and napkins on candlelit tables completed the friendly, comfortable and promising ambience of a good regional French restaurant. Georges had been right. It was very quiet. Only two other tables were occupied, one by a young couple holding hands across their table and gazing longingly at each other. As far as they were concerned the restaurant was empty. The other, halfway down the restaurant, was occupied by two men discussing the menu. Tony and Ginger exchanged understanding glances and were happy that Georges, without realising it, had put them at a safe distance from any interested listener.

"Now then," said Georges as soon as they were seated, "let us order our food and wine and then you must tell me this sad story." He signalled the waiting Pierre standing by a serving table just behind them. "If you would permit me," said Georges, "I can recommend the lobster bisque and the *crevettes*, and for the main course – I know you English love your steak and the fillet here is very good, but if you would like a typical French dish, the coq au vin is excellent, as is the veal provençale." After a short discussion it was decided. Tony ordered the lobster bisque and the coq au vin; Ginger some smoked salmon and a fillet steak *'au point'*; and Georges the *crevettes* and the veal. As it was a very special occasion to be together again, Georges suggested that a bottle of Chablis with the first course and a 1958 Pomerol

154

with the main would be suitable both for their meeting and for a toast to the memory of their other friends.

With their first glass of wine Tony began his explanation in detail – with Ginger's help – of the events surrounding Roddy Holmes's 'accidental' death, the burglary, Larry's murder by an intruder who was searching his papers, and the break-in to Ginger's apartment where the two of them had caught the villain, whose knife, however, did not appear to be the weapon that had killed Larry. It seemed, therefore, there was another villain at large involved in the search for this single wartime photograph. If they could identify which one had been taken they would probably uncover the identity of whoever was behind the crimes and to whom this single photo means so much. "You see, Georges, we need to compare one of the sets the burglar left behind – I have what was left of Larry's set with me – with a complete set. We cannot do that with Ginger's because his are locked away in a Devon farmhouse, and mine are in my cases in New York. So we thought you should be aware of the situation and we knew you would not mind us making the comparison with your set."

Georges Lebrun had remained silent throughout the entire account of what had happened and of their suspicions of the links between these events and the events of the AMCA mission. But at the last he looked at them, eyebrows raised with surprise. "Yes, of course I understand the importance of making that comparison in order to identify the picture, but I don't have my set any more. No."

Now it was Tony's and Ginger's turn to look surprised. "You don't have them? What have you done with them?"

"Done with them? I gave them to a Resistance museum in Nevers. Earlier this year I had a letter from the *Préfet* of Police in Nevers. He had just taken up his appointment on

155

promotion and was disappointed, when shown the museum, that it seemed to have been a little neglected. He wanted to revive it because he thought it important that future generations should be more aware of what so many had done to rescue the nation from an oppressive occupation. He consulted his predecessor, who had started the museum. This man had been in the Resistance movement and told the new *Préfet* that one of the Maquis groups that had worked in the area was Maquis François, led by myself. A "very brave and effective group", he had said. He had been given my real name and address and he wondered if I had anything – maps or photographs – I could donate to the museum which might illustrate how we operated. Naturally, I was interested, perhaps a little flattered, and said I would look through my memorabilia and do what I could to help."

"So what happened?"

"I thought about it and although I had a couple of old maps with some of our markings on them, it seemed to me that the unique, and most vivid, thing I had, which fitted exactly the *Préfet*'s request for "something to illustrate what you did", was the set of Roddy Holmes's photographs taken during operations. So I got in touch with the *Préfet* again and asked him if he thought they would be suitable. I must say his response almost overwhelmed me. He was enthusiastic about the prospect of having the honour of such a donation in his museum. So I arranged to take them down to Nevers myself, because I was curious to see the museum and also how they would be displayed."

"What was it like? The museum, I mean?"

"It's outside the town. In a house near the spot where the Saints' Day executions took place. That was before you and your friends arrived. We had not been long in our camp. I think I told you about it."

"Yes you did. The Germans caught the men out after curfew, didn't they?"

"That's right. They said they were bringing them into Nevers for questioning when they tried to escape. They were all killed. 'Shot trying to escape,' they said. All the same, the authorities had set up this museum in the house, with its own grounds quite nicely set out. Inside there are examples of some of the equipment used. Rifles, revolvers, radio sets. Some German uniforms; German guns and badges. Badges of Maquis François and Maquis Léon; also of the group working to the south-east of the town. And there is data of the numbers of Germans which we claim to have killed; the number of train derailments; number of targets bombed by the RAF and the USAAF. Quite well done, but lacking something . . . I'm not sure what. It lacks . . . lacks the *spirit* of the Resistance, if you know what I mean?"

"I think I can guess. It's hard to make museums live. But what about the photos? Did they put them on display while you were there?"

"No, they did not. The curator, a retired policeman, said the *Préfet* wanted them displayed in the centre of the section devoted to the 'The Fighting Maquis'. He would come down himself to inspect them when it was all ready. Clearly, the *Préfet* was very keen that they should be properly presented."

"What about captions, descriptions. How were they going to do that?"

"Well, shortly after receiving my set from Roddy I wrote a brief note on the back of each while the incidents were fairly fresh in my mind. When I got them out to take to the museum I copied the notes out and added as much as my memory would permit. The Curator said it would take a few weeks to organise and get the *Préfet*'s approval. He hoped I would visit the museum when it was all ready and he felt sure the *Préfet* would wish to meet me then. Only the week before last I had a letter from the curator saying the display was all ready, and would I let them know when I could go to see it. Unhappily, I have been too busy to go yet."

Tony realised he should not express the disappointment he felt about this further delay in identifying the vital photograph. "Well, that they asked you to make a contribution must be very pleasing for you, Georges. Whoever gave your name to the *Préfet* was paying you a tribute. Of course, it means we cannot now do the comparison we wanted. Perhaps we should not have worried you with . . ."

"But, no, my friend, of course you should have come to me. It was not and is not a 'worry', as you call it. I am as concerned as you are about whatever is going on. It is an attack on all of us. So what shall we do about seeing which photgraph has been stolen? I think we must go down there tomorrow. I shall cancel appointments. They are not as important as this thing is. So we shall go together, just like old times. Tonight we shall drink more, talk about those times, sleep, and tomorrow we can go to Nevers, to the museum and there perhaps solve this mystery."

His enthusiasm and willingness to help were infectious. "How far is it to Nevers from here?" asked Tony.

"Oh, I do not know exactly. Perhaps 250 or 300 kilometres."

"Well, that can certainly be done in a day, with time to spend there. But I have a problem, because I have to catch a flight from Orly at five-thirty in the afternoon and we have to hand the car back at the airport. Ginger also has to fly to America, but not until Friday from London. When we thought we could settle all this by coming quickly to see you, we had not reckoned with the need to go down to Nevers."

"No, of course not. How could you have known?" Georges replied. "But I think I have a solution, if you agree Tony . . ."

"Yes?"

"Yes, you see, you risk losing your flight if you try to go to Nevers, do what is necessary, and then return to Orly and hand in the car, no? But it would be possible for me to go to Nevers with Ginger tomorrow morning. You could take your car back to Orly and be in very good time for your flight to the United States. Ginger and I can return here and I will get a car to take him to Orly on Thursday morning. What time is your flight, Ginger?"

"Er, midday on Thursday."

"There, that's perfect, isn't it? And Ginger and I have the advantage of being able to dine together again tomorrow, yes?"

"That's even more perfect, Georges." Ginger gave Tony a smug smile. Tony scowled exaggeratedly as he pondered.

"I suppose you're right, Georges. But I agree with reluctance, not because I have any doubts about you and Ginger doing what is necessary, but because I resent missing another evening's conversation with good food and wine in your company – especially as I want to learn more from you about what is happening in France."

"Dear Tony. There will be other times. In future we must not let so much time pass between meetings. But", he said with renewed vigour, hunching his shoulders and raising his hands from the table, "the night is still young, you do not want to go to your beds yet, so we will have more wine." Turning, he signalled to the distant but ever-attentive figure of Monsieur Rambert. "Pierre, another bottle of the Pomerol, if you please. Now, my friends, what can I tell you?"

"Before you tell us anything, Georges, I have to go to the

toilet," said Ginger, standing up and making his way between the tables to the appropriately marked door at the side of the bar. As he was about to go through, the door opened and the figure of one of the two male diners emerged. For an instant they were face to face. Then the other turned quickly away and walked to his table as Ginger stared momentarily after him. Tony had seen the incident across Georges's shoulder. When he returned to the table Ginger looked straight at Tony and nodded. His message was understood.

"Georges, before we get into that bottle and our conversation, would you mind looking at those two types at the table behind you, near the bar, to see if you recognise them?"

Georges turned, looked, and turned back again. "No, I don't think I've ever seen them before. Why?"

"Just before Ginger's apartment was broken into we thought the villain might have found where he lived by following us. Then on our drive from Paris we thought we might have been followed by two men in a Mercedes which parked in the Place Chatelet just after we did. They also might have been sitting near us at the Espérance. We noticed those two sitting there when we came in. They certainly look similar. What do you think, Ginger?"

"I'm certain those two are the ones who stopped to buy bread when we were having our coffee break near Dourdan. They were in a Merc. I just ran into one of them as I was going to the toilet. I'm sure he was the one who bought the bread and was sitting near us in the Place."

Almost certainly aware by now that they were being talked about, and looking pointedly towards Georges's table, they had signalled Pierre for the bill, paid and left hurriedly. Georges beckoned Pierre and asked if he knew them. No, he did not. He did not think they had ever been in the restaurant before. They had come in just before Georges arrived.

"Well, I think it's clear that we *have* been followed and those two knew about our arrangements. The implication is that we've probably been under surveillance since Paris, or perhaps London. More and more it looks like a very serious business, Georges. They – whoever they are – seem very determined to get every copy of that photo, and of course they do not know that neither Ginger's nor mine are available. I wonder if we have inadvertently led them to you. You must take care."

"Yes, I see it is more serious than I had thought. We shall see what they do tomorrow when we split up. That will be interesting. But we are alert to them now. Ginger and I will – what do you say – keep our eyes skinned . . ."

"Peeled," said Ginger unnecessarily.

"Peeled. Even wide open, Ginger," he replied, smiling. "Frenchmen are expected to speak funny English, you know. But now let us talk and drink like the old comrades we are." Georges was again the happy extrovert they remembered so well. "First let us remember our absent friends." It was a sincere gesture. Georges pushed back his chair, the others followed, and they all stood and quietly drank a toast to Roddy and Larry. Georges began reminiscing, recalling incidents involving them both. Tony and Ginger made their own contributions as they had done on the evening of Roddy's funeral. Inevitably, they talked of Maquis Léon and Jean Boulanger. How Georges had found their relationship difficult until after the first François engagement, which had impressed Jean. After that they became true friends and worked well together. "Yet", said Georges, "a man to be respected but, unhappily, not loved." Georges was convinced

161

that his sudden withdrawal at the end of the mission was his loyal response to his party's instructions. Later, he said, there were rumours of a grouping of Communist forces preparing for a march on Paris as a prelude to a left-wing coup. Personally, he was not sure how much truth there had been in the rumour. He felt that if it were true, it was a foolhardy enterprise; it could never have succeeded. The army was loyal to the general and the rumour gave him the opportunity to assert his power. As to Jean Boulanger, he had not had proper medical attention after his wounds. He had spent some time in a sanatorium near Pau. Georges had written to him while he was there and had heard that a part of his lung had been taken away, though he was progressing well enough. He had also told him that his nephew Henri had become a *fonctionnaire*, a civil servant, in one of the regions – perhaps Cher. He was not sure, because he had political ambitions as a member of the Gaullist party, which did not please poor Jean very much! However, next time he wrote, Jean had left the sanatorium and gone to live in the Pyrénées somewhere.

"Yes, poor Jean," said Tony. "He sounds a lonely man. Not easy to maintain a relationship with him, but we must get in touch again sometime, perhaps sooner rather than later, bearing in mind he, too, has a set of Roddy's photos. But, tell me, Georges, what is happening here to your politics? We read of strikes and demonstrations. It sounds serious. Is the general and his government in trouble? If so, why is it happening?"

"My God, Tony there are several questions there. And behind them there are so many – what do say? – begged questions. Yes, it is serious. Millions of workers are on strike and the protest parades of the strikers give students and others a good opportunity to join the protests. But their protests are now looking more like rioting, not like students marching seriously but lawfully in favour of the workers. There is a lot of anger in the way they are behaving. Yet I do not feel that they are motivated only by left-wing thinking. I think the anger is the anger born of uncertainty and confusion. Many demonstrations have the traditional left-wing, radical views, but many are more right-wing because they are looking for an ideology that will restore their faith in France. It seems that those who are too young to have taken part in the war feel the shame of it even more than we do. And I do not think people generally – those in the regions, the countryside – are looking for a left-wing government to do this for them. They, too, are seeking a leadership that will restore their pride. This wish points to the General and his fierce – almost arrogant – patriotism. I cannot see another leader doing it. Yet it is true that because of what is happening he seems to have lost the confidence of the people, at least for the time being. Even there are rumours that he will resign. If he did, I think we would have an even more chaotic situation. I don't think it would solve anything."

"What would, Georges?"

"Oh, I wish I knew. You know, Tony, we French are always nationalistic and now, since the war, we are more so. Most of us want things to change compared with before the war, like you in Britain with your Beveridge Plan, health service and so on. But we also want to expurgate the sins of collaboration. We want to see signs that the French Government that passed French laws to send French Jews to concentration camps and their deaths, is completely repudiated and those who took part in those actions brought to justice. de Gaulle seems to want to pretend that the Vichy Government was not a French government. Yet some of those who did these things under Pétain, the head of the Vichy Government of so-called unoccupied France, and some of those who collaborated in occupied France, are active in government today. One of those who, it is said, was active in deporting French Jews and sending Frenchmen to work in Germany now holds a senior position in the General's government. That is unbelievable, isn't it? It is also said that others are in hiding, sheltered by the Church, my friend!

"So you see, Tony, we French are facing a moral and psychological dilemma. We want to be proud of our country again, and we want our country to be respected. And whenever we seek to raise the symbolic standard of '*la gloire de la France*', to see Marianne as a true heroine again, we do it by putting our trust in a highly centralised government. The great French Revolution, which some people in other countries saw as a beacon of hope while their governments feared its influence, did very little for ordinary people here – apart from giving them the right to hunt – but in the end it gave us a dictator and a very strong centralised government with an aggressive foreign policy. You know the saying, '*La France c'est L'État; L'État c'est La France.*' As for the present situation, we shall see very soon what will happen. If we hear nothing from the General in a few days, and we see the police in Paris getting tougher with the rioters, I think it will mean he has decided to carry on and will probably call a general election to test his public support."

Tony and Ginger were silent as they listened to this brave patriot's view of his country's troubles and pondered the problems he described. Then Tony spoke quietly. "Georges, my friend, thank you for your frankness. You told me something of this just after the war. You were very perceptive. I think all of us who were involved in fighting for the defeat of Germany and the liberation of your country are unhappy to see these signs of disunity, but you have helped me understand the reasons. I can see that France's experiences under occupation – which we in Britain did not have to endure – will be a powerful influence for a long time to come. The important thing for us to remember is that all those who chose the path of resistance, from whatever background, fought together bravely and successfully against the enemy."

With that the evening was complete. The mood, serious, thoughtful, and amiable as befitted their happy but unexpected reunion, had been set by Georges's eloquently expressed concerns. More conversation would have been anticlimactic. They were the last to leave Maison Madeleine, effusively thanked and well-wished on their journey by the attentive Pierre Rambert. Outside, Tony and Georges embraced and bid each other farewell, promising to be in touch more frequently, with Georges promising all his help in solving the mystery of the photograph and finding the thieves and murderers. "And watch out for those two types and their Mercedes – or perhaps some other car," said Tony as he gave Georges a final wave.

Chapter 9

Next morning Georges, as arranged, called for Ginger in his Citroën. Tony sat at a table outside the Espérance to see them drive off. He watched as closely as he could the cars going in their direction, to see if they were followed by the two men last seen in the restaurant. But the steady stream of traffic seemed to be of people hurrying to their work. There was no sign of villains.

With time to spare he drove at a leisurely pace back to Paris, stopping for coffee and again for lunch. He was certain he was not followed. It puzzled him that neither he nor Georges and Ginger were now being tailed. Had the clear indication in the restaurant the previous evening that they were now recognised simply warned them off? If so it did not say much for their expertise or their determination to discover the other sets containing the photograph they were targeting. Or did it mean they were confident that they had the information they needed? That was more worrying than knowing they were still being followed.

He completed the formalities of returning the car, and passed the time in the airport catching up on newspaper reading, noting a lengthy opinion expressed in *Le Monde* that the dislocation caused by the strikes and the disorder on the streets of Paris would endanger the Republic unless firmer action were taken by the government. Certainly, he thought, it was a dangerous time for France and for the

166

government of Gaullists. And, historically, such a time was when strong and sometimes desperate measures are often taken.

On the aircraft Tony's thoughts turned more to the coming dispute with his former employers over the terms for ending his contract. The events that had confronted him since his return from South America had distracted him from the vital needs of his situation. He badly wanted more legal advice. He must be sure to ring his friend Bill Walewsky, a lawyer formerly employed by the corporation, then by the Conference Board and now a semi-retired independent attorney who was very choosy about his briefs, to check on his rights under American employment law, and what bargaining opportunities he might have. Gradually, the wine he had drunk to make palatable the airline meal – a far cry from Maison Madeleine – and the boring drone of the cabin pressurisation sent him drifting into an uncomfortable sleep. Fitfully he dreamt he was at a table bargaining with former head-office colleagues, headed by General de Gaulle, for the purchase of a picture he could not see.

Georges and Ginger left the commuter traffic behind as they drove out of Chartres that morning and took the road to Orléans. It was sunny and warm and the French country-side, with its broad vistas, looked orderly and cared for. It seemed, thought Ginger, a good portent for a satisfying hot French summer. The strikes, the demonstrations they had discussed the previous evening, and the troubled French conscience were distant, physically and mentally. They went through Artenay and on to Orléans the historic city that in the Middle Ages saw the beginning of the end of the Hundred Years War when a young French maid with a military mind, destined for martyrdom, led a French army to recapture the town from the British and so inspired her countrymen and her king finally to wrench themselves free from the centuries-old 'joint' kingdom. Passing through the town brought back to Ginger's mind – not normally given to much thought on these matters – Tony's comment at a briefing on the historical and political background of their mission that a study of history was an opportunity to judge the way our forebears responded to dangers and challenges they faced but did not seek. Some historians, with a long hindsight and making judgements by the criteria of a different age, reinterpreted events, Tony had said, but he hoped that future writers would do justice to the bravery of ordinary people thrust into the fight to free Europe from military occupation. Ginger had not quite followed the argument, but agreed with its conclusion.

They decided to follow the broad sweep of the Loire down to Nevers rather than succumb to the temptation of a nostalgic tour through the area of their wartime operations, which they promised themselves on the way back. At Georges's suggestion they made a short stop at St-Benoît to admire the historic Benedictine abbey, but resisted crossing the river for a run through the vineyards up to the attractive town of Sancerre. They went through Gien and then stopped at the little town of La Charité for more refreshment before proceeding on to Nevers. Sitting outside a cafe by the bridge on the road that ran alongside the river, Ginger contentedly absorbed the placid scene, the clear sky, felt the warm spring sunshine and watched the thousand suns reflected in the flowing waters of the Loire. "Georges, you are very lucky living in a country with a beautiful countryside, romantic-looking towns and villages and the chance to escape the Northern chill and rain without going abroad. I've visited many countries but none has the attraction that this has – apart from home, of course. I really understand Tony's feeling for the place."

"Of course I am lucky, Ginger. But you know the saying that beauty is in the eye of the beholder. I don't believe that to be absolutely true. I think there is a state of beauty, which the eye of the beholder enhances – or rejects. I know many of my countrymen – me included – believe your country is one of the prettiest and most romantic, historically, in the world. And when we are in the mood to admire these beautiful scenes, perhaps we do not want to look at the troubles and difficulties on the other side of the picture. For short times we can indulge in that luxury, but at other times we must be realistic. So come on now, my friend, we must go."

Reaching Nevers, Georges took a road from the centre that led straight to the building to the south-west of the town housing the *Musée de la Resistance Française: à l'honneur des martyrs.* Georges parked the car in the small car park at the side of the house where there were just two other vehicles. By the gate there was a stone plaque headed 'Les Martyrs de Nevers de 1er Novembre 1943', beneath which were the names of the three men and the youth who were shot. They paused as Georges read the inscription to Ginger. Inside the entrance they stopped at the table manned by an old, bespectacled, grey-haired man wearing a Légion d'honneur ribbon in his lapel, whose task it was to collect entrance fees 'to contribute to the upkeep of the museum'. Georges told him that he was a donor to the museum, that he wished to see the curator, and handed him his card. The old man studied the card, looked at them both over the top of his spectacles, then pointed with his thumb in the direction of a closed door by the entrance to the main downstairs room. "*Par là, messieurs. Par là.*"

Georges gave a respectful knock on the door, then walked in. The room was stuffy and the atmosphere heavy with the smell of tobacco smoke. It contained a table on which, Ginger quickly noticed, were the paraphernalia of display and presentation – a roll of cartridge paper, scissors, marking pen, a pot of paste, and a desk laden with papers behind which sat a balding man, wearing steel-rimmed half-spectacles, with a greying Mexican moustache. He looked up with a frown and a far from friendly expression. Then recognition lit his features. "Monsieur Lebrun. It is yourself. I am happy to see you again. You should have told me you were coming. I would have met you." Georges explained that it was the unexpected arrival of his ex-comrades from England that had prompted his visit. Ginger was duly introduced and the curator was honoured to meet an English friend of Monsieur Lebrun who had fought for France.

Pleasantries over, Georges asked if his photographs were on display yet. "But certainly, monsieur. Follow me and I will show you. Monsieur le Préfet came down himself to approve the display. He had been asked by his predecessor to give it special attention." With Ginger carrying the packet of photos left from Larry's collection, the two of them followed the curator, who had left his Gauloise smouldering in an ashtray on his desk, into the main part (two rooms of the house knocked into one) of the museum. It was, Ginger thought, well set out with display boards, blown-up copies of old photos and newspaper headlines, cabinets containing equipment, weapons and so on. In the centre a large display panel with the heading 'Les Maquisards Combattants', also with headlines and text, prominently in the centre of which was a group of enlarged photographs easily recognisable as those of the mission's operations. As they approached Ginger frowned and stopped in his tracks. Georges looked round. "Anything the matter, Ginger?"

"They're not all there, Georges. There are fewer than I have in this packet."

"Are you sure?"

The curator was standing by the display regarding them uncomprehendingly.

"I'm sure." Ginger began to open the packet.

Georges turned to the curator. "Excuse us, monsieur. We wish to make a comparison with some other photographs we have . . ."

"But, monsieur, that is not necessary. These are the photos you sent us, which we have enlarged for effect and set out . . ."

"Yes, evidently, but we would still like to compare with some others . . ."

"But it is not . . ."

"If you please, monsieur," said Georges firmly. The curator shrugged and turned away.

They stood in front of the presentation and one by one matched the photos on display with those in Larry's collection. "How many left Ginger?"

"Three, and with the one that was stolen that makes four they have not used. We can identify three, but not the important one." They carefully examined the three they could identify. "One is the shot of the landmarks of the forest petrol dump, which, I suppose, is not very informative, and the other two seem to be the shots of the big ambush, the one containing the loot lorry. They have just left the

171

one showing you as Captain François talking to me and Larry. Why wouldn't they have shown the one of Tony and Léon? The mystery remains."

"I think we can find out a bit more while we are here. Monsieur," said Georges, turning to the curator again. "You have not used all the pictures I sent you. Where are the others?"

"Monsieur . . . er . . ." he spluttered, and he gave a Gallic shrug.

"Where . . . are . . . they . . . monsieur?" said Georges with great emphasis.

"Er . . . Monsieur le Préfet has them."

"The *Préfet*? In the name of God, why?"

"He wanted to know when the display was ready so that he could come down and inspect it before I put it up. He said it was an important display."

"And did he change it?"

"Yes, he came with a little note which he consulted as he examined the display. Then he said 'These three photos will not be needed', and he said he would see that they were sent back to you."

"How long ago?"

"Two weeks ago."

"Can you remember what the photos he removed were about?"

"No, monsieur, I regret." Another shrug. "I did not take much notice. My job is to display what I am given." Ginger was fairly certain he was not speaking the whole truth, even if he wasn't actually lying.

"I should like to telephone the *Préfet* from your office."

The curator had stopped trying to erect obstacles. "Certainly." He made a gesture towards his office.

Inside, Georges took the number from the curator and

dialled. It took some time to persuade the *Préfet*'s first line of defence to put him through. Ginger's French was not good enough to follow the conversation word by word, but it was sufficient for him to realise, if only from the pitch and volume of Georges's voice, that while it was the museum's right to decide what to show it would have been courteous to consult the donor, who had been invited to contribute, about what was decided and why. After all, as a former Maquis commander the donor would know best what was important and what was not. Then the explosive words "Monsieur Boulanger?" came through loud and clear. "Jean Boulanger? *Non? . . . Qui?*", then incredulously, "*Henri* Boulanger?" The rest was too rapid an exchange at a high pitch for him to get even a notion of what was said, but during the course of the exchange Ginger saw Georges scribble on a piece of paper. With the clearly understandable "*Merci, monsieur, et au revoir*," Georges replaced the receiver and turned to the curator. He shook him by the hand in the normal French manner and bade him "*au revoir*", also, perhaps, rather coolly. Taking the cue, Ginger followed the procedure with as much formality and as little warmth as he was capable of displaying. Georges said, "Come on Ginger, we must go." And they left.

They had just reached the gate when the curator called after them. "Monsieur, Monsieur . . ." He was waving an envelope. "Here are the originals of the photos we used in the display." Georges took the packet and thanked him. Not a word was said between them until they were in the car. Then, "Progress, Georges?"

"I do not know whether it is progress towards solving the mystery of the photo, my friend, but it is an interesting twist in the story, you might say. The *Préfet*'s predecessor, who suggested I be asked to contribute to the Museum, is none other than Jean Boulanger's nephew Henri, who ceased to be a senior officer in the gendarmerie and became *Préfet* of police, and is now a senior *fonctionnaire* – in the Gaullist Party, as I had heard. He has an office in Orléans."

"Then it was he who told the *Préfet* what to display and what not to?"

Georges nodded as he turned the car and drove out of the car park, heading back the way they came. "Then why did he exclude the ones he did?"

"He said that the shot of the petrol-dump marker was not very informative, as we suspected. And he said he thought we had too many of the big ambush compared with other operations. He said the rejected ones are in the post."

"Three is too many?"

"So he thought. But we are now on our way to see him to see if he can throw any light on our mystery. I could not go on questioning him from the curator's office, so I told him we had a problem we would like to discuss with him. I said we would call on him on our way back to Chartres."

"Did he remember any of us, did he say?"

"Oh yes, he remembered you and he asked about Tony. I told him he was in New York for a few days. I think we can see him without making you late. We have to go through Orléans, and it seems worth trying to fit it in. But we shall have to abandon going back through the old operational area. Sorry about that, but I promise to get you to Orly before midday tomorrow."

"All right by me," said Ginger, settling back in his seat.

So they followed in the reverse direction the road alongside the Loire through La Charité, Gien, St-Benoît and into Orléans from the south-west. Henri Boulanger's office in the building occupied by the Gaullist Party was near the Hôtel de Ville. He greeted them courteously. He had never been effusive in manner. Ginger remembered the brevity of his responses when Tony had questioned him about how he reached Maquis Léon. But because of his devotion to Jean Boulanger, his uncle, it mattered little then. "Capitaine François," he said with welcoming eyes in an impassive face as he came round from behind his desk, "and Sergeant Turner, I am happy to see you again." Georges responded warmly and Ginger, making no concessions to his host's mother tongue, said, "Good to see you again, Henri," noticing that he like everyone else was looking rounder, and certainly more mature.

"Please sit down. Excuse me for my small office," he said with a slightly deprecating smile. Now, what is this mystery of photographs you mentioned on the telephone, Monsieur Lebrun, and how can I help?"

Georges repeated what Tony and Ginger had told him in Chartres about the mysterious death of Roddy, the coincidental, or related, burglary of his house, Larry's murder, the attempted burglary of Ginger's apartment, all, it seemed, with the object of stealing one of the photos in the collections each had of some of the AMCA mission's operations. In his account of these events he turned to Ginger from time to time to check his memory. On occasions Ginger interrupted at what he thought were relevant points to add to the information. And in the exchanges that followed Georges conducted the conversation while asking Ginger for advice and confirmation. "The point is, Henri," Georges concluded, "we need to identify the subject matter of the missing photo before we can understand the importance of it to some person or persons – which should tell us who is responsible for these crimes."

"I think I can see your problem, but I do not see how I can help because I have never had a set of those photographs, and of course, as far as remembering operations at that time, I was, as you know, late in joining Maquis Léon and I only then went on those raids that my uncle required me to. I do not have, as you might say, the whole picture."

"But you advised your successor as *Préfet* in the Nièvre region to reject some of the pictures I sent to the Nevers museum at your suggestion."

"Ah, yes, but I explained on the telephone my reasons."

"Yes, you did, but perhaps you don't realise that one of your rejects seems to have included a copy of the photo that has been taken from two of the collections."

Henri Boulanger hesitated. "No, I did not. I did not see any special significance in any of them."

"We wondered if the mystery photo might have had something to do with the ambush of the convoy that included the lorry containing loot from Bordeaux?"

"That was before I got to Maquis Léon, wasn't it? So I can't say. But I think it unlikely. That lorry did not contain a great treasure. Some porcelain and jade and some paintings taken by the German commander of the convoy from the home of some poor Jews who were deported from Bordeaux."

"And the German officer who commanded the convoy was killed."

"Yes, so I was told, when my uncle was surprised by a German patrol. Do you know where the lorry went after liberation?"

"No. It was taken on the advice of the SOE agent in the region to the estate of a marquis who kept it hidden until Paris was liberated."

"And then?"

"We were told it had been handed to the authorities in Paris."

"Do you know what that meant? Who received it?"

"No we don't. It was not important to us at the time."

"But in view of what has happened, it may be important now. Perhaps you need to follow up on the SOE agent to see if what you heard about the loot being handed over was true. Maybe he will have the answer to your riddle, messieurs. I am sorry that on this I cannot help you."

"One more thing, if you please, Henri, do you know who the marquis might have been?"

"Unhappily, no. It was, as I say, before I joined my uncle. Much later, when I was *Préfet* at Nevers, there was an estate formerly the property of a Marquis de Ramatuelle by then owned by the marquise – the marquis having died – but she rarely visited it. I do not know of any in the Cher region."

"Well, thank you for your time, Monsieur Boulanger. Perhaps we should remind you that your uncle has a set of these photos and may be in danger from these criminals. He should be warned."

"I shall make it my duty to inform him of your fears. As you will understand, I owe him a great deal."

"Yes, we understand. He took great care of you in the war after your poor father was killed." Henri lowered his eyes from them and for a while looked uncomfortable. "How is Jean? We last heard he was living in the Pyrénées?"

"Yes, unfortunately he is not very well. The wound to his chest has turned bad for him. He had a lung taken away. He needs clean mountain air. I shall make a point of telling him all that you have said, and warn him of the danger."

"It would be nice if we could visit him to talk of old times. We know Tony Beckett would like to see him again. Your uncle was a great Maquis commander, and a good patriot. Where is he in the Pyrénées?"

Henri hesitated again. "Thank you for that. I know he

would be proud to hear you say such things. He had a great respect for Commander Beckett. However, I'm not sure a lot of visitors will be very good for him just now. He tires quickly. He is living in a small house in the mountains, just inside Spain above Roncesvalles. His house is called La Roche."

"Before we leave, monsieur, I must ask you, as a leading official in the Gaullist Party, will the government be able to handle these strikes and riots? Or will it fall?"

He seemed to be pleased to be asked a matter of such current importance. "Messieurs, I think you can be confident that the general will take strong action against these enemies of the Republic, and he will call an election which will confirm once and for all that France is safe in his hands."

Georges smiled and nodded his head in a sign of understanding and appreciation. "Thank you, Monsieur Boulanger, for that reassurance. And now, I regret, we must be on our way. I must get Monsieur Turner to Orly for a flight back to England in time for his trip to the United States."

"New York?"

"No. Washington. Tony Beckett is in New York."

"To be sure. Well then, *au revoir*. It has been very pleasant seeing you again. *Bon voyage*."

The trip back to Paris, requiring concentrated driving by Georges because they were later than they had wanted to be, was without conversation, apart from questions by Ginger to confirm his understanding of the discussion they had just left. As a result, Ginger, before falling into a doze, murmured, "We're really back to square one. Unless we wait for Jean to get back from Canada, or for Tony to unpack his crates in New York, now we can only try to find out if an old SOE agent is still alive. Tony's not going to like that. He hates negative results.'

178

Chapter 10

It was warm and airless as Tony Beckett walked into the passport-control area of the airport in New York on Thursday evening to join the shuffling queue of arrivals from many flights. He did not feel very good. He had slept for an hour or two, then restlessly dozed, irritated by his strange dream and trying to see reason in the recent strange and tragic events, hoping that Ginger would phone him in the morning with at least a clue; all the time mentally urging himself to forget all that for twenty-four hours and concentrate on the more urgent matter of his personal finances. It took half an hour for him to get through the immigration barrier and then began the wait by the baggage-reclaim carousel to collect his valise. Ahead was the scramble to get a cab into Brooklyn. No, he didn't feel at all good. He was in a very bad mood.

The cab he eventually caught was driven by a dark-skinned man, from somewhere in the Middle East to judge from the name and photograph on his licence, who kept up a conversation in scarcely understandable American English about his enthusiasm for America, the American way of life, and the freedom he enjoyed to go where he wanted and speak what he thought without fear. Tired and depressed though he was, Tony realised he was listening to an experience that reflected a life of repression and danger lived by many people – to whom he generally gave little thought – some of whom realised their dream of living in freedom, however poorly, while many did not. He tipped the man more generously than was normally expected when they arrived at Montague Terrace in Brooklyn Heights.

Inside the apartment he dropped his valise and cabin bag and went straight to the far window in the living room and looked out over the promenade that ran at the back of the properties. He looked across the East River to the southern end of Manhattan, already brightly lit. It was a magical view. The lights along The Battery, the waterfront and on the skyscrapers displaying the varied Manhattan skyline were reflected in the river, a mirror image broken only by the craft ceaselessly ploughing along the waterway. To the left was Staten Island and Ellis Island with its famous statue. To the right was Brooklyn Bridge. He had not had the opportunity to watch the scene very often, but it was a sight that never failed to enchant him. He felt better. It was strange, as he had noticed before, how the pace of life in New York was infectiously invigorating. He turned back into the room, switched on the lights, and walked over to the phone. He had made a note of Bill Walewsky's number in the plane. He prayed silently that he was not away, not out to dinner, not anywhere else at all, as he listened to the ringing tone. He had held, it seemed, for minutes and was about to hang up when he heard the deep, gravelly voice answer succintly, "Walewsky".

"Bill? Tony Beckett."

"For God's sake. Where the hell are you?" Bill Walewsky had a deep, rounded American accent; very third-generation New England and first-generation Harvard that concealed the Polish–Jewish origins of which he was nevertheless justly proud. He had a slow way of speaking, as if choosing each word and constructing each phrase with great deliberation.

It was comforting for his clients that his advice seemed so carefully thought out – which indeed it was.

"I'm in Henry Beckstein's apartment in Brooklyn Heights."

"Beckstein? He still alive?"

"I believe so. He's in Florida."

"Yeah? Florida? Maybe he's still alive, maybe not. It's hard to tell down there. So what's happening to you, Tony Beckett? Still trying to teach Wall Street how to conduct overseas investment properly?"

"Not any longer, Bill. Policy disagreement and I'm out. I need some Walewsky wisdom. I have a termination-of-contract dispute which is up for final negotiation tomorrow."

"*Tomorrow?*" There was a lengthy pause, then in slow, measured terms "Tony, it's nearly ten o'clock – p.m., that is. You have a negotiation tomorrow, a.m. I imagine, and you are telephoning me for advice, I assume . . ."

"No, Bill. The appointment is p.m."

"Oh! Oh! That makes all the difference, does it? We now have plenty of time, eh? Perhaps you're not aware that the work still has to be done tonight. Do you realise how long ago I gave up burning midnight oil over briefs? In the circumstances it would not be unreasonable of me to tell you to get lost, would it?"

"No, it wouldn't, Bill."

"OK, as long as we understand each other. Have you got a copy of your contract and of any letters or notes referring to the reasons given for your departure. Anything."

"Contract, yes. Only one letter confirming that I had to go, and an exchange of cables. Most of the argument took place over the phone and in their offices. Oh, and a letter regretting my going from the Chief Minister of Ciudad Guayana."

"How long a contract? How long did you serve? What termination terms?"

"Five-year contract. I served three. Six months notice on either side, or instant termination for 'social misbehaviour' or for damaging the company's reputation or its property maliciously . . . or words to that effect."

"Yeah, yeah. OK. Now, you have to bring all those things to me, tonight, at 1622 Arlington Avenue, East Side, where I have an apartment. Grab a cab, put your goddam arse in it and get it over here. I'll have a bottle of bourbon and two glasses waiting. And hurry. At my age I need plenty of beauty sleep. If I don't get it I'm not nice."

"Thanks Bill, I'll . . ."

"Yeah, I know. Just get here quickly. I'm tired already."

It was nearer eleven when Tony reached Bill Walewsky's smart East Side apartment. The elevator led straight into his entrance hall. They greeted each other with the restrained warmth and respect each felt for the other. Tony knew Bill from early days with the corporation, and from occasional subsequent meetings, as a highly skilled advocate and a friendly, cultured and generous human being. Bill's admiration of what he knew of Tony's wartime record was unrestrained. 'You British certainly have guts when you are up against it. You ignore the odds. And I'll never forget that you and the French were the first to take Hitler on when he raped my mother country, which you knew you could do little about at the time.' They sat in large enveloping easy chairs, papers and bourbon on a glass coffee table in front of them, facing a large window with floor-to-ceiling curtains on either side, looking across the East River towards the lights of Brooklyn, which Tony had just left. In just an hour and a half, after much questioning by Bill, they had worked out a negotiating position, a minimum acceptance figure, and a 'go for it' figure.

"What time is this historic confrontation taking place, Tony?"

"Two o'clock tomorrow afternoon at the corporation's offices on Wall Street."

"Same address?"

"Yes."

"Who are you seeing?"

"Karensky, the VP Operations, and Oscar Patterson, the treasurer. Patterson's not bad – he works to instructions. Karensky's ambitious and can be tough and unpleasant if thwarted."

"Yeah, I remember Karensky before he started climbing the executive ladder. He was brash then. Later, when he had climbed over a few people I met him again when he was defending a supplier against the corporation. I then judged him to be domineering and nasty when crossed. He gets nasty because when it comes to the crunch he's uncertain of himself. Basically no depth. He's of Polish extraction, you know. They're funny people," he said with a disarming grin. "Like the little girl, when they're good they're very good, but when they haven't got it they're lousy." He paused, then looked across at Tony with a little smile on his lips. "Like me to come with you? As your attorney? I'd like to face up Karensky again."

"Bill, that would be wonderful, of course. But I couldn't . . ."

"The fee is not negotiable, even to you, pal. It will be a bottle of bourbon – since you've drunk so much of mine tonight. OK? Now go, and let me get some sleep. I'll see you in the lobby of the Chase building at one-forty-five tomorrow. And don't be late. My time comes expensive."

183

They shook hands warmly, and the friendly grins they exchanged said everything they needed to say to each other. It was one-thirty in the morning when Tony returned to his apartment. Before closing the curtains and switching on the light he stood for a moment enjoying the view across the river, and in that moment he saw a figure with a broad-brimmed black trilby shielding his face get up from one of the benches along the promenade, look up at the windows of the apartments and move hurriedly away. Coincidence? His nervous imagination? Or did they after all overhear in France his – and Ginger's? – planned movements?

Telling Cels later about the meeting with the Strachan Corporation, Tony said that it was almost worth forfeiting six months' salary to see Karensky's face when they were shown in to his office the next afternoon. His jaw dropped visibly and his eyes widened with surprise. "Hello Jim," said Bill smoothly. "I'm glad to see you again." A phrase that did not express any great pleasure. "How are things?"

"Er . . . surprise. An unexpected pleasure," Karensky replied, regaining some composure. "Are you representing Beckett? You should have told us, Tony," he said, turning to him.

"Yes, I'm sorry, but there have been some unexpected events that required my urgent attention after getting back to the UK and I had too little time to prepare, but fortunately I have had the help of my excellent attorney – who you obviously remember."

Jim Karensky introduced Oscar Patterson then asked if they could be excused for a few minutes. They went into the outer office. Tony and Bill sat themselves at the table in the centre of the office and winked at each other. When Karensky and Patterson returned they sat themselves on the other side of the table. Just as Karensky was about to speak, Bill held up his hand and said, "Just to be sure that everything is above board I would like to place this tape recorder on the table. No doubt you would like to put yours there, too."

Karensky and Patterson exchanged glances. Then Karensky nodded and Patterson reached into his open briefcase and produced a recorder, which he put beside Bill's. There were half-smiles all round, then Karensky opened the discussion with a very brisk, "Well, I don't think this is a complicated issue. As we see it, Tony is entitled to six months' salary under contract, but we are prepared to extend that to a year's salary in view of his former good service. Naturally we'll meet all reasonable expenses associated with his return to the UK."

There was a long pause as Bill looked down at his papers and shuffled them before looking up with an amused smile on his face and fixing his eyes on Jim Karensky. "Now, Jim," he said slowly, "you know me well enough to realise I don't like playing silly buggers when I represent a client. It's a waste of time I can't spare even if you can. I'm prepared to regard that ridiculous offer you just made as an unfortunate joke and suggest we move on to negotiate seriously. As you say the issue is not complicated. I would just draw your attention to your letter confirming your decision to require Tony to leave, to the notes of the subsequent discussion in your office of the policy disagreement between you. And you may not have brought into your thinking on this matter the fact that Tony's proposal as to how your corporation could help the region's land-reform programme could have been a stabilising factor in that poor country. Now, I'm sure your stockholders would not want to think that corporation policy is opposed to helping to stabilise . . ."

Eyes blazing, Karensky broke in. "Bill, that's blatant blackmail. What the hell do you think you are doing?"

"No, Jim, listen to me. Just listen carefully and you will see what I am doing. I am pointing out that Tony's proposal was not designed to undermine the corporation's position, as you claimed, but was an attempt to improve the corporation's relationships with the local government there by cooperating in a scheme designed to remove local discontent, as the chief minister's letter shows. You already have a copy of it." Bill paused. Karensky looked uncertain of himself, and just as he seemed ready to speak Bill resumed having judged that his point had been taken. "Obviously you have a right to get rid of Tony, but not on the grounds you claim. So you have to pay him appropriate compensation. Now, we can argue about this for as long as you like. We can eventually bring in arbitrators and hand all the evidence over to them, if you wish. But I think we would both prefer to settle the matter quickly and between ourselves. Now, in the light of all that, here is what I think the settlement figure should be."

The negotiation was virtually over at that moment, though some subsequent pointless argument, and a bit of bluster from Karensky, and more Karensky–Patterson consultation in the outer office, followed before they shook hands on the terms proposed by Bill Walewsky. A letter of agreement was drawn up and signed. They shook hands again as they left. Bill's quiet but taunting "Well, it's been a pleasure doing business with you again, Jim. Call me if there's ever anything I can do." tested Jim Karensky's self-control. Going down in the crowded elevator Tony's bursting gratitude had to be restrained, but in the lobby he pumped Bill's arm and clapped him on the back until Bill was forced to protest. "Hey, go easy, Tony. It's poor recompense to disable me. It was no big deal. You had it by right. It's just a matter of playing it properly. You had two-years-and-three-month

186

salary owed under the contract, and all relocation *and* rehousing expenses as agreed by an independent auditor was not too hard to get – but maybe the compensation for loss of appointment equivalent to another year-and-a-half's salary was a bit of a bonus . . ."

"I'll say it was, Bill. I'll say. There's quite a bit of bourbon in that . . ."

"Yeah, well I had to be sure you could afford the fee . . . So what do you do now?"

"Well, let's find somewhere for a coffee and I'll bore you with a detailed description of an intriguing mystery I'm involved in in the UK. You deserve it after all you've just done for me."

"Oh my God! Why did I do it? Come on then."

It was over several cups of coffee that Tony described the mysterious and tragic pattern of events that occurred just after he returned to England, apparently connected with their wartime mission in France. Bill listened attentively, interrupting only to express sympathy at the deaths of Roddy and Larry and to ask an occasional question to clarify his understanding. When Tony had concluded Bill gazed into his empty cup for a few seconds, then looked up. "Clearly some goddam son of a bitch is desperately worried about something that your comrade Roddy photographed, in the process unwittingly signing his and Lawrence's death warrants and probably putting out contracts on you, Ginger Turner and maybe the Maquis leaders." He paused and looked down again. Tony could tell he had not finished, but by his manner seemed to be deliberating. Then, "But as I see it something more recent has happened or is happening that has turned what was a 25-year-old innocent snapshot into a death card today. Perhaps it will be something to do with the truck full of loot. Perhaps Mr Turner will have discovered what it is. But if not, all I can say to you from my experience is that the clue is there – somewhere. You just have to find it. Sounds simple, and I know it's what you've been trying to do. But when it seems you can't make any progress you have to go over every goddam piece of information very carefully and question it again and again. And keep asking yourself what new situation, and where, might have triggered such serious and deadly crimes now. Some idea about that will help pick out the clue in the information you probably already have."

"Bill, you're a good friend and a great counsellor. Your clarity of insight is a true gift. Strachan Corporation should never have let you go. I do appreciate . . ."

"OK. OK. Save the flattery, I've nothing more to give you now," Bill growled.

They walked together along to the subway to take their different lines. Before separating Bill took the tape recorder from his briefcase, extracted the tape and handed it to Tony. "There you are. Just in case you need it."

Tony thanked him. Shaking hands, Bill said, "With an agreement for almost four years' salary and relocation expenses in your pocket, and a live-in girlfriend on the way over, I kind of envy you. But pace yourself, pal. Pace yourself. You're not the vigorous young warrior you used to be, you know," and quickly ducked down the stairs to his platform.

When Tony emerged from the subway by Court Street at the top of Montague Street in Brooklyn Heights and walked slowly down towards the promenade along the East River, it was nearly six o'clock. He was contemplating with much satisfaction the momentous course of the day's events. As he was now financially secure for a few years at least, he could be more relaxed about searching for a job and for somewhere to live. Now, thanks to Bill Walewsky's advocacy h

188

could consider choices. He felt a trifle euphoric. As he came to the liquor store halfway down, he went in and ordered a case of bourbon and a case of Veuve Clicquot champagne to be sent to Bill's address. He also ordered half-a-dozen Pouilly Fumé and half-a-dozen Pomerol to be sent to his own apartment, to keep Cels and him from going dry over the weekend, and carried away a bottle of Bollinger. Farther down he went into a pizza parlour and took away a medium tomato, pepperoni and anchovy pizza, big enough for two. He would celebrate tonight. Unfortunately alone and at home, because he must not miss Ginger's telephone call. As he entered the apartment those more serious thoughts returned to his mind and he recalled Bill's comments on the subject of the mystery photograph. What had Ginger found out? Surely he will be phoning soon. Eleven o'clock in the evening in the UK. He must have got back from France by now – and he had to be on minder duty in the morning.

As an aperitif, half of the bottle of Bollinger was beyond compare. He drank the other half as an accompaniment to the pizza, for which inflicted indignity he apologised aloud to the bottle and mentally to his image of the great, matriarchal Madame Bollinger. Apart from the champagne it was an unsatisfactory way to celebrate a successful negotiation that gave him some years' security, but it sent him to bed replete and sleepy, and unfairly cursing Ginger for not telephoning. It seemed he had only been there five minutes when the shrill ringing woke him. He staggered to the lounge, blundered to the phone and grunted into the receiver. It was Ginger.

"Tony. Tony. Is that you? What's the matter? You sound awful."

"I *feel* awful, Ginger. I was fucking-well asleep."

"Oh! Of course. But Tony, can you just listen, please. Plans have changed. It's seven a.m. in London and I'm at the airport with my guv'nor and we are about to board a transatlantic flight. We have to come to New York to consult some lawyers. He wants a Saturday meeting before going on to Washington for the real business. The offices are not far from the New York Stock Exchange and I will have a free couple of hours once he is safely inside. Can we meet briefly somewhere nearby, because one or two things happened on the trip to Nevers which I should explain to you and there's no time now? Savvy?"

"Yes, OK, Ginger. Savvy. You want us to meet in New York. OK. What time? Let me think," and he forced his barely conscious brain to work out flight times and time-zone differences, "do you think your free time will be somewhere between one and two p.m?"

"Er . . ." then silence as Tony assumed, rightly, that Ginger was wrestling with his own mental arithmetic. "Yes, I guess that's about right."

"Well, you won't be far from Brooklyn Bridge. Let's meet at the Manhattan end of the footbridge by the towers holding the suspension cables. There's a viewpoint with a direction plaque there. I'll wait by that."

"OK. Between one and two . . ."

"Ginger. Quickly. Have we a solution?"

"Not really, but some funnies. I'll explain. Must go. Bye."

Tony, more awake now and deep in thought, slowly put the receiver back on its cradle. 'No solution, but some funnies.' What the hell did that mean? What could have happened in Nevers? He wished now that he had risked his meeting with the wretched Karensky by going with Georges and Ginger. But then he would probably also have missed getting Bill Walewsky's crucial help. In fact he would certainly have missed it because, although he did not realise it, he would undoubtedly have grasped the opportunity to call at Orléans as Georges and Ginger had done on the way back. Nonetheless, it was damned annoying having to wait, wondering, for – what? – about eleven hours. What should he do? He was too restless to go back to bed. He got up and walked to the window and looked out into the brightly lit night, across the small garden below, across the promenade. Under the lights along the promenade he could see on one bench a figure – probably a 'bum' – stretched out, oblivious to the passionate writhings of a couple on the next bench who were determined not to let discomfort calm their ardour. Beyond the promenade, he could hear the ceaseless rumble of traffic on Route 278 along the riverside just below his view. He could see the dim lights on the ends of the port-authority timber piers, the river full of rippling reflections under the moon, and the lights of the Manhattan skyscrapers beyond. It was not one of Nature's captivating views. It was almost entirely constructed and activated by man – industrious, flamboyant and ambitious – yet irrespective of the hour or the season it was a breathtaking sight. He felt calmer. He turned away, went to the long settee and swung it round so he could lie facing the window, watch the lights and wonder as he waited.

Waiting. The art of waiting. He remembered how he was surprised at first that so much time in soldiering was taken up with just waiting. Not just waiting to go on active service, but also while in the field. Waiting followed by shorter periods of intensive fighting. In 1940 in Belgium and France, and to some extent in 1942 in the Western Desert, it was defensive fighting. After he joined the SAS it was offensive, aggressive fighting. In both instances the waiting called for a discipline. Waiting for defensive action the nerve was touched with apprehension; the initiative was 'theirs'. Waiting for offensive action the nerve was alive with expectation; the initiative was ours; we played the cards. In either condition it was important to exclude from the mind any unpleasant possibilities. They did not exist, really; they were bad fantasies implanted by evil spirits.

There was that time in 1940 when they were waiting in the farmyard for the battalion transport to arrive to take on board the ammunition and food they badly needed. The battalion was late. Hardly surprising in view of the heavy rumble of battle to the north-east. They had been given the rendezvous by Company HQ. It looked all right on the map. Unfortunately, the bank of trees along the road that would have concealed the waiting vehicles did not exist. They were exposed. It was only a matter of time before the Stukas and Messerschmitts arrived, and there was only his team's old Lewis gun, and such rifle fire as they could muster, to defend them. Virtually sitting ducks. They had already heard a single-engined aircraft flying high above them. Probably a scout.

Just as the battalion transport arrived he heard the distinctive drone of the Stukas. He and his two comrades scanned the clear blue sky. Then he saw them: three, high above. Were they going past to another target? That was an example of waiting for defensive action, nerves tingling knowing there was nothing they could do but wait for the inevitable attack that would bring pain and death. Then it happened. He yelled the warning as the flight of Stukas turned, lined up and began their screaming dive.

In a curious, stupid way it was a bit of a relief: no more waiting. Now, aware of that inexplicable coolness he always felt under fire with which his vision became vividly clear, he could concentrate on holding the butt of the shaking,

192

clattering Lewis into his shoulder to put up a field of fire the Stukas would have to dive through. The tracers signalled the bullets' seemingly lazy course. The shriek of their engines and sirens as they followed each other into a near perpendicular dive was almost unbearable. He remembered seeing clearly the bombs leave the aircraft just before they pulled out of their dive. One, perhaps two, had gone through the thin veil of lead before he had to change the ammunition pan. One belched smoke as it turned at the bottom of its dive, wobbled and crashed in a field beyond the farm. The other two flew off at the end of their dives; perhaps damaged, perhaps not. But they had unloaded their deadly cargo. He had seen a lorry lifted in the air and fall in flames. He had seen a burst of orange flame and flying clods of earth in the middle of the farmyard that sent running figures hurtling out of control through the air, and he felt one side of the truck in which he and his team stood firing the Lewis lift up, as a flash of flame and a deep crunch sent earth and whining shrapnel spinning past them, then settle back again. Then the Stukas were gone. Now they had to change ammunition pans again and wait for the next onslaught.

Very different was the sensation when waiting for thirty-six hours on the airfield in the south of England for the right weather conditions for their drop into France for the start of the AMCA mission. Tension was mixed with anticipation, even eagerness to get on with the job they had trained long and hard for. The four of them had had a briefing in Scotland and then travelled down to the airfield not far from Cheltenham two days before expected departure. There they had been shown aerial photographs of 'their area', given maps to study and given a final briefing. It was there that Tony decided that Roddy and Jacques, the phantom officer, should go in first, make contact with the two Maquis leaders, check for security of future use the DZ they would drop on, and establish communications. He, Larry and Ginger would follow and bring with them in kitbags a limited supply of weapons and explosives.

They had been 'housed' in a tent on the perimeter of the airfield. The adrenaline level was high all round when they got the OK to go. He, Larry and Ginger stood in the dim light of a cloudy night sky as Roddy and Jacques waved and climbed aboard. They waited – and they waited – until the door opened and the two of them jumped out swearing angrily. "Fucking-well aborted. Bad weather over France," said Roddy in a rare display of frustration. Morale was low that night, and next day. Colonel Manley had come down and tried to cheer them up. Having had a final briefing they could not leave the security of the airfield. They had spent the day jogging round the field, kicking a ball about, and testing each other on the briefing. That evening, after another confirming briefing, they kitted up again and Roddy and Jacques moved out to the aircraft again, somewhat apprehensively. But this time they were 'lucky'.

And when their turn came, Tony, Larry and Ginger had boarded the aircraft expectantly: the mission was on, only to be aborted on the way to the DZ. As they waited another day, they knew that they must control the anger and frustration that was in them, which otherwise could affect the powers of calm judgement they were going to need.

All that was a different kind of waiting, Tony recalled, with some relief, as he fell into a deep sleep.

He woke with a start. Where was he? Had he landed safely in France? No. The noises outside were definitely mid-morning urban noises. Brooklyn! Ginger! And Cels! My God, what time is it? He looked at his watch: nearly eleven o'clock! Enough time, but not much to spare. Coffee, shave, shower, dressing, were accomplished competently in that order without undue haste, but without a pause until, ready to leave, he walked over to the window for another view. The promenade was bustling with an endless stream of runners, strollers, dog walkers, and people sitting on the benches reading their papers or just looking. The river was busy with a variety of craft, including strings of barges pushed along by tugs, and the tireless ferries to Staten Island. The Statue of Liberty on Ellis Island shone proudly in the morning sun, and as he moved closer to the glass he could just see to the left the bridge crossing from Bayonne to Staten.

It was as he turned his head back that the figure caught his attention. Whoever it was wore the same dark overcoat and broad-brimmed trilby that he had noticed before. He was leaning with his back against the railings that ran along the edge of the promenade, definitely gazing up towards the apartments. There was too much shadow from the hat and not enough time for Tony to see the face clearly, before he turned suddenly and moved off as if he was aware of Tony's move to the window. It could have been one of the men in the Mercedes – the one who bought the bread and sat with his companion near them in the Café Espérance and in Maison Madeleine. Tony had now twice seen the figure watching the apartment. That was not a coincidence. He watched the man retreat as he moved briskly away before turning right into one of the accessways, between the gardens, that would take him into Montague Terrace.

Tony knew it would be pointless rushing down. The man would be gone, along any of the streets that ran up from the terrace. The important point was that he had been followed right into Brooklyn – or his precise destination had been passed from London (or France?) to someone who was watching him. Either way it was unlikely that the attention he was being given was friendly, and it was almost certainly with the object of removing another of the remaining copies of the photograph. And that had already been proved to be a ruthless process. Although he did not have his set here in Brooklyn, the villains would assume he did. So vigilance and caution were the watchwords. But what about Ginger? Presumably he was under observation, too, though there could be no question of carrying his set of photos with him on a business trip, even if he had them. But he probably *was* carrying useful information for Tony. There was that reference to 'some funnies' arising from the journey to Nevers. Might the villains be aware of what those 'funnies' were, and want to prevent him passing on that knowledge?

His naturally suspicious mind recycled these and similar questions in his head as he left the apartment, made his way up Montague Street and turned into a coffee shop on the right. He climbed up the outside steps, took a cappuccino and a croissant and went and sat in the window. As he sat sipping his coffee and eating his croissant he pondered again the likelihood of a connection between the broad-brimmed watcher and Ginger's visit to Nevers – but at the same time he was watching the street outside. Satisfied there was no sign of surveillance he left the coffee shop, crossed the road and walked the length of Henry Street to Cadman Plaza, past the war memorial and up round the edge of the park that took him to the small flight of narrow steps up onto the footpath of Brooklyn Bridge.

On the few occasions he had been able to borrow Henry Beckstein's apartment he had always enjoyed this walk over the bridge to Manhattan and down to a little Irish bar-restaurant not far from Pier 17. To begin with the upward incline was quite sharp. Some strolled it, some walked it vigorously, while alongside the footpath the cycle track was well used by cyclists who, to the irritation of the pedestrians, did not always stay in their lane but seemed intent on seeing how closely they could brush past walkers without actually knocking them down. He had memorised the landmarks: the Jehovah's Witnesses' Watchtower back on the right-hand side; Sweeney Manufacturing; the old parking lot; and soon, down to the left, he could look back at the promenade behind Montague Terrace, and the endless stream of traffic on Route 278 below it. Pier 17 was on the left on the Manhattan side.

He had reached the level part of the bridge between the two suspension towers. People were grouped round the direction plaque at the viewpoint by the first tower. He had arranged to meet Ginger at the viewpoint area across the bridge by the other tower. He looked at his watch. He would be there by one o'clock and wait for however long it took. He walked on past the benches along the middle of the walkway where people gazed upstream towards the Queens-borough Bridge over to Roosevelt Island, or downstream towards Staten Island and the distant small but distinct figure of Liberty glinting in the sun. He was nearly there and strained his eyes through the bobbing heads to see if Ginger had arrived. Apparently not. He lessened his pace. No telling. He might have a long wait.

As he approached the viewpoint he scanned the faces of the crowd round the direction plaque. No sign of that ruddy face and thinning carroty hair. Then he saw him, hurrying, half-jogging up the inclined walkway from the Manhattan side, large brown envelope in hand. He waved and called, "Hi, Ginger," which, he later realised, was a mistake for at that instant events occurred with split-second rapidity. The figure in the broad trilby appeared from behind the left-hand pillar and pointed repeatedly at the oncoming Ginger. Tony looked at Ginger and then saw the cyclist in jeans and leather jacket, with a woolly hat pulled down over his forehead, pedalling hard behind him. Steel glinted in one of his hands. He yelled, "Ginger. Behind you. Knife. Quick." He saw Ginger turn, ducking as he did so, hand covering his head. The cyclist was on top of him and slashed upwards with deadly intent as Ginger tumbled to the walkway. Now the cyclist was coming straight on, large, threatening and very fast. Tony dodged to one side, ducked low and grabbed the tail of the jacket and pulled hard. He felt a searing pain across the back of his hand, but had the momentary satisfaction of seeing the figure fall and roll over across the walkway, a black bundle of cycle wheels and flailing arms. He stared at him for a second, then looked up to where he had seen Ginger fall. He was in time to see the trilby hat sprinting down the slope towards Manhattan as, much to his relief, he saw Ginger move, pick himself up and start towards him. "I'm OK, Tony. OK. You hurt?" Tony was pulling himself upright and making for the fallen cyclist. But he was too late. The man had rolled away, scrambled upright, leapt onto his cycle and pedalled off, twisting and dodging between pedestrians across the bridge to Brooklyn.

"I'm all right," he said as Ginger came panting alongside.

"Thanks for the warning . . . In saving chums from knife attacks . . . that's fifteen–all I guess."

"Guess so. But let's get that knife. It may tell us something," he said, nodding to where the weapon had slid out of the would-be-killer's hand as he fell.

"God, Tony, look at your hand!"

Tony looked down at the red streak across the back of his hand dripping blood onto the walkway. A number of people had gathered round, expressing sympathy and outrage, and advising him to get a 'cop' and visit a doctor. "Goddam muggers. Nowhere's safe. The cops are never where you want them. You get that hand looked at quickly, pal. Go find a cop. I'll be a witness." There was a chorus of nods and grunts of agreement.

"Yes. Thank you. I'm OK," he said as he wrapped his handkerchief round the wound. "This is only a scratch, but I'll get it seen to, and I'll try to find a cop on our way home. Thanks all the same," he said, looking at the volunteer witness, "but I don't think I need bother you. There are two of us who can describe what happened. Good of you, just the same. Goodbye," and he moved through the little throng to where Ginger was waiting carrying an object wrapped in a handkerchief, smiling a little at the muttered 'Limeys. You can tell by their funny accent. They don't like a fuss.'

Grabbing Ginger's arm, Tony led him back towards Brooklyn. "Let's find a bench farther along, away from scene, and sit so that you can tell me what happened in Nevers. It's no use going to the police. It will take too much time and lead to too many difficult questions. I'm fairly sure I've been followed to the US, I think by the sportsman who came out from behind that pillar and pointed you out to the cyclist. I think he might be the baguette eater from the Mercedes and one of our nearby companions in Chartres. Did you see him?"

"Vaguely. But I didn't recognise him. I had seen you wave and heard my name, then everything happened so quickly."

"Yes. Unwittingly, I gave you away. It seems to me they wanted to stop you telling me about Nevers. Why? What is it you now know?"

"Nothing crucial as far as I know . . ."

"But you mentioned 'some funnies' . . ."

"Yeah, but they were just a surprise or two, and some things I couldn't – can't – understand."

"OK. Let's sit on this bench." They had reached the centre of the bridge. "How long have you got?"

"Until about three."

"OK. Lets sit here, face each other as much as possible and watch each other's back. OK. Go right through that day in as much detail as you can remember. There's something there somewhere – I hope. Start from when you left Chartres."

Chapter 11

So Ginger described what happened after he and Georges had driven away from the Espérance; the stop at St-Benoît and what Georges had said about the Benedictine abbey; the stop at Gien and the short conversation there, then the arrival at the museum; the conversation with the curator and his reasons for excluding some photos from display; the discovery that Henri Boulanger was the former *Préfet* of police who had organised the display (which had been a bit of a 'funny'); and the conversation with Henri at Orléans. Tony remained quiet for most of the time, interrupting only to press for more detail, and to ask Ginger to try to recall word for word the conversations with the curator, the *Préfet* and Henri Boulanger.

"Somewhere in the post to Georges, then, are the photos which were excluded from the museum's display and which appear to include our mystery shot? When they arrive, Georges should be able to identify it for us?"

"So it seems. But that is another 'funny'."

"Why?"

"Well, when just as we left the museum the curator handed Georges his copies of the ones that had been displayed, why couldn't he have given him those others?"

"Mmmm. I see what you mean. Anything else? Anything at all?"

"No, I don't think so. I think you've squeezed it all out of me. Do you make anything of it?"

"No. Not yet. I've got to go over it all again very carefully. Thank you for finding time to tell me. By the way, does the knife tell us anything?"

Ginger had been nursing the wrapped weapon in his hand during his account of the trip. "No, not really. I had a quick glance as I picked it up. It looks like the usual kind of flick knife you can buy anywhere in America."

Tony lifted it by the tip of the blade and looked at the inscription. "A firm in Pittsburgh. That doesn't tell us anything." He closed it carefully and put it in his pocket, sat thinking for a moment, then looking at his watch pulled himself upright with a start. "Great heavens, it's half past two. You have to get back to your body-guarding. And I . . . Oh my God . . . Cels. I'm late for meeting Cels and I didn't leave a message."

"Ho, ho!" said Ginger not at all sympathetically. "Another black mark for you. Marching orders this time, I shouldn't wonder."

"Don't rub it in, you bugger. Come on, I'll walk with you to the Manhattan side."

"OK. When do we meet again?"

"I aim to be back sometime on Monday. I imagine you'll be later."

"Yes. Tuesday at the earliest. Perhaps later. Keep telephoning. Here, you'd better take this. Larry's set of photos," he said, handing Tony the envelope he had carried.

Tony sat fuming in the back of his cab as they crawled through the traffic to the top of Fifth Avenue with the driver giving Tony frequent eyebrow-raising shrugs in the mirror. Tony paid him with a generous tip and ran into the lobby of the Plaza Hotel. He did a circuit of the lobby before rushing to the desk. "Excuse me. My name is Beckett, B-e-c-k-e-t-t. Has anyone left a message for me?"

"Are you registered, sir?"

"No. Not yet," said Tony encouragingly.

"No, sir. No messages. There was a lady asking for messages a short time ago. She went toward the bar, sir. Would you care to register now?"

"Thank you, but I had better wait to see if it is my . . . my wife."

The desk clerk just looked at him and nodded. Tony walked away. Of course! The bar. He walked through the open doors and straightaway saw her elegant figure perched on a stool, martini glass in hand, deep in conversation with a very-dark-haired, dark-skinned gigolo-looking creature on the next stool. He walked up. "Hello, Cels."

She looked round. The glint in her eyes told him all was not well. "Good heavens! Tony Beckett! What are you doing here? This is my friend . . ."

"Francisco," volunteered the creature, flashing a set of white teeth.

"Francisco," she repeated.

"Yes it would be," said Tony, thinking extreme situations call for extreme measures. "I am Dr Beckett, her consultant psychiatrist. It's time she went back, I'm afraid. She's been out rather longer than we intended. You will excuse us, won't you Francisco. Good of you to look after her for a bit. I take it she wasn't troublesome? I got held up, I'm afraid."

Francisco looked confused and scared as he slid off his bar stool, muttering "Yes, of course. Nice to have met you" with notable insincerity, and turned away. Celia finished spluttering Martini over the counter, hissing, "Tony Beckett, you bastard, you bloody bastard. I'll never have anything to do with you again."

It was time for the balm. "Hello, Cels. That was for your own good, you know. Dusky, handsome bar lizards like that in uptown Manhattan aren't really to be trusted. I'm sorry to be late, but . . ."

"Don't treat me like a child, Tony. And not only were you late, but you didn't leave a message as you promised. What was I to think?"

He held on to the counter as he eased himself onto the recently vacated stool. "As I said, I'm sorry to be late, but Ginger and I ran into . . ."

"My God, Tony, look at your hand. You're bleeding . . ."

". . . a spot of trouble . . . That's why I'm bleeding-well late. Sorry."

She looked up at him staring at her, quizzically grinning, one questioning eyebrow raised. The icy glint in her eyes melted fast. "Oh, Tony," she whispered. "I'm sorry. What happened?"

"Let me get a drink and I'll tell you. Will you have another?" She nodded.

"I need a strong one." he said as he turned and ordered a martini and a manhattan. "Zen perrraps ze lady vill come vith me to . . ."

"Shut up." she said, smiling. "He was a nice kind gentleman just keeping me company while I was waiting. Now, tell me what happened."

He took a good gulp of his manhattan, took the blood-stained handkerchief from his wrist and refolded it to a cleaner side. Then, throwing her a shy kind of smile, he described how the arrangement to meet on Brooklyn Bridge had led to the knife attack first on Ginger then on him, with the trilby-hatted watcher fingering Ginger after Tony had identified him.

"So what is the information concerning the missing photo they didn't want Ginger to give you?"

"I don't know yet. There must be something in what happened on the trip to Nevers and Orléans that they believe will give their game away." And he went on to recall briefly what Ginger had told. "What I must do is go over his account precisely as he told me and shake it about. You could help me do that, except that . . ."

"Of course I'll help. What do you mean, 'except that'?"

He glanced down at his empty glass, looked over his shoulder and ordered another manhattan. "Well . . . well, now that Ginger and I have met and talked it's almost certain that I am a target, and I was thinking that it might be unwise for you to come to the apartment with me."

She frowned as she looked straight at him. "That's the second time you've made me angry since we met this afternoon. Don't for a moment think I'm going to let you be there on your own. Of course, if you don't want to be there yourself we can always register here . . ."

"Yes, I had thought of that, for your sake, but it's harder to be constantly vigilant in a hotel, with so many people around. If they have it in mind to break into the apartment, it's going to test them a bit. On the promenade side there are two sets of railings and a basement garden to negotiate before climbing up to the second-level balcony. At the front there are steps down to the street, a basement entrance alongside. Montague Terrace is a tree-lined street – fairly typical of the area."

"You sound like an estate agent. Anyway, it's settled then. I don't get the brush, at least not before you've seen the goods." She looked at him with a mischievous grin.

"Now who's 'being coarse', as your favourite admonition

puts it? But seriously, Cels, there's a nasty lot out there somewhere, able to pursue their objective in England, France and the United States, determined to remove incriminating evidence of some kind – determined enough to murder for it. Right now we don't know whether finding other copies of the mystery photograph or the information that Ginger has now passed to me is their prime objective. So we've got to keep our eyes open and our suspicious minds alert – without, I hope, spoiling our weekend – and that means if I sense any danger you must do exactly as I say, instantly. OK?"

"Of course, sir. Anything you say, sir. Your obedient servant as always . . ."

"That'll be the day. But no fooling, Cels. This *is* a matter of life or death. That's not being melodramatic. Two of my chums, brave men, have been killed by these bastards."

"Roddy was murdered as well as Larry?"

"Yes, I'm convinced of it. So, agreed?"

"Agreed. And" – Cels put her hand over Tony's on the bar – "you know, I've always wished I could have shared the excitements and thrills – and the fears – of your life. Perhaps more, if things had been different. Even to understand you at least as much as you understand me." He looked right into her softly enticing eyes that seemed to be inviting him to see a deep warmth where often before he had seen either passion or a danger signal. With a flicker of an eyelid it was gone, replaced with a happy smile and the teasing allure. Yes, what a partnership they might have made, in spite of her inner insecurity, Tony thought; yet I still only partly understand her.

"Thanks, Cels," he said quietly. "That was a nice thought." Then cheerfully, "Shall we have another drink, or shall we get going – fearlessly, as the novel might say, into the unknown?"

"Let's go. The concierge is looking after my case."

"OK. We'll collect that and get a cab at the door . . ."

"And go to Macy's."

Tony groaned. "God, Cels, you're just like every other woman. I thought you . . ."

"Well, you thought wrong. Come on. Macy's. Arriving in New York, I act just like every other woman. I'll show you the real difference when we get to Brooklyn Heights."

"Promises, promises."

After what was for Tony a boring hour in that internationally famous store, they queued for a cab with Tony holding a Macy's carrier bag containing a new skirt and blouse for Cels, watching the bustling throng of people, the endless stream of traffic and fuming at the queue-jumpers until Tony grabbed her by the hand. "Come on. It's every man for himself," he said and they ran for a Yellow cab he had spotted back in a traffic jam.

They arrived at Montague Terrace just after six o'clock. Tony busied himself with the wine deliveries that had been left outside the apartment door, while Celia made for the window and stared, captivated, at the view across the river to Manhattan. He took her case into the bedroom. "Only one bedroom I'm afraid." he said nonchalantly.

"For heaven's sake," she replied, admiring the view, "what sort of woman do you think I am?"

"Let you know later."

"Predator."

Celia sorted out her case and her purchases, while Tony sorted out the wine. They came together in the lounge for a glass of the Pouilly – insufficiently chilled, for which Tony apologised – and together gazed out of the window. Without mentioning it, Tony watched the figures on the promenade rather than the silhouette of Manhattan. He raised his glass. "Cheers, darling. I'm so glad we are able to be here together. One of our too-rare occasions." They faced each other and raised glasses, their eyes met and spoke, as lovers' eyes do, their messages of warmth, understanding and adoration. "When we've had our aperitif we might stroll up Montague Street and have a meal at a fairly nice restaurant I know. It's one of those hybrid establishments. Typically for these parts the menu is Americano-Franco-Italiano, so we should be able to get something we like. What do you think?"

"Sounds good to me. And if we're going to be seen together in public, let me do something about your wrist and get rid of that filthy handkerchief."

He submitted with reasonable grace. As she washed the wound and applied strips of sticking plaster to bring the edges of the cut together, then some gauze and a bandage, she said, "You should have this stitched, but I know you won't."

"Right both times," he replied with a grin. "Now, how would it be if, when we get back, and if it's not too late, you hear me run through Ginger's account of his trip, question me, and see if you can spot anything that might be sensitive to someone. Between us we might crack the problem. OK?"

"Yes, That'll be fun," she said.

"Maybe," he replied, "but it's serious too."

As they got ready to leave Tony said, "Now listen, Cels, if the villains have targeted me we are most vulnerable as we leave the apartment, as we walk up the road, as we return, and – especially – as we re-enter. So cling to me and do whatever I say."

"You can rely on me to cling to you," she said, gripping his arm. "It's quite exciting, isn't it?"

Tony grunted as he busied himself with lights and curtains, while Cels waited at the apartment door. "God, you do fuss, Tony." she said.

"Aye, that I do – on certain occasions."

The brightness of the day had gone when they stepped onto Montague Terrace. A quick glance to left and right confirmed that the street was deserted. No one behind the trees along the sidewalk, as far as he could see. As they walked past one of the gaps between the houses that gave access to the promenade, they both turned to look across to where the sun seemed balanced on the tops of the skyscrapers in downtown Manhattan, while a fresh breeze from the river fanned their faces. The usual steady stream of traffic edged its way down the centre of Montague Street between the parked cars, occasionally stopping as someone tried to park in too small a space or a delivery truck unloading goods held everything up while the klaxons shrilled their impatient, rude message. The sidewalks bustled with people hurrying down from the Court Street or Borough Hall subway stations, diving into stores and emerging with large brown-paper bags full of essential shopping which they hugged in front of them. Others emerged empty-handed and rushed to get home before the delivery boy.

The restaurant Tony had in mind was about halfway up on the right, on a corner. He had not mentioned that one of its advantages from his point of view was that large windows on both streets gave anyone inside who wanted it an excellent view of what was going on outside. And Tony wanted that. They were early enough to have a good choice of tables, and Tony indicated one in the far corner from which he could see through both windows over Celia's shoulder, his explanation being that it was better to be where they could watch other people than be stared at by them. They sipped manhattans while they studied the menu, from which after much discussion they both chose clam chowders as starters. To follow, Celia selected escalope of veal viennoise, and Tony tried to resist the prosaic choice of 12 oz chargrilled sirloin steak, but failed. A bottle of Californian Cabernet Sauvignon seemed to be the appropriate wine. "Elsewhere we would choose differently," said Tony half-apologetically.

Over the meal they chatted happily. Good friends, occasional lovers, each genuinely interested in the other's news. She told him about the state of the advertising business as she saw it – no longer bewitched by its glamorous image, and irritated by the people in it: those she regarded as precious and those who were unable to resist the attraction of the trappings of the fast life. Too often they were one and the same person. To be 'in' you had to keep up with the advertising community's modus vivendi. The fact that she could resist it she attributed – without any tone of self-aggrandisement – to the fact that she was a very good and experienced account executive. She did not have to fight for recognition by the 'in' crowd. In spite of periods of intense irritation and frustration, she still enjoyed her work – and the money was helpful.

"I bet it is," said Tony with a chuckle. "But don't you feel like chucking it in sometimes? Making a change?"

"Yes. The thought does occur to me sometimes, but change to what . . .?"

He looked at her searchingly. In her eyes he saw again the mixture of longing and fear, but now it was more longing than fear. Yet he could not hold her gaze; he could not respond. Feeling ashamed that he had raised the thought, he studied the tablecloth instead. She was looking for an answer, perhaps one he could not at present give. There had been hints earlier in the evening. Now, however, the uncertainty was his. He was totally absorbed with the mystery and the threat posed by people who were dangerously frightened by something that had occurred as long ago as 1944, and although he was financially secure for a while, his longer-term prospects were unclear. He felt he was in the same position as when he had left the army in 1946. What lay ahead? Was he now destined for a settled life at home? Or should he seek a job that could satisfy his continuing need for excitement – and remain footloose? At his age?

His uncertainty was the more acute as he had become aware that his relationship with Celia was changing. For years he had taken every opportunity to calm her dread of a stable relationship, which she believed from her childhood experience could only end in pain and unhappiness. But now she was more settled; more mature; the petulance less evident. Was she beginning to know what she wanted? For all the affection they shared, and for all the concern he had patiently exercised to help her come to terms with her fears, he had not thought of the possible consequences of achieving that aim. His musings – and the silence – were broken by the arrival of the waiter offering more coffee. The essence of the moment was gone. But he knew that she knew he had stepped back.

The waiter withdrew leaving them floundering in moments of awkward silence. Celia rescued them. "You know," she said brightly, raising a new subject in a new mood, "although you have told me bits about your experiences in the war when I've asked, I really don't know very much, particularly about AMCA. But I see how the deaths of

Roddy and Larry, and the mystery of the photograph, have brought those times back to you and revived a lot of feelings. I wish you would tell me more. The operation can't still be that secret, can it?"

His reply was accompanied by a smile and a nod of thanks for the change of subject, which he saw her acknowledge with a tilt of the head. "No, it's not that secret any more as a military operation. I suppose we still tend to treat it secretively because that is how it was, and we were trained to behave in a clandestine way. It's a way of thinking as well as a way of behaving; and it's a habit that's hard to lose."

"But what was it like living behind the lines – enemy territory – when any slip-up could lead to capture or death?"

"There was no difference between death and capture. You could be killed in fighting, and unfortunately if you were caught the chances were you would be killed anyway, probably after a pretty nasty bit of questioning by the Gestapo. You see, the army's high command had a touching faith that if we wore uniform, like the soldiers we were, we would be treated in accordance with the Geneva Convention, which laid down internationally recognised rules for the protection of prisoners of war. That faith was destroyed by Hitler's infamous order to his troops that the SAS and Commandos, must, when captured, be handed to the Gestapo for questioning and execution. 'These men are dangerous,' he proclaimed."

"Did you know about that at the time?"

"Oh yes."

"Wasn't that very unnerving? Affecting what you had to do?"

"I'm sure it did not adversely affect what we were about – it did not, for example, make us more cautious than we

212

needed to be to carry out our mission. I think I can honestly say we just did not think about the Hitler order."

"But you were terribly vulnerable. You must have known it. Didn't that add to your fear and affect your actions?"

"Cels, when you were in the WAAFs and bombed on airfields, you were afraid, weren't you?" Cels nodded. "But it did not alter your effectiveness as a WAAF officer, did it? You, and we, were trained – and had the instinct – to control our fear. It was called discipline: a blend of self-control and military training. I do not believe anyone is without fear. Some people let it dominate them; some treat it as a challenge and perform heroic deeds; while most of us control it as best we can and concentrate on getting the job done."

"Can I ask an impertinent question?" She did not wait for an answer. "When you were afraid, did you never feel the need for 'outside' support? Did you pray?"

"Mmmm. That's a tricky one. Well . . . yes, I did. Early in the war I felt the need, but for a time resisted it. You see, as a young man – you know, at the age when you have it all sorted out, ethics, religion, politics, the lot – I was pleased, genuinely pleased, to call myself a rationalist. Everything should be examined rationally and all questions could be answered rationally. Applying that rational analysis to questions of faith, I concluded it was unlikely that there was a God of the kind I had been taught to believe in at school and Sunday school. But the same rational thought told me I couldn't rationally *disprove* the existence of an almighty power. I could argue against the likelihood, but couldn't disprove it. I was agnostic rather than atheist – more probably, just mixed up. I suspect we all go through this process, but wartime certainly brings it to the fore in one's thinking.

Anyway, the first time I was under fire, in 1940, and found myself on the receiving end of a lot of the enemy's lethal intentions, which after a bit unnerved me, it was a matter of honour, believing in the correctness of 'rational thinking', not to pray to a God I did not believe in."

"Did that help? Did you stick to it?"

"Well, it didn't stop me being afraid, but I convinced myself I was being true to my convictions, and though tempted I honestly felt it unfair to seek His help if I did not believe He existed. Rational thinking, you see. But then as the pounding continued relentlessly, I lost my resolve. It was on the beaches at Dunkirk, when we had nothing with which we could hit back. I prayed."

"The Lord's Prayer?"

"Yes."

"How did you feel about that afterwards?"

"Well, I survived under both circumstances, so who do I thank? But, curiously, two things happened."

"What?"

"I found I was increasingly able to control my fear; and danger – the adrenaline it created, I suppose – gave me a kind of cold, clear-eyed perception of what was happening around me. I found I was relatively calm in action and seemed to have more time to react. Those responses stayed with me throughout the war and saved me, I now realise, on several occasions. Whenever I acknowledge that to myself, I have a mental picture of lots of believers nodding knowingly, laughing at my naivety and saying, 'Well, who helped you do that?'"

She smiled at what she thought was half an admission. "It's fascinating, Tony. And the second thing that happened?"

"Don't laugh. I questioned the wording of the Lord's Prayer."

"What? That was a bit arrogant, wasn't it? Not to mention testing your luck? It has been around for centuries, you know."

"Yes, I know. But it seemed to me that if I *had* been a believer and accepted that my God had given me free will, which we certainly have, to think for myself and to be responsible for my actions, it would be pretty helpless of me, for example, to have to ask Him to give me my daily bread, or to deliver me from evil, and rather impertinent to ask Him not to lead me into temptation. (Why would my God want to lead me to such things anyway?) Shouldn't I be doing much of this for myself? So I decided that rather than seek to be delivered of these things without any effort on my part, I would, when using the prayer, express my thanks for the sustenance I had, and ask for help in resisting temptation – without being clear what temptation I was supposed to resist – and for help in my fight against evil – which at that time, and without being smug, I, and so many like me, were convinced we were doing."

"Did you think so seriously then about these matters of belief and faith?"

"Well, when you're fighting in a war there's quite an incentive to do so. No better time, really. Many of us did, you know, and sometimes we even discussed it."

"With your chums on AMCA? Ginger and the rest?"

"Oh yes. As you might expect, Roddy was a committed Christian. He had thought about it a lot. Larry had been brought up in the traditional school, Church of England manner and accepted it without being committed. I guess that was the case with most of our generation. They were fairly happy with the way they were. Ginger was the most interesting one to talk with. He had had a relatively godless and educationless upbringing. He desperately wanted a spiritual anchor, but didn't know what to believe; he wanted to explore."

"Did you help him?"

"I doubt it. I was uncertain myself. A failed rationalist."

Celia gave a little laugh. "Sounds as if you became some kind of rationalist believer. Is that possible? Are you?"

He shrugged. "Oh, I don't know. I struggle to get my mind round the idea of a power that can create a swirling, moving, ever-growing universe in which there is a tiny planet blessed with a self-supporting natural system, inhabited by funny little quarrelsome creatures like us." Suddenly embarrassed, he looked away. "Look, Cels, we shouldn't have got into this kind of discussion. Much too serious for a nice evening like this."

She regretted her little laugh. "Perhaps it was wrong of me to have asked you those questions." Failing to catch his averted gaze, she reached for his hand across the table and said very quietly, "But, Tony, darling, in our different ways we both went through those years. They formed an indestructible link between all of us of that generation. And from time to time you and I have been very close. We didn't have time for more. They were episodes of comforting closeness which we both needed, and of glorious intimacy. You understood me better than anyone, and often I hated you for it. I thought if I was understood I would lose my independence . . ."

"Awkward witch, weren't you?"

"OK I was, and probably still am. But the point is, the lives we were living were inevitably separate, and now I want to try to understand better what you were doing, and how you felt. I loved it in the past when we had those times together and I persuaded you to talk a little – as far as 'keeping mum' allowed. For those short times I felt part of it, and had some of the sense of thrill. So I truly appreciate what you have just confided in me. It helps me understand, and I hope you will tell me more sometime – but I have a sneaking suspicion the roles have reversed and you feel you may be losing your independence. Right?"

"No, not really, Cels. It's just that I haven't talked about those experiences in years. Even forgotten a lot of it . . . until recent events have caused me to think back – as you noticed. I don't want to be thought of as a talker about such things. I hope you don't . . ."

"Never, Tony, my dear. Never."

He smiled his acknowledgement. "Cels . . . it will just take a bit of time . . . OK?"

"OK. So let's get back to the problem in hand. What is your guess as to what is behind these robberies and ghastly murders?"

"Well, the logical explanation is that there's a connection of some kind with the lorryload of loot we captured and sent away to be hidden, and which we believed was then handed to the French authorities. I was hoping for some evidence from Ginger's visit to Nevers. But it appears that the marquis who looked after it until the end of the war, at the suggestion of the SOE agent – and who then, we were told, passed it to the French Government – has died."

"Do you know if the marquis had any close relations? And what about this SOE man. Is he still around?"

"The answer in both cases is 'I don't know'. Apparently, Ginger did not ask about relatives when he heard that the marquis was dead. And I refrained from finding out about the SOE agent because I thought I would get the best lead from Georges Lebrun – whom I had to warn – and that visit led to Nevers. Now I certainly do need to find out about him. Back in London I can ring the association I belong to. It has files and records that might help. But now that we are into the subject once more, and you are asking the right questions, let's go back to the apartment and help me examine all the information Ginger brought back."

Chapter 12

They walked arm in arm back down Montague Street. It was dark, though the brightness of the lights in the shops and along the road mocked the night. The sidewalks were still bustling with people coming from or going to restaurants, shopping, or on their way to their apartments – a familiar American city scene. Yet, Tony thought, judging from his experience of New York, it was less frantic here in Brooklyn Heights, where there seemed to be something of a small-town atmosphere. As they reached Montague Terrace they could see through a gap onto the promenade that the sun had disappeared below the horizon beyond Manhattan and beyond the Hudson River, leaving only an orange reflection on the clouds in the west that contrasted with the greyness creeping in behind them.

"Let's walk to the promenade for a last look across the river," Tony suggested with a lightness that concealed his real motive.

They walked through the gap and leant on the railings to gaze at the skyline, ablaze with the lights in the skyscrapers.

"You always said the view was magic. You're right, Tony. It is."

Tony smiled his agreement as he turned his gaze in what he hoped was a casual manner to look up at the windows of the apartment. He frowned. Were the curtains drawn more closely than when he had arranged them? He had deliber-

219

ately set them – when Cels accused him of fussing – with a gap at either end of the bay, the ends where neighbours might most easily see anyone standing there. Surely the gap on one side was now completely shut? Or had he done it too much in the first place? Was his revived sixth sense telling him something was not quite right? He turned back towards the Manhattan skyline, the frown erased from his forehead.

"Well, lets go up, shall we?" he said, taking her arm and walking her towards the gap that led up to Montague Street.

"My, we are keen this evening, aren't we?" she said playfully, squeezing his arm.

"I'm always keen when I'm with you, but we have to lay down a little security drill first. When we get to the apartment I want you to stand to one side of the door with your back against the wall, while I go inside to make sure everything is OK."

"Oh, come on, Tony, you don't really think anyone . . ."

"Cels, we just don't know. There's a mystery: friends are dead and people have been attacked. In any case you promised to do as I say . . ."

"OK, OK."

"And when you are standing outside, whatever you hear inside, don't come in until I call you. If anything . . . er . . . really . . . er . . . untoward happens, get yourself off smartly and find someone who can call the police. Understood?"

"Tony . . ."

"Understood, Cels?" he demanded firmly.

She looked up at him, all the teasing gone, with a look of comprehension. "Sorry. Yes, understood. You suspect something, don't you?"

"Maybe."

They reached the landing of the apartment. Tony

motioned her to be quiet as they trod lightly towards the door. He pointed to the wall he wanted her to lean against. She nodded and stood with her back to it. Carefully, he took the keys from his pocket and selected the entry one, then centred it to the lock, ready to slide it in without a lot of scratching around. He put his right hand into his jacket pocket. Celia's eyes widened with surprise as she saw the flick knife with which he had been attacked on the bridge. It snapped open as he put the key in the lock, turned it, pushed open the door and leapt inside, in a swiftly coordinated movement. What Celia could not see was that once inside Tony reached the door of the lounge in two strides, barged it open, flicked down the light switch, dived onto the floor and rolled to the side where he knew there was a large armchair facing the window. He had worked out this series of moves as they walked back to the flat. He knew his sixth sense had been right when he heard a gasp and a hurried movement over at the bureau by the window – alongside the closed curtain! Quickly getting to his feet behind the chair, he saw a dark figure in a woolly hat turning from where he was searching a bureau drawer.

"Looking for something, chum?" he said as he pushed the chair forward to impede any rush forward by the intruder, who he could now see was black, tall and well built. As Tony advanced, waving the knife threateningly in front of him, the man reached for the handle of a baseball bat leaning against the bureau.

"Changed your weapon now that you've lost your knife, eh?" He saw the man lower his gaze toward the circling blade before making his move. He was more agile than Tony had expected. He leapt to his right, away from the knife, and in a simultaneous movement swung the bat in the direction of Tony's head. He wasn't near enough to make

221

contact, but it caused Tony to sway back and give his assailant time to move to his right again. Tony had to get nearer if he was going to tackle him before he did some damage. He ducked and lunged, but the man quickly side-stepped and raised the bat again. Tony realised he was circling towards the door, his only escape route. He lunged again, nearer that time, causing the man to shuffle back-wards. But he was almost at the door, baseball bat in his right hand high above his head, while Tony was bobbing and weaving, one eye on the raised bat, trying to make the feint that would force the man back to the centre of the room.

"Drop that bat or I'll shoot you in the back!"

The voice that suddenly broke the tension, coming from the doorway, was cold and tight, but easily recognised by Tony. Celia Southwood was standing behind the man, not with a gun but with one hand held to her mouth as if scared at having said such a thing. The man couldn't be sure; he turned his head to look behind him. It was the split-second chance Tony needed. He dropped the knife, leapt forward and grasped the raised wrist with both hands, then gave it a viscious twist, drawing a gasp from the man as the bat fell from his fingers. Twisting round, Tony pulled the arm over his shoulder, giving it a wrench as he did so, then thrust his hips into the man's waist as he bent over, and tugged and thrust his back up in true unarmed-combat fashion. The man came over his shoulder and landed with a loud thud on his shoulders, giving a loud gasp as his breath left him.

Instantly dropping to his knees beside the intruder, Tony quickly rolled him onto his face and, while he was still gasping for breath, bent his arms up behind him. "Quick, Cels, something to tie him with. Bedroom. Dressing-gown belt. Quick." Celia ran and returned within seconds that

222

seemed like half an hour to Tony, with a long dressing-gown belt. With his knee pressed hard into the small of his back, Tony swiftly tied the belt round each wrist and then put both together with another knot before passing the rest of the tie round the man's throat and back down to the wrists. He could not now move his arms without half-choking himself. He turned the man over again and, standing up, pulled off the woolly hat, grabbed the man's black curly hair and, not at all gently, jerked him into a sitting position. The man gasped and his eyes stared out from his dark face as he tried to suck in air through his constricted larynx. "Fuck you . . . Take this . . . this fucking thing off . . . I can't breathe," he croaked.

"No. Not yet, old chum. You've got to answer a few questions first. Just push your arms farther up your back and it'll ease the pressure on your throat. But just remember, I only have to tug your arms down to choke you. And I would take great pleasure in carving a few initials on you with this," he said, brandishing the open flick knife he had retrieved from the floor. "Now, who do you work for?" The man shook his head and looked defiantly at Tony, who sighed and with a quiet "Oh well" pushed the man's body forward and gave a sharp downward tug on the tied wrists. The noose tightened round his throat and he began coughing and gasping. Tony did not relent even as the man struggled for breath. His eyes bulged and his tongue came out as he tried to say something. Tony shouted in his ear. "You going to talk?" With a gasping, rasping croak coming from his throat, he nodded his head.

Tony eased the pressure and pulled him back to a sitting position. "Right then. Just don't try to fuck me about. Understand?" He nodded again.

"You were looking for photographs, right?

He looked up at Tony, surprised and puzzled, and slowly, reluctantly, nodded his head.

"What kind of photo? What would it show?"

He rolled his head from side to side. "I'm not sure. He said it would show some shot-up German trucks from the last war, and . . . and . . . some people in uniform."

"OK. But what particular picture were you looking for?"

"I don't know. He said I wouldn't be able to tell exactly what he wanted. I should just take him all the photos showing what looked like a lot of wrecked trucks with soldiers and civilians carrying weapons. Partisans, he called them, but I didn't know what that meant. Look, man, I don't know what this is all about. It was just a job. I needed the money."

"Someone hired you to do this?"

"Yeah. It was just a break-in job. I meant no harm, man."

"And you meant no harm this morning when you tried to kill my friend on Brooklyn Bridge and then attacked me?"

The man looked up again. The confusion and apprehension in his eyes was clearly visible. "I don't know what you're talking about. I wasn't on the bridge this morning."

"Oh, but I think you were and you attacked and tried to murder two people. There were witnesses. The authorities don't like that, even here in New York, and I can provide them with a very good case against you." Tony produced the knife he and Ginger had retrieved from the bridge, with which he had threatened the man that evening. Holding it by the blade he waved it in front of the man's face. "You see, I have a witness to prove that this was the knife used in that attack, and when I call the police I shall hand them the knife and ask them to check for prints. Mine will be there, but so will yours."

The man looked up, his eyes pleading. "No, man. Please don't call the police. It'll go bad for me. Please."

"Ah, so you have previous form, have you? Yes, that will be bad for you. I suppose you had to have some experience to be able to climb over the railings and up two levels, open a window to get in and shut the window after you – all without being seen. Quite skilled in the art of the burglar, but not much good as an assassin. The police will certainly enjoy saying they foiled an attempted murder and caught the would-be killer. Shall I call them in or would you rather sing."

The man nodded. "I'll talk. Please don't turn me in. I'll talk, but untie me first. My arms are killing me keeping them pushed up behind me."

Tony shook his head. "Oh no. Not yet, old chum. You've got to earn it. Who hired you?"

"I don't know who he was. I only saw him the once. He was a foreign guy. I met him through a friend. I ain't got no work, see? And up in the part of Harlem where I live, if you know the right people you can get jobs to do . . ."

"Criminal jobs – break-in, theft, even murder, eh?"

"OK. Yeah . . . but I gotta eat, ain't I?"

"That's a matter of opinion. Go on."

"Well, someone who wants a job done contacts Limpy. His real name is Jess. With some strong-arm buddies he controls the district where I live. He got his leg broke so bad in a robbery it didn't mend right. So he's called Limpy. If we get right with Limpy we know we'll get jobs. The punters tell Limpy what they want done. He asks a price to make an introduction to one of us he thinks can do the job. He arranges a meeting and the punter deals directly with us, but Limpy tells us the lowest price we should do the job for.

If we can get more that's OK with him, but it don't often happen that way. I expect Limpy tells the punter what we are likely to charge. Then Limpy expects us to give him ten per cent of what we get. He's got it made. He gets paid twice, and he don't have to do nothing. He's in the clear and we take the rap if we're caught."

"OK. So Limpy picked you for this 'job', and you met this punter. A foreigner, you say. Where from?"

"I don't know, I tell you. He spoke with an accent. Limpy had said he was from Europe someplace. He had a dark coat . . ."

"Did he have a hat?"

"Yes. As he left the coffee shop I saw him put on a dark hat . . ."

"Big brim?"

"Yeah, that's right – kinda foreign."

"And he hired you to kill my friend on Brooklyn Bridge? How much were you offered?"

"A thousand dollars. Two-fifty, then and seven-fifty when I'd done it."

"Life's cheap in Harlem."

"Well, yeah, I guess so. He said I had to stop him talking to another guy who would be waiting. I suppose that was you. He said he would be there to point out the target guy."

"Well you screwed that up. So why did you try to get me?"

"I was just trying to get away, man. You tried to stop me. I knew there were too many people who had seen me go for your friend."

"Then why were you just looking for photos instead of trying to knife me tonight?"

"I was told to do this after doing for your friend. He guessed you'd be someplace else if your friend had been done. I had to stop your friend telling you something then come and find the photos. So I had to try for the photos even if you might be here . . ."

"Hence the baseball bat – having lost your knife. You're not a very competent hoodlum, are you, chum?

"I didn't dare go back with nothing to show. This guy knows I screwed up on your friend. So I had to go for the photos. But I had to wait till dark."

"You've still got nothing to show. I guess you're in real trouble."

"Yeah, I sure am. You gotta help me. Someone's gotta help me. Because of you I screwed up on the bridge, and now you've stopped me getting the photos here. I'm a dead man when I get back to Harlem. I'm supposed to meet this guy when I get back tonight and I've got nothing to show." He shook his head, white eyes bulging, now showing real fear as he realised, under Tony's guidance, the danger of his situation.

"You were always going to screw up here, old chum. The photos you were supposed to search through aren't here. So you were given a bad steer on that, and now you have to take the rap."

"Jeez, not that, please. I told you all I can. What else can I do?" He was scared, and pleading.

Tony thought for a moment, then turning to Celia he said, "Cels, in the chest of drawers in the bedroom there's a camera. Bring it here, please." He went over to where the dejected villain sat effectively trussed up. "Come on, on your feet." He put his hand under his elbow to help him stand. "Over here by the bureau you were searching." He got him to the corner by the window, carefully picked up the baseball bat and leant it against the bureau, near him. Then he took

227

the camera from Cels and focused it on him standing by the bureau. Quickly he took two snaps. "Photos are the key evidence in this series of events," he said, smiling.

"What the fuck's going on?"

"I'm helping you, old chum," Tony replied, walking towards him. Taking the baseball bat between finger and thumb he moved it to the other side of the room. Then carefully wrapping his handkerchief round the handle of the open knife – "Don't want to smudge the prints too much" – he walked slowly back to where the intruder stood.

Watching Tony advance towards him, knife in hand, the man's face contorted in terror: his mouth opened, lips stretched across his teeth as if about to scream; his eyes widened; his chest heaved and as he made as if to run towards the door the binding round his throat tightened and he started to choke. "Oh no. For God's sake, no, man. Please don't." He dropped to his knees. "Please. I told you all I can. You can't kill me now."

Tony stopped and looked down at him. "It doesn't feel so good seeing someone come at you with a knife, does it?" The man shook his head, eyes still pleading. "Would you have spared my friend or me this morning if we had asked you to? Eh? I think not." The man was sobbing as Tony laid the flat of the blade against his neck. "From this position it wouldn't take much to do it, would it? A twist of the wrist and a quick slash round the neck and you start dying, unable to scream, drowning in your own blood . . ."

"Oh, Jesus, dear Jesus, please no," he whimpered. Defiance, bravado, pride all gone.

"Tony!!!"

It was a shout from Celia. Tony turned without removing the knife blade and looking straight into her eyes, gave a

228

reassuring slow shake of his head and whispered, "It's OK, Cels."

Turning back to the broken villain in front of him, he said, "Women are squeamish about blood, you know. But the likes of you and me aren't, are we? We don't mind slipping a knife into someone's throat, do we?" It was a question the man wasn't going to answer, his head shaking from side to side.

Tony stepped back and looked down at him. After a short pause he said, "OK, I'll give you just one chance to save your miserable hide." The sobbing stopped as he raised his head, eyes lit by a spark of hope. "Anything, man. Anything."

"You're going to meet your foreign gentleman tonight. You're going to tell him that you broke in here. You searched everywhere, but didn't find any photos, but I came in while you were here and in a struggle you managed to knife me. You think you killed me, but you're not sure. Anyway, I was pretty bad. You just left me here, threw the knife into the East River and went back to Harlem. OK so far?"

"Yeah, OK. But when he finds out you're not dead, I'm still a dead man."

"Not necessarily. It's up to you. You won't get all the rest of your blood money, will you?"

He shook his head. "I guess not."

"OK. I'll give you two hundred dollars to help you get out of Harlem as soon as you can after telling Limpy and this other guy what I've just told you. Get to another state. Lie low and wait. The man in the broad-brimmed hat won't stick around here once he finds out you didn't kill me and that we have departed. He and his friends will want to try to catch up with us back home. Whether or not you eventually

229

go back to Limpy and his bunch of hoodlums is up to you. Personally, I'd stay clear if I were you. You're not good enough to last in that sort of life. Sooner or later you'll screw up again and finish up in the river. Still, it's your miserable life.

But one thing is certain, if you go back on what we're agreeing, the photograph, the knife and the baseball bat will be handed to the police, and you'll be cooked. Before I leave I shall hand them to an attorney friend of mine, and, if I get the slightest hint that you've double-crossed me, he will get a telephone call from me or one of my friends. He will know what to do. Do you understand that? Understand? Just remember, I could kill you now and make it look like a fight, or I could call the police right away. So you're lucky for now, but you're not off the hook."

"Yeah, OK. I understand. Now, please untie me."

Tony leant over him and slashed the dressing-gown belt. Still threatening him with the knife he got hold of the man's hair and yanked him to his feet. The man grimaced and yelled as he tried to shake the circulation back into his arms. "Awright. Awright. I've got the message. Give me the two hundred and let me go."

Taking four fifties from his wallet, Tony handed them over, pointed to the door and still with knife in hand followed him down to the street. It was quite empty. He stood in the shadow of the doorway as he watched the wretched dupe make off in a loping run towards Montague Street. Back in the apartment he closed the door behind him and walked over to where Cels was leaning against a wall looking out of the window. "Celia Southwood, I thought I told you not to come into the room until I called. The one thing you must always do is obey orders."

She rushed towards him, fury in her eyes, her fists

clenched. "Tony bloody Beckett, you ungrateful bastard. Doing that to save your head from being bashed in nearly made me incontinent, and now you . . ."

He laughed and caught her by the shoulders before she could hammer his chest with her small fists, and, pulling her closer, tilted her chin and planted his lips on hers, mouth open, tongue probing. Her tense body resisted and she tried to pull her mouth away. But it was a short-lived defiance. With a little sigh of satisfaction she melted against him.

"Cels, darling, you were marvellous." He was smiling down at her. "It took a lot of courage and it gave me the instant I needed to get to him. Full marks for initiative and full marks for execution. How did you manage to time it so well?"

She looked up at him, smiling weakly.

"I had to hear what was going on otherwise I wouldn't have known when to send for the police – following your orders, sir," she replied with mild sarcasm. "So I tried to listen at the door. I heard you say something like 'You've changed your weapon'. Then I heard a kind of shuffling but no sound of actual fighting. I was worried, so I had a peep. Fortunately, our intruder friend had his back half to me and was edging to the door with that huge bat in his hand, which was keeping you at bay. I wished I had a gun, so, scared out of my pants, I decided to pretend I had one. I don't know what I'd have done if he had seen I hadn't before you had time to do something. Anyway, it worked, didn't it?"

"It certainly did. It was superb. You've earned yourself an award. See your leader later tonight!"

"Oh, sir, you wouldn't take advantage of your position, would you?"

"Without doubt. But meanwhile we must move, in case Mr Bighat comes to check us out. I guess he will be interviewing our chum soon now, so we haven't long. You go and

231

pack our things and I will ring the Plaza to see if they have a room. You never know, you might meet Francisco again. I'll also ring for a cab."

She put out her tongue at him as she made for the bedroom. "Oh, I do hope so. He was such a charming man." Skilfully avoiding the hand Tony swung at her posterior, she called from the door, "Do you feel sure our chum will keep his word?"

"Can't be certain, but I think he will. He was really scared, and I've given him a chance to get away before old Bighat finds out there's no police presence here, as there would be if there had been a dead or injured body."

"He was certainly frightened. You're a hard bastard when you get going, aren't you? You scared me. I really thought you were going to . . ."

"Ye of little faith. Come on. We've got a room . . . and a cab."

Chapter 13

It was quite late by the time they reached the Plaza, unpacked and settled down to a drink. Tony looked at her and said, "It's important that we re-examine what Ginger told me, and set a timetable for chasing up the fate of the loot lorry through the SOE man – if he's still around. It's frustrating that after all that has happened we still haven't identified the missing photo. Perhaps I can persuade the shipping company to let me dive into the crate containing my goods and chattels. But that's for tomorrow." He paused and, sipping his brandy, peered at her over the brim of the glass. "In fact, Cels, I think it all had better wait until tomorrow. As we get the reaction to that little burst of excitement at Montague Terrace, we may not give it the clear attention it requires. What do you say?"

"Anything you say, sir," she said, smiling.

"Glad you're learning." Then in a stage whisper, "I look forward to that day."

"Oh, very droll! Just for that you can wait while I use the bathroom. I know my rights."

"Mrs Pankhurst, I presume." There was no reply, but the bathroom door slammed shut.

When it opened again and Celia emerged, the room was filled with a refreshing and enticing perfume. One of the differences, Tony thought, between living carelessly on one's own and living with someone is that togetherness means

233

taking care to contribute to an environment both can enjoy. When he emerged, liberally dabbed with aftershave, towel wrapped round his waist, Cels was standing in front of the dressing table in a long pink nightdress held up at the shoulders by thin ribbons tied in bows, and through which Tony could see the outline of her still very seductive figure. She turned, taking a deep breath. "Mmmm. That's pretty enticing. What is it?" And as she faced him, unashamedly running her eyes over his half-naked torso, she added, "And so is that."

For seconds that seemed beyond normal time, each gazed admiringly and tenderly at the other. After years of knowing each other, though only intermittently as lovers, the attraction remained – probably stronger on each occasion as a result of a growing mutual understanding. It was Celia who broke the silence.

In a soft throaty voice she said, "After all the thrills of this evening I thought I would need nothing more than to have a deep sleep in your protective arms. But I was wrong. I'm not all that sleepy."

"That's not a problem. I'm not sleepy either." In fact Tony's adrenaline was still feeding his assertiveness. He moved towards her, took her in his arms and pulled her against him. They kissed, their mouths pressed openly, warmly together. Gently he pulled away. "I think we can dispense with this, pretty as it is," he said as he untied the shoulder straps of her nightdress. She smiled contentedly as he rolled it down her back and over her hips. Still holding her hands he stepped back half a pace to look admiringly at her nakedness.

"And we don't need that either," she said as she grabbed the towel and pulled it from his hips. Holding each other now by the shoulders at arm's length they brazenly gazed at each other, taking pleasure from what they saw and from being admired by their lover.

"God, you're lovely, Cels. How do you do it? You're body is as beautiful as I remember it the first time I saw it . . ."

"Rose-coloured specs, lover . . ."

"Not so. I can even recall the nervous excitement I felt. The first time between true lovers is a unique thrill, isn't it? The trembling expectation, the first sight of the nakedness, the promise of an approaching oneness, the confidence that each has chosen to give and accept the greatest of intimacies with this partner before all others, but also some anxiety not to disappoint the partner . . ."

"And you didn't."

"Later you know how to play to your partners needs and wishes in order to enhance her pleasure and deepen her satisfaction . . ." As he spoke he ran his hands over her breasts, lifting them in turn and moving his fingers slowly round her nipples before teasing them with his tongue and drawing them into his mouth. "Oh, Tony," she whispered as her head went back and she yielded to the sensation flowing from her breasts down through her body. With a sigh she opened her eyes and gazed straight into his. "Tony Beckett. What is it you do to me?" And putting her hands on his chest, she slid them slowly down his body as she lowered herself gracefully to her knees. With an approving "mmm", she grasped the column of flesh that stretched eagerly from his groin and pressed it to her lips. "Mr Beckett, 'tis you who are the beautiful one."

That night in bed their lovemaking was both passionate and hard in the manner that Tony knew usually followed an 'action'. She excited him with caresses and tongue, and with arms thrown back on the pillows happily accepted his firm and forceful act of love. Realising that the vigour of his passion had much to do with residual aggression, she was pleased that she was the willing haven of his plunging desire. Having earlier shared moments of concern and danger, they now lovingly shared the satisfying calming of their tensions.

Next morning when both were rested and refreshed, Tony reluctantly but determinedly focused both their minds on the urgent need to search for clues. "We have to get on with it, Cels," he said over coffee and toast. "There's just Ginger, Georges Lebrun, Jean Boulanger and me in the way of these villains' objective. I don't want to wait for another demonstration of their determination to wipe out the evidence that embarrasses them, which we appear to have. You know the circumstances of the two deaths and Jenny's robbery. Now let me go over again what Ginger told me about his trip with Georges Lebrun down to Nièvre; you question me on anything you think may help identify the reason for these damned events. I want to hear from you – a fresh mind on the case, so to speak – anything that strikes you as odd or not properly explained. OK?"

Celia nodded. "Right. Go ahead."

So Tony went over the whole of his and Ginger's experiences on their trip down to Chartres, the signs that they were followed, their discussion with Georges Lebrun and the circumstances leading to Georges sending his set of photographs to the Resistance museum near Nevers. He then repeated, as near word for word as he could recall, Ginger's account of their visit there and their surprise encounter with Henri Boulanger, the nephew of Jean, as the former *Préfet* of police.

Celia listened intently but interrupted from time to time with questions and occasional observations. How could they now find out exactly where the loot lorry was hidden after capture? How long was it there or was it moved elsewhere before being handed over to the authorities? To whom was it handed and by whom? Had Henri Boulanger been a mite too dismissive of the value of the loot considering the lorry was captured before he joined the Maquis? Tony answered thoughtfully, pointing out that identifying the marquis who hid the vehicle would depend on being able to contact the SOE agent, who might also know the circumstances surrounding its delivery to the French authorities – if indeed it had ever happened! He intended telephoning the organisation in London which might be able to help on that, as well as his removal agent to see if he could get into his crates – assuming they worked on a Sunday. As for Henri Boulanger's comment on the loot lorry, he may have heard talk of the contents from his uncle or others in the Maquis camp at the time.

"But the missing photos from Georges's collection are on the way back to him, aren't they?"

"Apparently so. And I must contact Georges about that. But if this affair runs true to form, the villains will find a way of extracting the picture they want so that when Georges receives the ones not used at the museum his set will simply match Larry's and Roddy's depleted sets. Bearing in mind the way they can stretch out to New York, my nasty suspicious mind suggests they could have a friend in the curator or in his office, or in the postal service, or even in Henri Boulanger's office. In any event, Cels – belt and braces, belt and braces."

"Quite. And that suggests Georges Lebrun is not now in danger. 'They' will know about his photos. Which leaves you, Ginger and Jean Boulanger in their way.

"That's right. Henri said he would warn his uncle, but I think I shall go and see him all the same, to see if he can throw any light on the mystery. He and I had a good, trusting relationship. So far, of the key AMCA people, he's been a kind of absentee player. My fault, of course. Perhaps I should have got in touch with him sooner."

"Good point. But tell me again how Roddy managed to get them safely processed in the middle of occupied France."

"A local friendly pharmacist, who Jacquie – the Phantoms man – used as a safe contact, developed them in his blacked-out kitchen . . . Of course . . . Of course, Cels. That's your best question yet. I know he returned all the negatives to Roddy . . . but might he remember? Might he have kept copies? . . . Is he still alive? Probably not, but it's worth following up. Damn it! I overlooked that as a line of enquiry. That means another early visit to France is in prospect. Thanks, Cels, we're nearly a partnership."

"What?" It was almost a scream. "Thanks for nothing, you bastard. I thought we *were* a partnership last night, not to mention other occasions! And not to mention intervening just in time yesterday when the villain was either going to escape or knock your brains out – or both! Try doing better on your own in future." She got up and stamped her way into the bedroom, slamming the door behind her.

Tony groaned and banged his forehead with the palms of his hands. "Oh God. What a fool." It was the old, quick-to-react, impetuous Cels, not as dead as he had thought, and his carelessness had resurrected her. He had meant the remark light-heartedly, but insensitively he had overlooked the possibility that in spite of her newly discovered wish for stability, her earlier fear of a happy relationship was not far below the surface. He walked into the bedroom. She was sitting on the edge of the bed looking out of the window. She was not crying, but her face was set and pale with anger.

238

"Cels, I'm so sorry. More sorry than I can say. I just didn't mean it that way, I . . ."

"Just didn't think, you mean. I know how much you've done to help me through my . . . my difficulties, and I really thought we understood each other. Now, I've so enjoyed being in this mystery with you, feeling I was helping – feeling . . . well, a part of you. It's what I hoped would happen. Then . . . then you throw me back like that. I know I mustn't expect too much, but . . ."

"Cels, Cels you are overreacting, my darling; you're reading into a flippant remark – a thoughtless one, I know – meanings that aren't there." He pulled her up from the bed, put his arms round her and tried to penetrate the resentful expression in her eyes. "Please believe me. I have enjoyed you being with me on this. And you have helped. Truly. And I want you to go on helping. It was just . . . just a comment, thoughtlessly chauvinistic, I suppose."

Her expression softened. "You suppose right. You are a bloody chauvinist anyway, Tony Beckett. I suppose your life would not have been what it was if you weren't. But don't bloody well be that way with me – too much." She managed a wry smile.

He pulled her to him and searched her eyes. "Armistice?"

She nodded. "Armistice. Peace depends on further negotiations." The kiss that followed augured well for those discussions.

They walked back to the sitting room. "Could you make some more coffee, Cels, while I begin the phoning?"

"Partners?" she said on the way to the kitchen.

"Partners," he replied from the bureau. His first call, to the removal agents, confirmed that the enquiry office was open and Leo Kaisler said he was there to help. Yes, he could give him the status of crates if he had his customer number, with the warning that if the crates were still in the warehouse it *might* be possible to get permission to open them, bearing in mind the containerisation and sailing might also have to be rescheduled. If the crates had already been containerised and, of course, if they were aboard, nothing could be done. Tony listened to all this while he dug out his customer number from his diary, persuading himself as he did so that he was on to a loser. He was right. The efficient Mr Kaisler returned with the news that Mr Beckett's crates had been containerised and were aboard a vessel which had sailed on Friday.

"Bad start, I'm afraid. And unfortunately I suspect that the office in London I want to ring about the SOE connection will be closed. Five hours on: middle of the afternoon, so if it were a weekday they would be open – but . . ." he murmured as Celia put a fresh cup of coffee in front of him. He searched his diary then dialled and waited. After a while he removed the phone from his ear and waved it in the air. "As I bloody well feared, ringing tone but no answer. Bugger it."

"Mr Beckett, please . . ."

"Yeah, I know but if you're a partner you must expect foul language." Then, swinging round to face her, he said "Cels, how long will your advertising presentation, or pitching, or whatever you call it, take tomorrow?"

"Impossible to say. Our agency is not the only one involved, but I don't know how many there are exactly. We know of one other, our main competitor in this field, but there could be at least one more. What's more, we could be asked to stay to the end, or even go over part of the presentation again. Why?"

"Sounds like all day, or into Tuesday?" Celia nodded.

"Look – and please don't be angry, partner – I think I have to act quickly to try to keep ahead of our villains' next moves now that they know Ginger has talked to me, that we are both still alive, and that we and Jean Boulanger still have photos they have not retrieved. I have to sort out the SOE question early tomorrow, try to find out about the pharmacist in the Morvan and go and talk to Jean down in the Pyrénées. I'll contact Georges Lebrun to see if he can join me on that."

"Which means you want to get back to London, then on to France?"

"Yeah, I'm afraid it does. Sorry, darling." He frowned apprehensively as he looked across at her. He was on dangerous ground. It might erupt.

"Quite a weekend, eh? A little different from what I expected . . ."

"I know, but Cels . . . Please . . ."

It was with a sad little smile that she said, "It's OK, Tony. I understand. It may have been different, but we did share the difference and I enjoyed that. I'll ring the desk to see if they can get you a flight."

"Thanks. Then I will ring Georges."

Georges's surprise at hearing from Tony again was soon followed by concern as he heard the account of events on Brooklyn Bridge and in the apartment in Brooklyn Heights, interrupting only with the occasional "*tiens*", "*sale type*", and "*merde*". He agreed immediately that they should try to find the pharmacist. "I remember well his shop with the small apartment over it containing the famous kitchen." He also agreed that they must confirm the warning to Jean Boulanger and seek his help. If they needed a hotel in St-Jean-Pied-de-Port for Monday or Tuesday, Georges recommended the Hotel de Navarre, where he had once spent a holiday. He would certainly make himself available on Monday and they could use his car to go down to the Morvan and to the Pyrénées. When he knew the time he would meet Tony at Orly. And, no, he had not yet received the photos that were being returned to him from the Resistance museum; the curator said they had been sent. The last piece of information further confirmed Tony's suspicions.

"Cels, I want you to do something. I don't know how long Ginger's assignment will be. I will ring him when I get to London, but I don't think he'll be back. I'll give you his number. Would you try it from time to time, and if you get him tell him what has happened and what I intend to do. Suggest that if he has the time, join me at the Hotel de Navarre in St-Jean-Pied-de-Port.

"OK. Now, you have a flight, check-in at 3 p.m. I've ordered a cab for 2 p.m."

"You're brilliant. Come on, then, let's go down and grab some lunch. I promise you a decent bottle of wine." He picked up his valise and the packet of Larry's photos. "Hang on to the room. I'll sort out the bill with you later."

On the plane Tony's thoughts oscillated between the narrowing number of explanations of the villains' sustained and merciless search for an old photograph, and the new relationship that was developing between Celia and himself. Her growing maturity and greater self-assurance were now apparent. He realised that he had missed the early signs, and had continued to think of her as a beautiful, enticing lover whose talents and true character were concealed and constrained by her own insecurity, which she protected with irascible outbursts. He had continued to be the sincere admirer and lover, with a patient, avuncular bent devoted to

242

helping her overcome the uncertainties that haunted her. It seemed that his efforts, and, no doubt, other influences in her life, had been more successful than he had realised. That there was little need now to treat her moods with a kind of amused tolerance had become painfully obvious in the last twenty-four hours. His careless remark about being 'almost partners' showed that, though she was still on a short fuse, her anger now was not born of a desire to avoid a personal commitment but of a feeling that she was not accepted in a commitment she thought she had. He deeply regretted his thoughtlessness just as he regretted his retreat when at dinner on Saturday she was signalling that she had come to terms with her instability and was looking for, at the least, his recognition of it. How blind he had been to those changes. Cels, the bewitching, sexy adolescent had, it seemed, become Celia the beautiful, seductive, reconciled and confident woman.

He had been blind, but then his mind had been primarily focused on the tragic loss of his friends and comrades, the unresolved explanations, and the continuing threats. Perhaps there was some excuse. Yet the real issue remained the photograph. There were still too many possible keys to the solution. Some help had come from Georges's and Ginger's trip to Nevers. While it meant that Georges was personally no longer at risk, it had introduced an unexpected dimension – the way his set of photos appeared to have been plundered. Whoever was behind it all was not only capable of commanding the services of burglars and murderers outside France, but was also able to pull a number of strings inside. Someone with power or with a lot of influence. Why had an old picture become so important to him – or them? Why so dangerously threatened by it? As he probed his memory and as the questions repeated themselves and revolved in his mind, he drifted into an unsatisfying, fitful sleep in which movement, conversation and noises in the aircraft interrupted his thoughts – and his dreams.

As he walked sleepily through the airport buildings he recalled that this was the third time in as many weeks that he had suffered the depressing experience of arriving at an international airport in the grey hours of the morning. It was the downside of long-distance air travel. He was never at his best at this time of the day even in normal circumstances, and certainly not after disturbed sleep when his biological clock was trying to cope with the abuses he was heaping on it. On the brighter side, arriving in England at least meant that the queue to fairly human immigration officials was shorter and quicker than the circuitous one to the automatons in the United States; and the deceptively disinterested customs officials seemed more welcoming than their fierce-eyed counterparts over there, who made the most innocent traveller feel guilty. So it was within an hour of landing that Tony found himself in a taxi heading through the tunnel towards Gloucester Road.

A walk to the shops to buy bread, milk, butter, coffee, fruit juice and croissants brought him to the threshold of life and a good breakfast pulled him through it. Finishing his second cup of coffee he decided he was again a paid-up member of the world community. And a thinking one; for it was curious that no one had attempted to burgle the flat, as might have been expected, while he was away. Which meant the opposition knew he had nothing of interest there, but knew of his visit to the United States. How? Where did that information come from? Something they had said within earshot of the two villains while they were dining with Georges in Chartres? Or Georges himself? The way he had apparently been deprived of the mystery photo was, in

244

contrast with the others, without personal danger! Surely not. No, that didn't bear thinking about. He knew Georges well enough to dismiss the idea immediately – a thought sent straight from the Devil. He felt ashamed.

Anyway, no new answers would be forthcoming until he had followed through the remaining lines of investigation. As it was useless beginning his telephoning until nine o'clock, he sat down and wrote his agenda: find out about the former SOE agent (from the association with an address and no name whose purpose was known only to those privileged by service to belong); see if Ginger is back; get times of flights to Orly; phone Georges and make arrangements to go to see if the old pharmacist in Chateauville is still alive; together go down to the Pyrénées to warn Jean Boulanger and see if he can throw light on the matter (if not resolved by then). He read it a couple of times. He could not think of additional lines of enquiry. Some might emerge later. It was a logical list and each approach could be fruitful.

When the telephone was answered on his first call, he asked to speak to the secretary, who then asked for his name and membership number. Then followed a short time of confusion while he explained why he was telephoning from London and not South America, where according to their records he was living. Tony explained and apologised for not notifying them of the change. But to meet the requirements of security he was asked to name the last covert operation he had been engaged in, name his CO at the time and one senior colleague. He waited until the voice confirmed he was who he claimed to be. Then followed Tony's fairly lengthy description of the situation he was facing and the wartime background to it, and why he needed to know if the SOE agent in that region in 1943–4 was still alive. If he was, would he be prepared to talk to Tony? Another pause until the properly cautious secretary returned with the welcome news that the former agent was living in Wiltshire. He would find out if he was prepared to see Tony, and call back.

That was a more hopeful result than Tony had expected. There was just time to find out if Ginger was back, before leaving the phone free for the return call. He was not surprised that there was no reply. The return call was not long in coming. Victor Atkinson, the man Tony was enquiring about, would be pleased to hear from him. He should telephone the following number and use the following secure word to prove his identity. (Clearly the system was working.) Tony, delighted that progress was being made, was profuse in his thanks.

The voice that answered the number in Wiltshire recalled immediately to Tony's mind the quiet "French schoolmaster" he had met by arrangement on the edge of a forest outside Château Chinon, and responded to the secure word with "Yes, good morning, Mr Beckett. I was expecting your call. The secretary told me something about what you want to discuss. I well remember our meeting in 1944. How are you?" It was a friendly introduction, which Tony responded to in similar vein. Victor Atkinson continued, "It would be nice to reminisce a bit about those times without fear of breaching security. I knew about your mission, of course – would like to hear how it all went. After the liberation we did our own debriefing, but we did not hear much about other operations. The Chinese walls between departments and organisations still existed – rightly, I suppose. Do you wish to arrange to come and see me? I could put you up for the night. There's a good pub for dinner nearby. Unfortu-

246

nately, my wife died last year so you would get short commons if you had to rely on me to feed you. Or would you rather talk on the phone?"

Tony recognised the sad chattiness of a lonely man. Of course he would like to see him again and hear his side of events, but in truth he should not spare the time. "I would very much like to come and talk with you, but unfortunately there is some urgency about my enquiries. Some people are in danger. If we can deal with it on the phone I would prefer it. When it's all over I would love to come and have a gossip."

"I quite understand. I shall look forward to seeing you later. I believe you want to know what happened to the lorry you captured containing works of art looted from or around Bordeaux."

"That's right. We think, though we can't be certain, that the recent murder of two of my comrades from that time, and the attack on me and another old chum, may be connected in some way with what happened to that little treasure." Tony went on to explain about the photographs.

"How dreadful. Why after all this time? Well, as you know, I arranged with a very sympathetic marquis, the Marquis de Ramatuelle . . ."

"Ah yes, his name has been mentioned . . ."

"Yes? He had a chateau west of Nevers; secluded, with stables and barns. He agreed to hide the '*objets*' in his cellars and cover the vehicle with a mound of hay in one of his barns. I was with him when the vehicle arrived, driven by a member of one of your Maquis, and accompanied by another Maquisard on a captured motorcycle who took the lorry driver away. And if I remember correctly, they precariously carried away a gift of wine from the marquis."

"You're right. Happily they got it back safely, and very welcome and good it was. Unfortunately, I never had a chance to thank him. You have a very good memory."

"Unfortunately only for some things. Those times remain fairly vivid for all of our generation, I suspect, but I can forget where I put something only yesterday. Don't you find that?"

"Yes I do. But what happened after the liberation?"

"The Marquis was anxious to get rid of the stuff. He got a message to me. It was just before I was called back for debriefing. We agreed that it all should be handed to the French authorities – preferably the military. General de Gaulle's great entry into Paris had taken place and he had been recognised by the Allies as ruler of France, but the civil authority was still being formed and lines of departmental responsibility were not clear. The Marquis and I accompanied the vehicle, this time driven by one of his own staff, to Paris to find the Headquarters of General de Lattre de Tassigny – one of France's most successful generals. By that time there was a liaison office connected with our and your sort of 'things', in a hotel near the Tuileries Gardens, so we went there first to explain our intentions. One of the liaison officers accompanied us to the de Tassigny HQ, where we explained how the marquis came by the loot and handed it over. The marquis was given some kind of receipt by the officer we handed it to. I understand the poor chap is dead now and his estate is in a bad state of repair."

"Well, that proves pretty conclusively that it didn't fall into the wrong hands."

"Certainly, it would be hard to prove that it had. In any case, if it did after that, no one would have a legitimate quarrel about it with you and your comrades."

"That's true . . . unless . . ."

248

"Unless what?

"Unless whoever is behind this knows only that our mission captured it, and knows nothing after that. Perhaps someone connected with the original convoy . . . and as far as we know of those guarding the convoy, only one might have got away following a subsequent small action, a member of the *Milice* . . . unless one or two of the *Wehrmacht* survived. Mmmm. That will be a harder nut to crack."

"Well, I must leave you to try to crack it. I've told you all I know."

"Thank you, but could I ask one more question? I hope you won't object to it."

"What is it?"

"As far as you know, was *all* the loot taken to Paris?"

"I see what you mean, but yes it was. I was there when it was unloaded and again when it was brought up from the cellars. I then went with the marquis into the cellar to have a look round. I'm sure nothing was missing."

"I'm most grateful. You've been very helpful and I will make a point of coming to see you when all this has been settled."

Tony put down the phone and sat thinking. He was now quite sure the loot had been properly handed over, but that confirmation did not entirely dispose of all the questions. There was still a chance that someone connected with the convoy was trying to find out what happened to it. Yet that hardly justified serial killing, assault and burglary – unless prompted by a situation of utter desperation. Desperation so long after the event? What would bring that about? Finding no answer to his own question, he turned to item three on the agenda and turned up the telephone numbers of BEA and Air France. If he was quick he could get a flight at midday, which meant Georges could meet him at about three in the afternoon. With luck they could be down in the Morvan by early evening. So, item four, telephone Georges at his office, brief him and set the rendezvous.

Georges Lebrun was waiting at the barrier when Tony emerged from the baggage hall. As he led him to his car he warned him that if they were to get to Chateauville by late afternoon or early evening they would have to "motor". What he meant by that was soon evident as he weaved his way, chiefly by a skilled use of accelerator, brake and continuous use of the horn, southward through the afternoon stream of vehicles in the Paris suburb. Not a word was exchanged during this part of the journey. A rather tense Tony had no intention of distracting Georges from his Le Mans-like concentration until they left congestion behind and reached more open country. In the more relaxed atmosphere that then followed, though with little slackening in speed, they talked. Georges wanted to know more about the attack on Ginger and Tony on Brooklyn Bridge, and the way Tony had dealt with the intruder in Montague Terrace.

"Whoever is controlling these events has a very long arm, my friend. One sees he has agents who can reach into the criminal communities in your country and in the United States, rather than carrying out these deeds himself – or themselves. The face of the man in the trilby hat, a Frenchman, it seems, meant nothing to you, did it?"

Tony shook his head.

"And nor did the appearance of the men in the Mercedes who followed you to Chartres and who sat near us in Maison Madeleine. They and the others were all working to order and may not even have known their ultimate employer. All of which means that the ultimate employer – the real villain

250

of the piece – has money or power, or both, and is engaged in no small vendetta. He – they – are playing for very high stakes."

"You are right, Georges. Exactly my feeling. But I also think it is something more than a relatively small amount of looted treasure – unless of course there was something worth more than met the eye in that load, in either money or political terms. Yet somehow I don't think it's a matter of financial value, because of the unanswered question: why, after all this time? As my old friend Bill Walewsky said to me in New York, 'Look for the reason that in the present time suddenly makes all this so deadly important to someone.' I can't think of anything about the present time that would suddenly so enhance the value of something as to make burglary and murder a necessity. Even if one of the paintings had been by a recognised old master, its value today would not have appreciated enough – even allowing for higher auction prices in the 1960s – to justify these crimes, would they, Georges?"

"I do not know. I am no art connoisseur. Instinctively I think you're right, but who knows what is driving this madman – or madmen – to these acts of violence? Perhaps someone discovered that what was thought to be a reasonable but undistinguished painting is in fact by a master? How would they discover that if they had not got the painting? If they have it, what is all the mayhem about? Or is it someone who was connected in some way with the removal of those objects from somewhere near Bordeaux, who has fallen on hard times and who recalls where some wealth might be found? But who in any of those photographs would that apply to? We know that the only people round what was left of the convoy after the ambush were our old comrades . . ."

251

"Only a few of whom knew what we found in that vehicle."

"Exactly. And the captured German officer and three or four *Milice*, all of whom were killed subsequently except, we think – or Léon thought – one. You know, we search repeatedly for an explanation associated with that ambush and with that load of stolen property, but we fail to find a satisfactory one. We cannot overlook the possibility that the explanation lies somewhere else."

"I know. It's naggingly infuriating. Let us hope we find the answer in a Chateauville pharmacy – if it is still there."

They had been travelling for about an hour and a half when Georges suggested stopping for a coffee. "We have made good time since leaving the Paris traffic," he said as he pulled up at a roadside cafe in Nogent. They went inside and Georges chose a table by the window, calling out his order for two espressos. As he sat down and looked out of the window, he said softly, "You know, Tony, since Fontainebleau I think we've had a tail again." It may have been from Orly, but if they were tucked into the traffic behind I would probably not have been able to spot them. It was a dark blue Citroën; two men. Let us see." They did not have long to wait. Even before the coffee arrived a Citroën with driver and passenger came through. It slowed down as it passed their parked car then drove on. "Aha. I think I was right. When we leave we shall see. If they are tailing us they will be waiting somewhere."

"Damn. How the hell could they have got to know about our meeting this afternoon? Unless I've been under surveillance since getting back to London. They could have been watching the flat. I didn't notice anything. I must be slipping."

"Perhaps they've put a more qualified team on to us. The Citroën is a commonplace car, not as noticeable as the

Mercedes, and perhaps the occupants are better at their jobs. Let us get on with our journey and we will see whether my suspicion is correct."

Barely ten kilometres down the road they passed a lay-by fairly deeply set behind a sward of grass, with picnic tables and refuse baskets, of the kind provided so well by the French. Near the exit, half-hidden by a bush, was a dark blue Citroën containing two figures. "Is that the one?" asked Tony as they drove past. "I think so – I'll tell you in a moment. Let us see if he moves out . . . Ah yes, there he comes. He's keeping his distance, and he's keeping pace with us. So, my friend, once more we are under surveillance. What will they want to do, I wonder? Are they just going to find out where we are going, or have they other activity in mind?"

"Let us ask them, Georges. Let's ask them. Get well ahead and round a bend so that we can get out and stop them."

Georges dropped down a gear and accelerated. Round a sharp curve he pulled into the side and braked. Both were quickly out and waited by the front of their car. As the Citroën came round the bend they stepped out into the road and held up their arms. The car skidded as its driver braked, then suddenly it accelerated and drove straight at them. There was nothing Tony and Georges could do but leap to either side of the road to Georges's shout of "*merde*". By the time they had picked themselves up the Citroën was disappearing round the next distant bend.

"Not one of our best ambushes, that, Georges. In fact it wasn't one of my best ideas."

"It was worth a try just the same. A more determined pair of tails than the last lot, I think. Quite ruthless. Did you get a look at them?"

"Only a quick look. They were strangers to me, but I think I could recognise them again.

"I suspect that's not the last we shall see of them." Georges looked at his watch. "Come on, we still have some way to go."

From there the journey down to the Loire and alongside it and into Nevers – the route followed by Georges and Ginger the previous week when Tony had flown to New York – was uneventful. Tony was more than content to gaze at the passing scenery and allow the beauty of the countryside and the character of the small towns along the way – Briare, Bonny, Cosne, La Charité – so typical of those regions of provincial France, rekindle his love for that country. It was late afternoon as they went through Nevers and took the road turning eastwards away from the river. They were well into the area of their wartime operations and silently shared a feeling of nostalgia and of being at home in the wooded undulations that had provided them with a sheltered base which had hidden them and from which they launched their raids and reconnaissance patrols. Half an hour later they entered Chateauville along a quiet road just off the main route.

Memories flooded into Tony's mind as he saw the charming Auberge de France set in its courtyard and, opposite, the *boulangerie, boucherie, épicerie*, and there, further down, the *pharmace*, just before the small tree-lined square opposite the church whose bells had once pealed a warning of the unexpected approach of a large German column. He recalled the mayor, so impatient for the liberation that his anti-Boche sentiments became more strident after the news of the Allied invasion. His views, more and more openly expressed, caused frequent altercations with the dignified and wise curé, who earlier in the war had supervised the burial deep in the high woods of a British bomber crew brought down nearby, and who advised patience and caution. He recalled the *patron* of the cafe: short, fat, balding, with half a Gauloise permanently between his lips and dressed always in collarless shirt and baggy trousers held loosely by braces. And he recalled the old pharmacist – stooped, spectacles low on a long thin nose that seemed barely to separate two twinkling eyes – who had risked discovery and death to develop Roddy's negatives, working calmly in his blacked-out kitchen. He always marvelled that these were a few *petits commerçants, campagnardes* and *petits fonctionnaires,* who found themselves unexpectedly at risk in an area of operations, yet who unquestioningly did whatever they could to help the mission and the Allied cause.

That the risks they ran were real was brutally demonstrated one weekend when not far away to the north of them, a column of German SS troops descended on Dun-lés-Places and in an orgy of reprisal shot the male inhabitants, set fire to the houses and then moved to neighbouring Montsauche for more killing, setting the town ablaze before they left. The attacks had been so sudden and in such strength that Tony and other members of the mission could do no more than listen to the gunfire and watch the dread, spiralling pillar of smoke on the horizon. The anger they felt at their inability to help had made them all double their efforts to seek out convoys to ambush, rail tracks to blow, and to find more targets for the RAF. There was little doubt that more of the enemy died as a result of those raids on the civilian population of those two rural towns.

They drew up in front of the pharmacy. Like all French villages Chateauville's main street looked deserted. Through the trees in the square they could see groups of men playing boules and they could hear loud drink-inspired conversation from the cafe beyond, at the entrance to which two men were involved in a hand-waving, critical discussion that seemed on the point of disturbing the peace. Tony smiled. He guessed the subject would be the most important one in the whole of rural France – the respective merits of local football teams – and would probably end with shouts of abuse and a handshake. The pharmacy, in common with the shops alongside, was shut. Tony turned to Georges. "Round the back. Remember? The door that opened to the stairs going up to his kitchen."

They walked to the square and up the side to the narrow alley running along the back of the shops. Their appearance temporarily halted both the game of boules and the animated conversation that accompanied it. For a few moments everything froze, then magically came to life again. Coming to the door leading up to the pharmacist's apartment over the shop, they knocked several times before a voice answered from above.

"Who is there? The pharmacy is shut. Are you ill? If not come back in the morning."

"No, monsieur, we are not ill, but we would like very much to talk to you, if you would be so kind. You see, we are looking for the pharmacist, Monsieur Phillipe – Monsieur André Phillipe. We are old friends of his from the time of the Occupation . . ."

"What?"

Georges repeated his request, shouting more loudly through the door.

"Wait, please, I'm coming down."

The sound of descending footsteps was followed by that of a bolt being drawn back and a key turning in the lock. The door was opened by a slim, olive-skinned man with thick, untidy dark hair and moustache. Frowning, he peered first at Tony, then Georges, as he bade them an uncertain "Good evening, gentlemen."

"We are sorry to trouble you so late in the day, Monsieur, but we have driven from Paris to find Monsieur Phillipe . . ."

"You say you were friends of his during the Occupation. But you are not from these parts."

"No, we are not. We were members of a Maquis group that operated nearby. Is Monsieur Phillipe here?"

Another searching look, then, "Come up, please."

Tony and Georges followed the cautious and taciturn young man up the stairs, past the door to the kitchen on the right and into a comfortably furnished living room. "Please sit down, gentlemen. Will you take a glass of wine? You must be in need of refreshment after your journey." They thanked him for his kindness and accepted. As he moved over to a cabinet containing glasses, he asked, "You say you were members of the Maquis groups round here. Do you remember the names of those groups?" Tony frowned with displeasure and looked across at Georges. "Yes, of course we do. They were Maquis François and Maquis Léon. I am sure that is known here. And my friend here" – gesturing towards Georges – "was Captain François. But why these questions? We simply want to know how we can find André Phillipe; he was the pharmacist here at that time and gave us valuable assistance."

"Yes, I know," the man said as he handed them glasses of red wine. He poured one for himself and raised his glass. "*Bon santé*, gentlemen." Tony and Georges responded in unison. The man went on, "André Phillipe is dead since a few years. I am called Fernand Brive – André was my uncle; my mother was his sister." He turned to Georges. "So you are Monsieur Georges Lebrun?" Georges nodded without troubling to disguise his surprise that Monsieur Brive knew his real name. "My uncle told me a lot about those times before he died. What was the nature of my uncle's help to you?" Georges let out a gasp of irritation and took from his pocket his wallet, from which he extracted a visiting card.

"I do not understand why you are so suspicious, monsieur. Your uncle helped us by developing and printing certain photographs for us there in that kitchen. It was very brave of him to do it at such a time. He knew he could have been caught. Here is my card. You will see I am exactly who I claim to be."

"Thank you, monsieur. I am quite satisfied. Yes, he was very proud of that work and especially proud of the letter of thanks signed by the great Mr Churchill he was given after the liberation."

"Ah, you know about that, too?" said Tony. "We gave those letters to friends who risked their lives to help us. There are others in this area. But can you now tell us how your uncle died? Did he die here?"

"No, he died in a small house on the outskirts of Nevers. He became very arthritic after the war was over. He had no children and he had insisted that I qualify as a pharmacist so that I could take over from him here. He was very kind to me. I respect his memory. He carried on – although the pain got increasingly severe – until I qualified and he supervised me in my first years. He then needed to move nearer to Nevers, where he could get better treatment and assistance in the house. I used to visit him as often as I could, and that was when he spoke to me about those times. He told me that when he felt lonely he would get some photos out and look at them. They reminded him of days of good comradeship. He showed them to me and sometimes described what he had been told had happened . . ."

"You mean he had a set of those photos?"

"A set? I do not know what is a set, but he had many. He said he always made an extra print in case it was needed. He had quite a collection of them. They gave him a lot of pleasure towards the end – at least until . . ."

"Until what?"

"One day when I visited him and he was reminiscing, I asked to see the photographs again and he became very agitated. He said he did not like them as much as he had. We must be very careful, he said, and I must not talk about them to anyone. Of course, I did not anyway. I had no occasion to."

"Did you find out why he had become disturbed."

"Not exactly. But when we were looking at the photos – we had them spread out on the table – and he was answering my questions, he kept shifting his gaze to a particular one, peering at it closely, saying, 'I hope not. I do hope not'. I said, 'Hope not what, uncle?' He looked at me and said, 'Better not to know, Fernand. Better not to know. Some knowledge can be dangerous.' I did not press him on it. I did not want to upset him. By this time he had become very absent-minded and sometimes got names confused and I thought his reactions were part of his mental vagabonding – if you understand me. But after he had gone, from time to time I wondered what his reaction that day really meant. Then a short time ago I had this telephone call asking where André Phillipe could be found – just as you did . . ."

Tony and Georges bristled with renewed interest. "When was this?"

"Some weeks ago . . ."

"And what did he say, this fellow?"

"As I said, he wanted to know where he could find my uncle – but I did not say he was my uncle. I did not like the voice. It was not *sympathique*, you know. I told him my name was Brive and that I was in charge of the pharmacy; that Monsieur Phillipe had retired and was now dead these several years. He was intrusive, this man. He wanted to know if he had died here and what had happened to his possessions. I said that it was none of his business and that in any case he had died in a house near Nevers, that all his things had been sold or destroyed, and the house had been demolished later to make way for a new development. I thought that would eliminate his interest, whatever it was. I did not tell him that I had supervised the disposal of uncle's belongings. I then said I was going to disconnect and did not want to hear from him again. Perhaps you can understand now why I was suspicious of you when you called."

"Yes, of course we can," said Tony. "So you disposed of all of André's things . . ."

"Well, not quite all. I kept back some pictures to hang on my walls, some glasses and cutlery, a carpet for my bedroom, but apart from that – yes. Of course, I inherited the proceeds as he had directed in his will. Why?"

"I am sure we are going to seem as intrusive as your telephone caller when we say we are interested in what happened to his personal mementos, so let me explain why before you answer. You have been very honest with us. Let us return the confidence and be honest with you," replied Tony. "I am going to ask my comrade Captain François," he continued, reverting to Georges's *nom de guerre*, "to recount to you a strange story of recent murderous events that have their origin somewhere in those past actions against the common enemy in which your uncle played a part."

Fernand Brive turned to Georges as he began his account of the events that had brought them to Chateauville: the AMCA mission, its activities, the purpose and importance of the photographs which André had developed; the sudden emergence of a threat to them all with the suspicious death of Roddy, the burglaries, Larry's murder, the attack on

260

Ginger and Tony, all perpetrated it seemed in order to remove a particular photo from their collections. The only way they could get to the bottom of the affair was to identify the photo that had been stolen and see why it should be dangerous to someone. "That is why, Monsieur Brive," Georges concluded, "we have expressed an impertinent interest in your uncle's personal possessions. We had hoped he had kept copies which might include the one that is causing the trouble. But it seems we are unlucky again if his collection of photos has been disposed of with his other . . ."

"But, no, gentlemen. Wait! I think I can help you." He rose and went to a chest of drawers and from the back of the bottom drawer withdrew an old cardboard box which he set on the table. "My uncle left this," he said as he lifted the lid, "with this note attached to it. You will see that he said, 'I want you to have these, Fernand, perhaps my most intimate possessions. Put the Churchill letter in a frame on the wall in the kitchen where I did my small bit for the cause' – You will see it there, gentlemen – 'and because you so enjoyed looking at them I leave you these photos instead of destroying them. But that task I charge you to do before you die. Until then, keep them out of sight. Unfortunately, in that record of heroic times there is also mischief.' "

"So you have his photographs, then," cried Tony excitedly.

"But yes, certainly. They are here," he said as he lifted from the box a small package wrapped in brown paper and tied with string.

"This is wonderful news for us, Monsieur Brive," exclaimed Georges. "We came with a faint hope but you have fulfilled our best expectation. May we examine them, please?"

"Why, of course." Fernand Brive opened the packet and spread the prints across the table. "I've kept them in the

261

order my uncle kept them in," he said, placing them neatly side by side as he went.

Tony and Georges moved round to the front of the table. "I can see already that there are more here than Roddy gave us," said Tony. "See here, there are four of the woods leading to the petrol dump. We only had two. Obviously, Roddy selected the clearest for our sets. Perhaps, monsieur you would not mind waiting while I go to our car to fetch the set that belonged to our poor dead comrade Larry Lawrence, so that we can compare them with yours."

When Tony returned, Fernand Brive had finished spreading his uncle's collection right across the table. Tony set out Larry's set below them, matching as best he could incident with incident. André Phillipe's collection was far bigger. "Of all the extra ones in your collection, I wonder how we identify the one that matters," said Georges half to himself.

"We just have to," replied Tony. "It's the only real chance we have had since this terrible business began. Look, we can start by assuming that the one we are searching for is not one of the additional petrol-dump scenes. They are not dissimilar from the ones left with Larry and Jenny, and they did not take those. For the same reason it is not included in these additional ones of the blown railway lines. The similar ones Roddy gave us are still in their sets. That reduces the number we have to concentrate on. Fernand, can you remember whereabouts it was in the spread-out collection that your uncle became concerned and worried?"

"Why, yes," replied Fernand Brive, leaning over the table and concentrating his gaze on the shots in the centre of the line. It was somewhere here: these German vehicles after an ambush."

"So it *was* to do with that convoy. The one that included the loot lorry, as we suspected," said Georges looking across at Tony. "But is there an additional photograph here? Together they peered at the two sets, matching each with the other showing the aftermath of the ambush."

"Ah!" cried Tony suddenly. "Look, Georges, this one is missing from Larry's set. See? Now what does it show that can explain the mystery? They looked closely at it, passing it back and forth.

"Not a lot, my friend. It's almost the same as that one there showing the wrecked vehicle and the captured *Wehrmacht* officer with his *Milice* troops," said Georges, his voice heavy with disappointment as he handed the print back to Tony. "What sort of wild chase are we on all this time?"

Tony took the print and looked at it again, moving over to the light. "Well, it is not identical with the other; it's taken from a slightly different angle. Roddy seems to have moved round a little to get in a shot of another wrecked vehicle behind. Oh, and look here, Georges, it includes another member of the wretched *Milice*, at the back there, with a moustache."

Georges moved over and peered again at the photo. "Ah, yes."

Then Tony tensed visibly as he looked more closely. "Oh, my God. Surely not. Georges, that figure. Does he remind you of anyone – if you mentally remove the moustache?"

It was Georges's turn to renew his examination of the print. "Well, yes. But it cannot be. He joined Léon's Maquis well after this ambush . . ."

"Yes, that's right. He found his way to the Léon Maquis after his father was captured and killed in Brest – as Jean Boulanger himself explained. But without that moustache that figure would bear a strong resemlence to the young Henri Boulanger. Perhaps it's a picture of Henri's younger brother who, Jean told us, he had left behind in Brest as he was not under suspicion. The proud Boulangers would be embarrassed at having a relative who was a *collaborateur* with the *Milice*, when their Resistance record – Léon, Henri's father, and of course Henri himself working with Léon – is so good. It could explain Henri's strange involvement with the selection of photos from your set for the Resistance museum in Nevers. That would be a reasonable explanation – but for one thing . . ."

"Yes, but for one dreadful thing . . ."

"In what conceivable circumstances can such a situation be an excuse for murder, attempted murder and armed robbery?" He paused for a moment, staring towards the kitchen, then turned to Georges. "You know, I have the feeling that the only person who can help us now we have this photo is the ailing Jean Boulanger somewhere in the Pyrénées."

"I agree with you."

"You have found something interesting, something helpful to you, gentlemen?" It was Fernand Brive, who had tried, unsuccessfully, to follow the exchanges between Tony and Georges as they had examined the newly found print, and who had been forgotten by them both as they puzzled over the meaning of their find.

"Yes, we think we have, Monsieur Brive. Thanks to your uncle, and thanks to you for your trust and kindness; we are sure the answer lies in this photograph – but we think we have to consult someone else to get it . . ."

"You mean Captain Léon? My uncle told me about him. A very brave man, he said."

"Yes, Captain Léon, Jean Boulanger, and he was a brave patriot. But I suppose, monsieur . . . I suppose . . ."

"Yes, what is it, monsieur?"

"I suppose you would not consider letting us borrow this

264

particular print for a few days. I can promise you we will guard it most carefully and return it to you unharmed. In a curious way I think your uncle, by keeping this extra set of photographs he developed during the war, is helping us once again in a dangerous situation."

Fernand Brive did not hesitate. "Of course, gentlemen. You may have this print for as long as you need it. I know my uncle would be eager to help you, and would expect me to make it possible. Please take it."

Their thanks were warm and sincere as they prepared to take their leave. Then Tony turned. "There's just one thing we should warn you about, Monsieur Brive. We are fairly sure we were followed on our journey from Paris, which suggests that the people concerned with these outrages may still be hunting copies of that picture just as they seem to be hunting us. We managed to lose them some miles away from here, but if they do trace us to Chateauville – bearing in mind that earlier phone call you had – I think you should be very cautious about responding to enquiries from strangers. As indeed you were with us!"

"Don't worry yourselves, gentlemen. I shall be."

Chapter 14

Luck was with Tony and Georges when they drove the short distance back to the Auberge de France. The proprietor was welcoming but not effusively so. Yes, rooms were available. After depositing their bags they met in the bar-dining room and over a glass of wine agreed that they should immediately contact Jean Boulanger and warn him of the purpose of their visit. Armed with the telephone number Georges had brought with him, Tony picked up the telephone. It was many rings later that a voice answered, slower speaking and huskier, but still recognisable as that of Jean Léon Boulanger. When Tony introduced himself there was another pause before Captain Léon, choking a little on his words expressed both surprise and delight at hearing again "since such a long time" from "my dear friend and comrade". He assured Tony, unconvincingly, that he was "*pas mal*", and it was when Jean asked about "our other comrades" that Tony, referring to the murders, attempted murders and burglaries, was able to explain the main purpose of their intended visit. "It appears," he said, "that the photo 'they' were anxious to remove from the sets was one of the big ambush at which we captured the lorry full of loot from Bordeaux . . ." "Yes, I remember it well," interjected Jean. "We left the loot hidden in a chateau."

"That's right," continued Tony. "There are two photos taken by Roddy of captured vehicles and enemy personnel.

)ne with a vehicle, the *Wehrmacht* officer and some *Milice*. 'he other shows another vehicle and another member of ne *Milice*. It seems that the second picture has been the arget of these villains. If you still have your set you will see he one I mean . . ." Tony waited while Jean Boulanger truggled to control a fit of coughing.

"Excuse me . . . Yes?"

"Which suggests that those responsible for these crimes vish to remove evidence of either the vehicle or the pris->ner. What we cannot understand is why such a picture is vorth murdering for, and who would stoop to such evil. So ve thought, if it is convenient, we would like to come and ee you – you might be able to help us solve the mystery."

"*Tiens* . . . how could that be?"

"Well, you were there at the time – in fact you took the >risoners away, ran into trouble and were wounded. You nay remember something we do not . . ." Tony waited again, >ut there was no immediate response from Jean, just more :learing of the throat and an audible gasping for breath .ntil he replied.

"I will try, my friend, but you may be mistaken in what you think. There is an evil behind what you have told me that I do not understand, He coughed again, and there was another wait. "What time will you be here in the Pyrénées?" Tony said they would leave early in the morning and probably take the route south to Clermont-Ferrand, then across via Aurillac and Montauban to the Pyrénées Atlantiques. It was unlikely that they would be there before late afternoon. They would telephone from the Hotel de Navarre to see if it was convenient to come up to see him. Jean understood and wished them a safe journey. "We shall look forward to seeing you, Jean. *Au revoir.*"

Tony replaced his receiver and turned to rejoin Georges.

He could not know that after Jean replaced his receiver h sat in deep thought for several minutes before lifting it agai to make another call.

They dined in the small, poorly lit, beamed dining roon with its large open fireplace in which the cold half-burr logs left from a cooler season still emitted a faint bu noticeable smell of wood fire, and its red-check tableclotl and red napkins. They were alone in the room. The à l carte menu was limited, but good. Local grilled trout, fo lowed by a boeuf bourguignon with a bottle of Côtes d Rhône, and then a cheese platter, provided a satisfying en to what had been a day of progress in their quest. The spoke little over the meal except to comment on the man changes, particularly in road construction and farm builc ing, since they had been there twenty years earlier.

Striking up conversation with the balding, moustache proprietor, whose blue apron tied round his ample girtl indicated he was also the chef, they learned that he hac taken over the Auberge only five years earlier, moving acros from Le Blanc in the Department of Indre, knew nothing o wartime events in and around Chateauville nor what hac happened to the curé or the mayor from that time. Facec with such minimal information, and with no time to seel out old friends – if they still existed – Tony and George promised themselves another visit when they could agair explore sites near Chateauville, and visit the martyrdom towns of Dun-les-Places and Montsauche.

Next morning, after an early, tradition breakfast of crois sants, fresh baguette, butter, jam and strong coffee, they se off on the road through Nevers. As they turned soutl towards Clermont, Georges asked Tony to recount his con versation with Jean. "Did he sound surprised about what you told him?"

"He was certainly surprised to hear from us and seemed equally surprised and concerned to hear about what had happened to Roddy and Larry, and the attempts on Ginger and me. He did not volunteer any explanation about the identity of the moustached *Milice* man. He seemed to think about it for a bit. His only comment was, 'I think you may be mistaken in what you think. There is an evil behind it which I do not understand.' "

"That was a little strange, wasn't it? How did he sound?"

Tony paused. "To judge from his voice, periods of coughing and noticeable shortness of breath, not very well, I fear. That old wound in his chest may be taking its toll."

They said little to each other as Georges worked their way round Clermont and continued southwards through the spectacular region of the Volcans d'Auvergne. At Massiac they branched off to Aurillac, following the road along the rivers Alagnon and Cère. They avoided the steep climb up to Aurillac and kept to a route round the south of the town and out towards Figeac. The road again became twisty and undulating as it had been through the Auvergne and Cantal. They had expected the route from Massiac to Montauban to be a slow part of the journey. It was, though Georges was uncompromising in his determination not to let it be a very slow part.

It was after they had negotiated the bends round the small villages of Sansac-de-Marmiesse and St-Mamet that Georges, who had properly been concentrating on the tortuous road ahead, looked in his driving mirror and with emotion that produced a swerve in his steering exclaimed, "*Merde! Merde alors!* They have found us again." Tony turned in his seat and saw through the rear window a dark blue Citroën with a driver and passenger in front, coming up behind them very fast. Before he turned back to the front, the car was close behind them, distractingly so as Georges negotiated the tight bends ahead.

"How the hell did they get on to us again?" Tony asked bitterly. "Did they get to Fernand Brive, or the proprietor of the Auberge de France? He did not have much feeling for the wartime scene in the Nièvre . . ."

"Or Captain Léon?"

Tony turned to look at Georges, focusing on the road and wrestling with the tight curves. "Surely not . . ."

"What the hell are they trying to do now?"

Georges glanced quickly at the driving mirror then back to the road again as they approached a very sharp bend with a deep drop on the nearside. They were travelling fast. Tony, feeling Georges's uncertainty, turned round to see the Citroën pulling alongside, its bonnet almost level with their rear windows. For an instant he could clearly see the grimly determined stare on the face of the driver. "I think they're going to force us off, Georges!"

"Or try to!" With a quick move of arm and foot, Georges dropped to a lower gear and accelerated as he edged the car round the sharp offside bend. The acceleration kept them ahead and as the road straightened out Georges swerved to the offside, pushing the persistent Citroën over to other side of the road just as a heavy lorry appeared from round the bend ahead. They both heard the scream of skidding tyres on the tarmac as the Citroën driver braked hard. Turning again, Tony saw the car swerving from side to side as the driver tried to correct the skid and then pull it back again. He could see the two figures in front rolling from side to side as the driver wrestled with the steering. "They're out of control," he called as Georges, slowing down, watched in the rear mirror. With a final screech of locked wheels the swaying, swerving Citroën turned broad

270

side on and headed straight for the bank across a grass verge on the offside of the road. It struck the high mound of grass with a loud bang and a clatter of breaking glass; then it rolled over onto its side, upper front wheel spinning.

Georges continued slowly until he could find a place to pull off the road. They both got out and ran back. The lorry that had forced the Citroën to skid out of its path had disappeared round the corner. Ahead of them the offside door on the upper side of the wreck was pushed open and one of the figures struggled out. Lying flat on the side of the car he helped his companion through the opening. Together they dropped to the ground. Dishevelled, blood on the face of one of them, they looked up to see Tony and Georges running towards them as they staggered to their feet. As of one mind they turned and started running back towards the corner where they had sought to ditch Tony and Georges, and disappeared round the bend.

As they got level with the crashed vehicle, Tony and Georges gave up the chase. "I don't think . . . we shall see any more . . . of them . . . on this journey," said Tony, panting. "And our priority . . . is still . . . to visit . . . Jean Boulanger . . . and we are still a long way off."

As they walked back to their own car a few vehicles passed by in both directions. None seemed to take notice of them. Their attention focused on the wreck. All slowed down as they came alongside it, then drove on.

Resuming their journey Tony complimented Georges on his skilful driving, which Georges acknowledged with a Gallic shrug. They agreed that they were honour bound to report the accident without, they hoped, having to go into detail. In Figeac they found the gendarmerie. Their account of seeing a smashed car beside the road evoked less interest than they had expected. "Thank you, gentlemen, it has already been reported twice. Thank you." To their relief, no questions were asked.

They took a quick lunch and then set off on the long stretch through Villefranche-de-Rouergue, Montauban, Tarbes and Pau to St-Jean-Pied-de-Port. The traffic was light and they made good time. In the car conversation was intermittent. For a while they pondered the unanswered question of how the villain's, or villains', hit men kept finding them. It seemed that here in France, in the United States and in England, they knew how to get information about their movements. Partly it could be explained by proficient tailing, as had happened in London, but other instances suggested some kind of network of informants, which in its turn suggested, once more, a source of power and influence. Tony was conscious of many unanswered questions, yet now that they had identified the missing photo he felt they were near to an explanation. It was one to which Jean Boulanger's memory might provide the key.

With clearer roads they made up a lot of time after leaving Villefranche and the tortuously twisting roads they had followed from Massiac. It was just after five-thirty that they mounted the rise that led into St-Jean-Pied-de-Port, the small Basque town, at the foot of a pass through the Pyrénées, that had at one time been at the centre of the old kingdom of Navarre. Over the brow of the hill they drove down the main street, with the old town wall on the left, into the marketplace. They pulled into a parking place by the Hotel de Navarre, the front terrace of which looked across to the bridge over the bubbling, fish-laden River Nive. They were glad to leave the car, stretch their legs, and walk up to the front terrace and into the hotel to claim their reservations.

"Ah!" exclaimed the clerk as Tony registered. "There is a

message for Monsieur Beckett." He turned away and picked up a folded piece of paper from the counter behind him, and handed it to Tony with a polite "If you please, monsieur". Tony flicked open the note. "Good God. It's from Ginger. He's here!" he cried as he read, 'Waiting for you on the garden patio – if you get here in time!' Come on, Georges." And anticipating the question the clerk smiled and waved a hand. "Follow the corridor, messieurs and through the door at the end."

Outside on the patio at a table by the swimming pool under a sun umbrella, glass of wine in hand, Ginger sat facing the door but admiring at the same time two lissom, suntanned figures in the briefest of bikinis, who were swimming in the pool. "Ah! I thought you'd never get here – but I was quite happy waiting for you," he said with the broadest of cheeky smiles.

"Ginger! Wonderful! How did you manage it?"

"I got back earlier than expected yesterday. My man's trip to Washington was cancelled after the visit to the lawyers. Luckily I was in when Celia phoned. She had been trying my number intermittently . . ."

"Good old Cels! How much did she tell you?"

"Not a lot. She was phoning between 'pitching sessions' – whatever that means. Anyway, she was in a hurry. She told me you had been visited by a villain in Brooklyn Heights, and that after giving a baseball hitter out after three strikes you sent him away with some money. I suppose that's the peacetime version of our old rule: if confronted face to face by an enemy, there can be no compromise, no delay. It's you or him. Act immediately and conclusively . . ."

"OK, OK. Ha-ha and all that. But there was more to it . . ."

"And she told me you and Georges now want to see Jean Boulanger."

"That's right, and now we have even more reason to see him."

"Oh? Going to fill me in?"

"Of course. But first let me phone Jean to find out when we can visit him. Meanwhile it's your privilege, as first here, to buy us all a drink."

Tony turned back into the hotel, ignoring the look that Ginger threw at him. At the telephone on the reception desk he dialled Jean's number. Again there was a fairly long wait before he heard Jean's husky "*Allo*". "*Jean, c'est moi, Tony, qui parle. Comment ça va?*"

"*Ah, Tony, mon ami. Oui, pas mal. Ça marche* . . . You have made good time . . . You had a good journey." Another pause for breath. No problems, eh?"

"No, no problems," said Tony, lying easily to avoid a long explanation on the telephone which he might need to repeat later, and puzzling over the possible motive for the question. A natural bit of politeness? Or some meaningful foreknowledge? "We are wondering, Jean, when it would be convenient to come to see you to talk about those matters I mentioned when I phoned earlier?" He waited again, this time through a longer silence. He began to think the connection had broken. Then,

"Tony, excuse me. Yes, you could come tomorrow morning . . . Perhaps I shall have some news to help you . . . and we will talk about old times, old comrades . . . over coffee and wine . . . eh?"

"That sounds like an excellent idea. But how do I get to you?"

"That's not so difficult. You take the road from St-Jean that goes up through the pass, as if you were going to Pamplona . . . You are climbing all the time until you come to a small village – Arnéguy – which is a frontier post. You'll

274

have your passport . . . but the guards will not trouble you – if they are there! Tony, excuse me a minute . . ." He waited until the fit of coughing had passed. "So, follow the road; it goes still upwards and very steep in parts with sharp bends, so pay attention. There are straight drops over the edge. Then you will come to a series of very tight curves and very steep ascent with a deep and wide valley on your left side before the country opens out like . . . like an alp, I think. Off the road on the left, on a small grass mound, is a monument to Roldan – I think you call him Roland – the hero who in the eighth century gallantly fought an army of Moors and lost . . . but gave France time to resist the invasion. I can see the monument from my window. Its my favourite view. So when you see that you are on top of the pass, just above Roncesvalles – where the battle was fought – and just opposite where I live. You look to the right and you will see a narrow road . . . just a track, perhaps . . . climbing up again . . . My house is about two kilometres up there . . . white, with red tiles on the roof. Is that clear, my friend?"

"Yes, very clear, thank you Jean. The road up through the pass to Pamplona until we reach the Roldan monument. OK?"

"Exactly. I shall look for you tomorrow. Go wisely."

"And you, Jean. *Au revoir.*"

Jean Boulanger replaced his receiver and sat staring out, down towards that small mound with its craggy granite monument to an historic resistance. Then he turned to the figure behind him. "Tony Beckett comes tomorrow morning."

As he walked back to the poolside Tony tried to recall the epic poem he had tried to learn at school – 'The Song of Roland'. He remembered the story, if not the words, of how Roland tried to call for help by blowing his hunting horn –

the oliphant, wasn't it? – until he bled at the mouth. Wrongly advised by a treacherous baron, the great King Charles ignored the call until it was too late. Roland saw his great friend Oliver killed before he himself perished. Yes, perhaps it was for the heroism in the legend that the view of the monument appealed to Jean.

A bottle of wine and glasses were waiting on the poolside table when Tony rejoined Georges and Ginger. Answering the two sets of raised, questioning eyebrows he said, "Jean wants us to visit him tomorrow. I did not go into any more detail about our concerns, but he said he might have some news that could help us – a little surprising, since he has not heard all of our story." He shook his head when Georges asked if he had given any indication what that news might be. "No. But I have the feeling that we are nearing the end of our quest."

"Is it far?"

"We take the road through the Pyrénées towards Pamplona, across the frontier and up to the top of the pass where there's a monument . . ."

"A monument to Roldan near Roncesvalles . . ."

"Correct, Georges. Jean looks out to the monument from his house."

"*Tiens.* So that is where he chose to spend his retirement. It is high in the mountains. The air must be very good for him."

"Somehow, Georges, I do not think he is there just for the air, however good that might be for his damaged lungs. I think he is a very sick man who is content to spend whatever time is left to him up there in the mountains, thinking about the past while he enjoys what he calls his favourite view – the monument – which I think appeals to something deep inside him."

They were silent as they thought of the implications of Tony's view of the lonely life of their ailing old comrade.

"The road there is very tortuous and steep. We should allow good time," said Georges rather pointlessly, because he felt someone should break the mood. Ginger was more to the point.

"Well, you all seem to know where we go next, how we get there and how we got this far. Now, will someone fill me in on what happened between Brooklyn Bridge and St-Jean Pied-something-or-the-other? Can we have an I-Group please?"

They were pleased to laugh at Ginger's plea and his reference to a half-forgotten army procedure whereby an officer in command called his key subcommanders together to inform them of the situation. "Of course, Ginger," said Tony. "Why don't we finish our drinks, go into the dining room and have an early dinner – I for one am hungry – and over the meal Georges and I will take you step by step along that route. We'll start with an amateur stake-out man in a large hat, and his baseball-bat-wielding hireling in a woolly hat, and go on to how an ex-SOE agent helped us from his lonely and sad retirement, and how dear old André Phillipe, the pharmacist, provided the missing clue from beyond the grave! Sounds rather good, doesn't it? OK, Ginger?"

It was OK.

Next morning the three of them set off in Georges's car and headed into the Pyrénées on the road to Pamplona. They climbed up to Arnéguy, where the frontier was marked by a simple pole barrier that stood open. They stopped at the customs post and Tony held Georges's passport out of the window for inspection, evoking a curt nod of the head and a wave of the hand from the bored inhabitant of the hut. They drove on. The scenery was spectacular, first on this side, then on that, as the road became steeper and as it twisted through the mountains. On this side were towering peaks, and on that were sheer drops, unnerving for those sitting that side until a sharp double bend brought the peaks and the abyss onto opposite sides. The predominant brown of the mountains was relieved by patches of green where trees grew in gullies or miraculously clung to steep slopes. But what gave the changing panorama a spectacular extra dimension was the way the sunlight and shadow kept shifting the perspective at every turn. It was as Jean had said, a long and tortuous climb, but rather more hair-raising for those in the car than he had indicated. Then as they neared the peak they could see across a wide deep valley and, slightly above them, a flatter landscape." The monument is up there, I think," said Georges, indicating with his head without taking his eyes off the road.

It was. At the top they saw the rugged block of stone inscribed with the name Roldan, with replicas of two medieval weapons, back from the road on their left. The small road to the right led to the small white house with red-tiled roof and brown shutters. Outside the door stood the figure of Jean, now white-haired and stooped, leaning on a stick. It was an emotional welcome, marked with that depth of sincerity and instantaneous understanding felt only in a reunion of old serving comrades. "Tony, dear friend; and brave Ginger; and good compatriot Captain François," Jean Boulanger exclaimed warmly, with tears filling the corners of his eyes as he embraced each in turn.

Behind his bent, limping walk as they followed him inside they saw how harshly the years since the war had dealt with him. He waved them to chairs round the small square table with a coffee pot, mugs, a bottle of wine and glasses in the centre. It did not surprise Tony that from the table you could see down the hill to the monument standing proudly and alone on the small grass mound that ran to the edge of the steep curved valley with mountains beyond. He noted, too, the single armchair close to the window. To the right of the table was an arch leading to a small kitchen in which a sink, a tap, a cooker and gas cylinder were just visible. To the left was a large fireplace with straight-back chairs on either side. In the corner an open wooden door showed the foot of an enclosed staircase. Behind him he he noticed as he sat down another wooden door, closed. The floor throughout was stone-paved. The only soft covering on it was a small rug in front of the fireplace. If the gods of health had punished Jean over the years, the gods of fortune had been no kinder. Tony felt a deep thrust of bad conscience, realising he had been unaware that one of his main commanders on the mission, a very brave and patriotic man with strong beliefs, was living in such poor circumstances. He deserved better.

As if reading Tony's mind Jean interrupted his thoughts with, "As you can see, my friends, it is not very big, but I have all I need. And now we are all together again – well, unhappily not all. But I am so pleased to see you." He was expressing genuine pleasure. He reached over and poured the coffee and in short sentences punctuated with breathlessness asked what each had been doing since they last met. Each brief account led to questions until they were able to ask him for his own news. He told them of the operations he had undergone to save his lungs, and to arrest the wasting of his leg – both conditions resulting, Tony reflected, from wounds suffered while serving with AMCA in defence of his country. Out of respect for Jean his visiting colleagues were patient. But the opportunity to move the discussion to the subject they came to pursue was provided by Jean himself. The coffee was finished and Jean, supporting himself with his stick, poured the wine. "Now, my friends, I think we have other, perhaps less pleasant things to talk about. But first let us drink to the memory of departed friends. *Salut*." They stood and touched glasses across the table and drank.

"Now, you said, Tony, that two of our comrades have recently been killed – murdered, you said – that you and Ginger had been attacked and that the foul types who did this have stolen photographs that poor Roddy took on the mission. So the motive, you think, has to be something connected with the mission, perhaps even the matter of the lorry of loot. Now, tell me, please, all that has happened.

"I think, Jean, it's important that, at the risk of boring you . . ."

"On such matters involving friends you cannot bore me."

Tony smiled and nodded. "It's important that we describe the whole sequence of events and then you will see why we have come to our conclusion. I will begin, but each of us has experiences of these events to add. And I must say at the start, the very fact that it is we, senior colleagues on the AMCA mission, who have been the victims of these attacks suggests a direct connection." He paused as he watched Jean nodding slowly as he peered into his glass. "Then I want to say, Jean, that coming here and having the pleasure of seeing you again – something we should have done long ago – has two purposes. First, we think you can help us discover who and what is behind these attacks at this time. Secondly, we wanted to warn you that as one who also holds a set of the photographs Roddy sent us and which probably includes the one that is the vital clue, you too are probably in danger from these villains, unless we can stop them. However, I believe your nephew Henri will already have warned you after Georges and Ginger met him in Orléans." Tony paused again as Jean's head came round suddenly to look up at him, frowning – a frown which was quickly replaced with a smile, and, "*Ah, oui. Merci, merci.*"

So Tony began his story with his discovery of the strange death of Roddy Holmes and the burglary on the day of his funeral when one photo was taken from his collection. With the others making their contributions, and taking over parts of the story such as Larry's murder, the visit to the Resistance museum in Nevers, and the episode on Brooklyn Bridge, they meticulously described the merciless trail. When it came to the discovery of the identity of the stolen photo, a sudden impulse made him omit any reference to finding it in the pharmacy in Chateauville. He was anxious to see Jean's reaction to the actual picture when they showed him. "And so, although we know at last which photo has provided the motive for all these attacks, we do not know why – whether it has to do with a vehicle or a person there at the time. So I would like to show it to you now."

Jean Boulanger, who had listened in silence to their long explanation, signalling his understanding solely by the changing expression on his face – frown, wide-eyed surprise, grimaces of disapproval – and occasionally nodding or shaking his head, suddenly heaved himself to his feet, grabbed his stick and said, "Wait, Tony. A moment, please." and pushing back his chair hobbled across to a cupboard in the corner, opened a drawer and extracted a small box which he threw onto the centre of the table as he returned. "My set," he said with a smile and a nod of his head.

"Oh yes, I have kept them and I look at them from time to time and think back to when we all devoted our lives to saving France and other occupied countries from tyranny, and I look down there" – he waved towards the window –

"to remind myself that it wasn't the first, or second, time when this had had to be done. Please open the box and spread the pictures out for me." Ginger carefully undid the box, untied the package inside and spread the contents across the table. Georges automatically reached across and swivelled them into chronological order, and Tony reached into his pocket for the copy brought from Fernand Brive. "You see, Jean, this shows a vehicle and in the background . . ."

Before he could finish Jean interrupted again. "A moment again, please, Tony", and he stretched across the table, put his finger on his copy of the crucial print and slid it away from the rest. "I think this is the one you have brought to show me, the clue to your mystery!" In Jean's quiet way it was a dramatic gesture and he looked round at the astonished faces, nodding his head, knowing he had got it right.

It was Tony who broke the tension that had gripped them. "Jean! Jean, you have known about this all along. How could you? Then you must know who is behind it, for God's sake!"

"No, I have not known about it all along. I only guessed the answer in the last two days. Since, in fact, you telephoned and spoke about the photographs of that ambush. I had begun to think about it when Georges called from Chartres, but it was only after your call yesterday, Tony, that I guessed what had happened."

"So it does not surprise you that, when we saw the photo and studied it carefully, we noticed that the member of the *Milice* with the moustache in the background had something of Henri's features, and therefore we thought it was probably Henri's young brother. But why is that identification so deadly important?" And to whom?"

Jean had settled back in his chair. He looked around. "Dear friends, you are right and you are wrong. You would understand what I'm about to tell you better if you had suffered the indignity of enemy occupation and felt the shame of being ruled by an enemy regime – though you, Captain François, will know what I am saying. You see, the *Milice* soldier in the picture is not Henri's brother, who was killed in one of your air raids on Brest. It is . . ."

Before he could finish the sentence, the door behind Tony burst open and through it lurched Henri, revolver in hand, shouting, "No . . . No . . . Uncle . . . Jean . . . you cannot. You must not . . . You said it would all be over today . . ."

"Henri! Are you mad? Are you so used to bloody action now that you think it solves everything? Which one of us do you want to kill? Me? So the others can then hand you to the gendarmes? Calm down. It *will* be all over." Henri was standing in between Tony and Ginger, slightly behind them. As Jean was rebuking the angry, distraught man, the merest of glances between them conveyed the necessary message. Ginger jabbed his elbow into Henri's crotch, and as he doubled up gasping for breath Tony grabbed his wrist, twisted the revolver from his grasp and forced his arm up behind his back, pressing his head down onto the table. Henri's wild intrusion was over in minutes. "You fool, Henri." cried Jean, still seated. "You think these gentlemen have forgotten everything? Let him up, Tony, he is past being dangerous now," he said as he gazed down at his nephew with an expression of pity mixed with sadness rather than anger. "Perhaps I should have the revolver. He is my responsibility – has been for years, though I do not seem to have discharged it properly. Henri, pull up a chair and listen to us."

"Yes, gentlemen, the *Milice* soldier with the moustache was Henri . . ."

"But how could that be Jean? He did not join your Maquis until after that ambush. You set off in the old Citroën with the *Wehrmacht* officer and the *Milice* prisoners to take them to Tony's camp, but got shot up by a German patrol, and only one . . . Oh! Unless . . ."

"Exactly, Georges. The one was Henri. You see it was sheer luck that we ambushed that particular convoy on which Henri was a guard. Henri had been sent to Bordeaux to serve in a unit under the command of that treacherous swine Darnand – one of whose colleagues is still in government, would you believe – and was detailed to accompany the convoy. After we ambushed it I recognised him at once. Until then I had thought he was with my dear brother in Brest. He was frightened and I signalled him to be quiet. We both knew how the Maquisards felt about the *Milice.* Then you, Tony, wanting to question them and protect them from our colleagues, told me to take them to your camp. As we drove away Henri told me how my brother had been tortured and killed by the Gestapo, and he had been forced to join the *Milice* . . ."

"Then you both must have been lucky to survive the German patrol."

Jean did not answer immediately. He looked down into his glass, lips pressed tightly together, the muscles at the corners of his jaw prominent. Then he looked straight at Tony. "It wasn't like that, Tony . . ."

"What do you mean?"

"I knew that if I was going to hide Henri for a while I could not let the others get to the camp and risk them telling you what I had done. There was no German patrol. Along the road I stopped the Citroën alongside a wood and told them I was going to deal with them myself and not take them to the camp where they would be executed anyway.

284

The officer claimed protection as a legitimate prisoner of war. I ignored him and marched Henri into the wood as if to shoot him. We hid where we could watch the others and as I expected they talked excitedly together then tore off their blindfolds, got out and started running towards the opposite ditch. I was ready and it took only a minute or two to finish them . . ."

There was a simultaneous gasp from Tony, Ginger and Georges. It was Ginger who vehemently shouted their common thought. "But that was bloody cold-hearted murder!"

"Yes, in your English way that's how you see it. I'm not proud of what I did, but remember, they were the enemy and they were trying to get away. They knew they were taking a risk. And don't forget, the Boche were our hated enemy, but the *Milice* were our detested enemy."

"But the wound in your leg. Surely you didn't . . ."

"Yes. I did it myself. I put a shot through my thigh muscle, carefully avoiding the bone, but, unfortunately, unintentionally doing it permanent damage. Part of my retribution, perhaps. But only a part. And then I had to hide Henri in a secure part of the wood. I got some food from the nearby village, and some different clothes. No one asked why I wanted them. I also had to hide the FFI Citroën which you supposed was lost in my imaginary brush with the patrol – which, incidentally, I salvaged after the mission was finished and you had all left."

"Oh, my God, Jean," said Tony, his voice heavy with sadness and disappointment. "It was all a deception . . . a bloody deception . . . and you were betraying our trust . . ."

"Yes, I deceived you, and I'm sorry I had to. But I was trying to protect my family's honour. The deception hurt no one except our enemy. Henri was not an enemy of France. He was a very young man who had acted bravely in the

285

Resistance with his father. Then he and his father were captured. It was obvious that his father, my brother, was in danger of hideous torture and execution because he had information about a Resistance group in Brest which the Germans wanted. Henri also had some useful information – he knew at least one other courier and an address or two. He did not know the Germans had also picked up other couriers, so they already knew what they were frightening Henri to reveal. They were masters at terrorising their prisoners especially when other members of their families were involved. They offered him the choice of enduring the agony of watching his father being tortured or joining the *Milice* and fighting for Germany so that his father could escape torture and just go to prison . . ."

"You just cannot know what a choice that was for me," shouted Henri. "You just cannot. They told me – I was tied to a chair; they had clubs and knives in their hands – I would not only have to watch my father being interrogated – and they said how merciless they were – but that I also would be tortured if I did not agree to serve the Reich. I loved my father. I admired him . . . What was I to do? What would you do? I was old enough to realise they might not keep their word and spare Papa, but there was a chance they would, and if I refused, his torture and death were certain. What could I do? Condemn him, or take that chance? They did not give me time to think. They were threatening me the whole time . . . Oh God . . ." He broke off with a sob, tears in his eyes, shaking his head in the agony, not of physical torture but of a tortured conscience.

For a minute or two everyone was silent. Then Jean spoke again. "Georges understands what we are saying here. He has lived close to this dilemma, which is France's dilemma. But you, Tony and Ginger, will probably see it differently.

But use your imaginations. What if you were facing that cruellest of tests: the choice between staying loyal to your country while condemning a loved one to a hideous death, or saving that loved one by betraying your country."

"Jean, of course we cannot feel this in the same way that you can. In England we have been spared the indignity – the shame – of being occupied. But, believe me, I have often thought of similar circumstances, where perhaps a comrade, someone I fought with, was at risk in that way, and his life or death was in my hands. I do not know what I would do. In any case imagining such a situation is a long way from experiencing the fearsome reality of it."

"Then try to imagine also how Henri felt, having made his dread choice, discovering that it had been in vain. His father was terribly tortured and then shot . . ."

"Yes, try to imagine that, Commander Beckett.". It was another miserable cry from Henri, springing up from his chair and pointing across at Tony. "It was so terrible when I heard that news. You cannot even imagine how it was . . . my dear father. I wanted to kill myself, and would have done if Uncle Jean had not stopped me, saying he knew my father would not have wanted that."

Tony waited while Henri settled back, the focus of sympathetic glances from round the table. Then he spoke quietly. "We can and do sympathise with you, Henri, and can understand the frightful position you were in and the horror of discovering what happened to your father. And Jean, while I now think you were probably justified in doing what you did to save Henri when you found him, it does not explain – nor remotely justify – what has happened since. The murders and the violence. It does not explain the part you or Henri have played in *those* tragic events. Do not forget, my friend, two of our old comrades have been brutally killed. Ginger and I might have gone the same way. All this because of something that happened over twenty years ago. Why, Jean? Do you know why?"

For a while Jean did not answer. He looked round at the serious, enquiring faces, and then at the frowning, worried face of his nephew opposite him. He struggled to his feet, picked up the revolver from the table, took his stick in his other hand and slowly walked the yard or so to the chair by the window. He lowered himself painfully into it and stared out onto the little plateau, the deep curving valley and the sun-tipped mountains beyond. "Well, my friends, I think you may now have understood Henri's fearful dilemma, but now with a heavy heart I have to say in respect of those sad events you just asked about Tony, that was another betrayal . . ."

"Uncle . . . please . . ."

"It's no use, Henri. Tony is right. Old comrades who fought with us to save France are dead because of it. We owe our friends the truth." He looked round the table. All eyes were on him except Henri's, who had buried his face in his hands. Then in a quiet voice he began. "You see, gentlemen, after the liberation of our country we were virtually without an agreed economic and social structure. There were the old patterns of departmental and regional administration, but many of those associated with it were tainted with pre-war corruption and inefficiency, and others with wartime collaboration. There was a chance of a fresh start; a new system which would have made the struggle doubly worth-while. Some people feared that, just as the French Revolu-tion led to a military dictatorship, we might follow the same path after the war.

"But in exile in London General de Gaulle and his friends had done a lot of work preparing for the restoration of order in post-liberation France. The political stakes were nigh. England and the other Allies wanted de Gaulle in charge and quickly recognised his as the legitimate government. Although they did not like him much, he was, as you would say, a safe bet. And in truth I think most of the people accepted him willingly. Propaganda from England had made him a hero, representative of what they called the true France, and people wanted stability. Perhaps more importantly, they felt that he more than anyone else would heal the wounds of conscience inflicted by defeat and occupation, and the shame of collaboration by some fellow citizens. It is strange, is it not, that a victor nation should suffer such a psychological trauma?

"And, of course, the people were right. The General set about restoring French pride with a will. He was ruthless in removing suggestions of our dependence on our Allies, not least by creating the myth that the forces of Resistance liberated us. We did not. We did a lot: we spied on the enemy, we passed back information, we identified targets for the bombers, we harassed the occupying forces, we disrupted communications and fought their convoys. But it was the Allied armies and air forces that forced the Boche from our country. Recognition of that was bad for de Gaulle's therapy. And in the short run his therapy has worked, but you English will be exasperated by the arrogance he has rebuilt in the process of making us believe in ourselves again . . ."

"Ah, Jean, agreed, agreed. I have been explaining to Tony the same story, *n'est-ce pas*, Tony?" Tony gave a brief nod. He was anxious for Jean to continue his explanation.

Jean smiled his acknowledgement of Georges's support. "So at that time there were opportunities for the ambitious, especially the politcally ambitious with a good Resistance record. And Henri was ambitious. I did not blame him for that. The young have to strive for what they want. He was soon accepted into the gendarmerie and was promoted quickly, and as he got higher his objectives in life advanced. He became *politically* ambitious. He saw France's future in Gaullism and his own future in that also, so he joined the Gaullist Party." Jean gave a resigned little chuckle. "You can guess that did not please me very much, but he was grown-up and it was his choice. I asked him to think very carefully about what he might be committing himself to. But I did not oppose him. The contact between us became less as he immersed himself in his job and his politics. When he became *Préfet* of police I was proud of him even though I did not like his politics. It is inevitable, is it not, that as you get older you have to accept that your young see things in a different light? Anyway, it is not too long since Henri told me he saw his future in the government of France and wanted to stand as a Gaullist candidate in the next elections – elections which the General has now just called . . ."

"Of course. Of course." It was Tony who interrupted. "How stupid of me. The declaration of elections was the new circumstance that Walewsky told me to look for. I see it now . . ."

All eyes turned towards him. "What do you mean?"

"A friend in America with whom I discussed those events, a lawyer named Walewsky, said that while we search for clues we should also search for the circumstance that made the removal of the target photograph so deadly important *now*, after it had been in existence for more than twenty years. That circumstance must be the the calling of these elections. If Henri was aiming for political office and public recognition he had to make sure that picture of him in *Milice* uniform would never see the light of day. That's right,

Henri, eh? And . . . and that makes you responsible for the murder of our comrades."

The wretched man sat with his head bowed, nodding slowly, clenching and unclenching his fists. "Oh, how I regret it all now. How I regret it. I did not mean it to involve killing. I knew about the photo because you had shown them to me from time to time, Jean. But it was not until I was interviewed for my candidacy and was questioned about my background and responded by referring to my Resistance work with my father, who was a war hero, and then with Maquis Léon, that I recognised the danger that picture held for me. Jean had told me you all had sets of them, and I thought that if I could put the right men onto the task of stealing them . . ."

"You knew how to get such men from your time with the gendarmerie, no?"

"Exactly. I knew where to find them. I used a pseudonym, of course, and never met them personally. It seemed simple. But the men went too far. They wanted the generous fees I had offered – at all costs."

"And when we became suspicious, you had enough friends in the gendarmerie who could keep you informed of our movements."

"That's right."

"But you must have known what your hirelings were doing?"

"Not until it was too late, and I still had to have the photos. After your visit to Nevers, Captain François and Monsieur Ginger, I worried that you might see a connection between me and the photo. I had to go on . . ."

"You had to go on in spite of knowing you were killing old comrades, eh? I think your moral judgements are des-

291

picable, Henri." It was Tony, in a savage tone and with an expression of disgust on his face.

"And you did *not* have to go on, Henri." Jean's cold intervention cut through the tense atmosphere. "You could have stopped. You could have tried to extricate yourself. You could have tried to make amends. I would have helped. Did you learn nothing from your time with me in the Maquis? Always reconnoitre a line of withdrawal before you attack. I realise you grew up in an environment in which killing resolved many problems. But it is not the same in peacetime. I used to think that violent revolution was the only way to change things. Well it can, but seldom in the way you mean it to. Most revolutions are not won by the revolutionists, but by the counter-revolutionists, and the original purpose of the upheaval is then lost. What you did was a betrayal, far worse than the betrayal of your country when you were put under frightening pressure to make a choice. This betrayal was a cold-hearted one. The only thing at stake was your ego. It was a betrayal of good friends and comrades. And it was a betrayal of what I did in the Nièvre to save your reputation and the reputation of our family."

"No! No, Jean. It wasn't meant like that." Again it was a cry of anguish and despair. Shaking his head, tears in his eyes, he looked up, pleading. "I am sorry. Truly sorry, Jean – gentlemen. Believe me. Please understand. Things were going well for me. I had been successful in the gendarmerie and when I became *Préfet*. Then friends in the party urged me to aim for a career in politics. I was bitterly ashamed of having been in the *Milice* and I knew there are people who spend their time searching for signs of past collaboration. We are not free of the divisions caused by the occupation. I knew that if my time with the *Milice* was discovered my career as well as my future would be finished. I thought that the only way I could be safe would be to remove the evidence – have the photgraphs stolen. Robbery is not so bad, is it? But as I said, it went wrong. I found I could not control what was happening. Even so, since you persistently investigated those crimes, gentlemen, my career *is* finished. Isn't that enough?"

"No, Henri, it is not." Again Jean's voice was cold. "You think robbery is not so bad. But you were stealing other people's memories to expunge your own. You had no right to do that and you were on a dangerous course. And when your men killed our friends you destroyed *their* hopes and *their* futures. Those are big debts that you carry. How can you . . ."

"Jean . . . you said it would all be settled today . . ." Again the miserably expressed wish.

"So it will be. So it will be." Jean rose unsteadily from his chair and came back to the table. Leaning on his stick he drew a folded piece of paper from his pocket. "Tony, this is a list of the criminals who were hired to steal – and who murdered – in your country, and who tried to kill you in the United States. Of course, they will probably have hired others, but at least this is a beginning. Henri provided the names at my . . . er . . . my request, and he and I will take it down to the police in St-Jean, and he will confess that he gave these names to a Monsieur Devereux – the pseudonym Henri used – who had claimed to be from the Sûreté. He will say he did not trouble to check on Monsieur Devereux as he should have done, but now believes the people were engaged in criminal activities. He may be regarded as an accessory to the crimes – that is a risk – but none of the crimes actually took place in France, apart from some

293

dangerous driving – which is not yet a crime here! Of course, he will be accused of negligence and he will have to resign his candidacy and his political ambitions will be dead."

Jean then took an envelope from his pocket and handed it to Tony. "This is a copy of the list of names, and no doubt you will wish to hand it to your police in England. It may not be easy to find them, but your police are very good and I'm sure they will succeed. I only regret, sincerely, that we cannot restore Roddy Holmes to his wife and family, nor Larry Lawrence to his brother. But I hope you can accept that we are doing what we can to end these dreadful events that have left an indelible stain on our relationships, while at the same time we try to restore some pride in our family – even if you think we do not deserve it. But please be good enough to remember that my brother and I fought honourably for France, and, in common with many others, with high hopes – hopes that may yet be destroyed by political manoeuvring. And Henri, too, fought bravely with his father in Brest and with us after I rescued him from the *Milice*. You could say he failed that foul test the Boche put to him if you put patriotism above all else. Perhaps we should – many soldiers, sailors and airmen do. I wish I was sure of the answer. What I am sure about is that the collaborators who are the real traitors are those who collaborated voluntarily – and there are many still free in this country. I am also sure that Henri will find a way to atone in good measure for what he chose wrongly to do to protect himself."

He turned and looked out of the window and, almost in an aside, murmured, "I now believe that the true good name of France will not be restored by jingoistic parading and posturing, much as it pleases people, but by the individual integrity of the majority of us. But we do feel the need for heroes."

294

He moved slowly round the table. "Come, Henri, let us go down now. You can drive me in your car." He picked up the revolver and put it in his pocket. "Georges, you can bring the others in your car. Perhaps we shall be able to meet later and have a drink to ... to at least a partially successful outcome." They moved towards the door. Tony, who with the others had listened quietly to Jean's commanding handling of his personal drama and his perceptive explanations, realised they had witnessed a cameo of some of the tragic consequences of a shamed yet proud nation. He felt compelled to temper his still deep anger at the callous way Henri had instigated a train of murder and violence with a signal of sympathy for Jean's dilemma. Unconsciously reverting to his *nom de guerre*, he called to him, "Léon, we understand you. You know we shall do everything to bring these villains to justice." He waved the envelope in the air. "Thank you, and *bon chance. Bon chance.*"

Jean Boulanger paused at the door and without looking round replied, "*Merci. Merci bien.* You also. And go wisely, my friend."

They walked down to Georges's car and watched as Henri, with Jean, drove past them down the road towards the monument. They followed them as they turned left onto the twisting road by the wide valley leading down to St-Jean-Pied-de-Port. The sun, at their backs and to the west, cast a wonderful light onto the mountains: bright on the high elevations and dark in the gullies, bringing the peaks and folds into ever-changing prominence as the bends in the road altered the perspective. Tony was content to leave it to Georges to negotiate the steep gradients and the breathtaking bends, while he wondered at the majesty of the vistas as they unfolded, until Georges's cry shattered the spell: "*Nom de Dieu alors!* What is happening there?" Looking ahead he saw Henri's car swerving from side to side on the narrow road now running alongside the deep valley. The drop was on the passenger side, where Jean was sitting. "Look at them," continued Georges. "Has the steering failed?" The car was moving erratically across the road. It seemed that both Henri and Jean were fighting with the wheel. For control? Or what? Then something fell from the window and bounced a couple of times on the edge of the road before spinning over the edge.

"What the hell?" cried Ginger.

"The revolver, I think," Tony replied quickly. "Was that what they were fighting for? No. They're still fighting . . .' And with Ginger peering between them from the back shouting, "Christ Almighty, look . . ." they watched in horror as the car swerved violently across the road, hit the bank on the mountainside and, with screeching tyres, spun through ninety degrees and at sickening speed leapt straight into the void. "No! No. Please God, no . . ." they shouted pointlessly as the car seemed to hang in the air for a second before diving sickeningly, fatally, into the deep valley. Georges skidded to a halt on the other side of the road. They scrambled out and ran to the edge. But they could see nothing, and weirdly, could hear nothing. Just an uncanny silence – as if the car and its occupants had just been spirited away.

"Oh, my God . . ." said Tony with a deep sob. "What an end! Poor Jean . . ."

"Bloody hell . . . How? Why?" yelled Ginger. Georges stood staring silently down as he crossed himself.

Tony gave a despairing little laugh. "I suppose you could say that was Henri's atonement. If it was, did he choose it, while Jean tried to stop him? Or was it the other way round? Or was it an accident? I suppose we shall never know." He turned. "Come on. There's nothing we can do here."

Silently and somberly they drove down to St-Jean, stopping to report at the frontier police at Arnéguy that they had seen a car with two occupants go over the edge of the road. They replied to what they thought were surprisingly few questions, left a note of their names and addresses and drove on. In St-Jean they also reported to the police that they had seen their two friends lose control of their car and plunge into the valley not far from the Roldan monument. They were all old comrades, together for the first time in years, and they'd been on their way to St-Jean for a small celebration. Something must have gone wrong with the car, as it swerved several times before going over the edge. "Well we shall never know the cause," said the captain of the gendarmerie flatly. "The car will be in a thousand pieces – if it is ever recovered. But that and the recovery of the bodies will be the responsibility of the Spanish," he added. "We will be in touch with them." Again they left their names and addresses and agreed to submit formal statements. And they left the names and brief descriptions of Jean and Henri Boulanger.

At the hotel they ordered a bottle of wine, walked straight through to the terrace in the garden, and found a table in a corner, away from other people. There they drank a toast – several toasts – to the memory of a loved and respected comrade, before Tony read the message he had been handed as he had passed the desk. It was from Celia, exuberantly proclaiming that he was not to leave before she arrived. She wanted to be there for 'the dénouement', and she wanted to enjoy the beauty of the Pyrénées. She would arrive 'tomorrow', but failed to say when tomorrow was! Tony smiled. She had missed the dénouement, which had turned out to be dramatically sad rather than thrilling. Partners though they might now be, it was as well she had not arrived yet. It would be hard for her to share the depth of their trauma, bearing in mind all that had gone before. For now he wanted to be alone with his remaining comrades. Later he would be glad of her company – and comfort.

It was after they had finished the second bottle of wine, during the drinking of which they had recalled personal memories of Jean the gallant and private patriot, that Tony, more from idle curiosity than premeditation, took from his pocket the envelope Jean had given him. Inside with the promised list of names was a handwritten letter. He read as the others talked. Then he looked up, stared away from the table, swallowed hard a couple of times, and cut into their conversation with a steely voiced, "We do know why and how. Listen to this: 'Dear friends and old comrades, tomorrow you will arrive to ask me if I can explain the crimes done to you, and the unforgivable murder of our dear comrades on account of a photograph taken during our operations against the enemy over twenty years ago.

'At first I was puzzled, but after your telephone call, Tony, I realised the ghastly truth – that Henri was responsible. Often in my lonely years here I have put those pictures on the table and relived some of those times – thinking of the things we did well and those we could have done better. But when I looked at that one photo that revealed Henri's disgrace, my heart was filled with a sadness that always made me weep, and filled me with dread that some day, somehow, it would get to the attention of the public or the authorities and Henri would be ruined, our good name besmirched, and our good deeds ignored. Henri has misguidedly brought trouble onto himself and me, and has unforgivably destroyed friends and devastated their families.

'Tomorrow I shall endeavour to explain how it all came

bout, and when you read this you will have heard me. I hope you will then understand better the cruel choice the very young, very frightened Henri had to make, and perhaps you will not be too hard on his memory. Try to understand him even if you cannot forgive him.

'Also, when you read this you will know that we have chosen what I hope will be seen by you and our other comrades as an honourable atonement. Drink to us, Tony, who have, *enfin*, tried to keep the faith. *Bon santé et au revoir.*'

"He planned it," said Tony quietly. "He said 'we have chosen' but to judge from the struggle in the car it was his decision. What a sacrifice to make – partly to atone and partly to save the honour of his family name. He said we should drink to 'something of a successful outcome', but I think it should be to gallantry of a special kind. Let's hope that that *is* successful."

Next morning the news of a tragic accident in the Pyrénées was on the front pages of the regional newspapers. Under the headline, '*Deux Héros de la Résistance Morts*', Tony read,

Le chef d'un maquis de la deuxième guerre mondiale, et son neveu un soldat dans la même groupe, ont été tués hier dans les Pyrénées, quand leur voiture a plongé 700 metres au fond d'un abîme. Monsieur Jean Boulanger, "Capitaine Léon" dans le maquis de Nièvre, et Monsieur Henri Boulanger, autrefois un Préfet de police, ont été membres d'une famille des patriotes Français. Le frère de M. Jean Boulanger, membre de la Résistance de Brest, était tué par la gestapo en '44 . . .

Tony was sitting on the terrace, a pot of cold coffee and a half-eaten croissant on the table in front of him. The crumpled pages of the paper were at his feet, where they

299

had dropped from his hands. His eyes stared vacantly into the distance. It was from that distant, timeless somewhere that he heard his name being called.

"Tony! Tony, darling!"

He came back to the present, and turning his head he saw the beautiful, elegant Celia waving as she hurried, smiling happily, towards him. As soon as he saw her he realised she was the balm, the understanding, loving presence he now needed.

"Cels! What a lovely surprise! I didn't know when 'tomorrow' would be."

"Eh? Oh, didn't I say in my message? Never mind. I'm here now. Are you all right?"

"Yes, I'm fine – now."

As they embraced and their lips met, a warmth of feeling – relief from drama, pleasure at meeting – flowed between them.

"Mmm. I care for that." As she looked around he realised she was unaware of the dramatic events of the last twenty-four hours.

"Tony, isn't this a lovely place?"

"No, Cels, it isn't. It's a sad and ghostly place." He took her hand. "Let's walk and I'll tell you all about it." Together they strolled towards the garden.

STUDIES
THE SERM
ON THE MOUNT

CW00685827

by

D. MARTYN LLOYD JONES

VOLUME ONE

ISBN: 979-8-89096-145-7

Printed: June 2023

Published and Distributed By:
Lushena Books
607 Country Club Drive, Unit E
Bensenville, IL 60106
www.lushenabks.com

ISBN: 979-8-89096-145-7

CONTENTS

Volume One: Matthew v. 1-48

PREFACE

THIS volume consists of thirty sermons preached for the most part on successive Sunday mornings in the course of my regular ministry at Westminster Chapel. It is being published for one reason only, namely, that I can no longer resist the pressure brought to bear on me by large numbers of people, some of whom heard the sermons when delivered and others who have read some of them in our church magazine. Such readers will need no word of explanation as to the form in which these sermons are published, but it may well be necessary in the case of others.

These chapters are reports of sermons taken down in shorthand (no tape-recording machine being available at that time). They have been subjected to a minimum amount of correction and alteration, and no attempt has been made to conceal, still less to expunge, the sermonic form. This has been quite deliberate and for several reasons.

I am profoundly convinced that the greatest need of the Church today is a return to expository preaching. I would emphasize both words and especially the latter. A sermon is not an essay and is not meant, primarily, for publication, but to be heard and to have an immediate impact upon the listeners. This implies, of necessity, that it will have certain characteristics which are not found and are not desirable in written studies. To prune it of these, if it should be subsequently published, seems to me to be quite wrong, for it then ceases to be a sermon and becomes something quite nondescript. I have a suspicion that what accounts for the dearth of preaching at the present time is the fact that the majority of printed books of sermons have clearly been prepared for a reading rather than a listening public. Their flavour and form are literary rather than sermonic.

Another characteristic of expository preaching is that it is not merely an exposition of a verse or passage, or a running commentary on it; what turns it into preaching is that it becomes a message and that it has a distinct form and pattern.

Furthermore, it must always be applied and its relevance shown to the contemporary situation.

I am constantly being asked to give lectures on expository preaching. I rarely accede to such requests, believing that the best way of doing this is to give examples of such preaching in actual practice. It is my hope that this volume with its many faults may help somewhat in that respect, but it could not possibly have done so if drastic excisions, and an attempt to produce a literary form, had been made.

Here they are then' warts and all'. Those who are not interested in exposition, and those who have no taste for preaching as such, will probably be irritated by stylistic blemishes, `the art of repetition' for the sake of emphasis, and what are termed `pulpit mannerisms' (as if they were worse than any other kind of mannerism!). All I ask is that they be read and considered for what they are and for what they set out to do.

My greatest hope and desire is that they may in some small way stimulate a new interest in expository preaching. It may encourage preachers to know that such sermons, lasting on an average forty minutes on Sunday mornings, can be preached in what is called a `down-town church' even in these days.

The two people who are most responsible for the appearance of the volume in print are Mrs. F. Hutchings who, almost miraculously, was able to take down the sermons in shorthand as they were delivered, and my daughter, Elizabeth Catherwood. Like many of my fellow preachers I acknowledge that my best and severest critic is my wife.

D. M. LLOYD JONES

Westminster Chapel,
Buckingham Gate,
London, S.W.1.

March, 1959

CHAPTER ONE

GENERAL INTRODUCTION

I-T is a wise rule in the examination of any teaching to proceed from the general to the particular. This is the only way of -avoiding the danger of `missing the wood because of the trees'. This rule is of particular importance in connection with the Sermon on the Mount. We must realize, therefore, that at the outset certain general questions have to be asked about this famous Sermon and its place in the life, thought and outlook of Christian people.

The obvious question with which to start is this: Why should we consider the Sermon on the Mount at all? Why should I call your attention to it and to its teaching? Well, I do not know that it is a part of the business of a preacher to explain the processes of his own mind and his own heart, but clearly no man should preach unless he has felt that God has given him a message. It is the business of any man who tries to preach and expound the Scriptures to wait upon God for leading and guidance. I suppose fundamentally, therefore, my main reason for preaching on the Sermon on the Mount was that I had felt this persuasion, this compulsion, this leading of the Spirit. I say that deliberately, because if I had been left to my own choice I would not have chosen to preach a series of sermons on the Sermon on the Mount. And as I understand this sense of compulsion, I feel the particular reason for doing so is the peculiar condition of the life of the Christian Church in general at the present time.

I do not think it is a harsh judgment to say that the most obvious feature of the life of the Christian Church today is, alas, its superficiality. That judgment is based not only on contemporary observation, but still more on contemporary observation in the light of previous epochs and eras in the life of the Church. There is nothing that is more salutary to the Christian life than to read the history of the Church, to read again of the great movements of God's Spirit, and to observe what has happened in the

Church at various times. Now I think that anyone who looks at the present state of the Christian Church in the light of that background will be driven to the reluctant conclusion that the outstanding characteristic of the life of the Church today is, as I have said, its superficiality. When I say that, I am thinking not only of the life and activity of the Church in an evangelistic sense. In that particular respect I think everybody would agree that superficiality is the most obvious characteristic. But I am thinking not only of modern evangelistic activities as compared and contrasted with the great evangelistic efforts of the Church in the past-the present-day tendency to boisterousness, for example, and the use of means which would have horrified and shocked our fathers; but I also have in mind the life of the Church in general where the same thing is true, even in such matters as her conception of holiness and her whole approach to the doctrine of sanctification.

The important thing for us is to discover the causes of this. For myself I would suggest that one main cause is our attitude to the Bible, our failure to take it seriously, our failure to take it as it is and to allow it to speak to us. Coupled with that, perhaps, is our invariable tendency to go from one extreme to the other. But the main thing, I feel, is our attitude towards the Scriptures. Let me explain in a little more detail what I mean by that.

There is nothing more important in the Christian life than the way in which we approach the Bible, and the way in which we read it. It is our textbook, it is our only source, it is our only authority. We know nothing about God and about the Christian life in a true sense apart from the Bible. We can draw various deductions from nature (and possibly from various mystical experiences) by which we can arrive at a belief in a supreme Creator. But I think it is agreed by most Christians, and it has been traditional throughout the long history of the Church, that we have no authority save this Book. We cannot rely solely upon subjective experiences because there are evil spirits as well as good spirits; there are counterfeit experiences. Here, in the Bible, is our sole authority.

Very well; it is obviously important that we should approach this Book in the right manner. We must start by agreeing that merely to read the

Bible is not enough in and of itself. It is possible for us to read the Bible in such a mechanical manner that we derive no benefit from doing so. That is why I think we have to be careful with every kind of rule and regulation in the matter of discipline in the spiritual life. It is a good thing to read the Bible daily, but it can be quite profitless if we merely do so for the sake of being able to say we read the Bible daily. I am a great advocate of schemes of Bible reading, but we have to be careful that in our use of such schemes we are not content just to read the portion for the day and then to rush off without thought and meditation. That can be quite profitless. Our approach to the Bible is something which is of vital importance.

Now the Bible itself tells us this. You remember the apostle Peter's famous remark with regard to the writings of the apostle Paul. He says that there are things in them which are 'hard to be understood, which they that are unlearned and unstable wrest . . . unto their own destruction'. What he means is this. They read these Epistles of Paul, yes; but they are twisting them, they are wresting them to their own destruction. You can easily read these Epistles and be no wiser at the end than you were at the beginning because of what you have been reading into what Paul says, wresting them to your own destruction. Now that is something which we must always bear in mind with regard to the whole of the Bible. I can be seated with the Bible in front of me; I can be reading its words and going through its chapters; and yet I may be drawing a conclusion which is quite false to the pages in front of me.

There can be no doubt at all that the commonest cause of all this is our tendency so often to approach the Bible with a theory. We go to our Bibles with this theory, and everything we read is controlled by it. Now we are all quite familiar with that. There is a sense in which it is true to say that you can prove anything you like from the Bible. That is how heresies have arisen. The heretics were never dishonest men; they were mistaken men. They should not be thought of as men who were deliberately setting out to go wrong and to teach something that is wrong; they have been some of the most sincere men that the Church has ever known. What was the matter with them? Their trouble was this: they evolved a theory and they were rather pleased with it; then they went back with this theory to the Bible, and they seemed to find it everywhere. If you read half a verse and emphasize over-much some other half verse elsewhere, your theory is soon proved. Now obviously this is something of which we have to be very wary. There is nothing so dangerous as to come to the Bible with a theory, with preconceived ideas, with some pet idea of our own, because the moment we do so, we shall be tempted to overemphasize one aspect and under-emphasize another.

Now this particular danger tends chiefly to manifest itself in the matter of the relationship between law and grace. That has always been true in the Church from the very beginning and it is still true today. Some so emphasize the law as to turn the gospel of Jesus Christ with its glorious liberty into nothing but a collection of moral maxims. It is all law to them and there is no grace left. They so talk of the Christian life as something that we have to do in order to make ourselves Christian, that it becomes pure legalism and there is really no grace in it. But let us remember also that it is equally possible so to overemphasize grace at the expense of law as, again, to have something which is not the gospel of the New Testament.

Let me give you a classical illustration of that. The apostle Paul, of all men, constantly had to be facing this difficulty. There was never a man whose preaching, with its mighty emphasis upon grace, was so frequently misunderstood. You remember the deduction some people had been drawing in Rome and in other places. They said, `Now then, in view of the teaching of this man Paul, let us do evil that grace may abound, for, surely, this teaching is something that leads to that conclusion and to no other. Paul has just been saying, "Where sin abounded grace did much more abound"; very well, let us continue in sin that more and more grace may abound.' `God forbid', says Paul; and he is constantly having to say that. To say that because we are under grace we therefore have nothing at all to do with law and can forget it, is not the teaching of the Scriptures. We certainly are no longer under the law but are under grace. Yet that does not mean that we need not keep the law. We are not under the law in the sense that it condemns us; it no longer pronounces judgment or condemnation on us. No ! but we are meant to live it, and we are even meant to go beyond it. The argument of the apostle Paul is that I should live, not as a man who is under the law, but as Christ's free man. Christ kept the law, He lived the law; as this very Sermon on the Mount emphasizes, our righteousness must exceed that of the scribes and Pharisees. Indeed, He has not come to abolish the law; every jot and tittle has to be fulfilled and perfected. Now that is something which we very frequently find forgotten in this attempt to put up law and grace as antitheses, and the result is that men and women often completely and entirely ignore the law.

But let me put it in this way. Is it not true to say of many of us that in actual practice our view of the doctrine of grace is such that we scarcely ever take the plain teaching of the Lord Jesus Christ seriously? We have so emphasized the teaching that all is of grace and that we ought not to try to imitate His example in order to make ourselves Christians, that we are virtually in the position of ignoring His teaching altogether and of saying that it has nothing to do with us because we are under grace. Now I wonder how seriously we take the gospel of our Lord and Saviour Jesus Christ. The best way of concentrating on that question is, I think, to face the Sermon on the Mount. What is our view, I wonder, of this Sermon? Supposing that at this point I suggested that we should all write down on paper our answers to the following questions: What does the Sermon on the Mount mean to us? Where does it come in our lives and what is its place in our thinking and outlook? What is our relationship to this extraordinary Sermon that has such a prominent position in these three chapters in the Gospel according to St. Matthew? I think you would find the result would be very interesting and perhaps very surprising. Oh, yes, we know all about the doctrine of grace and forgiveness, and we are looking to Christ. But here in these documents, which we claim to be authoritative, is this Sermon. Where does it come in our scheme?

Now that is what I mean by background and introduction. However, let us take it a step further, by facing together another vital question. For whom is the Sermon on the Mount intended? To whom does it apply? What is really the purpose of this Sermon; what is its relevance? Now, here, there have been a number of conflicting opinions. There was once the so-called `social gospel' view of the Sermon on the Mount. What it comes to is this, that the Sermon is in reality the only thing that matters in the New Testament, that there, in it, is the basis of the socalled social gospel. The principles, it was said, were there laid down as to how life should be lived by men, and all we have to do is to apply the Sermon on the Mount. We can thereby produce the kingdom of God on earth, war will be banished and all our troubles will be ended. That is the typical social gospel view, but we do not need to waste time with it. It has already become out-moded; it is to be found only amongst certain people whom I can describe as remnants and relics of the mentality of thirty years ago. The two world wars have shaken that view to its very foundation. Critical as we may be in many respects of the Barthian movement in theology, let us pay it this tribute: it has once and for ever made the social gospel look utterly ridiculous. But of course the real answer to this view of the Sermon on the Mount is that it has always ignored the Beatitudes, those statements with which the Sermon begins- 'Blessed are the poor in spirit'; `Blessed are they that mourn.' As I hope to show you, these statements mean that no man can live the Sermon on the Mount in and of himself, and unaided. The advocates of the social gospel, having conveniently ignored the Beatitudes, have then rushed on to a consideration of the detailed injunctions, and have said, `This is the gospel.'

Another view, which is perhaps a little more serious for us, is that which regards the Sermon on the Mount as nothing but an elaboration or an exposition of the Mosaic law. Our Lord, it is maintained, realized that the Pharisees and scribes and other teachers of the people were misinterpreting the law, as given by God to the people through Moses; what He does, therefore, in the Sermon on the Mount is to elaborate and expound the Mosaic law, giving it a higher spiritual content. That is a more serious view, obviously; and yet I feel it is totally inadequate if for no other reason than that it, also, fails to take account of the Beatitudes. The Beatitudes immediately take us into a realm that is beyond the law of Moses completely. The Sermon on the Mount does expound and explain the law at certain points-but it goes beyond it.

Then the next view I want to mention is what we may call the 'dispensational' view of the Sermon on the Mount. Probably many of you are familiar with it. It has been popularized in certain 'Bibles'. (I never like these adjectives; there is only one Bible, but we unfortunately tend to talk about 'So-and-so's Bible'.) There are, then, certain teachings which have been made popular in this way, and which teach a dispensational view of the Sermon on the Mount, saying that it has nothing whatsoever to do with modern Christians. They say our Lord began to preach about the kingdom of God, and the preaching of the Sermon on the Mount was in connection with the inauguration of this kingdom. Unfortunately, they continue, the Jews did not believe His teaching. So our Lord could not establish the kingdom, and therefore, almost as a kind of afterthought, the death on the cross came in, and as another afterthought the whole Church and the whole Church age came in, and that will persist up to a certain point in history. Then our Lord will return with the kingdom and again the Sermon on the Mount will be introduced. That is the teaching; it says, in effect, that the Sermon on the Mount has nothing to do with us. It is meant 'for the kingdom age'. It was meant for the people to whom He was preaching; it will be meant again in the millennial age. It is the law of that age and of the kingdom of heaven, and has nothing whatsoever to do with Christians in the meantime.

Now obviously this is a serious matter for us. This view is right or else it is not. According to this view I need not read the Sermon on the Mount; I need not be concerned about its precepts; I need not feel condemned because I am not doing certain things; it has no relevance for me. It seems to me that the answer to all that can be put like this. The Sermon on the Mount was preached primarily and specifically to the disciples. 'When he was set, his disciples came unto him: and he opened his mouth, and taught them, saying. . .' Now the whole presupposition is that it is preached to them. Take, for instance, the words which He spoke to them when He said, We are the salt of the earth'; 'Ye are the light of the world.' If the Sermon on the Mount has nothing to do with Christian people now, we must never say that we are the salt of the earth, or that we are the light of the world, for that does not apply to us. It applied to the first disciples; it will apply to some people later on. But, in the meantime, it has nothing to do with us. We must likewise ignore the gracious promises in this Sermon. We must not say that we must let our light so shine before men that they may see our good works and glorify our Father which is in heaven. If the whole Sermon on the Mount is inapplicable to modern Christians, all that is irrelevant. But clearly our Lord was preaching to these men and telling them what they were to do in this world, not only while He was here, but after He had gone. It was preached to people who were meant to practise it at that time and ever afterwards.

Not only that. To me another very important consideration is that there is no teaching to be found in the Sermon on the Mount which is not also found in the various New Testament Epistles. Make a list of the teachings of the Sermon on the Mount; then read your Epistles. You will find that the teaching of the Sermon on the Mount is there also. Now all the Epistles are meant for Christians today; so if their teaching is the same as that of the Sermon on the Mount, clearly its teaching also is meant for Christians today. That is a weighty and important argument. But perhaps I can put it best like this. The Sermon on the Mount is nothing but a great and grand and perfect elaboration of what our Lord called His `new commandment'. His new commandment was that we love one another even as He has loved us. The Sermon on the Mount is nothing but a grand elaboration of that. If we are Christ's, and our Lord has meant that word for us, that we should love one another even as He loved us, here we are shown how to do it.

The dispensational view is based on a wrong conception of the kingdom of God. This is where the confusion arises. I agree, of course, that the kingdom of God in one sense has not been established on the earth yet. It is a kingdom which is to come; yes. But it is also a kingdom which has come. `The kingdom of God is among you', and `within you'; the kingdom of God is in every true Christian, and in the Church. It means `the reign of God', `the reign of Christ'; and Christ is reigning today in every true Christian. He reigns in the Church when she acknowledges Him truly. The kingdom has come, the kingdom is coming, the kingdom is yet to come. Now we must always bear that in mind. Whenever Christ is enthroned as King, the kingdom of God is come, so that, while we cannot say that He is ruling over all in the world at the present time, He is certainly ruling in that way in the hearts and lives of all His people.

There is nothing, therefore, so dangerous as to say that the Sermon on the Mount has nothing to do with modern Christians. Indeed, I will put it like this: it is something which is meant for all Christian people. It is a perfect picture of the life of the kingdom of God. Now I have no doubt at all in my own mind that that is why Matthew put it in his Gospel at the beginning. It is agreed that Matthew was writing his Gospel especially for the Jews. That was his set desire. Hence all this emphasis upon the kingdom of heaven. And what was Matthew out to emphasize? Surely it was this. The Jews had a false, materialistic conception of the kingdom. They thought the Messiah was one who was coming to give them political emancipation. They were looking forward to someone who would deliver them from the bondage and yoke of the Roman Empire. They always thought of the kingdom in an external sense, a mechanical, military, materialistic sense. So Matthew puts the true teaching concerning the kingdom in the very forefront of his Gospel, for the great purpose of this Sermon is to give an exposition of the kingdom as something which is essentially spiritual. The kingdom is primarily something `within you'. It is that which governs and controls the heart and mind and outlook. Far from being something which leads to great military power, it is to be `poor in spirit'. In other words, we are not told in the Sermon on the Mount, `Live like this and you will become Christian'; rather we are told, `Because you are Christian live like this.' This is how Christians ought to live; this is how Christians are meant to live.

But to complete this part of our argument we must face another difficulty. Some say, `Surely the Sermon on the Mount teaches that we have our sins forgiven only if we forgive others? Doesn't our Lord say, "If ye forgive not men their trespasses, neither will your Father forgive your trespasses"? Is not that law? Where is grace there? To be told that if we do not forgive, we shall not be forgiven, is not grace.' Thus they seem to be able to prove that the Sermon on the Mount does not apply to us. But if you say that, you will have to take almost the whole of Christianity out of the gospel. Remember also that our Lord taught exactly the same thing in His parable, recorded at the end of Matthew xviii, of the steward who committed an offence against his master. This man went to his master and pleaded with him to forgive him; and his master forgave him. But he refused to forgive an underling who was likewise in debt to him, with the result that his master withdrew his forgiveness and punished him. Our Lord comments on this: `So likewise shall my heavenly Father do also unto you, if ye from your hearts forgive not every one his brother their trespasses.' That is exactly the same teaching. But does it teach that I am forgiven only because I have forgiven? No, the teaching is, and we have to take this teaching seriously, that if I do not forgive, I am not forgiven. I explain it like this: the man who has seen himself as a guilty, vile sinner before God knows his only hope of heaven is that God has forgiven him freely. The man who truly sees and knows and believes that, is one who cannot refuse to forgive another. So the man who does not forgive another does not know forgiveness himself. If my heart has been broken in the presence of God I cannot refuse to forgive; and, therefore, I say to any man who is imagining fondly that his sins are to be forgiven by Christ, though he does not forgive anybody else, Beware, my friend, lest you wake up in eternity and find Him saying to you, `Depart from me; I never knew you.' You are misinterpreting the doctrine, the glorious doctrine of the grace of God. The man who is truly forgiven and knows it, is a man who forgives. That is the meaning of the Sermon on the Mount at this point.

We shall be going into this in detail later. Here let me just put one last question. Having considered the people to whom the Sermon on the Mount applies, let us ask ourselves this: Why should we study it? Why should we try to live it? Let me give you a list of answers. The Lord Jesus Christ died to enable us to live the Sermon on the Mount. He died. Why? `That he might ... purify unto himself a peculiar people, zealous of good works,' says the apostle Paul-the apostle of grace (see Tit. ii. 14). What does he mean? He means that He died in order that I might now live the Sermon on the Mount. He has made this possible for me.

The second reason for studying it is that nothing shows me the absolute need of the new birth, and of the Holy Spirit and His work within, so much as the Sermon on the Mount. These Beatitudes crush me to the ground. They show me my utter helplessness. Were it not for the new birth, I am undone. Read and study it, face yourself in the light of it. It will drive you to see your ultimate need of the rebirth and the gracious operation of the Holy Spirit. There is nothing that so leads to the gospel and its grace as the Sermon on the Mount.

v Another reason is this. The more we live and try to practise this Sermon on the Mount, the more shall we experience blessing. Look at the blessings that are promised to those who do practise it. The trouble with much holiness teaching is that it leaves out the Sermon on the Mount, and asks us to experience sanctification. That is not the biblical method. If you want to have power in your life and to be blessed, go straight to the Sermon on the Mount. Live and practise it and give yourself to it, and as you do so the promised blessings will come. `Blessed are they which do hunger and thirst after righteousness: for they shall be filled.' If you want to be filled, don't seek some mystic blessing; don't rush to meetings hoping you will get it. Face the Sermon on the Mount and its implications and demands, see your utter need, and then you will get it. It is the direct road to blessing.

But this is what I want to leave in your minds. I suggest to you it is the best means of evangelism. Surely we all ought to be urgently concerned about this at the present time. The world today is looking for, and desperately needs, true Christians. I am never tired of saying that what the Church needs to do is not to organize evangelistic campaigns to attract outside people, but to begin herself to live the Christian life. If she did that, men and women would be crowding into our buildings. They would say, `What is the secret of this?' Almost every day we read that the real secret of communism at the present time is that it seems to be doing something and giving people something. I am told repeatedly, as I talk to young people and read books, that communism is conquering as it is in the modern world because people feel that its adherents are doing things and are sacrificing for what they believe. That is how they are gaining their members. Now there is only one way to counter that, and that is to show we have something infinitely bigger and greater. It has been my privilege to meet comparatively recently more than one person converted from communism, and in each case it has not been as a result of some intellectual sermon or argument but as the result of this communist seeing in some simple Christian a more thorough-going practice of self-abnegation and concern for others than he or she had ever thought of.

Let me enforce this by quoting something I read some time ago. A one-time Law Minister in the Indian Government was a great man called Dr. Ambedkar, an out-caste himself and a leader of the out-castes in India. At the time of which I am speaking he was taking a great interest in the teachings of Buddhism, and attended a great Conference of twenty-seven countries in Ceylon which had met together to inaugurate a world fellowship of Buddhists. He gave as his chief reason for attending the Conference, his desire to discover to what extent the religion of Buddha was a live thing. He said at the Conference, `I am here to find out to what extent there is dynamic in the Buddhist religion as far as the people of this country are concerned.' There was the leader of the out-castes turning to Buddhism, and examining it. He said, `I want to find if it is alive. Has it something to give to these masses of my fellow out-castes? Has it dynamic in it? Is it something that can uplift people?' But the real tragedy about this able, learned man is that he had already spent much time in America and Great Britain studying Christianity. And it was because he had found it was not a live thing, because he had found an absence of dynamic in it, that he was now turning to Buddhism. Though he had not accepted Buddhism, yet he was seeking to find whether this was the power he was looking for. That is the challenge that comes to you and to me. We know Buddhism is not the answer. We claim to believe that the Son of God has come into the world and has sent His own Holy Spirit into us, His own absolute power that will reside in men and make them live a quality of life like His own. He came, I say, and lived and died and rose again and sent the Holy Spirit in order that you and I might live the Sermon on the Mount.

Do not say it has nothing to do with us. Why, it has everything to do with us! If only all of us were living the Sermon on the Mount, men would know that there is dynamic in the Christian gospel; they would know that this is a live thing; they would not go looking for anything else. They would say, `Here it is.' And if you read the history of the Church you will find it has always been when men and women have taken this Sermon seriously and faced themselves in the light of it, that true revival has come. And when the world sees the truly Christian man, it not only feels condemned, it is drawn, it is attracted. Then let us carefully study this Sermon that claims to show what we ought to be. Let us consider it that we may see what we can be. For it not only states the demand; it points to the supply, to the source of power. God give us grace to face the Sermon on the Mount seriously and honestly and prayerfully until we become living examples of it, and exemplifiers of its glorious teaching.

CHAPTER TWO

GENERAL VIEW AND ANALYSIS

I_N the last chapter we considered the background and introduction to the Sermon on the Mount. Although I want to -advance from that now, we must again consider it as a whole before we come to its details and to its specific statements. It seems to me to be a very good thing indeed, and a very vital thing, to do this. I do not mean by that, that I am about to embark on a study of what we may call the technicalities. Learned authorities are very fond of discussing, for example, whether the Sermon on the Mount as recorded in Matthew v, vi and vii is identical with that which is recorded in Luke vi. Many of you are probably familiar with all the arguments about that. For myself I am frankly not very concerned: indeed, I do not hesitate to say, I am not very interested. I am not decrying the value of a careful discussion and study of the Scriptures in that way; but I do feel constantly the need to warn myself and everybody else against becoming so immersed in the mechanics of Scripture that we miss its message. While we should be concerned about the harmony of the Gospels and similar problems, God forbid, I say, that we should regard the four Gospels as some kind of intellectual puzzle. The Gospels are not here for us to try to draw out our perfect schemes and classifications; they are here for us to read in order that we may apply them, that we may live them and practise them.

l I do not intend, therefore, to spend time considering such technical questions. There have been various classifications and subdivisions of the Sermon as recorded in these three chapters; there has been much argument and disputation on this kind of question-how many Beatitudes are there, seven, eight or nine? Others can spend their time on such problems if they like, but it seems to me that the important thing is not the numericals, as it were, but that we face the Beatitudes themselves. Thus I trust I shall not disappoint anyone who is interested in that kind of study.

I can never forget, in this connection, a man who, whenever I met him, always impressed upon me the fact that he was a great Bible student. 1 suppose in one sense he was, but his life was unfortunately very far removed from that which one finds described in the pages of the New Testament. Yet Bible study was his hobby and that is the thing of which I am afraid. You can be a Bible student in that mechanical sense. As people spend their time in analysing Shakespeare, so some people spend their time in analysing the Scriptures. An analysis of Scripture is all right as long as it is in a very subordinate position, and as long as we are careful it does not so grip us, that we become interested only in an objective, intellectual sense. It is a unique Word, and it must not be approached just as any other book is approached. I do increasingly understand those Fathers and saints of the Church in the past who used to say that we should never read the Bible except on our knees. We need this constant reminder as we approach the Word of God, that it is indeed and in truth the Word of God speaking directly to us.

The reason, then, why I believe it is important for us to take the Sermon as a whole before we come to the details, is this constant danger of `missing the wood because of the trees'. We are all of us ready to fix on certain particular statements, and to concentrate on them at the expense of others. The way to correct that tendency, I believe, is to realize that no part of this Sermon can be understood truly except in the light of the whole. Some good friends have already said to me, `I am going to be most interested when you come to state exactly what is meant by "Give to him that asketh thee" ', etc. That is a betrayal of a false attitude to the Sermon on the Mount. They have jumped to particular statements. There is a great danger at this point. The Sermon on the Mount, if I may use such a comparison, is like a great musical composition, a symphony if you like. Now the whole is greater than a collection of the parts, and we must never lose sight of this wholeness. I do not hesitate to say that, unless we have understood and grasped the Sermon on the Mount as a whole, we cannot understand properly any one of its particular injunctions. I mean that it is idle and useless and quite futile to confront anybody with any particular injunction in the Sermon on the Mount unless such a person has already believed, and accepted, and has indeed already conformed to, and is living, the Beatitudes.

That is where the so-called `social application of the Sermon on the Mount to modern needs' idea is such a complete fallacy and such a heresy. People have often applied it in this way. For example, they will select this matter of `turning the other cheek'. They take that out of the Sermon and isolate it, and, on the basis of that, they have denounced all forms of war as being unchristian. I do not want to discuss the question of pacifism now; all I am concerned to show is this, that you cannot take that particular injunction and hold it up to an individual, or to a nation, or to the world, unless that particular individual, or that particular nation, or the whole world is already living and practising and conforming to the Beatitudes. All the particular injunctions which we shall consider follow the Beatitudes with which the Sermon starts. That is what I mean when I say that we must start by a kind of synoptic, general view of the whole before we even begin to consider the particular parts. In other words, everything in this Sermon, if we treat it rightly, and if we are to derive benefit from considering it, must be taken in its setting; and, as I have just been emphasizing, the order in which the statements come in the Sermon is really of supreme importance. The Beatitudes do not come at the end, they come at the beginning, and I do not hesitate to say that unless we are perfectly clear about them we should go no further. We have no right to go further.

There is a kind of logical sequence in this Sermon. Not only that, there is certainly a spiritual order and sequence. Our Lord does not say these things accidentally; the whole thing is deliberate. Certain postulates are laid down, and on the basis of those, certain other things follow. Thus I never discuss any particular injunction of the Sermon with a person until I am perfectly happy and clear in my mind that that person is a Christian. It is wrong to ask anybody who is not first a Christian to try to live or practise the Sermon on the Mount. To expect Christian conduct from a person who is not born again is heresy. The appeals of the gospel in terms of conduct and ethics and morality are always based on the assumption that the people to whom the injunctions are addressed are Christian.

Now that is obvious in any one of the Epistles, and it is equally obvious here. Take any Epistle you like. You will find that the sub-division in each one of them is the same; always doctrine first, then deductions from doctrine. The great principles are laid down and a description is given of the Christians to whom the letter is written. Then, because of that, or because they believe that, `therefore' they are exhorted to do certain things. We always tend to forget that every New Testament letter was written to Christians and not to non Christians; and the appeals in terms of ethics in every Epistle are always addressed only to those who are believers, to those who are new men and women in Christ Jesus. This Sermon on the Mount is exactly the same.

Very well; let us try to give a kind of general division of the contents of the Sermon on the Mount. Here again you will find it is almost true to say that every man has his own classification and sub-division. In a sense, why shouldn't he? There is nothing more futile than to ask, `What is the correct sub-division and classification of the contents of this Sermon?' There are various ways in which it can be sub-divided. The one that commends itself to me is as follows. I would divide the Sermon up into general and particular. The general part of the Sermon occupies v. 3 to v. 16. There you have certain broad statements with regard to the Christian. Then the remainder of the Sermon is concerned with particular aspects of his life and conduct. First the general theme, and then an illustration of this theme in particular.

But we can sub-divide it a little further for the sake of convenience. In V. 3-10 you have the character of the Christian described in and of itself. That is, more or less, the Beatitudes which are a description of the character of the Christian in general. Then v. i i, 12, I would say, show us the character of the Christian as proved by the reaction of the world to him. We are told, `Blessed are ye, when men shall revile you, and persecute you, and shall say all manner of evil against you falsely, for my sake. Rejoice, and be exceeding glad: for great is your reward in heaven: for so persecuted they the prophets which were before you.' In other words, the character of the Christian is described positively and negatively. First we see the sort of man he is, and then we are told, because he is that, certain things happen to him. Yet it is still a general description. Then, obviously, v. 13-16 is an account of the relationship of the Christian to the world, or, if you prefer it, these verses are descriptive of the function of the Christian in society and in the world, and these descriptions of him are emphasized and elaborated, and then are summed up, as it were, in exhortation: `Let your light so shine before men, that they may see your good works, and glorify your Father which is in heaven.'

There, then, is a general account of the Christian. From there on, I suggest, we come to what I may call the particular examples and illustrations of how such a man lives in a world like this. Here we can sub-divide like this. In v. 17-48 we have the Christian facing the law of God and its demands. You will remember the various sub-divisions. A general description of his righteousness is given. Then we are told of his relationship towards such matters as murder, adultery and divorce; then how he should speak and then his position with regard to the whole question of retaliation and self-defence, and his attitude towards his neighbour. The principle involved is that the Christian is primarily concerned about the spirit rather than the letter. This does not mean that he ignores the letter, but he is more concerned about the spirit. The whole error of the Pharisees and the scribes was that they were interested only in the mechanical. The Christian view of the law is one that is concerned about the spirit, and is interested in the details only as they are an expression of the spirit. That is worked out in terms of a number of particular examples and illustrations.

The whole of chapter vi, I suggest,' relates to the Christian as living his life in the presence of God, in active submission to Him, and in entire dependence upon Him. If you read chapter vi at your leisure I think you will come to that conclusion. It is all along concerned about the Christian in his relationship to the Father. Take, for instance, the first verse: `Take heed that ye do not your alms before men, to be seen of them: otherwise ye have no reward of your Father which is in heaven.' It continues like that from beginning to end, and at the end we are told practically the same thing. `Therefore take no thought, saying, What shall we eat? . . . or,

Wherewithal shall we be clothed? (for after all these things do the Gentiles seek:) for your heavenly Father knoweth that ye have need of all these things. But seek ye first the kingdom of God, and his righteousness; and all these things shall be added unto you.' There, I say, is a description of the Christian as a man who knows he is always in the presence of God, so that what he is interested in is not the impression he makes on other men, but his relationship to God. Thus, when he prays, he is not interested in what other people are thinking, whether they are praising his prayers or criticizing them; he knows he is in the presence of the Father, and he is praying to God. Also, when he does his alms, it is God he has in mind all along. Furthermore, as he meets problems in life, his need of food and clothing, his reaction to external events, all are viewed in the light of this relationship which he bears to the Father. This is a very important principle with regard to the Christian life.

Then chapter vii can be regarded in general as an account of the Christian as one who lives always under the judgment of God, and in the fear of God. `Judge not, that ye be not judged.' `Enter ye in at the strait gate.' `Beware of false prophets.' `Not every one that saith unto me, Lord, Lord, shall enter into the kingdom of heaven; but he that doeth the will of my Father which is in heaven.' Moreover the Christian is likened to a man who builds a house which he knows is going to be tested.

There, I think, we have not only a general analysis of the Sermon on the Mount, but also a very complete portrayal and representation of the Christian. Certain things always characterize the Christian, and these are certainly the three most important principles. The Christian is a man who of necessity must be concerned about keeping God's law. I mentioned in chapter one the fatal tendency to put up law and grace as antitheses in the wrong sense. We are not `under the law' but we are still meant to keep it; the `righteousness of the law' is meant to be `fulfilled in us', says the apostle Paul in writing to the Romans. Christ coming `in the likeness of sinful flesh, .. . condemned sin in the flesh'. Well; why? `That the righteousness of the law might be fulfilled in us, who walk not after the flesh, but after the Spirit' (Rom. viii. 3, 4). So the Christian is a man who is always concerned about living and keeping the law of God. Here he is reminded how that is to be done.

Again one of the essential and most obvious things about a Christian is that he is a man who lives always realizing he is in the presence of God. The world does not live in this way; that is the big difference between the Christian and the nonChristian. The Christian is a man whose every action should be performed in the light of this intimate relationship to God. He is not, as it were, a free agent. He is a child of God, so that everything he does, he does from this standpoint of being wellpleasing in His sight. That is why the Christian man, of necessity, should view everything that happens to him in this world entirely differently from everybody else. The New Testament emphasizes that everywhere. The Christian is not worried about food and drink and housing and clothing. It is not that he says these things do not matter, but they are not his main concern, they are not the things for which he lives. The Christian sits loosely to this world and its affairs. Why? Because he belongs to another kingdom and another way. He does not go out of the world; that was the Roman Catholic error of monasticism. The Sermon on the Mount does not tell you to go out of life in order to live the Christian life. But it does say that your attitude is entirely different from that of a non-Christian, because of your relationship to God and because of your utter dependence upon Him. The Christian therefore should never worry about his circumstances in this world because of his relationship to God. That, again, is fundamental about the Christian.

The third thing is equally true and fundamental. The Christian is a man who always walks in the fear of God-not craven fear, because `perfect love casteth out' that fear. Not only does he approach God in terms of the Epistle to the Hebrews, `with reverence and godly fear', but he lives his whole life like that. The Christian is the only man in the world who does live always with and under this sense of judgment. He must do so because our Lord tells him to do so. He tells him his building is going to be judged, the test of life is going to come. He tells him not to say, `Lord, Lord,' nor to rely upon his activities in the Church as being of necessity sufficient, because judgment is coming, and judgment by One who sees the heart. He does not look at the sheep's clothing outside but at the inward parts. Now the Christian is a man who always remembers that. I said earlier that the final charge that will be laid against us modern Christians is the charge of superficiality and glibness. This is manifested at this point more than anywhere else, and that is why it is a good thing for us to read about Christians living in past ages. These New Testament people lived in the fear of God. They all accepted the teaching of the apostle Paul when he said, `We must all appear before the judgment seat of Christ; that every one may receive the things done in his body, according to that he hath done, whether it be good or bad' (2 Cor. v. io). That is addressed to Christians. Yet the modern Christian does not like that; he says he will have nothing to do with it. But that is the teaching of the apostle Paul as it is the teaching of the Sermon on the Mount. `We must all appear before the judgment seat of Christ'; `Knowing, therefore, the terror of the Lord.' Judgment is coming and it is going to `begin at the house of God', where it should begin, because of the claim we make. It is all impressed upon us here in the final section of the Sermon on the Mount. We should always be living and walking, distrustful of the flesh, distrustful of ourselves, knowing we have to appear before God and be judged by Him. It is a `strait gate', it is a `narrow way', this way that leads to life which is life indeed.

How important it is, then, to look at this Sermon in general before we begin to argue with one another about what it means when it tells us to turn the other cheek, and so on. People always jump to these particulars and it is an utterly false approach to the Sermon.

Let me now lay down a number of controlling principles which should govern the interpretation of this Sermon. What is of supreme importance is that we must always remember that the Sermon on the Mount is a description of character and not a code of ethics or of morals. It is not to be regarded as law-a kind of new `Ten Commandments' or set of rules and regulations which are to be carried out by us-but rather as a description of what we Christians are meant to be, illustrated in certain particular respects. It is as if our Lord says, `Because you are what you are, this is how you will face the law and how you will live it.' It follows from this that each particular injunction is not to be considered and then applied mechanically or by rule of thumb, for that would of necessity make it ridiculous. People come to this Sermon and say something like this: `Take that injunction, "if any man will sue thee at the law, and take away thy coat, let him have thy cloke also." If you did that you would soon have nothing left in the wardrobe.' That is the kind of approach that must not be made. You must not take separate injunctions and say, `This is to be applied.' That is not the way to look at it. What is inculcated is that I should be in such a spirit that under certain circumstances and conditions, I must do just that-throw in the cloke, or go the second mile. This is no mechanical rule to be applied; but I am such a person that, if it is God's will and for His glory, I do so readily. All I am and have are His, and are no longer mine. It is a particular illustration of a general principle and attitude.

I find this relationship of the general to the particular something which is very difficult to put into words. Indeed I suppose one of the most difficult things in any realm or department of thought is to define what this relationship is. The nearest I can get to my own satisfaction is to put it like this. The relation of any particular injunction to the whole life of the soul is the relationship, I think, of the artist to the particular rules and laws that govern what he is doing. Take, for example, the realm of music. A man may play a piece of great music quite accurately; he may make no mistakes at all. And yet it may be true to say of him that he did not really play Beethoven's Moonlight Sonata. He played the notes correctly, but it was not the Sonata. What was he doing? He was mechanically striking the right notes, but missing the soul and the real interpretation. He wasn't doing what Beethoven intended and meant. That, I think, is the relationship between the whole and the parts. The artist, the true artist, is always correct. Even the greatest artist cannot afford to neglect rules and regulations. But that is not what makes him the great artist. It is this something extra, the expression; it is the spirit, it is the life, it is the whole' that he is able to convey. There, it seems to me, is the relationship of the particular to the general in the Sermon on the Mount. You cannot divorce, you cannot separate them. The Christian, while he puts his emphasis upon the spirit, is also concerned about the letter. But he is not concerned only about the letter, and he must never consider the letter apart from the spirit.

Let me, then, try to summarize it in this way. Here are some negative tests to apply. If you find yourself arguing with the Sermon on the Mount at any point, it means either that there is something wrong with you or else that your interpretation of the Sermon is wrong. I find that very valuable. As I read this Sermon something hits me and I want to argue with it. Well, I repeat, it means either that my whole spirit is wrong and I am not living and exemplifying the Beatitudes: or else I am interpreting that particular injunction in a wrong and false way. It is a very terrible sermon, this Sermon on the Mount. Be very careful as you read it, and especially when you talk about it. If you criticize this Sermon at any point you are really saying a great deal about yourself. Let us, therefore, in the words of James, `be swift to hear, slow to speak, slow to wrath'.

Again, if our interpretation makes any injunction appear to be ridiculous then we can be certain our interpretation is wrong. You see the argument; I have already mentioned it earlier in the illustration of the coat and the cloak. Such an interpretation, I repeat, must be wrong, for nothing that our Lord ever taught can be ridiculous.

Finally, if you regard any particular injunction in this Sermon as impossible, once more your interpretation and understanding of it must be wrong. Let me put it like this. Our Lord taught these things, and He expects us to live them. His last injunction, you remember, to these men whom He sent out to preach was, `Go ye therefore, and teach all nations, baptizing them in the name of the Father, and of the Son, and of the Holy Ghost: teaching them to observe all things whatsoever I have commanded you.' Now here in this Sermon are those very things. He meant them to be taught, He meant them to be practised. Our Lord Himself lived the Sermon on the Mount. The apostles lived the Sermon on the Mount, and if you take the trouble to read the lives of the saints down the centuries, and the men who have been most greatly used of God, you will find that, every time, they have been men who have taken the Sermon on the Mount not only seriously but literally. You read the life of a man like

Hudson Taylor and you will find he literally lived it, and he is not the only one. These things were taught by the Lord and were meant for us, His people. This is how the Christian is meant to live.

There was a time when the designation applied to the Christian was that he was a `God-fearing' man. I do not think you can ever improve on that- a `God-fearing' man. It does not mean craven fear, it does not mean `the fear that hath torment', but it is a wonderful description of the true Christian. He is of necessity, as we are reminded very forcibly in the seventh chapter of this Gospel, a man who lives in the fear of God. We can say of our blessed Lord Himself that His life was a God-fearing life. You see how important that view of the Christian is. So often, as I have been pointing out, modern Christians, who may be able to give very bright and apparently thrilling testimonies of some experience they have had, do not suggest that they are God-fearing people, but give the impression of being men of the world, both in dress and appearance, and in a kind of boisterousness and easy confidence.

So we must not only take the injunctions of the Sermon seriously. We must also check our particular interpretation in the light of the principles I have given. Beware of the spirit of arguing against them; beware of making them ridiculous; and beware of so interpreting them as to regard any one of them as impossible. Here is the life to which we are called, and I maintain again that if only every Christian in the Church today were living the Sermon on the Mount, the great revival for which we are praying and longing would already have started. Amazing and astounding things would happen; the world would be shocked, and men and women would be drawn and attracted to our Lord and Saviour Jesus Christ.

May God give us grace to consider this Sermon on the Mount and to remember that we are not to sit in judgment on it, but that we ourselves are under judgment, and that the building we are erecting in this world and in this life will have to face His final test and the ultimate scrutiny of the eye of the Lamb of God that once was slain.

CHAPTER THREE

AN INTRODUCTION TO THE BEATITUDES

W"E have now finished our general analysis of the Sermon and so can begin to consider this first section, the Beatitudes, this delineation of the Christian man in his essential features and characteristics. I am not, as I have said, concerned with the argument whether there are seven, eight or nine Beatitudes. What matters is not how many Beatitudes there are, but that we should be perfectly clear as to what is said about the Christian. First I want to look at this in general, because again I feel there are certain aspects of this truth which can only be grasped as we take it as a whole. In biblical study, it should invariably be the rule that you must start with the whole before you begin to pay attention to the parts. There is nothing so likely to lead to heresy and error as to start with the parts rather than the whole. The only man who is at all capable of carrying out the injunctions of the Sermon on the Mount is the man who is perfectly clear in his mind with regard to the essential character of the Christian. Our Lord says that this is the only kind of person who is truly `blessed', that is, `happy'. Someone has suggested that it might be put like this; this is the sort of man who is to be congratulated, this is the sort of man to be envied, for he alone is truly happy.

Happiness is the great question confronting mankind. The whole world is longing for happiness and it is tragic to observe the ways in which people are seeking it. The vast majority, alas, are doing so in a way that is bound to produce misery. Anything which, by evading the difficulties, merely makes people happy for the time being, is ultimately going to add to their misery and problems. That is where the utter deceitfulness of sin comes in; it is always offering happiness, and it always leads to unhappiness and to final misery and wretchedness. The Sermon on the Mount says, however, that if you really want to be happy, here is the way. This and this alone is the type of person who is truly happy, who is really blessed. This is the sort of person who is to be congratulated. Let us look at him, then, in general, by taking a kind of synoptic view of these

Beatitudes before we come to deal with them one by one. It will be seen that I am adopting a somewhat leisurely procedure with this Sermon and I am doing so quite deliberately. I have already referred to the people who are anxiously wanting to know what is going to be said about `going the second mile', for example. No; we need to spend a long time with `the poor in spirit' and `the meek' and terms such as these before we go on to those interesting questions which are so thrilling and exciting. We are to be interested primarily in character before we consider conduct.

There are certain general lessons, I suggest, to be drawn from the Beatitudes. First, all Christians are to be like this. Read the Beatitudes, and there you have a description of what every Christian is meant to be. It is not merely the description of some exceptional Christians. Our Lord does not say here that He is going to paint a picture of what certain outstanding characters are going to be and can be in this world. It is His description of every single Christian.

I pause with that for just a moment, and emphasize it, because I think we must all agree that the fatal tendency introduced by the Roman Catholic Church, and indeed by every branch of the Church that likes to use the term `Catholic', is the fatal tendency to divide Christians into two groups-the religious and the laity, exceptional Christians and ordinary Christians, the one who makes a vocation of the Christian life and the man who is engaged in secular affairs. That tendency is not only utterly and completely unscriptural; it is destructive ultimately of true piety, and is in many ways a negation of the gospel of our Lord Jesus Christ. There is no such distinction in the Bible. There are distinctions in offices-apostles, prophets, teachers, pastors, evangelists, and so on. But these Beatitudes are not a description of offices; they are a description of character. And from the standpoint of character, and of what we are meant to be, there is no difference between one Christian and another.

Let me put it like this. It is the Roman Catholic Church that canonizes certain people, not the New Testament. Read the introduction to almost any New Testament Epistle and you will find all believers addressed as in the Epistle to the Church at Corinth, `called to be saints'. All are `canonized', if you want to use the term, not some Christians only. The idea that this height of the Christian life is meant only for a chosen few, and that the rest of us are meant to live on the dull plains, is an entire denial of the Sermon on the Mount, and of the Beatitudes in particular. We are all meant to exemplify everything that is contained here in these Beatitudes. Therefore let us once and for ever get rid of that false notion. This is not merely a description of the Hudson Taylors or the George Mallers or the Whitefields or Wesleys of this world; it is a description of every Christian. We are all of us meant to conform to its pattern and to rise to its standard.

The second principle I would put in this form; all Christians are meant to manifest all of these characteristics. Not only are they meant for all Christians, but of necessity, therefore, all Christians are meant to manifest all of them. In other words it is not that some are to manifest one characteristic and others to manifest another. It is not right to say some are meant to be `poor in spirit', and some are meant to `mourn', and some are meant to be `meek', and some are meant to be `peacemakers', and so on. No; every Christian is meant to be all of them, and to manifest all of them, at the same time. Now I think it is true and right to say that in some Christians some will be more manifest than others; but that is not because it is meant to be so. It is just due to the imperfections that still remain in us. When Christians are finally perfect, they will all manifest all these characteristics fully; but here in this world, and in time, there is a variation to be seen. I am not justifying it; I am simply recognizing it. The point I am emphasizing is that we are every one of us meant to manifest all of them together and at the same time. Indeed, I think we can even go further and say that the character of this detailed description is such, that it becomes quite obvious, the moment we analyse each Beatitude, that each one of necessity implies the other. For instance, you cannot be `poor in spirit' without `mourning' in this sense; and you cannot mourn without `hungering and thirsting after righteousness'; and you cannot do that without being one who is `meek' and a `peacemaker'. Each one of these in a sense demands the others. It is impossible truly to manifest one of these graces, and to conform to the blessing that is pronounced upon it, without at the same time inevitably showing the others also. The Beatitudes are a complete whole and you cannot divide them; so that, whereas one of them may be more manifest perhaps in one person than in another, all of them are there. The relative proportions may vary, but they are all present, and they are all meant to be present at the same time.

That is a vitally important principle. But the third is perhaps even more important. None of these descriptions refers to what we may call a natural tendency. Each one of them is wholly a disposition which is produced by grace alone and the operation of the Holy Spirit upon us. I cannot emphasize this too strongly. No man naturally conforms to the descriptions here given in the Beatitudes, and we must be very careful to draw a sharp distinction between the spiritual qualities that are here described and material ones which appear to be like them. Let me put it like this. There are some people who appear to be naturally `poor in spirit'; that is not what is described here by our Lord. There are people who appear to be naturally `meek'; when we deal with that statement I hope to be able to show you that the meekness which Christ talks about is not that which appears to be natural meekness in an ordinary unregenerate person. These are not natural qualities; nobody by birth and by nature is like this.

This is a rather subtle matter and people are often in difficulty about it in this way. They say, `I know a person who does not claim to be a Christian, never goes to a place of worship, never reads the Bible, never prays, and frankly tells us he is not interested in these things at all. But, you know, I have a feeling that he is more of a Christian than many people who do go to a place of worship and who do pray. He is always nice and polite, never says a harsh word or expresses an unkind judgment, and is always doing good.' Such people look at certain characteristics in the person they are considering and say, `There are the Beatitudes obviously staring me in the face; this person must be a Christian though he denies the entire faith.' That is the kind of confusion that often arises through failure to be clear at this particular point. In other words, it will be our business to show that what we have here in each individual case is not a description of a natural temper, it is rather a disposition that is produced by grace.

Take this man who by 'nature appears to be such a fine Christian. If that is really a condition or a state which conforms to the Beatitudes, I suggest it is quite unfair, for it is a matter of natural temperament. Now a man does not determine his natural temperament, though he governs it up to a point. Some of us are born aggressive, others are quiet; some are alert and fiery, others are slow. We find ourselves as we are, and these nice people who are so frequently brought forward as an argument against the evangelical faith are in no sense responsible for being like that. The explanation of their condition is something biological; it has nothing to do with spirituality, and nothing to do with man's relationship to God. It is purely animal and physical. As people differ in their physical appearance, so they differ in temperament; and if that is what determines whether a man is a Christian or not, I say it is totally unfair.

But, thank God, that is not the position at all. Any one of us, every one of us, whatever we may be by birth and nature, is meant as a Christian to be like this. And not only are we meant to be like this; we can be like this. That is the central glory of the gospel. It can take the proudest man by nature and make him a man who is poor in spirit. There have been some wonderful and glorious examples of that. I would suggest there has never been a naturally prouder man than John Wesley; but he became a man who was poor in spirit. No; we are not concerned about natural dispositions or what is purely physical and animal, or what appears to simulate the Christian character. I am hoping to be able to show you this when we come to an analysis of these things, and I think you will very soon see the essential difference between them. Here are characteristics and dispositions that are the result of grace, the product of the Holy Spirit, and therefore possible for all. They cut right across all natural states and natural dispositions. That, I think you will agree, is a vital and essential principle, so that as we come to look at these individual descriptions, not only must we not confuse them with natural tempers, but we must be very careful at the same time not to define them in such terms. All along we must be drawing our distinction in a spiritual manner and on the basis of the New Testament teaching.

Let us now consider the next principle. These descriptions, I suggest, indicate clearly (perhaps more clearly than anything else in the entire realm of Scripture) the essential, utter difference between the Christian and the non-Christian. This is the thing that should really concern us; and that is why I say it is most important to consider this Sermon on the Mount. This is not just a description of what a man does; the real point is this difference between the Christian and the non-Christian. The New Testament regards that as something absolutely basic and fundamental; and, as I see things at the present time, the first need in the Church is a clear understanding of this essential difference. It has become blurred; the world has come into the Church and the Church has become worldly. The line is not as distinct as it was. There were times when the distinction was clear cut, and those have always been the greatest eras in the history of the Church. We know, however, the arguments that have been put forward. We have been told that we have to make the Church attractive to the man outside, and the idea is to become as much like him as we can. There were certain popular padres during the first world war who mixed with their men, and smoked with them, and did this, that, and the other with them, in order to encourage them. Some people thought that, as a result, when the war was over, the ex-service men would be crowding into the churches. Yet it did not happen, and it never has happened that way. The glory of the gospel is that when the Church is absolutely different from the world, she invariably attracts it. It is then that the world is made to listen to her message, though it may hate it at first. That is how revival comes. That must also be true of us as individuals. It should not be our ambition to be as much like everybody else as we can, though we happen to be Christian, but rather to be as different from everybody who is not a Christian as we can possibly be. Our ambition should be to be like Christ, the more like Him the better, and the more like Him we become, the more we shall be unlike everybody who is not a Christian.

Let me show you this in detail. The Christian and the nonChristian are absolutely different in what they admire. The Christian admires the man who is `poor in spirit', while the Greek philosophers despised such a man, and all who follow Greek philosophy, whether intellectually or practically, still do exactly the same thing. What the world says about the true Christian is that he is a weakling, an apology for a man, or that he isn't manly. Those are its expressions. The world believes in self-confidence, self-expression and the mastery of life; the Christian believes in being `poor in spirit'. Take the newspapers and see the kind of person the world admires. You will never find anything that is further removed from the Beatitudes than that which appeals to the natural man and the man of the world. What calls forth his admiration is the very antithesis of what you find here. The natural man likes an element of boastfulness, but that is the very thing that is condemned in the Beatitudes.

Then, obviously, they must be different in what they seek. `Blessed are they which do hunger and thirst.' After what? Wealth, money, status, position, publicity? Not at all. `Righteousness.' And righteousness is being right with God. Take any man who does not claim to be a Christian and who is not interested in Christianity. Find out what he is seeking and what he really wants, and you will see it is always different from this.

Then, of course, they are absolutely different in what they do. That follows of necessity. If they admire and seek different things, they very clearly do different things. The result is that the life which is lived by the Christian must be an essentially different life from that of the man who is not a Christian. The non-Christian is absolutely consistent. He says he lives for this world. `This', he says, `is the only world, and I am going to get all I can out of it.' Now the Christian starts by saying he is not living for this world; he regards this world as but the way of entry into something vast and eternal and glorious. His whole outlook and ambition is different. He feels, therefore, that he must be living in a different way. As the man of the world is consistent, so the Christian also ought to be consistent. If he is, he will be very different from the other man; he cannot help it. Peter puts it perfectly in the second chapter of his first Epistle when he says that if we truly believe that we are a people who have been called `out of darkness into his marvellous light', we must believe that this has happened to us in order that we might show forth His praises. Then he goes on to say: `I beseech you as strangers and pilgrims (those of you who are in this world), abstain from fleshly lusts, which war against the soul; having your conversation honest among the Gentiles:

41

that, whereas they speak against you as evildoers, they may by your good works, which they shall behold, glorify God in the day of visitation' (i Pet. ii. I i, 12). That is nothing but an appeal to their sense of logic.

Another essential difference between men is in their belief as to what they can do. The man of the world is very confident as to his own capacity and is prepared to do anything. The Christian is a man, and the only man in the world, who is truly aware of his own limitations.

I hope to deal with these things in detail in later chapters, but these are some of the essential, obvious, surface differences between the Christian and the non-Christian. There is nothing, surely, which exhorts us more than this Sermon on the Mount to be what we are meant to be, and to live as we are meant to live; to be like Christ by being a complete contrast to everyone who does not belong to Christ. I trust, therefore, that any of us who may have been guilty of trying to be like the man of the world in any respect will not do so any longer and will see what an utter contradiction it is of our faith.

Perhaps I can put it all finally in this concept. The truth is that the Christian and the non-Christian belong to two entirely different realms. You will notice the first Beatitude and the last Beatitude promise the same reward, `for theirs is the kingdom of heaven.' What does this mean? Our Lord starts and ends with it because it is His way of saying that the first thing you have to realize about yourself is that you belong to a different kingdom. You are not only different in essence; you are living in two absolutely different worlds. You are in this world; but you are not of it. You are among those other people, yes; but you are citizens of another kingdom. This is the vital thing that is emphasized everywhere in this passage.

What is meant by this kingdom of heaven? You will find certain people saying that there is a difference between the `kingdom of heaven' and the `kingdom of God'; but my difficulty is to know what the difference is. Why does Matthew talk about the kingdom of heaven rather than the kingdom of God? Surely the answer is that he was writing primarily for the Jews, and to the Jews, and his chief object, perhaps, was to correct the Jewish conception of the kingdom of God or the kingdom of heaven. They had got into this materialistic way of looking at the kingdom; they were thinking of it politically and in a military sense, and our Lord's whole object here is to show that His kingdom is primarily a spiritual one. In other words He says to them, `You must not think of this kingdom primarily as anything earthly. It is a kingdom in the heavens, which is certainly going to affect the earth in many different ways, but it is essentially spiritual. It belongs to the heavenly rather than to the earthly and human sphere.' What is this kingdom, then? It means, in its essence, Christ's rule or the sphere and realm in which He is reigning. It can be considered in three ways as follows. Many times when He was here in the days of His flesh our Lord said that the kingdom of heaven was already present. Wherever He was present and exercising authority, the kingdom of heaven was there. You remember how on one occasion, when they charged Him with casting out devils by the power of Beelzebub, He showed them the utter folly of that, and then went on to say, `If I cast out devils by the Spirit of God, then the kingdom of God is come unto you' (Mt. xii. 28). Here is the kingdom of God. His authority, His reign was actually in practice. Then there is His phrase when He said to the Pharisees, `the kingdom of God is within you', or, `the kingdom of God is among you'. It was as though He were saying, `It is being manifested in your midst. Don't say "look here" or "look there". Get rid of this materialistic view. I am here amongst you; I am doing things. It is here.' Wherever the reign of Christ is being manifested, the kingdom of God is there. And when He sent out His disciples to preach, He told them to tell the cities which received them not, `Be ye sure of this, that the kingdom of God is come nigh unto you.'

It means that; but it also means that the kingdom of God is present at this moment in all who are true believers. The Roman Catholic Church has tended to identify this kingdom with the Church, but that is not right, because the Church contains a mixed multitude. The kingdom of God is only present in the Church in the hearts of true believers, in the hearts of those who have submitted to Christ and in whom and among whom He reigns. You remember how the apostle Paul puts it in language reminiscent of that of Peter. In writing to the Colossians he gives thanks to the Father 'who hath delivered us from the power of darkness, and hath translated us into the kingdom of his dear Son' (Col. i. 13). The 'kingdom of his dear Son' is 'the kingdom of God', it is 'the kingdom of heaven', it is this new kingdom into which we have entered. Or, again, in his letter to the Philippians he says, 'Our conversation is in heaven,' or, 'Our citizenship is in heaven.' We are here on earth, we obey the powers that be, we live our lives in this way. Yes; but 'our citizenship is in heaven; from whence also we wait for a Saviour' (Phil. iii. 20, Rv). We who recognize Christ as our Lord, and in whose lives He is reigning and ruling at this moment, are in the kingdom of heaven and the kingdom of heaven is in us. We have been translated into the 'kingdom of his dear Son'; we have become a 'kingdom of priests'.

The third and last way of looking at the kingdom is this. There is a sense in which it is yet to come. It has come; it is coming; it is to come. It was here when He was exercising authority; it is here in us now; and yet it is to come. It will come when this rule and reign of Christ will be established over the whole world even in a physical and material sense.

The day is coming when the kingdoms of this world will have become 'the kingdoms of our Lord, and of his Christ', when

> Jesus shall reign where'er the sun
> Doth his successive journeys run;
> His kingdom stretch from shore to shore,
> Till moons shall wax and wane no more.

It will then have come, completely and entirely, and everything will be under His dominion and sway. Evil and Satan will be entirely removed; there will be 'new heavens and a new earth, wherein dwelleth righteousness' (2 Pet. iii. i 3), and then the kingdom of heaven will have come in that material way. The spiritual and the material will become one in a sense, and all things will be subject to His sway, that 'at the name of Jesus every knee should bow, of things in heaven, and things in earth, and things under the earth; and that every tongue should confess that Jesus Christ is Lord, to the glory of God the Father' (Phil. ii. io, ii).

There, then, is the general account of the Christian which is given in the Beatitudes. Do you see how essentially different he is from the non-Christian? The vital questions which we therefore ask ourselves are these. Do we belong to this kingdom? Are we ruled by Christ? Is He our King and our Lord? Are we manifesting these qualities in our daily lives? Is it our ambition to do so? Do we see that this is what we are meant to be? Are we truly blessed? Are we happy? Have we been filled? Have we got peace? I ask, as we have looked together at the general description, what do we find ourselves to be? It is only the man who is like that who is truly happy, the man who is truly blessed. It is a simple question. My immediate reaction to these Beatitudes proclaims exactly what I am. If I feel they are harsh and hard, if I feel that they are against the grain and depict a character and type of life which I dislike, I am afraid it just means I am not a Christian. If I do not want to be like this, I must be `dead in trespasses and sins'; I can never have received new life. But if I feel that I am unworthy and yet I want to be like that, well, however unworthy I may be, if this is my desire and my ambition, there must be new life in me, I must be a child of God, I must be a citizen of the kingdom of heaven and of God's dear Son.

Let every man examine himself.

CHAPTER FOUR

BLESSED ARE THE POOR IN SPIRIT

W_E come now to a consideration of the first of the Beatitudes, `Blessed are the poor in spirit: for theirs is the kingdom of heaven.' As I have already indicated in our last study, it is not surprising that this is the first, because it is obviously, as I think we shall see, the key to all that follows. There is, beyond any question, a very definite order in these Beatitudes. Our Lord does not place them in their respective positions haphazardly or accidentally; there is what we may describe as a spiritual logical sequence to be found here. This, of necessity, is the one which must come at the beginning for the good reason that there is no entry into the kingdom of heaven, or the kingdom of God, apart from it. There is no-one in the kingdom of God who is not poor in spirit. It is the fundamental characteristic of the Christian and of the citizen of the kingdom of heaven, and all the other characteristics are in a sense the result of this one. As we go on to expound it, we shall see that it really means an emptying, while the others are a manifestation of a fullness. We cannot be filled until we are first empty. You cannot fill with new wine a vessel which is partly filled already with old wine, until the old wine has been poured out. This, then, is one of those statements which remind us that there has to be a kind of emptying before there can be a filling. There are always these two sides to the gospel; there is a pulling down and a raising up. You remember the words of the ancient Simeon concerning our Lord and Saviour when he held Him as an Infant in his arms. He said, `this child is set for the fall and rising again of many.' The fall comes before the rising again. It is an essential part of the gospel that conviction must always precede conversion; the gospel of Christ condemns before it releases. Now that is obviously something which is fundamental. If you prefer me to put it in a more theological and doctrinal form, I would say that there is no more perfect statement of the doctrine of justification by faith only than this Beatitude: `Blessed are the poor in spirit: for theirs (and theirs only) is the kingdom of heaven.' Very well then, this is the foundation of everything else.

But not only that. It is obviously, therefore, a very searching test for every one of us, not only as we face ourselves, but especially as we come to face the whole message of the Sermon on the Mount. You see, it at once condemns every idea of the Sermon on the Mount which thinks of it in terms of something that you and I can do ourselves, something that you and I can carry out. It negatives that at the very beginning. That is where it is such an obvious condemnation of all those views which we considered earlier, which think of it as being a new law, or in terms of bringing in a kingdom amongst men. We do not hear so much of that talk now, but it still lingers and it was very popular in the early part of this century. Men talked about `bringing in the kingdom', and always used as their text the Sermon on the Mount. They thought of the Sermon as something that can be applied. You have to preach it and then men immediately proceed to put it into practice. But this view is not only dangerous, it is an utter denial of the Sermon itself, which starts with this fundamental proposition about being `poor in spirit'. The Sermon on the Mount, in other words, comes to us and says, `There is the mountain that you have to scale, the heights you have to climb; and the first thing you must realize, as you look at that mountain which you are told you must ascend, is that you cannot do it, that you are utterly incapable in and of yourself, and that any attempt to do it in your own strength is proof positive that you have not understood it.' It condemns at the very outset the view which regards it as a programme for man to put into operation immediately, just as he is.

Before we go on to deal with it from what we might call a more spiritual standpoint, there is one matter concerning the rendering of this verse which has to be considered. There are those who tell us that it should read `Blessed in spirit are the poor'. They seem to derive a certain amount of justification for that from the parallel passage in Luke vi. 2o, where you will read, `Blessed be ye poor' without any mention of `poor in spirit'. So they would regard it as a commendation of poverty. But surely that must be entirely wrong. The Bible nowhere teaches that poverty as such is a good thing. The poor man is no nearer to the kingdom of heaven than the rich man, speaking of them as natural men. There is no merit or advantage in being poor. Poverty does not guarantee spirituality. Clearly, therefore, the passage cannot mean that. And if you take the whole paragraph in Luke vi, I think it becomes perfectly clear that our Lord was even there speaking of `poor' as meaning `not being possessed by the worldly spirit', poor in the sense, if you like, that you do not rely upon riches. That is the thing that is condemned, this reliance on riches as such. And obviously there are many poor people who rely upon riches exactly as many rich people do. They say, `If only I had so-and-so', and they are jealous of those who have it. Now if they are in that condition they are not blessed. So it cannot be poverty as such.

I have had to emphasize this point because most of the Roman Catholic commentators and their imitators in Anglicanism are very fond of interpreting this statement in that sense. They regard it as scriptural authority for the assumption of voluntary poverty. Their patron saint is Francis of Assisi and they regard him and his type as those who alone conform to the statement of this Beatitude. They say that it refers to those who have deliberately made themselves poor, and turned their backs upon wealth. You will find that the late Bishop Gore in his book on the Sermon on the Mount definitely teaches that. It is the characteristic `Catholic' interpretation of this particular statement. But obviously, for the reasons I have been deducing, that is to do violence to Scripture.

What our Lord is concerned about here is the spirit; it is poverty of spirit. In other words, it is ultimately a man's attitude towards himself. That is the thing that matters, not whether he is wealthy or poor. Now here we have a perfect illustration of one of those general principles that we laid down earlier when we said that these Beatitudes indicate more clearly than anything else in Scripture the utter and essential difference between the natural man and the Christian. We saw that there is a clear-cut division between these two kingdoms-the kingdom of God and the kingdom of this world, the Christian man and the natural-a complete, absolute distinction and division. Now there is perhaps no statement that underlines and emphasizes that difference more than this `Blessed are the poor in spirit'. Let me show you the contrast. This is something which is not only not admired by the world; it is despised by it. You will never find a greater antithesis to the worldly spirit and outlook than that which you find in this verse. What emphasis the world places on its belief in self-reliance, self-confidence and self-expression! Look at its literature. If you want to get on in this world, it says, believe in yourself. That idea is absolutely controlling the life of men at the present time. Indeed I would say it is controlling the whole of life outside the Christian message. What, for instance, is the essence of good salesmanship according to modern ideas? It is giving the impression of confidence and assurance. If you want to impress your customer that is the way you must do it. The same idea is put into practice in every realm. If you want to succeed in a profession, the great thing is to give the impression that you are a success, so you suggest that you are more successful than you actually are, and people say, `That is the man to go to'. That is the whole principle on which life is run at the present time-express yourself, believe in yourself, realize the powers that are innate in yourself and let the whole world see and know them. Self-confidence, assurance, self-reliance. And it is in terms of that fundamental belief that men think they can bring in the kingdom; it is the whole basis of the fatal assumption that by Acts of Parliament alone you can produce a perfect society. Everywhere we see displayed this tragic confidence in the power of education and knowledge as such to save men, to transform them and make them into decent human beings.

Now in this verse we are confronted by something which is in utter and absolute contrast to that, and it is tragic to see how people view this kind of statement. Let me quote the criticism which a man offered a few years ago on that famous hymn of Charles Wesley, `Jesu, Lover of my soul'. You will remember the verse in which Wesley says:

> Just and holy is Thy name, I am all
> unrighteousness; Vile and full of sin I am,
> Thou art full of truth and grace.

This he ridiculed and asked, `What man desiring a post or job would dream of going to an employer and saying to him, "Vile and full of sin I am"? Ridiculous!' And he said it, alas, in the name of what he regards as Christianity. You see what a complete misunderstanding of this first Beatitude that reveals. As I am going to show you, we are not looking at men confronting one another, but we are looking at men face to face

51

with God. And if one feels anything in the presence of God save an utter poverty of spirit, it ultimately means that you have never faced Him. That is the meaning of this Beatitude.

But neither is this Beatitude popular in the Church today. It was this I had in mind earlier when I regretted the amazing and obvious contrast between so much that is true of the Church now and that which was true in past ages, especially in the Puritan era. There is nothing so unchristian in the Church today as this foolish talk about `personality'. Have you noticed it-this tendency to talk about the `personality' of speakers and to use such phrases as `What a wonderful personality that man has'? Incidentally, it is tragic to observe the way in which those who speak thus seem to define personality. It is generally something purely fleshly and carnal, and a matter of physical appearance.

But, and this is still more serious, this attitude is generally based upon a confusion between self-confidence, selfassurance and self-expression on the one hand, and true personality on the other. Indeed, I have noticed at times a tendency even to fail to appreciate what is regarded by the Bible as the greatest virtue of all, namely, humility. I have heard people on a Committee discuss a certain candidate and say, `Yes, very good; but he is rather lacking in personality,' when my opinion of that particular candidate was that he was humble. There is a tendency rather to exalt a certain aggressiveness and self-assurance, and to justify a man's making use of himself and his own personality and trying to put it forward, or as the horrible phrase has it, `to put it across'. The advertisements that are being increasingly used in connection with Christian work proclaim this tendency very loudly. You read the old records of the activities of God's greatest workers, the great evangelists and others, and you observe how self-effacing they were. But, today, we are experiencing something that is almost a complete reversal of this. Advertisements and photographs' are being put into the foreground.

v What does it mean? `We preach not ourselves,' says Paul, `but Christ Jesus the Lord.' When he went to Corinth, he tells us, he went `in weakness, and in fear, and in much trembling'. He did not step onto the platform with confidence and assurance and ease, and give the impression of a great personality. Rather, the people said of him, `His appearance is weak and his speech contemptible.' How far we tend to wander from the truth and the pattern of the Scriptures. Alas! How the Church is allowing the world and its methods to influence and control her outlook and life. To be `poor in spirit' is not as popular even in the Church as it once was and always should be. Christian people must re-think these matters. Let us not take things on their face value; let us above all avoid being captivated by this worldly psychology; and let us realize from the outset that we are in the realm of a kingdom which is unlike everything that belongs to this `present evil world'.

Let us come more positively to this subject, however. What does it mean to be poor in spirit? Once more let me give you certain negatives. To be `poor in spirit' does not mean that we should be diffident or nervous, nor does it mean that we should be retiring, weak or lacking in courage. There are certain people, it is true, who, reacting against this self-assertion which the world and the Church foolishly describe as `personality', think that it does mean just that. We have all met those naturally unobtrusive people who, far from pushing themselves forward, always stand in the background. They are born like that and may even be naturally weak, retiring and lacking in a sense of courage. We emphasized earlier the fact that none of the things which are indicated in the Beatitudes are natural qualities. To be `poor in spirit', therefore, does not mean that you are born like that. Let us get rid of that idea once and for ever.

Neither does it mean that we are to become what I can best describe as imitators of Uriah Heep. Many, again, have mistaken being `poor in spirit' for that. I remember once having to go to preach at a certain town. When I arrived on the Saturday evening, a man met me at the station and immediately asked for my bag, indeed he almost took it from my hand by force. Then he talked to me like this. `I am a deacon in the church where you are preaching tomorrow', he said, and then added, `You know, I am a mere nobody, a very unimportant man, really. I do not count; I am not a great man in the Church; I am just one of those men who carry the bag for the minister.' He was anxious that I should know what a humble man he was, how 'poor in spirit'. Yet by his anxiety to make it known he was denying the very thing he was trying to establish. Uriah Heep-the man who thus, as it were, glories in his poverty of spirit and thereby proves he is not humble. It is an affectation of something which he obviously does not feel. This is a danger which confronts many people, though not as much today as once it did. There was a time when it was the curse of the Church, and affected men's very appearance and even their gait! It did great harm to the cause of Christ, and the moderns have reacted violently against it, and in some cases have obviously gone to the other extreme. I am far from being a defender of clerical dress; but if I had to defend either it or the attire of a man who deliberately goes out of his way to avoid giving the impression that he is a minister, I should undoubtedly defend clerical dress. I heard a man describing a minister of religion the other day and he seemed to be greatly impressed by the fact that the minister did not look like one. 'He does not look like a preacher,' he said. 'He looks like a prosperous man of affairs.' I am not interested in men's personal appearance, but I am suggesting that a man of God should not look like a 'prosperous man of affairs', and he certainly should not go out of his way to give that impression. That but shows that he has far too great a concern about himself and the impression he is making. No, no; we are not to be concerned about these things ; we are to be concerned about the spirit. The man who is truly 'poor in spirit' need not worry so much about his personal appearance and the impression he makes; he will always give the right impression.

Then again, to be 'poor in spirit' is not a matter of the suppression of personality. This also is very important. There are those who would agree with all we have been saying but who would then interpret being 'poor in spirit' in that way and would urge the necessity for a man to repress his true personality. This is a great subject which can best be illustrated here by taking one example. The type of thing we are considering is seen in the story of Lawrence of Arabia. You will remember that in his attempt to efface himself and to suppress his own personality he went to the extent of even changing his name and becoming 'Aircraftman Shaw' just an ordinary man in the Royal Air Force. You recall how he met his death tragically in a bicycle accident, and how he was hailed as a wonderful example of humility and self-abnegation. Now to be poor in spirit does not mean that you have to do that sort of thing. It does not mean that you have to change your name and falsely crucify yourself or assume another character and personality in life. That is utterly unscriptural and quite unchristian. That kind of behaviour often impresses the world, and even impresses Christians also, for they regard it as wonderfully humble. You will find that there is always this subtle temptation to think that the only man who is truly `poor in spirit' is the man who makes a great sacrifice, or, after the manner of the monks, retires out of life and its difficulties and responsibilities. But that is not the biblical way. You do not have to go out of life in order to be `poor in spirit'; you do not have to change your name. No; it is something in the realm of your spirit.

We can go one step further and say that to be `poor in spirit' is not even to be humble in the sense in which we speak of the humility of great scholars. Generally speaking, the truly great thinker is a humble man. It is `a little learning' that `is a dangerous thing'. Now to be `poor in spirit' does not mean that, because that humility is produced by an awareness of the vastness of knowledge and is not of necessity a true humility of spirit in the scriptural sense.

If those are the negatives then what is the positive aspect of being `poor in spirit'? I think the best way to answer that question is to put it in terms of Scripture. It is what Isaiah said (1vii. 15) : `For thus saith the high and lofty One that inhabiteth eternity, whose name is Holy; I dwell in the high and holy place, with him also that is of a contrite and humble spirit, to revive the spirit of the humble, and to revive the heart of the contrite ones.' That is the quality of spirit, and you have endless illustrations of it in the Old Testament. It was the spirit of a man like Gideon, for instance, who, when the Lord sent an angel to him to tell him the great thing he was to do, said, `No, no, this is impossible; I belong to the lowest tribe and to the lowest family in the tribe.' That was not Uriah Heep, it was a man who really believed what he said and who shrank from the very thought of greatness and honour, and thought it was incredible. It was the spirit of Moses, who felt deeply unworthy of the task that was laid upon him and was conscious of his insufficiency and inadequacy. You find it in David, when he said, `Lord, who am I that thou shouldst come to me?' The thing was incredible to him; he was astonished by it. You get it in Isaiah in exactly the same way. Having had a vision, he said, `I am a man of unclean lips'. That is to be `poor in spirit', and it can be seen right through the Old Testament.

But let us look at it in the New Testament. You see it perfectly, for instance, in a man like the apostle Peter who was naturally aggressive, self-assertive, and self-confident-a typical modern man of the world, brimful of this confidence and believing in himself. But look at him when he truly sees the Lord. He says, `Depart from me; for I am a sinful man, 0 Lord.' Look at him afterwards as he pays his tribute to the apostle Paul, in 2 Peter iii. 15, i6. But observe that he never ceases to be a bold man; he does not become nervous and diffident. No, he does not change in that way. The essential personality remains; and yet he is `poor in spirit' at the same time. Or look at it as you see it in the apostle Paul. Here was a man, again with great powers, and obviously, as a natural man, fully aware of them. But in reading his Epistles you will find that the fight he had to wage to the end of his life was the fight against pride. That is why he kept on using the word `boasting'. Any man gifted with powers is generally aware of them; he knows he can do things, and Paul knew this. He has told us in that great third chapter of the Epistle to the Philippians about his confidence in the flesh. If it is a question of competition, he seems to say, he fears no-one; and then he gives us a list of the things of which he can boast. But having once seen the risen Lord on the road to Damascus all that became `loss', and this man, possessed of such tremendous powers, appeared in Corinth, as I have already reminded you, `in weakness and fear and much trembling'. That is the position right through, and as he goes on with the task of evangelism, he asks, `Who is sufficient for these things?' If any man had a right to feel `sufficient' it was Paul. Yet he felt insufficient because he was `poor in spirit'.

But, of course, we see this most of all as we look at the life of our Lord Himself. He became a Man, He took upon Him `the likeness of sinful flesh'. Though He was equal with God He did not clutch at the prerogatives of His Godhead. He decided that while He was here on earth He would live as a man, though He was still God. And this was the result. He said, `I can do nothing of myself.' It is the God-Man speaking. `I can do nothing of myself.' He said also, `The words that I speak unto you I speak not of myself: but the Father that dwelleth in me, he doeth the works' (Jn. xiv. io). `I can do nothing, I am utterly dependent upon Him.' That is it. And look at His prayer life. It is as you watch Him praying, and realize the hours He spent in prayer, that you see His poverty of spirit and His reliance upon God.

That, then, is what is meant by being `poor in spirit'. It means a complete absence of pride, a complete absence of selfassurance and of self-reliance. It means a consciousness that we are nothing in the presence of God. It is nothing, then, that we can produce; it is nothing that we can do in ourselves. It is just this tremendous awareness of our utter nothingness as we come face to face with God. That is to be `poor in spirit'. Let me put it as strongly as I can, and I do so on the basis of the teaching of the Bible. It means this, that if we are truly Christian we shall not rely upon our natural birth. We shall not rely upon the fact that we belong to certain families; we shall not boast that we belong to certain nations or nationalities. We shall not build upon our natural temperament. We shall not believe in and rely upon our natural position in life, or any powers that may have been given to us. We shall not rely upon money or any wealth we may have. The thing about which we shall boast will not be the education we have received, or the particular school or college to which we may have been. No, all that is what Paul came to regard as `dung', and a hindrance to this greater thing because it tended to master and control him. We shall not rely upon any gifts like that of natural `personality', or intelligence or general or special ability. We shall not rely upon our own morality and conduct and good behaviour. We shall not bank to the slightest extent on the life we have lived or are trying to live. No; we shall regard all that as Paul regarded it. That is `poverty of spirit'. There must be a complete deliverance from and absence of all that. I say again, it is to feel that we are nothing, and that we have nothing, and that we look to God in utter submission to Him and in utter dependence upon Him and His grace and mercy. It is, I say, to experience to some extent what Isaiah experienced when, having seen the vision, he said, `Woe is me ! ... I am a man of unclean lips'-that is `poverty of spirit'. As we find ourselves in competition with other men in this world we say, `I am a match for them'. Well, that is all right in that realm, if you like. But when a man has some conception of God, he of necessity feels `as one dead', as did the apostle John on the Isle of Patmos, and we must feel like that in the presence of God. Any natural spirit that is in us goes out, because it is not only exposed in its smallness and weakness, but its sinfulness and foulness become apparent at the same time.

Let us then ask ourselves these questions. Am I like that, am I poor in spirit? How do I really feel about myself as I think of myself in terms of God, and in the presence of God? And as I live my life, what are the things I am saying, what are the things I am praying about, what are the things I like to think of with regard to myself? What a poor thing it is, this boasting of the things that are accidental and for which I am not responsible, this boasting of things that are artificial and that will count as nothing at the great day when we stand in the presence of God. This poor self! That hymn of Lavater's puts it perfectly: `Make this poor self grow less and less', and `O Jesus Christ, grow Thou in me.'

How does one therefore become `poor in spirit'? The answer is that you do not look at yourself or begin by trying to do things to yourself. That was the whole error of monasticism. Those poor men in their desire to do this said, `I must go out of society, I must scarify my flesh and suffer hardship, I must mutilate my body.' No, no, the more you do that the more conscious will you be of yourself, and the less `poor in spirit'. The way to become poor in spirit is to look at God. Read this Book about Him, read His law, look at what He expects from us, contemplate standing before Him. It is also to look at the Lord Jesus Christ and to view Him as we see Him in the Gospels. The more we do that the more we shall understand the reaction of the apostles when, looking at Him and something He had just done, they said, `Lord, increase our faith.' Their faith, they felt, was nothing. They felt it was so weak and so poor. `Lord, increase our faith. We thought we had something because we had cast out devils and preached Thy word, but now we feel we have nothing; increase our faith.'

Look at Him; and the more we look at Him, the more hopeless shall we feel by ourselves, and in and of ourselves, and the more shall we become `poor in spirit'. Look at Him, keep looking at Him. Look at the saints, look at the men who have been most filled with the Spirit and used. But above all, look again at Him, and then you will have nothing to do to yourself. It will be done. You cannot truly look at Him without feeling your absolute poverty, and emptiness. Then you say to Him,

> Nothing in my hand I bring, Simply to
> Thy cross I cling.

Empty, hopeless, naked, vile. But He is the all-sufficient One-

> Yea, all I need, in Thee to find, 0 Lamb of
> God, I come.

CHAPTER FIVE

BLESSED ARE THEY THAT MOURN

WE come now to a consideration of the second Beatitude - 'Blessed (or happy) are they that mourn: for they shall be comforted.' This, like the first, stands out at once, and marks off the Christian as being quite unlike the man who is not a Christian and who belongs to the world. Indeed the world would, and does, regard a statement like this as utterly ridiculous-Happy are those who mourn ! The one thing the world tries to shun is mourning; its whole organization is based on the supposition that that is something to avoid. The philosophy of the world is, Forget your troubles, turn your back upon them, do everything you can not to face them. Things are bad enough as they are without your going to look for troubles, says the world; therefore be as happy as you can. The whole organization of life, the pleasure mania, the money, energy and enthusiasm that are expended in entertaining people, are all just an expression of the great aim of the world to get away from this idea of mourning and this spirit of mourning. But the gospel says, `Happy are they that mourn.' Indeed they are the only ones who are happy! If you turn to the parallel passage in Luke vi you will find it is put in a still more striking manner, because there the negative is employed. `Woe unto you that laugh now!' our Lord says, `for ye shall mourn and weep.' This saying condemns the apparent laughter, joviality and happiness of the world by pronouncing a woe upon it. But it promises blessing and happiness, joy and peace to those who mourn. These preliminary statements, then, concerning the Christian are obviously of primary importance.

Once more it is clear, that we have here something which is entirely spiritual in its meaning. Our Lord did not say that those who mourn in a natural sense are happy, meaning by `mourning', the sorrow experienced because of the death of someone. No, this is a spiritual mourning. As we saw that poverty of spirit was not something financial, but something essentially spiritual, so this again is something entirely spiritual and has nothing to do with our natural life in this world. All these Beatitudes have reference to a spiritual condition and to a spiritual attitude. Those who are commended are those who mourn in spirit; they, says our Lord, are the happy people.

This, as we have seen, is something which is never found in the world, and it presents a striking contrast to what is found there. But, again, I am constrained to say that this is something which is not as evident in the Church today as it once was and as it is in the New Testament. In a sense, as I said earlier, that is really our main reason for considering this Sermon on the Mount. We are concerned about the state and life of the Church at the present time. I have no hesitation again in asserting that the failure of the Church to have a greater impact upon the life of men and women in the world today is due entirely to the fact that her own life is not in order. To me there is nothing more tragic or short-sighted or lacking in insight than the assumption, made by so many, that the Church herself is all right and all she has to do is to evangelize the world outside. Every revival proves clearly that men who are outside the Church always become attracted when the Church herself begins to function truly as the Christian Church, and as individual Christians approximate to the description here given in these Beatitudes. So we must start with ourselves, and see why, unfortunately, this description of the Christian as one who `mourns' is one that makes us feel that somehow or another this is not as evident in the Church today as it once was.

The explanation of this is fairly obvious. It is partly a reaction against the kind of false puritanism (I say false puritanism, not puritanism) which, let us be frank, was too much in evidence towards the end of the last century and the beginning of the present one. It often manifested itself in an assumed piety. It was not natural; it did not come from within; but people affected and assumed a pious appearance. It almost gave the impression that to be religious was to be miserable; it turned its back upon many things that are perfectly natural and legitimate. In that way a picture was given of the Christian man that was not attractive, and, I think, there has been a violent reaction against it, a reaction so violent that it has gone to the other extreme.

But I also think that another explanation of this is the idea which has gained currency that if we as Christians are to attract those who are not Christian we must deliberately affect an appearance of brightness and joviality. Thus many try to assume a kind of joy and happiness which is not something that rises from within, but is something which is put on. Now probably that is the main explanation of the absence of this characteristic of mourning in the life of the Church today. It is this superficiality, this glibness or joviality that is almost unintelligent. It is this endeavour to appear to be something and to cut a certain figure, instead of a life arising from within, which controls and determines the whole of our appearance and behaviour.

I sometimes think, however, that the ultimate explanation of it all is something still deeper and still more serious. I cannot help feeling that the final explanation of the state of the Church today is a defective sense of sin and it defective doctrine of sin. Coupled with that, of course, is a failure to understand the true nature of Christian joy. There is the double failure. There is not the real, deep conviction of sin as was once the case; and on the other hand there is this superficial conception of joy and happiness which is very different indeed from that which we find in the New Testament. Thus the defective doctrine of sin and the shallow idea of joy, working together, of necessity produce a superficial kind of person and a very inadequate kind of Christian life.

Now this is obviously extremely important, especially as regards the matter of evangelism. It is not surprising that the Church is failing in her mission if her dual conception of sin and joy are thus defective and inadequate. And, therefore, it comes to pass that so much evangelism, whether organized on a large or a small scale (in spite of all that is claimed for it in figures and results), is obviously not affecting the life of the Church deeply. Indeed, the very statistics prove the failure in this respect. For this reason it is surely a very fundamental subject for us to consider. That is why it is so important that we should approach it all in terms of this Sermon on the Mount, which starts with negatives. We have to be poor in spirit before we can be filled with the Holy Spirit. Negative, before positive. And here again is another example of exactly the same thing-conviction must of necessity precede conversion, a real sense of sin must come before there can be a true joy of salvation. Now that is the whole essence of the gospel. So many people spend all their lives in trying to find this Christian joy. They say they would give the whole world if they could only find it, or could be like some other person who has it. Well, I suggest that in ninety-nine cases out of a hundred this is the explanation. They have failed to see that they must be convicted of sin before they can ever experience joy. They do not like the doctrine of sin. They dislike it intensely and they object to its being preached. They want joy apart from the conviction of sin. But that is impossible; it can never be obtained. Those who are going to be converted and who wish to be truly happy and blessed are those who first of all mourn. Conviction is an essential preliminary to true conversion.

It is of the greatest importance, then, that we should know exactly what our Lord means when He thus says, `Happy are those who mourn.' We shall discover the answer as we look at the teaching of the New Testament in general with regard to this subject. Let us start, for instance, with our Lord Himself. We, as Christians, are made, we are told by the Bible, after the image and the pattern of the Lord Himself. A Christian is one who is to be like the Lord Jesus Christ. He is `the firstborn among many brethren'; that is the ultimate standard of what you and I are to be like. Very well; let us look at Him. What do we find?

One thing we observe is that we have no record anywhere that He ever laughed. We are told He was angry; we are told that He suffered from hunger and thirst; but there is actually no record of laughter in His life. I know an argument from silence can be a dangerous one, and yet we must pay due attention to that fact. We remember the prophecy concerning Him in the book of the prophet Isaiah, where we are told He was to be a `man of sorrows, and acquainted with grief', that His visage would be so marred that none would desire Him. That is the prophecy concerning Him, and as you look at these accounts of Him in the New Testament Gospels you will see that the prophecy was literally fulfilled. There is an indication in John viii. 57, that our Lord looked very much older than He actually was. You remember He had said, `Abraham rejoiced to see my day' and they looked at Him and said, `Thou art not yet fifty years old, and hast thou seen Abraham?' This was spoken to one just over thirty, and I tend to agree with the interpreters who argue from this statement that our Lord looked much older than He really was. There is, then, no record of laughter in His life. But we are told that He wept at the grave of Lazarus (Jn. xi. 35). That was not because His friend was dead, because He had gone to raise Him from the dead. He knew that in a moment Lazarus was going to live again. No, it is something very different, something we are going to consider together. We are told also that He wept over Jerusalem as He looked at the city just before the end (see Lk. xix. 41-44). That is the picture which you find as you look at our Lord in these Gospels, and we are meant to be like Him. Compare it, not only with the world, but also with this assumed brightness and joviality which so many Christians seem to think is the right portrait of the Christian. I think you will see at once the amazing and striking contrast. There is nothing of that in our Lord.

Again, let us look at the teaching of the apostle Paul as it is to be seen, for example, in Romans vii. We are to be like this apostle, and like the other apostles and the saints of all centuries, if we are to be truly Christian. Let us remember, then, that the Christian is a man who knows what it is to cry out, `O wretched man that I am! who shall deliver me from the body of this death?' That tells us something of what is meant by mourning. Here is a man who was so grief stricken about himself that he cries out in that agony. All Christians are meant to be like that. A Christian man knows that experience of feeling utterly hopeless about himself, and says about himself, as did Paul, `In me (that is, in my flesh,) dwelleth no good thing'. He knows the experience of being able to say, `the good that would I do not: but the evil which I would not, that I do'. He is fully aware of this conflict between the law in the mind and the law in the members, and all this wretched struggling and striving. But listen again to what Paul says in Romans viii. You know there are some people who consider that what is described in Romans vii was only a phase in Paul's experience, and that he left it, turned over a new leaf and went to the eighth chapter of Romans where he no longer knew what it was to mourn. But this is what I read in verse 23 of that chapter, `And not only they, but ourselves also, which have the firstfruits of the Spirit, even we ourselves groan within ourselves, waiting for the adoption, to wit, the redemption of our body.' Or, again, writing in 2 Corinthians v, he says that `we that are in this tabernacle do groan, being burdened': he describes himself as `earnestly desiring to be clothed upon with our house which is from heaven'. He puts all this even more explicitly in the Pastoral Epistles, in which he writes to Timothy and Titus to tell them how they are to teach other people. He says that `the aged men' are to be `sober, grave, temperate'. Indeed even `the young men' are to be `sober minded'. There is none of your glib joviality and brightness here. Even young Christians ought not to affect this appearance of such a wonderful joy that they always wear a bright smile on their face in order to show the world how happy they are.

I have selected these few passages at random. I could supplement them from the writings of the other New Testament writers. What does it all mean? I think the best way we can put it is this. To `mourn' is something that follows of necessity from being `poor in spirit'. It is quite inevitable. As I confront God and His holiness, and contemplate the life that I am meant to live, I see myself, my utter helplessness and hopelessness. I discover my quality of spirit and immediately that makes me mourn. I must mourn about the fact that I am like that. But obviously it does not stop there. A man who truly faces himself, and examines himself and his life, is a man who must of necessity mourn for his sins also, for the things he does. Now the great experts in the life of the spirit have always recommended self-examination. They all recommend and practise it themselves. They say it is a good thing for every man to pause at the end of the day and meditate upon himself, to run quickly over his life, and ask, `What have I done, what have I said, what have I thought, how have I behaved with respect to others?' Now if you do that any night of your life, you will find that you have done things which you should not have done, you will be conscious of having harboured thoughts and ideas and feelings which are quite unworthy. And, as he realizes these things, any man who is at all Christian is smitten with a sense of grief and sorrow that he was ever capable of such things in action or in thought, and that makes him mourn. But he does not stop merely at things he has done, he meditates upon and contemplates his actions and his state and condition of sinfulness, and as he thus examines himself he must go through that experience of Romans vii. He must become aware of these evil principles that are within him. He must ask himself, `What is it in me that makes me behave like that? Why should I be irritable? Why should I be bad tempered? Why am I not able to control myself? Why do I harbour that unkind, jealous and envious thought? What is it in me?' And he discovers this war in his members, and he hates it and mourns because of it. It is quite inevitable. Now this is not imagination; it is actual experience and true to fact. It is a very thorough-going test. If I object to this kind of teaching, it just means that I do not mourn and therefore I am not one of the people who, our Lord says, are blessed. If I regard this as nothing but morbidity, something a man should not do, then I am simply proclaiming the fact that I am not spiritual, and that I am unlike the apostle Paul and all the saints, and I am contradicting the teaching of the Lord Jesus Christ Himself. But if I bemoan these things in myself, I am truly mourning.

Yet the Christian does not stop even at that. The man who is truly Christian is a man who mourns also because of the sins of others. He does not stop at himself. He sees the same thing in others. He is concerned about the state of society, and the state of the world, and as he reads his newspaper he does not stop at what he sees or simply express disgust at it. He mourns because of it, because men can so spend their life in this world. He mourns because of the sins of others. Indeed, he goes beyond that and mourns over the state of the whole world as he sees the moral muddle and unhappiness and suffering of mankind, and reads of wars and rumours of wars. He sees that the whole world is in an unhealthy and unhappy condition. He knows that it is all due to sin; and he mourns because of it.

That is why our Lord Himself mourned, that is why He was `a man of sorrows, and acquainted with grief'; that is why He wept at the grave of Lazarus. He saw this horrid, ugly, foul thing called sin which had come into life and introduced death into life, and had upset life and made life unhappy. He wept because of that; He groaned in His spirit. And as He saw the city of Jerusalem rejecting Him and bringing upon itself its own damnation, He wept because of it. He mourned over it and so does His true follower, the one who has received His nature. In other words, he must mourn because of the very nature of sin itself, because it has ever entered into the world and has led to these terrible results. Indeed he mourns because he has some understanding of what sin means to God, of God's utter abhorrence and hatred of it, this terrible thing that would stab, as it were, into the heart of God, if it could, this rebelliousness and arrogance of man, the result of listening to Satan. It grieves him and he mourns because of it.

There, then, is the New Testament teaching with respect to this matter. That is what is meant by mourning in this spiritual sense in the New Testament. Perhaps we can best put it like this. It is the very antithesis of the spirit and mind and outlook of the world, which, as our Lord puts it, `laughs now'. Look at the world outside, even in a time of war. It still tries to go on not looking at the true situation, ignoring it and being happy. `Let us eat, drink, and be merry', is its motto. It laughs, and says, `Don't dwell too much upon these things'. To mourn is the exact opposite. The Christian man's attitude is essentially different.

We do not stop at this point, however, otherwise our description of the Christian is going to be an incomplete one. Our Lord in these Beatitudes makes a complete statement and it must be taken as such. `Blessed are they that mourn', He says, `for they shall be comforted.' The man who mourns is really happy, says Christ; that is the paradox. In what respect is he happy? Well, he becomes happy in a personal sense. The man who truly mourns because of his sinful state and condition is a man who is going to repent; he is, indeed, actually repenting already. And the man who truly repents as the result of the work of the Holy Spirit upon him, is a man who is certain to be led to the Lord Jesus Christ. Having seen his utter sinfulness and hopelessness, he looks for a Saviour, and he finds Him in Christ. No-one can truly know Him as his personal Saviour and Redeemer unless he has first of all known what it is to mourn. It is only the man who cries out, `O wretched man that I am! who shall deliver me?' who can go on to say, `I thank God through Jesus Christ our Lord.' Now this is something that follows as the night the day. If we truly mourn, we shall rejoice, we shall be made happy, we shall be comforted. For it is when a man sees himself in this unutterable hopelessness that the Holy Spirit reveals unto him the Lord Jesus Christ as his perfect satisfaction. Through the Spirit he sees that Christ has died for his sins and is standing as his advocate in the presence of God. He sees in Him the perfect provision that God has made and immediately he is comforted. That is the astounding thing about the Christian life. Your great sorrow leads to joy, and without the sorrow there is no joy.

Now this is not only true at conversion; it is something that continues to be true about the Christian. He finds himself guilty of sin, and at first it casts him down and makes him mourn. But that in turn drives him back to Christ; and the moment he goes back to Christ, his peace and happiness return and he is comforted. So that here is something that is fulfilled at once. The man who mourns truly is comforted and is happy; and thus the Christian life is spent in this way, mourning and joy, sorrow and happiness, and the one should lead to the other immediately.

But there is not only this immediate comfort offered to the Christian. There is another comfort, that which we may call `the blessed hope', elaborated by the apostle Paul in Romans viii to which we have already made reference. He says that at the present moment even we who `have the firstfruits of the Spirit, even we ourselves groan within ourselves, waiting for the adoption, to wit, the redemption of our body'. `For we are saved by hope', he continues, and we are confident that `the sufferings of this present time are not worthy to be compared with the glory which shall be revealed'. In other words, as the Christian looks at the world, and even as he looks at himself, he is unhappy. He groans in spirit; he knows something of the burden of sin as seen in the world which was felt by the apostles and by the Lord Himself. But he is immediately comforted. He knows there is a glory coming; he knows that a day will dawn when Christ will return, and sin will be banished from the earth. There will be `new heavens and a new earth, wherein dwelleth righteousness'. 0 blessed hope! 'Blessed are they that mourn: for they shall be comforted.'

But what hope has the man who does not believe these things? What hope has the man who is not a Christian? Look at your world; read your newspaper. What can you bank upon? Fifty years ago they used to bank on the fact that man was rapidly improving and getting better. You cannot do that now. You cannot bank on education; you cannot bank on the United Nations any more than you could on the League of Nations. All that has been tried and failed. What hope is there for the world? There is none. There is no comfort for the world now. But for the Christian man who mourns because of sin and because of the state of the world, there is this comfort-the comfort of the blessed hope, the glory that yet remains. So that even here, though he is groaning, he is happy at the same time because of the hope that is set before him. There is this ultimate hope in eternity. In that eternal state we shall be wholly and entirely blessed, there will be nothing to mar life, nothing to detract from it, nothing to spoil it. Sorrow and sighing shall be no more; all tears shall be wiped away; and we shall bask for ever and ever in the eternal sunshine, and experience joy and bliss and glory unmixed and unspoiled. `Happy are they that mourn: for they shall be comforted.' How true it is. Unless we know that, we are not Christian. If we are Christian, we do know it, this joy of sins forgiven and the knowledge of it; the joy of reconciliation; the joy of knowing that God takes us back when we have fallen away from Him; the joy and contemplation of the glory that is set before us; the joy that comes from anticipation of the eternal state.

Let us, then, try to define this man who mourns. What sort of a man is he? He is a sorrowful man, but he is not morose. He is a sorrowful man, but he is not a miserable man. He is a serious man, but he is not a solemn man. He is a sober-minded man, but he is not a sullen man. He is a grave man, but he is never cold or prohibitive. There is with his gravity a warmth and attraction. This man, in other words, is always serious; but he does not have to affect the seriousness. The true Christian is never a man who has to put on an appearance of either sadness or joviality. No, no; he is a man who looks at life seriously; he contemplates it spiritually, and he sees in it sin and its effects. He is a serious, sober-minded man. His outlook is always serious, but because of these views which he has, and his understanding of truth, he also has `a joy unspeakable and full of glory'. So he is like the apostle Paul, `groaning within himself', and yet happy because of his experience of Christ and the glory that is to come. The Christian is not superficial in any sense, but is fundamentally serious and fundamentally happy. You see, the joy of the Christian is a holy joy, the happiness of the Christian is a serious happiness. None of that superficial appearance of happiness and joy! No, no; it is a solemn joy, it is a holy joy, it is a serious happiness; so that, though he is grave and sober-minded and serious, he is never cold and prohibitive. Indeed, he is like our Lord Himself, groaning, weeping, and yet, `for the joy that was set before him' enduring the cross, despising the shame.

That is the man who mourns; that is the Christian. That is the type of Christian seen in the Church in ages past, when the doctrine of sin was preached and emphasized, and men were not merely urged to take a sudden decision. A deep doctrine of sin, a high doctrine of joy, and the two together produce this blessed, happy man who mourns, and who at the same time is comforted. The way to experience that, obviously, is to read the Scriptures, to study and meditate upon them, to pray to God for His Spirit to reveal sin in us to ourselves, and then to reveal to us the Lord Jesus Christ in all His fullness. `Blessed are they that mourn: for they shall be comforted.'

CHAPTER SIX

BLESSED ARE THE MEEK

IN our consideration of the Beatitudes as a whole, we have already found that there are certain general characteristics -which apply to them all. As we come to study each Beatitude separately we find that this proves to be so in detail. Here once more, therefore, we must point out that this Beatitude, thi ; particular description of the Christian, causes real surpris' because it is so completely and entirely opposed to everything which the natural man thinks. `Blessed are the meek: for they shall inherit the earth.' World conquest-possession of the whole universe-given to the meek, of all people! The world thinks in terms of strength and power, of ability, self-assurance and aggressiveness. That is the world's idea of conquest and possession. The more you assert yourself and express yourself, the more you organize and manifest your powers and ability, the more likely you are to succeed and get on. But here comes this astounding statement, `Blessed are the meek: for they shall inherit the earth'-and they alone. Once more, then, we are reminded at the very beginning that the Christian is altogether different from the world. It is a difference in quality, an essential difference. He is a new man, a new creation; he belongs to an entirely different kingdom. And not only is the world unlike him; it cannot possibly understand him. He is an enigma to the world. And if you and I arc not, in this primary sense, problems and enigmas to the non-Christians around us, then this tells us a great deal about our profession of the Christian faith.

This statement must have come as a great shock to .the Jews of our Lord's own day; and there can be no doubt, as we agreed at the beginning, that Matthew was writing primarily for the Jews. He places the Beatitudes in the forefront of the Gospel for that reason. They had ideas of the kingdom which, you remember, were not only materialistic but military also, and to them the Messiah was one who was going to lead them to victory. So they were thinking in terms of conquest and fighting in a material sense, and immediately our Lord dismisses all that. It is as though He says, `No, no, that is not the way. I am not like that, and my kingdom is not like that.'-'Blessed are the meek: for they shall inherit the earth.' It is a great contrast to the Jews' way of thinking.

But further, this Beatitude comes, alas, in the form of a very striking contrast to much thinking within the Christian Church at the present time. For is there not a rather pathetic tendency to think in terms of fighting the world, and sin, and the things that are opposed to Christ, by means of great organizations? Am I wrong when I suggest that the controlling and prevailing thought of the Christian Church throughout the world seems to be the very opposite of what is indicated in this text? `There', they say, `is the powerful enemy set against us, and here is the divided Christian Church. We must all get together, we must have one huge organization to face that organized enemy. Then we shall make an impact, and then we shall conquer.' But `Blessed are the meek', not those who trust to their own organizing, not those who trust to their own powers and abilities and their own institutions. Rather it is the very reverse of that. And this is true, not only here, but in the whole message of the Bible. You get it in that perfect story of Gideon where God went on reducing the numbers, not adding to them. That is the spiritual method, and here it is once more emphasized in this amazing statement in the Sermon on the Mount.

As we approach this statement let us first of all try to look at it in its relationship to the other Beatitudes. Clearly it follows on from what has gone before. There is an obvious logical connection between these different Beatitudes. Each one suggests the next and leads to the next. They are not spoken haphazardly. There is first of all that fundamental postulate about being `poor in spirit'. That is the primary fundamental spirit that leads in turn to a condition of mourning as we become aware of our sin; and that in turn leads to this spirit of meekness. But-and I want to emphasize this-we not only find this logical connection between them. I would point out, also, that these Beatitudes as they proceed become increasingly difficult. In other words, what we are now considering is more searching, more difficult, more humbling and even more humiliating than anything we have looked at hitherto in our consideration of this Sermon on the Mount. We can look at it like this. The first

Beatitude asks us to realize our own weakness and our own inability. It confronts us with the fact that we have to face God, not only in the Ten Commandments and the moral law, but also in the Sermon on the Mount, and in the life of Christ Himself. Anybody who feels that he, by his own strength, can accomplish all that, has not started to be a Christian. No, it makes us feel we have nothing; we become `poor in spirit', we are truly helpless. Anyone who thinks that he can live the Christian life himself is proclaiming that he is not a Christian. When we realize truly what we have to be, and what we have to do, we become inevitably `poor in spirit'. That in turn leads to that second state in which, realizing our own sinfulness and our own true nature, realizing that we are so helpless because of the indwelling of sin within us, and seeing the sin even in our best actions, thoughts and desires, we mourn and we cry out with the great apostle, `O wretched man that I am! who shall deliver me from the body of this death?' But here, I say, is something which is still more searching'Blessed are the meek'.

Now why is this? Because here we arc reaching a point at which we begin to be concerned about other people. Let me put it like this. I can see my own utter nothingness and helplessness face to face with the demands of the gospel and the law of God. I am aware, when I am honest with myself, of the sin and the evil that are within me, and that drag me down. And I am ready to face both these things. But how much more difficult it is to allow other people to say things like that about me! I instinctively resent it. We all of us prefer to condemn ourselves than to allow somebody else to condemn us. I say of myself that I am a sinner, but instinctively I do not like anybody else to say I am a sinner. That is the principle that is introduced at this point. So far, I myself have been looking at myself. Now, other people are looking at me, and I am in a relationship to them, and they are doing certain things to me. How do I react to that? That is the matter which is dealt with at this point. I think you will agree that this is more humbling and more humiliating than everything that has gone before. It is to allow other people to put the searchlight upon me instead of my doing it myself.

Perhaps the best way of approaching this is to look at it in terms of certain examples. Who is this meek person? What is he like? Well, there are many illustrations one can give. I have merely selected some which I regard as the most important and striking. Take certain of the Old Testament characters, for instance. Look at the portrait of that great gentleman--in many ways, I think, the greatest gentleman in the Old Testament-Abraham, and as you look at him you see a great and wonderful portrait of meekness. It is the great characteristic of his life. You remember his behaviour with respect to Lot, and how he allows the younger man to assert himself and take the first choice and does it without a murmur and without a complaint-that is meekness. You see it again in Moses, who is actually described as the most meek man on the face of the earth. Examine his character and you see the same thing, this lowly conception of himself, this readiness not to assert himself but rather to humble and to abase himself-meekness. There were wonderful possibilities ahead of him, all the possibility of the court of Egypt and his position as the son of Pharaoh's daughter. But how truly he evaluated it all, saw it as it was, and humbled himself completely to God and His will.

The same is true of David, especially in his relations with Saul. David knew he was to be king. He had been informed, he had been anointed; and yet how he suffered Saul and Saul's unjust and unkind treatment of him! Read the story of David again and you will see meekness exemplified in a most extraordinary manner. Again, take Jeremiah and the unpopular message that was given to him. He was called upon to speak the truth to the people-not the thing he wanted to do-while the other prophets were saying smooth and easy things. He was isolated. He was an individualist-non-co-operative they would call him today-because he did not say what everybody else was saying. He felt it all bitterly. But read his story. See how he suffered it all and allowed the unkind things to be said about him behind his back, and how he went on delivering his message. It is a wonderful example of meekness.

Come, however, to the New Testament, and here you will see it again and again. Look at the portrait of Stephen and you will see this text illustrated. Look at it in the case of Paul, that mighty man of God.

Consider what he suffered at the hands of these different churches and at the hands of his own countrymen and various other people. As you read his letters you will see this quality of meekness coming out, and especially as he writes to the members of the church at Corinth who had been saying such unkind and disparaging things about him. It is again a wonderful example of meekness. But of course we must come to the supreme example, and stand and look at our Lord Himself. `Come unto me,' He said, `all ye that labour ... and I will give you rest ... I am meek and lowly in heart.' You see it in the whole of His life. You see it in His reaction to other people, you see it especially in the way He suffered persecution and scorn, sarcasm and derision. Rightly was it said of Him, `A bruised reed shall he not break, and smoking flax shall he not quench.' His attitude towards His enemies, but perhaps still more His utter submission to His Father, show His meekness. He said, `The words that I speak unto you, I speak not of myself', and `the Father that dwelleth in me, he doeth the works'. Look at Him in the Garden of Gethsemane. Look at the portrait of Him which we find in Philippians ii where Paul tells us that He did not regard His equality with God as a prerogative at which to clutch or something to hold on to at all costs. No, He decided to live as a Man, and He did. He humbled Himself, became as a servant and even went to the death on the cross. That is meekness; that is lowliness; that is true humility; that is the quality which He Himself is teaching at this point.

Well then, what is meekness? We have looked at the examples. What do we see in them? First, let us notice again that it is not a natural quality. It is not a matter of a natural disposition, because all Christians are meant to be like this. It is not only some Christians. Every Christian, whatever his natural temperament or psychology may be, is meant to be like this. Now we can prove that very easily. Take these various characters whom I have mentioned, apart from our Lord Himself, and I think you will find that in every case we have a man who was not like this by nature. Think of the powerful, extraordinary nature of a man like David, and yet observe his meekness. Jeremiah similarly lets us into the secret. He says he was almost like a boiling cauldron, and yet he was still meek. Look at a man like the apostle Paul, a master mind, an extraordinary personality, a strong character; yet consider his utter humility and meekness. No, it is not a matter of natural disposition; it is something that is produced by the Spirit of God.

Let me emphasize it by putting it like this. Meekness does not mean indolence. There are people who appear to be meek in a natural sense; but they are not meek at all, they are indolent. That is not the quality of which the Bible is speaking. Nor does it mean flabbiness-I use the term advisedly. There are people who are easy-going, and you tend to say how meek they are. But it is not meekness; it is flabbiness. Nor does it mean niceness. There are people who seem to be born naturally nice. That is not what the Lord means when He says, `Blessed are the meek.' That is something purely biological, the kind of thing you get in animals. One dog is nicer than another, one cat is nicer than another. That is not meekness. So it does not mean to be naturally nice or easy to get on with. Nor does it mean weakness in personality or character. Still less does it mean a spirit of compromise or `peace at any price'. How often are these things mistaken. How often is the man regarded as meek who says, `Anything rather than have a disagreement. Let's agree, let's try to break down these distinctions and divisions; let's smooth over these little things that divide; let's all be nice and joyful and happy.'

No, no, it is not that. Meekness is compatible with great strength. Meekness is compatible with great authority and power. These people we have looked at have been great defenders of the truth. The meek man is one who may so believe in standing for the truth that he will die for it if necessary. The martyrs were meek, but they were never weak; strong men, yet meek men. God forbid that we should ever confuse this noble quality, one of the noblest of all the qualities, with something merely animal or physical or natural.

My last negative would be that meekness is not merely a matter of outward manner, but also, and still more, of inward spirit. A well-known hymn which inculcates the spirit of meekness tells us to `stay the angry blow', and of course it is right. But if we are to be truly meek we must not only `stay the angry blow', we must get into that state and condition in which we do not feel like doing it at all. We must control the lips and the mouth, and not say the things we feel like saying. You cannot spend time with a verse like this without its humbling you. It is true Christianity; it is the thing for which we are called and for which we are meant.

What, then, is meekness? I think we can sum it up in this way. Meekness is essentially a true view of oneself, expressing itself in attitude and conduct with respect to others. It is therefore two things. It is my attitude towards myself, and it is an expression of that in my relationship to others. You see how inevitably it follows being `poor in spirit' and `mourning'. A man can never be meek unless he is poor in spirit. A man can never be meek unless he has seen himself as a vile sinner. These other things must come first. But when I have that true view of myself in terms of poverty of spirit, and mourning because of my sinfulness, I am led on to see that there must be an absence of pride. The meek man is not proud of himself, he does not in any sense glory in himself. He feels that there is nothing in himself of which he can boast. It also means that he does not assert himself. You see, it is a negation of the popular psychology of the day which says `assert yourself', `express your personality'. The man who is meek does not want to do so; he is so ashamed of it. The meek man likewise does not demand anything for himself. He does not take all his rights as claims. He does not make demands for his position, his privileges, his possessions, his status in life. No, he is like the man depicted by Paul in Philippians ii. `Let this mind be in you, which was also in Christ Jesus.' Christ did not assert that right to equality with God; He deliberately did not. And that is the point to which you and I have to come.

Then let me go further; the man who is meek is not even sensitive about himself. He is not always watching himself and his own interests. He is not always on the defensive. We all know about this, do we not? Is it not one of the greatest curses in life as a result of the fall-this sensitivity about self? We spend the whole of our lives watching ourselves. But when a man becomes meek he has finished with all that; he no longer worries about himself and what other people say. To be truly meek means we no longer protect ourselves, because we see there is nothing worth defending. So we are not on the defensive; all that is gone. The man who is truly meek never pities himself, he is never sorry for himself. He never talks to himself and says, `You are having a hard time, how unkind these people are not to understand you'. He never thinks: `How wonderful I really am, if only other people gave me a chance.' Self-pity! What hours and years we waste in this! But the man who has become meek has finished with all that. To be meek, in other words, means that you have finished with yourself altogether, and you come to see you have no rights or deserts at all. You come to realize that nobody can harm you. John Bunyan puts it perfectly. `He that is down need fear no fall.' When a man truly sees himself, he knows nobody can say anything about him that is too bad. You need not worry about what men may say or do; you know you deserve it all and more. Once again, therefore, I would define meekness like this. The man who is truly meek is the one who is amazed that God and man can think of him as well as they do and treat him as well as they do. That, it seems to me, is its essential quality.

It must then go on and express itself in our whole demeanour and in our behaviour with respect to others. It does so like this. A person who is of the type that I have been describing must of necessity be mild. Think again of the examples; think again of the Lord Jesus Christ. Mild, gentle, lowly-those are the terms. Quiet, of a quiet spirit-I have already quoted the terms-`meek and lowly'. In a sense the most approachable Person this world has ever seen was the Lord Jesus Christ. But it also means that there will be a complete absence of the spirit of retaliation, having our own back or seeing that the other person pays for it. It also means, therefore, that we shall be patient and long-suffering, especially when we suffer unjustly. You remember how Peter puts that in the second chapter of his first Epistle, that we should `follow his steps: who did no sin, neither was guile found in his mouth: who, when he was reviled, reviled not again; when he suffered, he threatened not; but committed himself to him that judgeth righteously'. It means patience and long-suffering even when we are suffering unjustly. There is no credit, Peter argues in that chapter, if, when we are buffeted for our faults, we take it patiently; but if we do well and suffer for it and take it patiently, then that is the thing that is praiseworthy in the sight of God. That is meekness. But it also means that we are ready to listen and to learn; that we have such a poor idea of ourselves and our own capabilities that we are ready to listen to others. Above all we must be ready to be taught by the Spirit, and led by the Lord Jesus Christ Himself. Meekness always implies a teachable spirit. It is what we see again in the case of our Lord Himself. Though he was the Second Person in the blessed Holy Trinity, He became man, He deliberately humbled Himself to the extent that He was dependent entirely upon what God gave Him, what God taught Him and what God told Him to do. He humbled Himself to that, and that is what is meant by being meek. We must be ready to learn and listen and especially must we surrender ourselves to the Spirit.

Finally, I would put it like this. We are to leave everything—ourselves, our rights, our cause, our whole future—in the hands of God, and especially so if we feel we are suffering unjustly. We learn to say with the apostle Paul that our policy must be this, `Vengeance is mine; I will repay, saith the Lord'. We need not repay, we just deliver ourselves into the hands of God. The Lord will revenge; He will repay. We have nothing to do. We leave ourselves and our cause, and our rights and everything with God, with a quietness in spirit and in mind and heart. Now all this, we shall see later, is something that is abundantly illustrated in the various detailed teachings of this Sermon on the Mount.

Now notice what happens to the man who is like this. `Blessed are the meek; for they shall inherit the earth.' What does that mean? We can summarize it very briefly. The meek already inherit the earth in this life, in this way. A man who is truly meek is a man who is always satisfied, he is a man who is already content. Goldsmith expresses it well when he says: `Having nothing yet bath all.' The apostle Paul has put it still better, for he says, `as having nothing, and yet possessing all things.' Again, in writing to the Philippians, he says in effect, `Thank you for sending your present. I like it, not because I wanted anything, but I like the spirit that made you send it. Yet as for myself, I have all things and abound.' He has already said to them, `I know both how to be abased, and I know how to abound' and `I can do all things through Christ which strengtheneth me'. Notice, too, the striking way in which he expresses the same thought in i

Corinthians iii. After telling his readers that they need not be jealous or concerned about these things, he says, `All things are yours', everything; `whether Paul, or Apollos, or Cephas, or the world, or life, or death, or things present, or things to come; all are yours; and ye are Christ's; and Christ is God's.' All things are yours if you are meek and truly Christian; you have already inherited the earth.

But obviously it has a future reference also. `Do ye not know', says Paul again to these Corinthians, in i Corinthians vi, `do ye not know that the saints shall judge the world?' You are going to judge the world, you are going to judge angels. You will then have inherited the earth. In Romans viii, he puts it this way. We are children, `and if children, then heirs; heirs of God, and joint-heirs with Christ.' That is it; we are going to inherit the earth. `If we suffer', he says to Timothy, `we shall also reign with him.' In other words, `Do not be worried about your suffering, Timothy. You be meek and suffer and you shall reign with Him. You are going to inherit the earth with Him.' But I think it is all to be found in those words of our Lord in Luke xiv. i i : `Whosoever exalteth himself shall be abased; and he that humbleth himself shall be exalted.'

There, then, is what is meant by being meek. Need I emphasize again that this is obviously something that is quite impossible to the natural man? We shall never make ourselves meek. The poor people who went off and made themselves monks were trying to make themselves meek. We shall never do it. It cannot be done. Nothing but the Holy Spirit can humble us, nothing but the Holy Spirit can make us poor in spirit and make us mourn because of our sinfulness and produce in us this true, right view of self and give us this very mind of Christ Himself. But this is a serious matter. Those of us who claim to be Christian claim of necessity that we have already received the Holy Spirit. Therefore we have no excuse for not being meek. The man who is outside has an excuse, for it is impossible to him. But if we truly claim that we have received the Holy Spirit, and this is the claim of every Christian, we have no excuse if we are not meek. It is not something that you do and I do. It is a character that is produced in us by the Spirit. It is the direct fruit of the Spirit. It is offered to us and it is possible for us all. What have we to do? We must face this Sermon on the Mount; we must meditate upon this statement about being meek; we must look at the examples; above all we must look at the Lord Himself. Then we must humble ourselves and confess with shame, not only the smallness of our stature, but our utter imperfection. Then we must finish with that self which is the cause of all our troubles, so that He who has bought us at such a price may come in and possess us wholly.

CHAPTER SEVEN

RIGHTEOUSNESS AND BLESSEDNESS

T I--- HE Christian's concern is to view life in this world in the light of the gospel; and, according to the gospel, the trouble with mankind is not any one particular manifestation of sin, but rather sin itself. If you are anxious about the state of the world and the threat of possible wars, then I assure you that the most direct way of avoiding such calamities is to observe words such as these which we are now considering, 'Blessed are they which do hunger and thirst after righteousness: for they shall be filled.' If every man and woman in this world knew what it was to `hunger and thirst after righteousness' there would be no danger of war. Here is the only way to real peace. All other considerations eventually do not touch the problem, and all the denunciations that are so constantly made of various countries and peoples and persons will not have the slightest effect upon the international situation. Thus we often waste our time, and God's time, in expressing our human thoughts and sentiments instead of considering His Word. If every human being knew what it was to `hunger and thirst after righteousness', the problem would be solved. The greatest need in the world now is for a greater number of Christians, individual Christians. If all nations consisted of individual Christians there would be no need to fear atomic power or anything else. So the gospel, which seems to be so remote and indirect in its approach, is actually the most direct way of solving the problem. One of the greatest tragedies in the life of the Church today is the way in which so many are content with these vague, general, useless statements about war and peace instead of preaching the gospel in all its simplicity and purity. It is righteousness that exalts a nation, and the most important thing for all of us is to discover what righteousness means.

In this particular statement in the Sermon on the Mount we are looking at another of the characteristics of the Christian, a further description of the Christian man. Now, as we have seen, it is very important that we should take it in its logical place in the series of statements that have been made by our Lord. This Beatitude again follows logically from the previous ones; it is a statement to which all the others lead. It is the logical conclusion to which they come, and it is something for which we should all be profoundly thankful and grateful to God. I do not know of a better test that anyone can apply to himself or herself in this whole matter of the Christian profession than a verse like this. If this verse is to you one of the most blessed statements of the whole of Scripture you can be quite certain you are a Christian; if it is not, then you had better examine the foundations again.

Here is an answer to the things we have been considering. We have been told that we must be `poor in spirit', that we must `mourn', and that we must be `meek'. Now here is the answer to all that. For, even though this Beatitude belongs logically to all the others that have gone before, it is none the less true to say that it introduces a slight change into the whole approach. It is a little less negative and more positive. There is a negative element here, as we shall see, but there is a more positive element. The others, as it were, have been causing us to look at ourselves and to examine ourselves; here we begin to look for a solution, and thus there is a slight change in the emphasis. We have been looking at our own utter helplessness and weakness, our utter poverty of spirit, our bankruptcy in these spiritual matters. And having looked at ourselves, we have seen the sin that is within us and that mars God's perfect creation of man. Then we saw the delineation of meekness and all that it represents. All along, we were concerned with this terrible problem of the self-that self-concern, and interest, that selfreliance which leads to our miseries and which is the ultimate cause of war, whether between individuals or nations, that selfishness and self-centredness that turns in upon self and deifies self, that horrible thing that is the cause of all unhappiness ultimately. And we have seen that the Christian man is one who bemoans and regrets and hates it all. Here we turn and look for the solution, for the deliverance from self for which we long.

In this verse we have one of the most notable statements of the Christian gospel and everything that it has to give us. Let me describe it as the great charter for every seeking soul, the outstanding declaration of the Christian gospel to all who are unhappy about themselves and their spiritual state, and who long for an order and quality of life that they have not hitherto enjoyed. We can also describe it as one of the most typical statements of the gospel. It is very doctrinal; it emphasizes one of the most fundamental doctrines of the gospel, namely, that our salvation is entirely of grace or by grace, that it is entirely the free gift of God. This is its great emphasis.

The simplest way, perhaps, to approach the text is just to look at its terms. It is one of those texts that divides itself for us, and all we have to do is to look at the meaning of the various terms which are used. Obviously therefore the one to start with is the term `righteousness'. `Blessed-or happy-are they which do hunger and thirst after righteousness.' They are the only truly happy people. Now the whole world is seeking for happiness; there is no question about that. Everybody wants to be happy. That is the great motive behind every act and ambition, behind all work and all striving and effort. Everything is designed for happiness. But the great tragedy of the world is that, though it gives itself to seek for happiness, it never seems to be able to find it. The present state of the world reminds us of that very forcibly. What is the matter? I think the answer is that we have never understood this text as we should have done. `Blessed are they which do hunger and thirst after righteousness.' What does it mean? Let me put it negatively like this. We are not to hunger and thirst after blessedness; we are not to hunger and thirst after happiness. But that is what most people are doing. We put happiness and blessedness as the one thing that we desire, and thus we always miss it; it always eludes us. According to the Scriptures happiness is never something that should be sought directly; it is always something that results from seeking something else.

Now this is true of those outside the Church and of many inside the Church as well. It is obviously the tragedy of those who are outside the Church. The world is seeking for happiness. That is the meaning of its pleasure mania, that is the meaning of everything men and women do, not only in their work but still more in their pleasures. They are trying to find happiness, they are making it their goal, their one objective. But they do not find it because, whenever you put happiness before righteousness, you will be doomed to misery. That is the great message of the Bible from beginning to end. They alone are truly happy who are seeking to be righteous. Put happiness in the place of righteousness and you will never get it.

The world, it is obvious, has fallen into this primary and fundamental error, an error which one could illustrate in many different ways. Think of a man who is suffering from some painful disease. Generally the one desire of such a patient is to be relieved of his pain, and one can understand that very well. No-one likes suffering pain. The one idea of this patient, therefore, is to do anything which will relieve him of it. Yes; but if the doctor who is attending this patient is also only concerned about relieving this man's pain he is a very bad doctor. His primary duty is to discover the cause of the pain and to treat that. Pain is a wonderful symptom which is provided by nature to call attention to disease, and the ultimate treatment for pain is to treat the disease, not the pain. So if a doctor merely treats the pain without discovering the cause of the pain, he is not only acting contrary to nature, he is doing something that is extremely dangerous to the life of the patient. The patient may be out of pain, and seems to be well; but the cause of the trouble is still there. Now that is the folly of which the world is guilty. It says, `I want to get rid of my pain, so I will run to the pictures, or drink, or do anything to help me forget my pain.' But the question is, What is the cause of the pain and the unhappiness and the wretchedness? They are not happy who hunger and thirst after happiness and blessedness. No. `Blessed are they which do hunger and thirst after righteousness : for they shall be filled.'

This is equally true, however, of many within the Church. There are large numbers of people in the Christian Church who seem to spend the whole of their life seeking something which they can never find, seeking for some kind of happiness and blessedness. They go round from meeting to meeting, and convention to convention, always hoping they are going to get this wonderful thing, this experience that is going to fill them with joy, and flood them with some ecstasy. They see that other people have had it, but they themselves do not seem to get it. So they seek it and covet it, always hungering and thirsting; but they never get it.

Now that is not surprising- We are not meant to hunger and thirst after experiences; we are not meant to hunger and thirst after blessedness. If we want to be truly happy and blessed, we must hunger and thirst after righteousness. We must not put blessedness or happiness or experience in the first place. No, that is something that God gives to those who seek righteousness. Oh, the tragedy that we do not follow the simple teaching and instruction of the Word of God, but are always coveting and seeking this experience which we hope we are going to have. The experiences are the gift of God; what you and I are to covet and to seek and to hunger and thirst for is righteousness. Very well, that is a very important negative. But there are others.

What does this righteousness mean? It does not mean, of course, what is talked about so much at the present time, a sort of general righteousness or morality between nations. There is a great deal of talk about the sanctity of international contracts, and the honouring of bonds, and keeping your word, and straight dealing and fair play and all the rest of it. Well, it is not for me to denounce all that. It is all right as far as it goes; that is the kind of morality that was taught by the Greek pagan philosophers and it is very good. But the Christian gospel does not stop at that; its righteousness is not that at all. There are men who can talk eloquently about that kind of righteousness who know very little, it seems to me, about personal righteousness. Men can wax eloquent about how countries threaten the peace of the world and break their contracts, who at the same time are disloyal to their wives and disloyal to their own marriage contracts and the solemn vows they have taken. The gospel is not interested in that kind of talk; its conception of righteousness is much deeper than that. Neither does righteousness mean merely a general respectability or a general morality. I cannot stop with these various points; I merely mention them in passing.

Much more important and much more serious from the truly Christian standpoint is, I think, the fact that it is not right to define righteousness in this connection even as justification. There are those who turn up their Concordance and look at this word 'righteousness' (and of course you will find it in many places) and say it stands for justification. The apostle Paul uses it like that in the Epistle to the Romans, where he writes about 'the righteousness of God which is by faith'. There, he is talking about justification, and in such cases the context will generally make it perfectly plain to us. Very often it does mean justification; but here, I suggest, it means more. The very context in which we find it (and especially its relation to the three Beatitudes that have gone before) insists, it seems to me, that righteousness here includes not only justification but sanctification also. In other words, the desire for righteousness, the act of hungering and thirsting for it, means ultimately the desire to be free from sin in all its forms and in its every manifestation.

Let me divide that a little. It means a desire to be free from sin, because sin separates us from God. Therefore, positively, it means a desire to be right with God; and that, after all, is the fundamental thing. All the trouble in the world today is due to the fact that man is not right with God, for it is because he is not right with God that he has gone wrong everywhere else. That is the teaching of the Bible everywhere. So the desire for righteousness is a desire to be right with God, a desire to get rid of sin, because sin is that which comes between us and God, keeping us from a knowledge of God, and all that is possible to us and for us with God and from God. So I must put that first. The man who hungers and thirsts after righteousness is the man who sees that sin and rebellion have separated him from the face of God, and longs to get back into that old relationship, the original relationship of righteousness in the presence of God. Our first parents were made righteous in the presence of God. They dwelt and walked with Him. That is the relationship such a man desires.

But it also means of necessity a desire to be free from the power of sin. Having realized what it means to be poor in spirit and to mourn because of sin within, we naturally come to the stage of longing to be free from the power of sin. The man we have been looking at in terms of these Beatitudes is a man who has come to see that the world in which he lives is controlled by sin and Satan; he sees that he is under the control of a malign influence, he has been walking `according to the prince of the power of the air, the spirit that now worketh in the children of disobedience'. He sees that `the god of this world' has been blinding him to various things, and now he longs to be free from it. He wants to get away from this power that drags him down in spite of himself, that `law in his members' of which Paul speaks in Romans vii. He wants to be free from the power and the tyranny and the thraldom of sin. You see how much further and how much deeper it goes than vague general talk- of a relationship between nation and nation, and things of that kind.

But it goes further still. It means a desire to be free from the very desire for sin, because we find that the man who truly examines himself in the light of the Scriptures not only discovers that he is in the bondage of sin; still more horrible is the fact that he likes it, that he wants it. Even after he has seen it is wrong, he still wants it. But now the man who hungers and thirsts after righteousness is a man who wants to get rid of that desire for sin, not only outside, but inside as well. In other words, he longs for deliverance from what you may call the pollution of sin. Sin is something that pollutes the very essence of our being and of our nature. The Christian is one who desires to be free from all that.

Perhaps we can sum it all up like this. To hunger and thirst after righteousness is to desire to be free from self in all its horrible manifestations, in all its forms. When we considered the man who is meek, we saw that all that really means is that he is free from self in its every shape and form-self-concern, pride, boasting, self-protection, sensitiveness, always imagining people are against him, a desire to protect self and glorify self. That is what leads to quarrels between individuals, that is what leads to quarrels between nations; self-assertion. Now the man who hungers and thirsts after righteousness is a man who longs to be free from all that; he wants to be emancipated from self-concern in every shape and form.

Until now I have been putting it rather negatively; but let me put it positively like this. To hunger and thirst after righteousness is nothing but the longing to be positively holy. I cannot think of a better way of defining it. The man who hungers and thirsts after righteousness is the man who wants to exemplify the Beatitudes in his daily life. He is a man who wants to show the fruit of the Spirit in his every action and in the whole of his life and activity. To hunger and thirst after righteousness is to long to be like the New Testament man, the new man in Christ Jesus. That is what it means, that the whole of my being and the whole of my life shall be like that. Let me go further. It means that one's supreme desire in life is to know God and to be in fellowship with Him, to walk with God the Father, the Son and the Holy Spirit in the light. 'Our fellowship', says John, 'is with the Father, and with his Son Jesus Christ.' He also says, 'God is light, and in him is no darkness at all'. To be in fellowship with God means to be walking with God the Father, Son and Holy Spirit in the light, in that blessed purity and holiness. The man who hungers and thirsts after righteousness is the man who longs for that above everything else. And in the end that is nothing but a longing and desire to be like the Lord Jesus Christ Himself. Look at Him; look at His portrait in these Gospels; look at Him when He was here on earth in His incarnate state; look at Him in His positive obedience to God's holy law; look at Him in His reaction to other people, His kindness, His compassion, His sensitive nature; look at Him in His reaction to His enemies and all that they did to Him. There is the portrait, and you and I, according to the New Testament doctrine, have been born again and have been fashioned anew after that pattern and image. The man, therefore, who hungers and thirsts after righteousness, is the man who wants to be like that. His supreme desire is to be like Christ.

Very well, if that is righteousness, let us look at the other term, 'Blessed are they which do hunger and thirst after righteousness.' Now this is most important because it brings us to the practical aspect of this matter. What does it mean to 'hunger and thirst'? Obviously it does not mean that we feel we can attain unto this righteousness by our own efforts and endeavour. That is the worldly view of righteousness which concentrates on man himself and leads to the individual pride of the Pharisee, or to the pride of one nation as against other nations regarding itself as being better and superior. It leads to those things which the apostle Paul lists in Philippians iii and which he there dismisses as 'dung', all self-confidence, all belief in self. `To hunger and thirst' cannot mean that, because the first Beatitude tells us that we must be `poor in spirit' which is a negation of every form of self-reliance.

Well, what does it mean? It obviously means some simple things like these. It means a consciousness of our need, of our deep need. I go further, it means a consciousness of our desperate need; it means a deep consciousness of our great need even to the point of pain. It means something that keeps on until it is satisfied. It does not mean just a passing feeling, a passing desire. You remember how Hosea says to the nation of Israel that she is always, as it were, coming forward to the penitent form and then going back to sin. Her righteousness, he says, is as `a morning cloud'-it is here one minute and gone the next. The right way he indicates in the words-`then shall we know, if we follow on to know the Lord.' `Hunger' and `thirst'; these are not passing feelings. Hunger is something deep and profound that goes on until it is satisfied. It hurts, it is painful; it is like actual, physical hunger and thirst. It is something that goes on increasing and makes one feel desperate. It is something that causes suffering and agony.

Let me suggest another comparison. To hunger and thirst is to be like a man who wants a position. He is restless, he cannot keep still; he is working and plodding; he thinks about it, and dreams about it; his ambition is the controlling passion of his life. To `hunger and thirst' is like that; the man `hungers and thirsts' after that position. Or it is like a longing for a person. There is always a great hunger and thirst in love. The chief desire of the one who loves is to be with the object of his love. If they are separated he is not at rest until they are together again. `Hungering and thirsting'. I need not use these illustrations. The Psalmist has summed it up perfectly in a classical phrase: `As the hart panteth after the water brooks, so panteth my soul after thee, 0 God. My soul thirstetli for God, for the living God.' He is hungering and thirsting after Him-that is it. Let me quote some words of the greatJ. N. Darby which I think put this exceedingly well. He says, `To be hungry is not enough; I must be really starving to know what is in His heart towards me.' Then comes the perfect statement of the whole thing. He says, `When the prodigal son was hungry he went to feed upon husks, but when he was starving, he turned to his father.' Now that is the whole position. To hunger and thirst really means to be desperate, to be starving, to feel life is ebbing out, to realize my urgent need of help. `Hungering and thirsting after righteousness'-`as the hart panteth after the water brooks, so panteth---so thirsteth-- my soul after thee, 0 God.'

Lastly, let us look briefly at what is promised to the people who are like that. It is one of the most gracious, glorious statements to be found in the entire Bible. `Happy, happy', `blessed', `to be congratulated' are those who thus hunger and thirst after righteousness. Why? Well, `they shall be filled', they shall be given what they desire. The whole gospel is there. That is where the gospel of grace comes in; it is entirely the gift of God. You will never fill yourself with righteousness, you will never find blessedness apart from Him. To obtain this, `all the fitness He requireth, is to see your need of Him', nothing more. When you and I know our need, this hunger and starvation, this death that is within us, then God will fill us, He will give us this blessed gift. `Him that cometh to me I will in no wise cast out.' Now this is an absolute promise, so if you really are hungering and thirsting after righteousness you will be filled. There is no question about it. Make sure you are not hungering and thirsting after blessedness. Hunger and thirst after righteousness, long to be like Christ, and then you will have that and the blessedness.

How does it happen? It happens-and this is the glory of the gospel-it happens immediately, thank God. `They shall be filled' at once, in this way--that in inediately we desire this truly, we are justified by Christ and His righteousness and the barrier of sin and guilt between us and God is removed. I trust there is no-one who is uncertain or unhappy about that. If you believe truly on the Lord Jesus Christ, if you believe that on that cross He was dying for you and for your sin, you have been forgiven; you have no need to ask for forgiveness, you have been forgiven. You have to thank God for it, you are filled with that righteousness immediately, the righteousness of Christ is imputed to you. God looks at you in the righteousness of Christ and He no longer sees the sin. He sees you as a sinner whom He has forgiven. You are no longer under the law, you are under grace; you are filled with the righteousness of Christ in this whole matter of your standing before God and your justification-glorious, wondrous truth. The Christian, therefore, should always be a man who knows that his sins are forgiven. He should not be seeking it, he should know he has it, that he is justified in Christ freely by the grace of God, that he stands righteous at this moment in the presence of the Father. So he can say with Augustus Toplady:

> The terrors of law and of God With me can have nothing to do; My Saviour's obedience and blood Hide all my transgressions from view.

Thank God it happens immediately.

But, it is also a continuing process. By this I mean that the Holy Spirit, as already shown, begins within us His great work of delivering us from the power of sin and from the pollution of sin. We have to hunger and thirst for this deliverance, from the power and from the pollution. And if you hunger and thirst for that you will get it. The Holy Spirit will come into you and He will work in you `both to will and to do of his good pleasure'. Christ will come into you, He will live in you; and as He lives in you, you will be delivered increasingly from the power of sin and from its pollution. You will be able to be more than conqueror over all these things that assail you, so that not only do you get this answer and blessing immediately, it goes on continuously as you walk with God and with Christ, with the Holy Spirit living in you. You will be enabled to resist Satan, and he will flee from you; you will be able to stand against him and all his fiery darts, and the whole time the work of getting rid of the pollution will be going on within you.

But of course, finally, this promise is fulfilled perfectly and absolutely in eternity. There is a day coming when all who are in Christ and belong to Him shall stand in the presence of God, faultless, blameless, without spot and without wrinkle. All blemishes will have gone. A new and perfect man in a perfect body. Even this body of my humiliation shall be transformed and glorified and be like the glorified body of Christ. We shall stand in the presence of God, absolutely perfect in body, soul and spirit, the whole man filled with a perfect, complete and entire righteousness which we shall have received from the Lord Jesus Christ. In other words we have a paradox once more. Have you noticed the apparent contradiction in Philippians iii? Paul says, `Not as though I had already attained, either were already perfect', and then a few verses further on he says, `Let us therefore, as many as be perfect.' Is it a contradiction of what he has just been saying? Not at all; you see the Christian is perfect, and yet he is to become perfect. `Of him', he says in writing to the Corinthians, `are ye in Christ Jesus, who of God is made unto us wisdom, and righteousness, and sanctification, and redemption.' At this moment I am perfect in Christ, and yet I am being made perfect. `Not as though I had already attained, either were already perfect; but I follow after ... I press toward the mark.' Yes, he is addressing those who are Christians, those who are already perfect in this matter of understanding concerning the way of righteousness and justification. Yet his exhortation to them in a sense is, `let us therefore go on to perfection.'

I do not know what you feel about this, but to me it is fascinating. You see the Christian is one who at one and the same time is hungering and thirsting, and yet he is filled. And the more he is filled the more he hungers and thirsts. That is the blessedness of this Christian life. It goes on. You reach a certain stage in sanctification, but you do not rest upon that for the rest of your life. You go on changing from glory into glory `till in heaven we take our place'. `Of his fullness have we received and grace upon grace', grace added to grace. It goes on and on; perfect, yet not perfect; hungering, thirsting, yet filled and satisfied, but longing for more, never having enough because it is so glorious and so wondrous; fully satisfied by Him and yet a supreme desire to `know him, and the power of his resurrection, and the fellowship of his sufferings, being made conformable unto his death; if by any means I might attain unto the resurrection of the dead.'

Are you filled? are you blessed in this sense? are you hungering and thirsting? Those are the questions. This is the gracious, glorious promise of God to all such: `Blessed are they which do hunger and thirst after righteousness: for they shall be filled.'

CHAPTER EIGHT

THE TESTS OF SPIRITUAL APPETITE

WT dealt with verse 6 in general in the last chapter. I propose to continue our study of it in this, because I feel that what we considered then is not enough. We can never exhaust this great statement, and certainly if we are to derive anything approaching the full benefit from a consideration of it, we must also look at it in a slightly more practical manner than we have done so far. I do so because in many ways this is one of the key Beatitudes, it is one of the most vital of all.

We have realized that in this Beatitude we begin to turn away from an examination of self, to God. This is, of course, a vital matter, for it is this whole question of how to turn to God that causes so many to stumble. We are entitled, therefore, to say that this is the only way of blessing. Unless we 'hunger and thirst' after righteousness, we shall never have it, we shall never know the fullness which is here promised to us. Therefore, because it is such a vital matter, we must come back to it. I suggested earlier that the very essence of the Christian salvation is given us in this verse. It is a perfect statement of the doctrine of salvation by grace only.

Furthermore, this Beatitude is of exceptional value because it provides us with a perfect test which we can apply to ourselves, a test not only of our condition at any given time, but also of our whole position. It operates in two main ways. It is a very wonderful test of our doctrine, and also a very thoroughgoing, practical test of where, exactly, we stand.

Let us consider it, first, as a test of our doctrine. This one Beatitude deals with what I would describe as the two commonest objections to the Christian doctrine of salvation. It is very interesting to observe how people, when they have the gospel presented to them, generally have two main objections to it, and what is still more interesting is that the two objections are so often found in the same people. They tend to change their position from one to the other. First of all, when they hear this announcement, `Blessed are they which do hunger and thirst after righteousness: for they shall be filled', when they are told that salvation is altogether of grace, that it is something that is given by God, which they cannot merit, which they can never deserve, and about which they can do nothing except receive it, they immediately begin to object and say, `But that is making the thing much too easy. You say that we receive this as a gift, that we receive forgiveness and life, and ourselves do nothing. But surely,' they say, `salvation cannot be as easy as that.' That is the first statement.

Then, when one points out to them that it must be like that because of the character of the righteousness about which the text speaks, they begin to object and to say that that is making it much too difficult, indeed so difficult as to make it impossible. When one tells them that one has to receive this salvation as a free gift, because what is required is that we should be fit to stand in the presence of God, who is light, and in whom is no darkness at all, when they hear that we should be like the Lord Jesus Christ Himself and that we should conform to these various Beatitudes, they say, `Now that is making it impossible for us'. They go astray, you see, about this whole question of righteousness. Righteousness to them means just being decent and moral up to a certain level. But we saw in our last chapter that that is a totally wrong definition of it. Righteousness ultimately means being like the Lord Jesus Christ. That is the standard. If we want to face God and spend eternity in His holy presence, we must be like Him. No-one can be in the presence of God who has any vestige of sin remaining in him; a righteousness is demanded that is absolutely perfect. That is what we have to attain unto. And, of course, the moment we realize that, then we see that it is something we ourselves cannot do, and realize that we must therefore receive it as helpless paupers, as those who have nothing in our hands at all, as those who take it entirely as a free gift.

Now this one statement deals with both those aspects. It deals with those people who object to the fact that this evangelical presentation of the gospel makes it too easy, those people who tend to say, as I once heard someone say who had just been listening to a sermon which emphasized human activity in this matter of salvation, `Thank God there is something for us to do after all'. It shows that that kind of person just admits that he or she has never understood the meaning of this righteousness, has never seen the real nature of sin within, and has never seen the standard with which God confronts us. Those who have really understood what righteousness means never object to the fact that the gospel `makes it too easy'; they realize that apart from it they would be left entirely without hope, utterly lost. `Nothing in my hand I bring, Simply to Thy cross I cling'-is the statement of everyone who has truly seen the position. Therefore, to object to the gospel because it `makes things too easy', or to object to it because it makes things too difficult, is just virtually to confess that we are not Christians at all. The Christian is one who admits that the statements and the demands of the gospel are impossible, but thanks God that the gospel does the impossible for us and gives us salvation as a free gift. `Blessed are they', therefore, `which do hunger and thirst after righteousness: for they shall be filled.' They can do nothing, but as they hunger and thirst for it, they shall be filled by it. There, then, is the test of our doctrinal position. And it is a very thoroughgoing test. But let us ever remember that the two aspects of the test must always be applied together.

Let us now consider the practical test. This is one of those statements which reveal to us exactly where we are in this Christian life. The statement is categorical-they who hunger and thirst after righteousness `shall be filled', and therefore they are happy, they are the people to be congratulated, they are the truly blessed. That means, as we saw in the last chapter, that we are filled immediately, in one sense, namely that we are no longer seeking forgiveness. We know we have had it. The Christian is a man who knows he has been forgiven; he knows he is covered by the righteousness of Jesus Christ, and he says, `Therefore being justified by faith, we have peace with God'. Not, we are hoping to have it. We have it. The Christian has this immediate filling; he is completely satisfied concerning the matter of his standing in the presence of God; he knows that the righteousness of Christ is thus imputed to him and that his sins have been forgiven. He also knows that Christ, by the Holy Spirit, has come to dwell within him. His essential problem of sanctification is also solved. He knows that Christ has been made unto him of God `wisdom, and righteousness, and sanctification, and redemption'. He knows that he is already complete in Christ so that he is no longer hopeless even about his sanctification. There is an immediate sense of satisfaction about that also; and he knows that the Holy Spirit is in him and that He will continue to work in him `both to will and to do of his good pleasure'. Therefore he looks forward, as we saw, to that ultimate, final state of perfection without spot or wrinkle or blemish or any such thing, when we shall see Him as He is and we shall be like Him, when we shall indeed be perfect, when even this body which is `the body of our humiliation' shall have been glorified and we shall be in a state of absolute perfection.

Very well then; if that is the meaning of filling, we must surely ask ourselves questions such as these: Are we filled? Have we got this satisfaction? Are we aware of this dealing of God with us? Is the fruit of the Spirit being manifested in our lives? Are we concerned about that? Are we experiencing love to God and to other people, joy and peace? Are we manifesting long-suffering, goodness, gentleness, meekness, faith and temperance? They that do hunger and thirst after righteousness shall be filled. They are filled, and they are being filled. Are we, therefore, I ask, enjoying these things? Do we know that we have received the life of God? Are we enjoying the life of God in our souls ? Are we aware of the Holy Spirit and all His mighty working within, forming Christ in us more and more? If we claim to be Christian, then we should be able to say yes to all these questions. Those who are truly Christian are filled in this sense. Are we thus filled? Are we enjoying our Christian life and experience? Do we know that our sins are forgiven? Are we rejoicing in that fact, or are we still trying to make ourselves Christian, trying somehow to make ourselves righteous? Is it all a vain effort? Are we enjoying peace with God? Do we rejoice in the Lord alway? Those are the tests that we must apply. If we are not enjoying these things, the only explanation of that fact is that we are not truly hungering and thirsting after righteousness. For if we do hunger and thirst we shall be filled. There is no qualification at all, it is an absolute statement, it is an absolute promise-'Blessed are they which do hunger and thirst after righteousness: for they shall be filled.'

The question that now remains is obviously this: How can we tell whether we are hungering and thirsting after righteousness? That is the vital thing; that is all we have to be concerned about. I suggest the way to discover the answer is to study the Scriptures, as, for example, Hebrews xi, because there we have some great and glorious examples of people who did hunger and thirst after righteousness and were filled. Go through the whole of the Bible and you will discover the meaning of this, especially in the New Testament itself. Then you can supplement scriptural biography by reading about some of the great saints who have adorned the Church of Christ. There is ample literature concerning this matter. Read the Confessions of St. Augustine, or the lives of Luther, of Calvin, and of John Knox. Read the lives of some of the outstanding Puritans and the great Pascal. Read the lives of those mighty men of God of 200 years ago in the evangelical awakening, for example the first volume of John Wesley's journal, or the astounding biography of George Whitefield. Read the life of John Fletcher of Madeley. I have not time to mention them all: there are men who enjoyed this fullness, and whose holy lives were a manifestation of it. Now the question is, how did they arrive at that? If we want to know what hungering and thirsting means, we must study the Scriptures and then go on to see it more on our own level by reading the lives of such people, and if we do so, we come to the conclusion that there are certain tests which we can apply to ourselves to discover whether we are hungering and thirsting after righteousness or not.

The first test is this: Do we see through all our own false righteousness? That would be the first indication that a man is hungering and thirsting after righteousness. Until he has come to see that his own righteousness is nothing, is, as the Scripture puts it, but `filthy rags', or, to use a stronger term, the particular term that the apostle Paul used and which some people think should not be used from a Christian pulpit, the term used in Philippians iii, where Paul speaks of all the wonderful things he had been doing and then tells us that he counts them all as 'dung'-dung, refuse, putrefying refuse. That is the first test. We are not hungering and thirsting after righteousness as long as we are holding with any sense of self-satisfaction to anything that is in us, or to anything that we have ever done. The man who hungers and thirsts after righteousness is the man who knows what it is to say with Paul, `In me (that is, in my flesh,) dwelleth no good thing'. If we still want to pat ourselves on the back, and feel a sense of satisfaction in the things we have done, it indicates perfectly clearly that we are still trusting and holding on to our own righteousness. If we are in any sense prone to defend ourselves, well, that means that we are just holding on still to some righteousness of our own. And as long as we do that we shall never be blessed. We see that to be hungering and thirsting in this sense is, as John Darby puts it, to be starving, to realize we are dying because we have nothing. That is the first step, seeing all false righteousness of our own as `filthy rags' and as `refuse'.

But it also means that we have a deep awareness of our need of deliverance and our need of a Saviour; that we see how desperate we are, and realize that unless a Saviour and salvation are provided, we really are entirely without hope. We must recognize our utter helplessness, and see that, if someone does not come and take hold of us, or do something to us, we are altogether lost. Or let me put it like this. It means that we must have a desire within us to be like those saints to whom I have made reference. That is a very good way of testing ourselves. Do we long to be like Moses or Abraham or Daniel or any of those men who lived in the subsequent history of the Church to whom I have referred? I must add a warning, however, because it is possible for us to want to be like these people in the wrong way. We may desire to enjoy the blessings which they enjoyed without really desiring to be like them. Now, there is a classical example of this in the story of that false prophet, Balaam. You remember he said, `Let me die the death of the righteous, and let my last end be like his!' Balaam wanted to die like the righteous but, as a wise old Puritan pointed out, he did not want to live like the righteous. That, indeed, is true of many of us. We want the blessings of the righteous; we want to die like them. Of course we do not want to be unhappy on our deathbed. We want to enjoy the blessings of this glorious salvation. Yes;

but if we want to die like the righteous we must also want to live like the righteous. These two things go together. `Let me die like the righteous.' If I could but see the heavens open and yet go on living as I am, I should be happy! But it does not work like that. I must long to live like them if I want to die like them.

There, then, are some of the preliminary tests. But if I leave it like that we may come to the conclusion that we have nothing to do but to be entirely passive, and to wait quietly for something to happen. That, however, it seems to me, is to do much violence to these terms, `hungering and thirsting'. There is an active element in them. People who really want something always give some evidence of that fact. People who really desire something with the whole of their being do not sit down, passively waiting for it to come. And that applies to us in this matter. So I am going to apply some more detailed tests as to whether we are truly hungering and thirsting after righteousness. Here is one of them. The person who is truly hungering and thirsting after righteousness obviously avoids everything that is opposed to such a righteousness. I cannot obtain it myself, but I can refrain from doing things that are obviously opposed to it. I can never make myself like Jesus Christ, but I can stop walking in the gutters of life. That is a part of hungering and thirsting.

Let us sub-divide that. There are certain things in this life that are patently opposed to God and His righteousness. There is no question about that at all. We know they are bad; we know they are harmful; we know they are sinful. I say that to hunger and thirst after righteousness means avoiding such things just as we would avoid the very plague itself. If we know there is an infection in a house, we avoid that house. We segregate the patient who has a fever, because it is infectious, and obviously we avoid such persons. The same is equally true in the spiritual realm.

But it does not stop at that. 'I suggest that if we are truly hungering and thirsting after righteousness we shall not only avoid things that we know to be bad and harmful, we shall even avoid things that tend to dull or take the edge off our spiritual appetites. There are so many things like that, things that are quite harmless in themselves and which arc perfectly legitimate. Yet if you find that you are spending much of your time with them, and that you desire the things of God less, you must avoid them. This question of appetite is a very delicate one. We all know how, in the physical sense, we can easily spoil our appetite, dull its edge, so to speak, by eating things between meals. Now it is like that in the spiritual realm. There are so many things that I cannot condemn in and of themselves. But if I find I spend too much of my time with them, and that somehow I want God and spiritual things less and less, then, if I am hungering and thirsting after righteousness, I shall avoid them. I think it is a commonsense argument.

Let me give another positive test. To hunger and thirst after righteousness means we shall remind ourselves of this righteousness actively. We shall so discipline our lives as to keep it constantly before us. This subject of discipline is of vital importance. I am suggesting that unless we day by day voluntarily and deliberately remind ourselves of this righteousness which we need, we are not very likely to be hungering and thirsting after it. The man who truly hungers and thirsts after it makes himself look at it every day. `But', you say, `I am so tremendously busy. Look at my agenda. Where have I time?' I say, if you are hungering and thirsting after righteousness you will find time. You will order your life, you will say, `First things must come first; there is a priority in these matters, and though I have to do this, that and the other, I cannot afford to neglect this because my soul is in bondage."Where there is a will there is a way.' It is amazing how we find time to do the things we want to do. If you and I are hungering and thirsting after righteousness, a good deal of time every day will be spent in considering it.

But let us go further. The next test I would apply is this. The man who is hungering and thirsting after righteousness always puts himself in the way of getting it. You cannot create it yourself; you cannot produce it. But at any rate you do know there are certain ways in which it seems to have come to these people about whom you have been reading, so you begin to imitate their example. You remember that blind man,

Bartima°us. He could not heal himself. He was blind; do what he would and what others would, he could not get back his sight. But he went and put himself in the way of getting it. He heard that Jesus of Nazareth was going that way, so he took up his stand on the high road. He got as near as he could. He could not give himself sight, but he put himself in the way of getting it. And the man who hungers and thirsts after righteousness is the man who never misses an opportunity of being in those certain places where people seem to find this righteousness. Take, for example, the house of God, where we meet to consider these things. I meet people who talk to me about their spiritual problems. They have these difficulties; they so want to be Christian, they say. But somehow or other something is lacking. Quite frequently I find that they do not often go to the house of God, or that they are very haphazard in their attendance. They do not know what it is to hunger and thirst after righteousness. The man who really wants it says, `I cannot afford to lose any opportunity; wherever this is being talked about I want to be there.' It is common sense. And then, of course, he seeks the society of people who have this righteousness. He says, `The oftener I am in the presence of godly and saintly men the better it is for me. I see that person has it; well, I want to talk to that person, I want to spend my time with such a person. I do not want to spend so much time with others who do me no good. But these people, who have this righteousness, I am going to keep close to them.'

Then, reading the Bible. Here is the great textbook on this matter. I ask a simple question again. I wonder whether we spend as much time with this Book as we do with the newspaper or with the novels or with the films and all other entertainments -wireless, television and all these things. I am not condemning these things as such. I want to make it completely clear that that is not my argument. My argument is that the man who is hungering and thirsting after righteousness and has time for such things should have more time for this-that is all I am saying. Study and read this Book. Try to understand it; read books about it.

And then, prayer. It is God alone who can give us this gift. Do we ask Him for it? How much time do we spend in His presence? I have referred to the biographies of these men of God. If you read them, and if you are like me, you will feel ashamed of yourself. You will find that these saints spent four or five hours daily in prayer, not just saying their prayers at night when they were almost too weary to do so. They gave the best time of their day to God; and people who hunger and thirst after righteousness know what it is to spend time in prayer and meditation reminding themselves of what they are in this life and world and what is awaiting them.

And then, as I have already said, there is the need for reading the biographies of the saints and all the literature you can lay your hands on about these things. This is how the man acts who really wants righteousness, as I have proved by the examples I have given. To hunger and thirst after righteousness is to do all that and, having done it, to realize that it is not enough, that it will never produce it. The people who hunger and thirst after righteousness are frantic. They do all these things; they are seeking righteousness everywhere; and yet they know that their efforts are never going to lead to it. They are like Bartima:us or like the importunate widow of whom our Lord spoke. They come back to the same person until they get it. They are like Jacob struggling with the angel. They are like Luther, fasting, sweating, praying, not finding; but going on increasingly in his helplessness until God gave it to him. The same is true of all the saints of all ages and countries. It does not matter whom you look at. It seems to work out like this: it is only as you seek this righteousness with the whole of your being that you can truly discover it. You can never find it yourself. Yet the people who sit back and do nothing never seem to get it. That is God's method. God, as it were, leads us on. We have done everything, and having done all we are still miserable sinners : and then we see that, as little children, we are to receive it as the free gift of God.

Very well; these are the ways in which we prove whether we are hungering and thirsting after this righteousness or not. Is it the greatest desire of our life? Is it the deepest longing of our being? Can I say quite honestly and truly that I desire above everything else in this world truly to know God and to be like the Lord Jesus Christ, to be rid of self in every shape and form, and to live only, always and entirely to His glory and to His honour?

Let me conclude this chapter with just a word in this practical sense. Why should this be the greatest desire of every one of us? I answer the question in this way. All who lack this righteousness of God remain under the wrath of God and are facing perdition. Anybody who dies in this world without being clothed with the righteousness of Jesus Christ goes on to utter hopelessness and wretchedness. That is the teaching of the Bible, that is what the Bible says. `The wrath of God abideth on him.' It is only this righteousness that can fit us to be right with God and to go to heaven and to be with Him and to spend eternity in His holy presence. Without this righteousness we are lost and damned and doomed. How amazing it is that this is not the supreme desire in the life of everybody! It is the only way to blessing in this life and to blessing in eternity. Let me put to you the argument of the utter hatefulness of sin, this thing that is so dishonouring to God, this thing that is dishonouring in itself, and dishonouring even to us. If only we saw the things of which we are guilty so continually in the sight of God, and in the sight of utter holiness, we should hate them even as God Himself does. That is a great reason for hungering and thirsting after righteousness-the hatefulness of sin.

But lastly I put it in a positive form. If only we knew something of the glory and the wonder of this new life of righteousness, we should desire nothing else. Therefore let us look at the Lord Jesus Christ. That is how life should be lived, that is what we should be like. If only we really saw it. Look at the lives of His followers. Wouldn't you really like to live like those men, wouldn't you like to die like them? Is there any other life that is in any way comparable to it-holy, clean, pure, with the fruit of the Spirit manifesting itself as `love, joy, peace, long-suffering, gentleness, goodness, faith, meekness, temperance'. What a life, what a character. That is a man worthy of the name of man; that is life as it should be. And if we see these things truly, we shall desire nothing less; we shall become like the apostle Paul and we shall say, `That I may know him, and the power of his resurrection, and the fellowship of his sufferings, being made conformable unto his death; if by any means I might attain unto the resurrection of the dead.' Is that your desire? Very well, `Ask, and it shall be given you; seek, and ye shall find; knock (and go on knocking), and it shall be opened unto you.' `Blessed are they which do hunger and thirst after righteousness: for they shall be filled'-with `all the fullness of God'.

CHAPTER NINE

BLESSED ARE THE MERCIFUL

T f 1 HIS particular statement, `Blessed are the merciful: for they shall obtain mercy', is a further stage forward in the description, given in these Beatitudes, of the Christian man. I say deliberately that it is a further stage forward because there is again a change in the type and kind of description. In a sense we have so far been looking at the Christian in terms of his need, of his consciousness of his need. But here there is a kind of turning-point. Now we are concerned more with his disposition, which results from everything that has gone before. That is true, of course, of the subsequent Beatitudes also. We have already seen some of the results which follow when a man has truly seen himself, and especially when he has seen himself in his relationship to God. Here, now, are some further consequences which must inevitably be manifested when one is truly Christian. So that again we can emphasize the fact that our Lord clearly chose these Beatitudes carefully. He did not speak haphazardly. There is a definite progression in the thought; there is a logical sequence. This particular Beatitude comes out of all the others, and especially is it to be noted that it is in a very sharp and welldefined logical connection with the immediately preceding one, `Blessed are they which do hunger and thirst after righteousness: for they shall be filled.' I would emphasize once more that it is idle to take any statement of the Sermon on the Mount at random, and to try to understand it, without taking it in the context of the whole, and especially in the context of these descriptions which are here given of the character and the disposition of the Christian man.

`Blessed are the merciful.' What a searching statement that is! What a test of each one of us, of our whole standing and of our profession of the Christian faith! Those are the happy people, says Christ, those are the people to be congratulated. That is what man should be like-merciful. This is perhaps a convenient point at which to emphasize once more the searching character of the whole of this statement which we call the

Beatitudes. Our Lord is depicting and delineating the Christian man and the Christian character. He is obviously searching us and testing us, and it is good that we should realize that, if we take the Beatitudes as a whole, it is a kind of general test to which we are being subjected. How are we reacting to these searching tests and probings? They really tell us everything about our Christian profession. And if I dislike this kind of thing, if I am impatient with it, if I want instead to be talking about communism, if I dislike this personal analysis and probing and testing, it simply means that my position is entirely contrary to that of the New Testament man. But if I feel, on the other hand, that though these things do search and hurt me, nevertheless they are essential and good for me, if I feel it is good for me to be humbled, and that it is a good thing for me to be held face to face with this mirror, which not only shows me what I am, but what I am in the light of God's pattern for the Christian man, then I have a right to be hopeful about my state and condition. A man who is truly Christian, as we have already seen, never objects to being humbled. The first thing that is here said about him is that he should be `poor in spirit', and if he objects to being shown that there is nothing in him, then that is not true of him. So these Beatitudes taken as a whole do provide a very searching test.

They are searching also, I think, in another way, a fact which is borne out very strikingly in the particular Beatitude we are looking at now. They remind us of certain primary, central truths about the whole Christian position. The first is this. The Christian gospel places all its primary emphasis upon being, rather than doing. The gospel puts a greater weight upon our attitude than upon our actions. In the first instance its main stress is on what you and I essentially are rather than on what we do. Throughout the Sermon our Lord is concerned about disposition. Later, He is going to talk about actions; but before He does that He describes character and disposition. And that of course is, as I am trying to show, essentially the New Testament teaching. A Christian is something before he does anything; and we have to be Christian before we can act as Christians. Now that is a fundamental point. Being is more important than doing, attitude is more significant than action. Primarily it is our essential character that matters. Or let me put it like this. We are not called upon as

Christians to be, or to try to be, Christian in various respects. To be Christian, I say, is to possess a certain character and therefore to be a certain type of person. So often that is misinterpreted and people think that what the New Testament exhorts us to do is to try to be Christian in this and that respect, and to try to live as a Christian here and there. Not at all: we are Christians and our actions are the outcome of that.

Going a step further, we can put it like this. We are not meant to control our Christianity; our Christianity is rather meant to control us. From the standpoint of the Beatitudes, as indeed from the standpoint of the whole of the New Testament, it is an entire fallacy to think in any other way, and to say, for example, 'To be truly Christian I must take up and use Christian teaching and then apply it.' That is not the way our Lord puts it. The position rather is that my Christianity controls me; I am to be dominated by the truth because I have been made a Christian by the operation of the Holy Spirit within. Again I quote that striking statement of the apostle Paul which surely puts it so perfectly-'I live; yet not I, but Christ liveth in me.' He is in control, not I; so that I must not think of myself as a natural man who is controlling his attitude and trying to be Christian in various ways. No, His Spirit controls me at the very centre of my life, controls the very spring of my being, the source of my every activity. You cannot read these Beatitudes without coming to that conclusion. The Christian faith is not something on the surface of a man's life, it is not merely a kind of coating or veneer. No, it is something that has been happening in the very centre of his personality. That is why the New Testament talks about rebirth and being born again, about a new creation and about receiving a new nature. It is something that happens to a man in the very centre of his being; it controls all his thoughts, all his outlook, all his imagination, and, as a result, all his actions as well. All our activities, therefore, are the result of this new nature, this new disposition which we have received from God through the Holy Spirit.

That is why these Beatitudes are so searching. They tell us, in effect, that as we live our ordinary lives we are declaring all the time exactly what we are. That is what makes this matter so serious. By the way we react we manifest our spirit; and it is the spirit that proclaims the man in terms of Christianity. There are people, of course, who as a result of a strong human will can control their actions very largely. Yet in these other respects they are always proclaiming what they are. All of us are proclaiming whether we are `poor in spirit', whether we `mourn', whether we are `meek', whether we `hunger and thirst', whether we are `merciful', or whether we are not. The whole of our life is an expression and a proclamation of what we really are. And as we confront a list like this, or as we look at this extraordinary portrait of the Christian drawn by our Lord, we are forced to look at ourselves and examine ourselves and ask ourselves these questions.

The particular question here is: Are we merciful? The Christian, according to our Lord, is not only what we have seen him to be already, but he is also merciful. Here is the blessed man, here is the man to be congratulated; one who is merciful. What does our Lord mean by this? First let me just mention one negative which is of importance. It does not mean that we should be `easy-going', as we put it. There are so many people today who think that being merciful means to be easy-going, not to see things, or if we do see them, to pretend we have not. That, of course, is a particular danger in an age like this which does not believe in law or discipline, and in a sense does not believe in justice or righteousness. The idea today is that man should be absolutely free minded, that he has the right to do just what he likes. The merciful person, many people think, is one who smiles at transgression and law breaking. He says, `What does it matter? Let's carry on.' He is a flabby kind of person, easygoing, easy to get on with, to whom it does not matter whether laws are broken or not, who is not concerned about keeping them.

Now that, obviously, is not what is meant by our Lord's description of the Christian at this point, and for very good reasons. You may recall that when we considered these Beatitudes as a whole, we laid great stress upon the fact that none of them must ever be interpreted in terms of natural disposition, because if you start thinking of these Beatitudes in such terms you will find they are grossly unfair. Some are born like this, some are not; and the man who is born with this easy-going temperament has a great advantage over the man who is not. But that is a denial of the whole of biblical teaching. This is not a gospel for certain temperaments; nobody has an advantage over anybody else when they are face to face with God. `All have come short of the glory of God', `every mouth has been stopped' before God. That is the New Testament teaching, so that natural disposition must never be the basis of our interpretation of any one of the Beatitudes.

There is, however, a very much stronger reason than that for saying that what is meant by `merciful' is not being easy-going. For when we interpret this term we must remember that it is an adjective that is applied specially and specifically to God Himself. So that whatever I may decide as to the meaning of `merciful' is true also of God, and the moment you look at it like that you see that this easy-going attitude that doesn't care about breaking the law is unthinkable when we are talking about God. God is merciful; but God is righteous, God is holy, God is just: and whatever our interpretation of merciful may be it must include all that. `Mercy and truth are met together', and if I can think of mercy only at the expense of truth and law, it is not true mercy, it is a false understanding of the term.

What is mercy? I think perhaps the best way of approaching it is to compare it with grace. You notice in the introduction to the so-called Pastoral Epistles that the apostle brings in a new term. Most of his other Epistles start by saying `grace and peace' from God the Father and the Lord Jesus Christ; but in his Pastoral Epistles he says, `grace, mercy, and peace', and there is thus an interesting distinction implied between grace and mercy.The best definition of the two that I have ever encountered is this: `Grace is especially associated with men in their sins; mercy is especially associated with men in their misery.' In other words, while grace looks down upon sin as a whole, mercy looks especially upon the miserable consequences of sin. So that mercy really means a sense of pity plus a desire to relieve the suffering. That is the essential meaning of being merciful; it is pity plus the action. So the Christian has a feeling of pity. His concern about the misery of men and women leads to an anxiety to relieve it. There are many ways in which one could illustrate that. For example, to have a merciful spirit means the spirit that is displayed when you suddenly find yourself in the position of having in your power someone who has transgressed against you. Now the way to know whether you are merciful or not is to consider how you feel towards that person. Are you going to say, `Well now, I am going to exert my rights at this point; I am going to be legal. This person has transgressed against me; very well, here comes my opportunity'? That is the very antithesis of being merciful. This person is in your power; is there a vindictive spirit, or is there a spirit of pity and sorrow, a spirit, if you like, of kindness to your enemies in distress? Or, again, we can describe it as inward sympathy and outward acts in relation to the sorrows and sufferings of others. Perhaps an example is the best way of illustrating this. The great New Testament illustration of being merciful is the parable of the Good Samaritan. On his journey he sees this poor man who has been in the hands of robbers, stops, and goes across the road to where he is lying. The others have seen the man but have gone on. They may have felt compassion and pity yet they have not done anything about it. But here is a man who is merciful; he is sorry for the victim, goes across the road, dresses the wounds, takes the man with him and makes provision for him. That is being merciful. It does not mean only feeling pity; it means a great desire, and indeed an endeavour, to do something to relieve the situation.

But let us go from that to the supreme example of all. The perfect and central example of mercy and being merciful is the sending by God of His only begotten Son into this world, and the coming of the Son. Why? Because there is mercy with Him. He saw our pitiable estate, He saw the suffering, and, in spite of the law breaking, this was the thing that moved Him to action. So the Son came and dealt with our condition. Hence the whole necessity for the doctrine of the atonement. There is no contradiction between justice and mercy, or mercy and truth. They have met together. Indeed John the Baptist's father put this very clearly when, having understood what was happening by the birth of his son, he thanked God that at last the mercy promised to the fathers had arrived, and then proceeded to thank God that the Messiah had come `through the tender mercy of our God'. That is the idea, and he realized it at the very beginning. It is all a matter of mercy. It is God, I say, looking down upon man in his pitiful condition as the result of sin, and having pity upon him. The grace that is there in regard to sin in general now becomes mercy in particular as God looks at the consequences of sin. And, of course, it is something that is to be observed constantly in the life and behaviour of our blessed Lord Himself.

That, then, is more or less a definition of what is meant by being merciful. The real problem, however, in this Beatitude is raised by the promise, `for they shall obtain mercy'; and perhaps there is no other Beatitude that has been misunderstood quite so frequently as this one. For there are people who would interpret it like this. They say, `If I am merciful towards others, God will be merciful towards me; if I forgive, I shall be forgiven. The condition of my being forgiven is that I forgive.' Now the best way to approach this problem is to take it with two parallel statements. First there is that well-known statement in the Lord's prayer which is an exact parallel to this, `Forgive us our trespasses, as we forgive them that trespass against us', or, `Forgive us our debts, as we forgive our debtors'. There are those who interpret this as meaning that if you forgive, you will be forgiven, if you do not, you will not be forgiven. Some people refuse to recite the Lord's prayer for this reason.

Then there is a similar statement recorded in the parable of the debtors in Matthew xviii. Here a cruel servant who was in debt was asked by his master for payment. The man did not have the money to pay so he besought his master to forgive him his debt. His master had mercy upon him and forgave him all that he owed. But, you remember, this man went outside and demanded payment from somebody under himself who owed him a comparatively trivial debt. That man in turn prayed and besought him and said, `Have patience with me, and I will pay thee all'. But he would not listen and cast him into prison until he could pay him the utmost farthing. But other servants, seeing this, reported it to their lord. On hearing their account he called for this cruel and unjust servant and said to him in effect, `Very well; in view of your action I am going to repeal what I said to you'; and he cast him into prison, saying he should remain there until he had paid the utmost farthing. Our Lord ends the parable by saying, `So likewise shall my heavenly Father do also unto you, if ye from your hearts forgive not every one his brother their trespasses.'

Here again people at once begin to say, `Well; does not that clearly teach that I am forgiven by God only as I forgive others and to the extent that I forgive others?' It is an amazing thing to me that anybody could ever arrive at such an interpretation, and that for two main reasons. First, if you and I were to be judged strictly on those terms, it is very certain that not one of us would be forgiven and not one of us would ever see heaven. If the passage is to be interpreted in that strictly legal manner forgiveness is impossible. It is amazing that people can think like that, not realizing they are condemning themselves as they do so.

The second reason is still more striking. If that is the interpretation of this Beatitude and the parallel passages, then we must cancel the whole doctrine ofgrace from the New Testament. We must never again say that we are saved by grace through faith, and that not of ourselves; we must never read those glorious passages which tell us that `while we were yet sinners, Christ died for us', even `when we were enemies, we were reconciled to God', or `God was in Christ, reconciling the world unto himself'. They must all go; they are all nonsense; and they are all untrue. Scripture, you see, must be interpreted by Scripture; we must never interpret any Scripture in such a manner as to contradict other Scriptures. We must `rightly divide the word of truth', and we must see that there is a conformity of doctrine to doctrine.

When we apply this to the statement before us, the explanation is perfectly simple. Our Lord is really saying that I am only truly forgiven when I am truly repentant. To be truly repentant means that I realize I deserve nothing but punishment, and that if I am forgiven it is to be attributed entirely to the love of God and to His mercy and grace, and to nothing else at all. But I go further; it means this. If I am truly repentant and realize my position before God, and realize that I am only forgiven in that way, then of necessity I shall forgive those who trespass against me.

"Let me put it like this. I have taken the trouble to point out in each case how every one of these Beatitudes follows the previous one. This principle was never more important than it is here. This Beatitude follows all the others; therefore I put it in this form. I am poor in spirit; I realize that I have no righteousness; I realize that face to face with God and His righteousness I am utterly helpless; I can do nothing. Not only that. I mourn because of the sin that is within me; I have come to see, as the result of the operation of the Holy Spirit, the blackness of my own heart. I know what it is to cry out, `0 wretched man that I am! who shall deliver me?' and desire to be rid of this vileness that is within me. Not only that. I am meek, which means that now that I have experienced this true view of myself, nobody else can hurt me, nobody else can insult me, nobody can ever say anything too bad about me. I have seen myself, and my greatest enemy does not know the worst about me. I have seen myself as something truly hateful, and it is because of this that I have hungered and thirsted after righteousness. I have longed for it. I have seen that I cannot create or produce it, and that nobody else can. I have seen my desperate position in the sight of God. I have hungered and thirsted for that righteousness which will put me right with God, that will reconcile me to God, and give me a new nature and life. And I have seen it in Christ. 1 - have been filled; I have received it all as a free gift.

Does it not follow inevitably that, if I have seen and experienced all that, my attitude towards everybody else must be completely and entirely changed? If all that is true of me, I no longer see men as I used to see them. I see them now with a Christian eye. I see them as the dupes and the victims and the slaves of sin and Satan and of the way of the world. I have come to see them not simply as men whom I dislike but as men to be pitied. I have come to see them as being governed by the god of this world, as being still where once I was, and would be yet but for the grace of God. So I am sorry for them. I do not merely see them and what they do. I see them as the slaves of hell and of Satan, and my whole attitude toward them is changed. And because of that, of course, I can be and must be merciful with respect to them. I differentiate between the sinner and his sin. I see everybody who is in a state of sin as one who is to be pitied.

But I would take you again to the supreme example. Look at Him there upon the cross, who never sinned, who never did any harm to anyone, who came and preached the truth, who came to seek and save that which was lost. There He is, nailed and suffering agonies on that cross, and yet what does He say as He looks upon the people who are responsible for it? `Father, forgive them.' Why? `For they know not what they do.' It is not they, it is Satan; they are the victims; they are being governed and dominated by sin. `Father, forgive them; for they know not what they do.' Now you and I are to become like that. Look at Stephen the martyr attaining to that. As they are stoning him, what does he say? He prays to his heavenly Father and cries, `Lay not this sin to their charge.' `They do not know what they are doing, Lord', says Stephen; `they are mad. They are mad because of sin; they do not understand me as Thy servant; they do not understand my Lord and Master; they are blinded by the god of this world; they do not know what they are doing. Lay not this sin to their charge. They are not responsible.' He has pity upon them and is merciful with respect to them. And that, I say, is to be the condition of every one who is truly Christian. We are to feel a sense of sorrow for all who are helpless slaves of sin. That is to be our attitude towards people.

I wonder whether we have recognized this as the Christian position even when people were using us despitefully and maligning us. As we shall see later in this Sermon on the Mount, even when they are doing that, we are still to be merciful. Do you not know something about this in experience? Have you not felt sorry for people who show from the expression on their faces the bitterness and the anger they feel? They are to be pitied. Look at the things aboutwhich they get angry, showing that their whole central spirit is wrong; so unlike Christ, so unlike God who has forgiven them everything. We should feel a great sorrow for them, we should be praying to God for them and asking Him to have mercy upon them. I say that all this follows of necessity if we have truly experienced what it means to be forgiven. If I know that I am a debtor to mercy alone, if I know that I am a Christian solely because of that free grace of God, there should be no pride left in me, there should be nothing vindictive, there should be no insisting upon my rights. Rather, as I look out upon others, if there is anything in them that is unworthy, or that is a manifestation of sin, I should have this great sorrow for them in my heart.

All these things then follow inevitably and automatically. That is what our Lord is saying here. If you are merciful, you have mercy in this way. You already have it, but you will have it every time you sin, because when you realize what you have done you will come back to God and say, `Have mercy upon me, O God.' But remember this. If, when you sin, you see it and in repentance go to God, and there on your knees immediately realize that you are not forgiving somebody else, you will have no confidence in your prayers; you will despise yourself. As David puts it, `If I regard iniquity in my heart, the Lord will not hear me.' If you are not forgiving your brother, you can ask God for forgiveness, but you will have no confidence in your prayer, and your prayer will not be answered. That is what this Beatitude says. That is what our Lord said in the parable of the unjust steward. If that unrighteous, cruel servant would not forgive the servant who was under him, he was a man who had never understood forgiveness or his relationship to his master. Therefore he was not forgiven. For the one condition of forgiveness is repentance. Repentance means, among other things, that I realize that I have no claim upon God at all, and that it is only His grace and mercy that forgive. And it follows as the night the day that the man who truly realizes his position face to face with God, and his relationship to God, is the man who must of necessity be merciful with respect to others.

It is a solemn, serious and, in a sense, terrible thing to say that you cannot be truly forgiven unless there is a forgiving spirit in you. For the operation of the grace of God is such, that when it comes into our hearts with forgiveness it makes us merciful. We proclaim, therefore, whether we have received forgiveness or not by whether we forgive or not. If I am forgiven, I shall forgive. None of us has by nature a forgiving spirit. And if you now have such a spirit, you have it for one reason only. You have seen what God has done for you in spite of what you deserve, and'you say, `I know that I am truly forgiven; therefore, I truly forgive.' `Blessed are the merciful: for they shall obtain mercy.' Because they have already obtained mercy, therefore they are merciful. As we go on through the world we fall into sin. The moment we do so we need this mercy and we get it. And remember the end. In 2 Timothy i. 16-18 Paul inserts a note about Onesiphorus whom he recalls as one who had compassion on him and who visited him when he was a prisoner in Rome. Then he adds: `The Lord grant unto him that he may find mercy of the Lord in that day.' Oh yes, we shall need it then; we shall need it at the end, at the day of judgment when every one of us stands before the judgment seat of Christ and has to give an account of the deeds done in the body. For certain, there will be things which are wrong and sinful, and we shall need mercy in that day. And, thank God, if the grace of Christ is in us, if the spirit of the Lord is in us, and we are merciful, we shall obtain mercy in that day. What makes me merciful is the grace of God. But the grace of God does make me merciful. So it comes to this. If I am not merciful there is only one explanation; I have never understood the grace and the mercy of God; I am outside Christ; I am yet in my sins, and I am unforgiven.

`Let every man examine himself.' I am not asking you what sort of life you are living. I am not asking whether you do this, that or the other. I am not asking whether you have some general interest in the kingdom of God and His house. I am simply asking this. Are you merciful? Are you sorry for every sinner even though that sinner offends you? Have you pity upon all who are the victims and the dupes of the world and the flesh and the devil? That is the test. `Blessed-happy-are the merciful: for they shall obtain mercy.'

CHAPTER TEN

BLESSED ARE THE PURE IN HEART

W "E come now to what is undoubtedly one of the greatest utterances to be found anywhere in the whole realm of Holy Scripture. Anyone who realizes even something of the meaning of the words, `Blessed are the pure in heart: for they shall see God', can approach them only with a sense of awe and of complete inadequacy. This statement, of course, has engaged the attention of God's people ever since it was first uttered, and many great volumes have been written in an attempt to expound it. Obviously, therefore, one cannot hope to deal with it in any exhaustive sense in just one chapter. Indeed, no-one can ever exhaust this verse. In spite of all that has been written and preached, it still eludes us. Our best plan, perhaps, is just to~ try to grasp something of its central meaning and emphasis.

Once again it is important, I feel, to consider it in its setting, and to study its relationship to the other Beatitudes. As we have seen, our Lord did not select these statements at random. Clearly there was a definite sequence of thought, and it is our business to try to discover this. Of course we must always be very careful as we do that. It is interesting to try to discover the order and the sequence in Scripture; but it is very easy to impose upon the sacred text our own ideas as to order and sequence. An analysis of the books of the Bible can be a very useful thing indeed. But there is always the danger that, by imposing our analysis on the Scripture, we shall thereby distort its message. As we seek in this way to discover the order we must bear that warning in mind.

I suggest that the following is a possible way of understanding the sequence. The first question which must be answered is, why is this statement put here? You would have thought, perhaps, that it should have come at the beginning, because the vision of God has always been regarded by God's people as the summum bonum. It is the ultimate goal of every endeavour. To `see God' is the whole purpose of all religion. And yet here it is, not at the beginning, not at the end, not even in the exact middle. That, at once, must raise the question in our minds, why does it come just here? A possible analysis, which commends itself to me, is as follows. I regard the sixth verse as providing the explanation. It comes, as I think we saw when we dealt with it, in the centre; the first three Beatitudes lead up to it and these other Beatitudes follow it. If we regard verse six as a kind of watershed, I think it helps us to understand why this particular statement comes at this point.

Now the first three Beatitudes were concerned with our need, our consciousness of need-poor in spirit, mourning because of our sinfulness, meek as the result of a true understanding of the nature of self and its great ego-centricity, that terrible thing that has ruined the whole of life. These three emphasize the vital importance of a deep awareness of need. Then comes the great statement of the satisfaction of the need, God's provision for it, `Blessed are they which do hunger and thirst after righteousness: for they shall be filled.' Having realized the need, we hunger and thirst, and then God comes with His wondrous answer that we shall be filled, fully satisfied. From there on we are looking at the result of that satisfaction, the result of being filled. We become merciful, pure in heart, peacemakers. After that, there is the outcome of all this, `persecuted for righteousness' sake'. That, I suggest, is the way of approach to this passage. It leads up to the central statement about hungering and thirsting and then describes the results that follow. In the first three we are going up one side of the mountain, as it were. We reach the summit in the fourth, and then we come down on the other side.

But there is a closer correspondence even than that. It seems to me that the three Beatitudes which follow the central statement in verse six correspond to the first three that lead up to it. The merciful are those who realize their poverty of spirit; they realize that they have nothing in themselves at all. As we have seen, that is the most essential step to becoming merciful. It is only when a man has reached that view of himself that he will have the right view of others. So we find that the man who realizes he is poor in spirit and who is utterly dependent upon God, is the man who is merciful to others. It follows from that, that this second statement which we are now considering, namely, `blessed are the pure in heart', also corresponds to the second statement in the first group, which was, `blessed are they that mourn'. What did they mourn about? We saw that they were mourning about the state of their hearts; they were mourning about their sinfulness; they were mourning, not only because they did things that were wrong, but still more because they ever wanted to do wrong. They realized the central perversion in their character and personality; it was that which caused them to mourn. Very well then; here is something which corresponds to that-'blessed are the pure in heart.' Who are the pure in heart? Essentially, as I am going to show you, they are those who are mourning about the impurity of their hearts. Because the only way to have a pure heart is to realize you have an impure heart, and to mourn about it to such an extent that you do that which alone can lead to cleansing and purity. And in exactly the same way, when we come to discuss the `peacemakers' we shall find that the peacemakers are those that are meek. If a person is not meek he is not likely to be a peacemaker.

I do not want to stay longer with this matter of order, but I think it is a possible way of discovering what underlies the precise arrangement which our Lord adopted. We take the three steps in order of need; then we come to the satisfaction; then we look at the results that follow and find that they correspond precisely to the three that lead up to it. This means that, in this amazing and glorious statement about `blessed are the pure in heart: for they shall see God' which comes at this particular point, the emphasis is upon the purity of heart and not upon the promise. If we look at it from that standpoint, I think it will enable us to see why our Lord took this precise order.

Here, then, we are face to face with one of the most magnificent, and yet one of the most solemnizing and searching, statements which can be found anywhere in Scripture. It is, of course, the very essence of the Christian position and ofthe Christian teaching. `Blessed are the pure in heart.' That is what Christianity is about, that is its message. Perhaps the best way of considering it is once more to take the various terms and to examine them one by one.

We begin of course with the `heart'. Here, I repeat, is something which is very characteristic of the gospel. The gospel of Jesus Christ is concerned about the heart: all its emphasis is upon the heart. Read the accounts which we have in the Gospels of the teaching of our blessed Lord, and you will find that all along He is talking about the heart. The same is true in the Old Testament. Our Lord undoubtedly put this emphasis here because of the Pharisees. It was His great charge against them always that they were interested in the outside of the pots and platters and ignored the inside. Looked at externally, they were without spot. But their inward parts were full of ravening and wickedness. They were most concerned about the external injunctions of religion; but they forgot the weightier matters of the law, namely, love to God and the love of one's neighbour. So here our Lord puts this great emphasis upon it again. The heart is the whole centre of His teaching.

Let us for a moment consider this emphasis in terms of a few negatives. He puts His emphasis upon the heart and not upon the head. 'Blessed are the pure in heart.' He does not commend those who are intellectual; His interest is in the heart. In other words we have to remind ourselves again that the Christian faith is ultimately not only a matter of doctrine or understanding or of intellect, it is a condition of the heart. Let me hasten to add that the doctrine is absolutely essential; the intellectual apprehension is absolutely essential; understanding is vital. But it is not only that. We must ever beware lest we stop at giving only an intellectual assent to the faith or to a given number of propositions. We have to do that, but the terrible danger is that we stop at that. When people have had merely an intellectual interest in these matters it has often-times been a curse to the Church. This applies not only to doctrine and theology. You can have a purely mechanical interest in the Word of God, so that merely to be a student of the Bible does not mean that all is well. Those who are interested only in the mechanics of exposition are in no better position than the purely academic theologians. Our Lord says that this is not essentially a matter of the head. It is that, but it is not only that.

But again, why is it that He puts His emphasis upon the heart rather than upon externalities and conduct? The Pharisees, you will remember, were always ready to reduce the way of life and righteousness to a mere matter of conduct, ethics and behaviour. How this gospel finds us all out! Those of you who dislike the intellectual emphasis were probably saying `Amen', as I emphasized that first point. `Yes, that is quite right', you said, `it is not intellectual, it is the life that matters.' Be careful! for Christianity is also not primarily a matter of conduct and external behaviour. It starts with this question: What is the state of the heart?

What is meant by this term, `the heart'? According to the general scriptural usage of the term, the heart means the centre of the personality. It does not merely mean the seat of the affections and the emotions. This Beatitude is not a statement to the effect that the Christian faith is something primarily emotional, not intellectual or pertaining to the will. Not at alt. The heart in Scripture includes the three. It is the centre of man's being and personality; it is the fount out of which every thing else comes. It includes the mind; it includes the will; it includes the heart. It is the total man; and that is the thing which our Lord emphasizes. `Blessed are the pure in heart'; blessed are those who are pure, not merely on the surface but in the centre of their being and at the source of their every activity. It is as deep as that. Now that is the first thing; the gospel always emphasizes that. It starts with the heart.

Then, secondly, it emphasizes that the heart is always the seat of all our troubles. You remember how our Lord put it,'Out of the heart proceed evil thoughts, murders, adulteries, fornications, thefts, false witness, blasphemies'. The terrible, tragic fallacy of the last hundred years has been to think that all man's troubles are due to his environment, and that to change the man you have nothing to do but to change his environment. That is a tragic fallacy. It overlooks the fact that it was in Paradise that man fell. It was in a perfect environment that he first went wrong, so to put man in a perfect environment cannot solve his problems. No, no; it is out of `the heart' that these things arise. Take any problem in life, anything that leads to wretchedness; find out its cause, and you will always discover that it comes from the heart somewhere, from some unworthy desire in somebody, in an individual, in a group or in a nation. All our troubles arise out of this human heart which, we are told by

Jeremiah, is 'deceitful above all things, and desperately wicked: who can know it?' In other words, the gospel not only tells us that all these problems arise out of the heart, but that they do so because the heart of man, as the result of the fall and as the result of sin, is, as Scripture puts it, desperately wicked and deceitful. Man's troubles, in other words, are at the very centre of his being, so that merely to develop his intellect is not going to solve his problems. We should all be aware that education alone does not make a good man; a man may be highly educated and yet be an utterly wicked person. The problem is in the centre, so that mere schemes for intellectual development cannot put us right. Neither can these efforts to improve the environment do so alone. Our tragic failure to realize this is responsible for the state of the world at this moment. The trouble is in the heart, and the heart is desperately wicked and deceitful. That is the problem.

Now we come to the second term. 'Blessed', says our Lord, 'are the pure in heart', and you see again how packed with doctrine these Beatitudes are. We have just been looking at the human heart. Is anybody prepared to say in the light of that, that man can make himself a Christian? You can see God only when you are pure in heart, and we have just seen what we are by nature. It is a complete antithesis; nothing could be further removed from God. What the gospel proposes to do is to bring us out of the terrible pit and to raise us up to the heavens. It is supernatural. Therefore let us look at it in terms of definition. What does our Lord mean by 'pure in heart'? It is generally agreed that the word has at any rate two main meanings. One meaning is that it is without hypocrisy; it means, if you like, 'single'. You remember our Lord talks about the evil eye later on in this Sermon on the Mount. He says, 'If therefore thine eye be single, thy whole body shall be full of light. But if thine eye be evil, thy whole body shall be full of darkness.' This pureness of heart, therefore, corresponds to 'singleness'. It means, if you like, 'without folds'; it is open, nothing hidden. You can describe it as sincerity; it means single-minded, or single-eyed devotion. One of the best definitions of purity is given in Psalm lxxxvi. I I, 'Unite my heart to fear thy name'. The trouble with us is our divided heart. Is not that my whole problem face to face with God? One part of me wants to know God and worship God and please God; but another part wants something else. You remember the way Paul expresses it in Romans vii; `For I delight in the law of God after the inward man: but I see another law in my members, warring against the law of my mind, and bringing me into captivity to the law of sin which is in my members.' Now the pure heart is the heart that is no longer divided, and that is why the Psalmist, having understood his trouble, prayed the Lord to `unite my heart to fear thy name'. `Make it one', he seems to say; `make it single, take out the pleats and the folds, let it be whole, let it be one, let it be sincere, let it be entirely free from any hypocrisy.'

But that is not the only meaning of this term `purity'. It also obviously carries the further meaning of `cleansed', `without defilement'. In Revelation xxi. 27 John tells us concerning the people who are to be admitted into the heavenly Jerusalem that is to come, that `there shall in no wise enter into it any thing that defileth, neither whatsoever worketh abomination, or maketh a lie: but they which are written in the Lamb's book of life'.

In Revelation xxii. 14 we read, `Blessed arc they that do his commandments, that they may have right to the tree of life, and may enter in through the gates into the city. For without are dogs, and sorcerers, and whoremongers, and murderers, and idolaters, and whosoever loveth and maketh a lie.' Nothing that is unclean or impure, or has any defiling touch about it, shall enter into the heavenly ,Jerusalem.

But perhaps we can perfectly express it by saying that being pure in heart means to be like the Lord Jesus Christ Himself, `who did no sin, neither was guile found in his mouth'--perfect and spotless and pure and entire. Analysing it a little we can say that it means we have an undivided love which regards God as our highest good, and which is concerned only about loving God. To be pure in heart, in other words, means to keep `the first and great commandment', which is that `Thou shalt love the Lord thy God with all thy heart, and with all thy soul, and with all thy mind.'

Reducing it still further, it means that we should live to the glory of God in every respect, and that that should be the supreme desire of our life. It means that we desire God, that we desire to know Him, that we desire to love Him and to serve Him. And our Lord states here that only those who are like that shall see God. That is why I say that this is one of the most solemnizing statements in Holy Scripture. There is a parallel one in the Epistle to the Hebrews which speaks of `holiness, without which no man shall see the Lord'. I cannot understand people who object to the preaching of holiness (I am not referring to the theories about it; I am talking about preaching holiness itself in the New Testament sense), because we have this plain, obvious statement of Scripture that without it `no man shall see the Lord'. Now we have been looking at what holiness really means. I ask once more, therefore, whether there is any folly greater than the folly of imagining that you can ever make yourself a Christian. The whole object of Christianity is to bring us to the vision of God, to see God.

What then is necessary before I can see God? Here is the answer. Holiness, a pure heart, an unmixed condition of being. Yet men and women would reduce all this to just a little matter of decency, of morality or an intellectual interest in the doctrines of the Christian faith. But nothing less than the whole person is involved. `God is light, and in him is no darkness at all.' In the spiritual realm you cannot mix light and darkness, you cannot mix black and white, you cannot mix Christ and Belial. There is no connection between them. Obviously, therefore, only those who are like Him can see God and be in His presence. That is why we must be pure in heart before we can see God.

What is meant by the vision of God? What is meant by saying we shall `see' God? Here again is a matter which has been often written about throughout the long history of the Christian Church. Some of the great Fathers and the early teachers in the Church were much attracted by it and gave a great deal of thought to the problem. Did it really mean that in the glorified state we should see God with the naked eye or not? That was their great problem. Was it objective and visible, or was it purely spiritual? Now it seems to me that, ultimately, that is a question that cannot be answered. I can only put evidence before you. There are statements made in Scripture which seem to indicate one or the other. But at any rate we can say this much. You remember what happened to Moses. On one occasion God took him aside and placed him in the cleft of a rock and said He was going to give Moses a vision of Himself, but told him that he should see only His back parts, suggesting, surely, that to see God is impossible. The theophanies of the Old Testament, namely, those occasions when the Angel of the Covenant appeared in the form of man, surely suggest that this seeing is impossible in a physical sense.

Then you remember the statements made by our Lord Himself. He turned to the people and said on one occasion, `Ye have neither heard his voice at any time, nor seen his shape'suggesting that there is a `shape'. Again He said, `Not that any man hath seen the Father, save he which is of God, he hath seen the Father.' `You have not seen the Father,' said our Lord in effect to the people; `but I who am of God have seen the Father.' `No man bath seen God at any time; the only begotten Son, which is in the bosom of the Father, he hath declared him.' There are the statements by which we are confronted. Then you remember, on another occasion He said, `He that bath seen me bath seen the Father', one of the most cryptic of all the statements. This is what Scripture says on the matter, and it does seem to me that, on the whole, it is unprofitable to spend our time on it. We just do not know. The very Being of God is so transcendent and eternal that all our efforts to arrive at an understanding are doomed at the very outset to failure. Scripture itself, it seems to me--I say it with reverence-does not attempt to give us an adequate conception of the Being of God. Why? Because of the glory of God. Our terms are so inadequate, and our minds are so small and finite, that there is a danger in any attempt at a description of God and His glory. All we know is that there is this glorious promise that, in some way or other, the pure in heart shall see God.

I suggest, therefore, that it means something like this. As with all the other Beatitudes, the promise is partly fulfilled here and now. In a sense there is a vision of God even while we are in this world. Christian people can see God in a sense that nobody else can. The Christian can see God in nature, whereas the nonChristian cannot. The Christian sees God in the events of history. There is a vision possible to the eye of faith that no-one else has. But there is a seeing also in the sense of knowing Him, a sense of feeling He is near, and enjoying His presence. You remember what we are told about Moses in that great eleventh chapter of the Epistle to the Hebrews. Moses endured `as seeing him who is invisible'. That is a part of it, and that is something that is possible to us here and now. `Blessed are the pure in heart.' Imperfect as we are, we can claim that even now we are seeing God in that sense; we are `seeing him who is invisible'. Another way we see Him is in our own experience, in His gracious dealings with us. Do we not say we see the hand of our Lord upon us in this and that? That is part of the seeing of God.

But of course that is a mere nothing as compared with what is yet to be. `Now we see through a glass, darkly.' We see in a way we had not seen before, but it is all still much of an enigma. But then we shall see `face to face'. `Beloved, now are we the sons of God,' John says, `and it doth not yet appear what we shall be: but we know that, when he shall appear, we shall be like him; for we shall see him as he is.' This is surely the most amazing thing that has ever been said to man, that you and I, such as we are, pressed with all the problems and troubles of this modern world, are going to see Him face to face. If we but grasped this, it would revolutionize our lives. You and I are meant for the audience chamber of God; you and I are being prepared to enter into the presence of the King of kings. Do you believe it, do you know it as true of you? Do you realize that a day is coming when you are going to see the blessed God face to face? Not as in a glass, darkly; but face to face. Surely the moment we grasp this, everything else pales into insignificance. You and I are going to enjoy God, and to spend our eternity in His glorious and eternal presence. Read the book of the Revelation, and listen to the redeemed of the Lord as they praise Him and ascribe all glory to Him. The blessedness is inconceivable, beyond our imagination. And we are destined for that. `The pure in heart shall see God', nothing less than that. How foolish we are to rob ourselves of these glories that are here held out before our wondering gaze. Have you in a partial sense already seen God? Do you realize you are being prepared for this, and do you set your affection on it? `Set your affection on things above, not on things on the earth.' Are you looking at these things which are unseen and eternal? Do you spend time in meditating upon the glory that yet awaits you? If you do, the greatest concern of your life will be to have a pure heart.

But how can our hearts become pure? Here again-is a great theme which has occupied attention throughout the centuries. There are two great ideas. First there are those who say there is only one thing to do, that we must become monks and segregate ourselves from the world. `It is a whole-time job', they say. `If I am going to have this pure heart, I have not time for anything else.' There you have the whole idea of monasticism. We must not stay with that, but I would simply point out in passing that it is utterly unscriptural. It is not to be found in the New Testament, for it is something you and I can never do. All such efforts at self-cleansing are doomed to failure. The way of the Scriptures is rather this. All you and I can do is to realize the blackness of our hearts as they are by nature, and as we do so we shall join David in the prayer, `Create in me a clean heart, 0 God; and renew a right spirit within me'. We shall join Joseph Hart in saying:

'Tis thine to cleanse the heart,
To sanctify the soul,
To pour fresh life in every part
And new create the whole.

You can start trying to clean your heart, but at the end of your long life it will be as black as it was at the beginning, perhaps blacker. No! it is God alone who can do it, and, thank God, He has promised to do it. The only way in which we can have a clean heart is for the Holy Spirit to enter into us and to cleanse it for us. Only His indwelling and working within can purify the heart, and He does it by working in us `both to will and to do of his good pleasure'. Paul's confidence was this, that `he which bath begun a good work in you will perform it until the day of Jesus Christ'. That is my only hope. I am in His hands, and the process is going on. God is dealing with me, and my heart is being cleansed. God has set His hand to this task, and I know, because of that, that a day is coming when I shall be faultless and blameless, without spot or wrinkle, without any defilement. I shall be able to enter into the gate of the holy city, leaving everything that is unclean outside, solely because He is doing it.

That does not mean that I therefore remain passive in the matter. I believe that the work is God's; but I also believe what James says, `Draw nigh to God, and he will draw nigh to you.' I want God to draw nigh to me, because, if He does not, my heart will remain black. How is God going to draw nigh to me? You `draw nigh to God, and he will draw nigh to you', says James. `Cleanse your hands, ye sinners; and purify your hearts, ye double minded.' The fact that I know that I cannot ultimately purify and cleanse my heart in an absolute sense does not mean that I should walk in the gutters of life waiting for God to cleanse me. I must do everything I can and still know it is not enough, and that He must do it finally. Or listen again to what Paul says: `It is God which worketh in you both to will and to do of his good pleasure.' Yes, but `mortify therefore your members which are upon the earth'. Strangle them, get rid of them, get rid of everything that stands between you and the goal you are aiming at. `Mortify', put it to death. `If ye through the Spirit', he says again to the Romans, `do mortify the deeds of the body, ye shall live.'

All I have tried to say can be put like this. You are going to see God ! Do you not agree that this is the biggest, the most momentous, the most tremendous thing that you can ever be told? Is it your supreme object, desire and ambition to see God? If it is, and if you believe this gospel, you must agree with John, `Every man that hath this hope in him purifieth himself, even as he is pure.' The time is short, you and I have not long to prepare. The Great Reception is at hand; in a sense the ceremonial is all prepared; you and I are waiting for the audience with the King. Are you looking forward to it? Are you preparing yourself for it? Don't you feel ashamed at this moment that you are wasting your time on things that not only will be of no value to you on that great occasion, but of which you will then be ashamed. You and I, creatures of time as we appear to be, are going to see God and bask in His eternal glory for ever and ever. Our one confidence is that He is working in us and preparing us for that. But let us also work and purify ourselves `even as he is pure'.

CHAPTER ELEVEN

BLESSED ARE THE PEACEMAKERS

A_S we come to consider this further characteristic of the Christian man, we are once more constrained to suggest - -that there is nothing in the whole range of Scripture which so tests and examines and humbles us as these Beatitudes. Here in this statement, `Blessed are the peacemakers,' we have a further outcome and outworking of being filled by God. According to the scheme which we outlined in the last chapter we can see how this corresponds to `blessed are the meek'. I suggested there that there was this correspondence between the Beatitudes which preceded and followed the statement in verse 6-poverty of spirit and being merciful can be regarded together, the mourning for sin and being pure in heart are similarly connected, and, in exactly the same way, the meekness and being peacemakers correspond to each other; and the link between them is always that waiting upon God for that fullness which He alone can give.

Here, then, we are reminded once more that the outworking in the Christian of the Christian life is altogether and entirely different from everything that can be known by any man who is not a Christian. That is the message which recurs in every one of these Beatitudes and which, obviously, our Lord desired to emphasize. He was establishing an entirely new and different kingdom. As we have seen in all our previous studies, there is nothing more fatal than for the natural man to think that he can take the Beatitudes and try to put them into practice. Here once more this particular Beatitude reminds us that this is utterly impossible. Only a new man can live this new life.

We can see that this statement must have come as a very great shock to the Jews. They had the idea that the coming kingdom of the Messiah was to be a military one, a national, materialistic one. People are always ready to materialize the great promises of Scripture (they are still doing it) and the Jews fell into that fatal error. Here our Lord reminded them again at the very beginning that their whole idea was a complete fallacy. They thought the Messiah when He came would set Himself up as a great King, and that He would deliver them from all their bondage and would thus establish the Jews above everybody else as the conquering and the master race. You remember that even John the Baptist seems to have clung to that conception when he sent his two disciples and asked his famous question, `Art thou he that should come? or look we for another?' `I know all about these miracles', he seems to say, `but when is the big thing going to take place?' And you remember how the people were so impressed after our Lord had performed that great miracle of the feeding of the five thousand that they began to say, `This is He undoubtedly', and then they went, we are told, and tried to `take him by force, to make him a king'. It was always like that. But here our Lord says to them, in effect, `No, no; you do not understand. Blessed are the peacemakers. My kingdom is not of this world. If it were, then My citizens would be fighting for this sort of thing. But it is not that; you are entirely wrong in your whole outlook upon it.' And then He gives them this Beatitude and stresses that principle once more.

Surely this should impress us at the present time. Never, perhaps, was there a more appropriate word for this modern world of ours than this Beatitude which we are studying together. There is perhaps no clearer pronouncement of what the Scriptures, and the New Testament gospel especially, have to say about the world, and life in this world, than this. And of course, as I have been trying to point out as we have faced each of these Beatitudes, it is a very highly theological statement. Now I say that again deliberately, for there is no section of the New Testament that has been so misunderstood and abused as the Sermon on the Mount. You remember how it used to be the habit (especially in the early years of this century, and it still lingers) for certain people to say that they had no interest in theology at all, that they utterly disliked the apostle Paul and regarded it as a calamity that he had ever become a Christian; `that Jew', they said, `with his legalistic notions, who came along and foisted his legalism upon the glorious, delightful and simple gospel of Jesus of Nazareth.' They were not interested in the New Testament Epistles at all, but they were tremendously interested, they said, in the Sermon on the

Mount. That was the great need of the world. All that was needed was to take seriously this beautiful idealism thus presented by the Master Teacher of Galilee. All we had to do was to study it and to try to persuade one another to put it into practice. `Not theology', they said; `that has been the curse of the Church. What is needed is this beautiful ethical teaching, this marvellous, moral uplift which is to be found here in the Sermon on the Mount.' The Sermon on the Mount was their favourite portion of Scripture because they maintained it was so un-theological, so utterly lacking in doctrine and dogma and all such wasteful interest.

We are reminded here of the utter folly and futility of such a view of this glorious portion of Scripture. Let me put it like this. Why are peacemakers blessed? The answer is that they are blessed because they are so absolutely unlike everybody else. The peacemakers are blessed because they are the people who stand out as being different from the rest of the world, and they are different because they are the children of God. In other words, I say, we are again plunged immediately into New Testament theology and doctrine.

Let me vary my question. Why are there wars in the world? Why is there this constant international tension? What is the matter with the world? Why have we had these world wars in this century? Why is there a threat of further war and all this unhappiness and turmoil and discord amongst men? According to this Beatitude, there is only one answer to these questionssin. Nothing else; it is just sin. So immediately you are back at the doctrine of man and the doctrine of sin-theology, in fact. The peacemaker, you see, has become different from what he was; there again is essential theology. The explanation of all our troubles is human lust, greed, selfishness, self-centredness; it is the cause of all the trouble and the discord, whether between individuals, or between groups within a nation, or between nations themselves. So you cannot begin to understand the problem of the modern world unless you accept the New Testament doctrine with regard to man and sin, and here it is at once suggested to us.

Or look at it in this way. Why is there so much trouble and difficulty in maintaining peace in the world? Think of all the endless international conferences that have been held in this present century to try to produce peace. Why have they all failed and why are we now coming to the state when very few of us seem to have any confidence in any conference that men may choose to hold? What is the explanation of all this? Why did the League of Nations fail? Why does the United Nations Organization seem to be failing? What is the matter? Now I suggest to you that there is only one adequate answer to that question; it is not political, it is not economic, it is not social. The answer once more is essentially and primarily theological and doctrinal. And it is because the world in its folly and blind ness will not recognize this, that it wastes so much time. The trouble, according to the Scripture, is in the heart of man, and until the heart of man is changed, you will never solve his problem by trying to make manipulations on the surface. If the source of the trouble is in the fountain and the origin from which the stream comes, is it not obviously a waste of time and money and energy to be pouring chemicals into the stream in an attempt to cure the condition? You must go to the source. There is the essential trouble; none of these things can possibly work while man remains what he is. The tragic folly of this twentieth century is our failure to see that. And, alas, it is not only the failure which is found in the world, it is a failure to be found even in the Church herself. How often has the Church been preaching nothing but these human efforts and endeavours, preaching the League of Nations and the United Nations. It is a contradiction of biblical doctrine. Do not misunderstand me. I am not saying you should not make all these efforts internationally; but I am saying that the man who pins his faith to these things is a man who is not regarding life and the world from the standpoint of Scripture. According to the Scripture, the trouble is in the heart of man and nothing but a new heart, nothing but a new man can possibly deal with the problem. It is `out of the heart' that evil thoughts, murders, adultery, fornication, jealousy, envy, malice and all these other things proceed; and while men are like that there will be no peace. What is in, will inevitably come out. I say once more, therefore, that there is nothing I know of in Scripture which so utterly condemns humanism and idealism as this Sermon on the Mount, which has always apparently been the humanists' favourite passage of Scripture. Clearly they have never understood it. They have evacuated it of its doctrine, and have turned it into something which is entirely different.

This teaching, then, is something which is of prime importance at the present hour, because it is only as we see our modern world in proper perspective through these New Testament eyes that we shall even begin to understand it. Are you surprised that there are wars and rumours of wars? You should not be if you are a Christian; indeed you should regard it as a strange and extraordinary confirmation of the biblical teaching. I remember some twenty years ago shocking certain nice Christian people because I could not be very enthusiastic about what was then called the Kellogg pact. I happened to be at a Christian meeting when the news came through of the Kellogg pact, and I remember a very worthy deacon in that meeting getting up and proposing that the meeting should not take its customary form of sharing experiences and considering problems of the spiritual life, but that the whole meeting ought to be given to talking about this Kellogg pact. To him it was such a wonderful thing, it was something that was going to outlaw war for ever, and he was amazed at my lack of enthusiasm. I think I need say no more. Our approach must be doctrinal and theological. The trouble is in the heart of man, and while it is there, these manipulations on the surface cannot possibly deal with the problem in any final sense.

Bearing all that in mind, let us look at this great word positively. The great need of the world today is for a number of peacemakers. If only we were all peacemakers there would be no problems, there would be no troubles. What then is a peacemaker? Obviously again, it is not a matter of natural disposition. It does not mean an easy-going person, it does not mean your `peace at any price' person. It does not mean the sort of man who says, `Anything to avoid trouble'. It cannot mean that. Have we not agreed all along that none of the Beatitudes describe natural dispositions? But not only that. These easy-going, peace-at-anyprice people are often lacking in a sense of justice and righteousness; they do not stand where they should stand; they are flabby. They appear to be nice; but if the whole world were run on such principles and by such people it would be even worse than it is today. So I would add that your true peacemaker is not an 'appeaser', as we say today. You can postpone war by appeasement; but it generally means that you are doing something that is unjust and unrighteous in order to avoid war. The mere avoidance of war does not make peace, it does not solve the problem. This generation ought to know that with particular certainty. No; it is not appeasement.

What is it, then, to be a peacemaker? He is one about whom we can say two main things. Passively, we can say that he is peaceable, for a quarrelsome person cannot be a peacemaker. Then, actively, this person must be pacific, he must be one who makes peace actively. He is not content to 'let sleeping dogs lie', he is not concerned about maintaining the status quo. He desires peace, and he does all he can to produce peace and to maintain it. He is a man who actively sees that there should be peace between man and man, and group and group, and nation and nation. Obviously, therefore, I think we can argue that he is a man who is finally and ultimately concerned about the fact that all men should be at peace with God. There, essentially, is the peacemaker, both passively and actively, negatively and positively pacific, one who not only does not make trouble, but who goes out of his way to produce peace.

What does this involve and imply? Clearly, in view of what I have been saying, it implies the necessity of an entirely new outlook. It must involve a new nature. To sum it up in a phrase, it means a new heart, a pure heart. There is, as we have seen, a logical order in these matters. It is only the man of a pure heart who can be a peacemaker because, you remember, we saw that the person who did not have a pure heart, who had a heart which was filled with envy, jealousy and all such horrible things, could never be a peacemaker. The heart must be cleansed of all that before one can possibly make peace. But we do not even stop at that. To be a peacemaker obviously means that one must have an entirely new view of self, and here you see how it links up with our definition of the meek. Before one can be a peacemaker one really must be entirely delivered from self, from selfinterest, from self-concern. Before you can be a peacemaker you really must be entirely forgetful of self because as long as you are thinking about yourself, and shielding yourself, you cannot be doing the work properly. To be a peacemaker you must be, as it were, absolutely neutral so that you can bring the two sides together. You must not be sensitive, you must not be touchy, you must not be on the defensive. If you are, you will not be a very good peacemaker.

v Perhaps I can best explain it like this. The peacemaker is one who is not always looking at everything in terms of the effect it has upon himself. Now is not that the whole trouble with us by nature? We look at everything as it affects us. `What is the reaction upon me? What is this going to mean to me?' And the moment we think like that there is of necessity war, because everybody else is doing the same thing. That is the explanation of all the quarrelling and discord. Everybody looks at it from the self-centred point of view. `Is this fair to me? Am I having my rights and dues?' They are not interested in the causes they should be serving, or the great thing that brings them all together, this Church, Society, or Organization. It is, `How is this affecting me? What is this doing to me?' Now that is the spirit that always leads to quarrels, misunderstandings and disputes, and it is a negation of being a peacemaker.

The first thing, therefore, we must say about the peacemaker is that he has an entirely new view of himself, a new view which really amounts to this. He has seen himself and has come to see that in a sense this miserable, wretched self is not worth bothering about at all. It is so wretched; it has no rights or privileges; it does not deserve anything. If you have seen yourself as poor in spirit, if you have mourned because of the blackness of your heart, if you have truly seen yourself and have hungered and thirsted after righteousness, you will not stand any longer on your rights and privileges, you will not be asking, `What about nie in this?' You will have forgotten this self. Indeed, can we not agree that one of the best tests of whether we are truly Christian or not is just this: Do I hate my natural self? Our Lord said, `He that loveth his life (in this world) shall lose it.' By this He meant loving ourselves, the natural man, the natural life. That is one of the best tests of whether we are Christian or not. Have you come to hate yourself, your natural self? Can you say with Paul, `O wretched man that I am'? If you have not, and if you cannot, you will not be a peacemaker.

The Christian is a man who has two men in him, the old and the new. He hates the old and says to him, 'Silence! leave me alone ! I have finished with you.' He has a new view of life, and this obviously implies that he has a new view of others also. He is concerned about them; he has come to see them objectively, and is now trying to see them in the light of the biblical teaching. The peacemaker is the man who does not talk about people when they are offensive and difficult. He does not ask, `Why are they like that?' He says, `They are like that because they are still being governed by the god of this world, "the spirit that now worketh in the children of disobedience." That poor person is a victim of self and of Satan; he is hell bound; I must have pity and mercy upon him.' The moment he begins to look at him like that he is in a position to help him, and he is likely to make peace with him. So you must have an entirely new view of the other person.

It also means an entirely new view of the world. The peacemaker has only one concern, and it is the glory of God amongst men. That was the Lord Jesus Christ's only concern. His one interest in life was not Himself, but the glory of God. And the peacemaker is the man whose central concern is the glory of God, and who spends his life in trying to minister to that glory. He knows that God made man perfect, and that the world was meant to be Paradise, so when he sees individual and international disputes and quarrelling, he sees something that is detracting from the glory of God. This is the thing that concerns him, nothing else. Very well; with these three new views this is what follows. He is a man who is ready to humble himself, and he is ready to do anything and everything in order that the glory of God may be promoted. He so desires this that he is prepared to suffer in order to bring it to pass. He is even prepared to suffer wrong and injustice in order that peace may be produced and God's glory magnified. You see he has finished with himself and with self-interest and self-concern. He says, `What matters is the glory of God and the manifestation of that amongst men.' So that if his suffering is going to lead to that, he will endure it.

Now that is the theory. But what about the practice? This is very important, because to be a peacemaker does not mean that you sit in a study and theoretically work out this principle. It is in practice that you prove whether you are a peacemaker or not. So I do not apologize for putting it very simply, indeed in almost an elementary manner. How does this work out in practice? First and foremost it means that you learn not to speak. If only we could all control our tongues there would be much less discord in this world. James, with his practical turn of mind, puts it perfectly: `Be swift to hear, slow to speak, slow to wrath.' That, I say, is one of the best ways of being a peacemaker, that you just learn not to speak. When, for example, something is said to you, and the temptation is to reply, do not do it. Not only that; do not repeat things when you know they are going to do harm. You are not a true friend when you tell your friend something unkind that was said about him by somebody else. It does not help; it is a false friendship. Moreover, apart from anything else, unworthy and unkind things are not worth repeating. We must control our tongues and our lips. The peacemaker is a man who does not say things. He often feels like saying them, but for the sake of peace he does not. The natural man is so strong in us. You often hear Christian people say, `I must express my mind'. What if everybody were like that! No; you must not excuse yourself or talk in terms of what you are by nature. As Christians you are meant to be new men, made after the image and pattern of the Lord Jesus Christ, `swift to hear, slow to speak, slow to wrath.' If I were preaching on the international situation my one main comment at the present time would be this. I believe there is far too much talking going on in the international realm; I cannot see it does any good to be constantly blackguarding another nation. It is never a good thing to say these unkind, unpleasant things. You can organize for war; you can organize for peace; but stop talking. One of the first things in making peace is to know when not to speak.

The next thing I would say is that we should always view any and every situation in the light of the gospel. When you face a situation that tends to lead to trouble, not only must you not speak, you must think. You must take the situation and put it into the context of the gospel and ask, `What are the implications of this? It is not only I who am involved. What about the Cause? what about the Church? what about the Organization? what about all the people who are dependent? what about the people who are right outside?' The moment you think of it like that you are beginning to make peace. But as long as you are thinking of it in a personal sense there will be war.

The next principle which I would ask you to apply would be this. You must now become positive and go out of your way to look for means and methods of making peace. You remember that mighty word, `If thine enemy hunger, feed him.' There is your enemy, who has been saying terrible things about you. Well, you have not answered him, you have controlled your tongue. Not only that, you have said, `I can see it is the Devil that is in him and therefore I must not answer him. I must have pity and pray that God will deliver him and show him himself as the dupe of Satan.' Good; that is the second step. But you must go beyond that. He is hungry, things have gone wrong for him. Now you begin to seek for ways of relieving him. You are becoming positive and active. It may mean sometimes that you, as we put it so foolishly, have to humble yourself and approach the other person. You have to take the initiative in speaking to him, perhaps apologizing to him, trying to be friendly, doing everything you can to produce peace.

And the last thing in the practical realm is that, as peacemakers, we should be endeavouring to diffuse peace wherever we are. We do this by being selfless, by being lovable, by being approachable and by not standing on our dignity. If we do not think of self at all, people will feel, `I can approach that person, I know I shall get sympathy and understanding, I know I shall get an outlook which is based upon the New Testament.' Let us be such people that all will come to us, that even those who have a bitter spirit within them will somehow feel condemned when they look at us, and perhaps may be led to speak to us about themselves and their problems. The Christian is to be a man like that.

Let me sum it all up like this: the benediction pronounced on such people is that they `shall be called the children of God'. Called means `owned'. `Blessed are the peacemakers: for they shall be "owned" as the children of God.' Who is going to own them? God is going to own them as His children. It means that the peacemaker is a child of God and that he is like his Father. One of the most glorious definitions of the being and character of God in the Bible is contained in the words, `the God of peace, that brought again from the dead our LordJesus' (Heb. xiii. zo). And Paul, in his Epistle to the Romans, speaks twice of'the God of peace' and prays that his readers will themselves be granted peace by God the Father. What is the meaning of the advent? Why did the Son of God ever come into this world? Because God, though He is holy and just and righteous and absolute in all His qualities, is a God of peace. That is why He sent His Son. Where did war come from? From man, from sin, from Satan. Discord was brought into the world in that way. But this blessed God of peace has not, I say it with reverence, `stood upon His dignity'; He has come, He has done something. God has made peace. He has humbled Himself in His Son to produce it. That is why the peacemakers are `children of God'. What they do is to repeat what God has done. If God stood upon His rights and dignity, upon His Person, every one of us, and the whole of mankind, would be consigned to hell and absolute perdition. It is because God is a `God of peace' that He sent His Son, and thus provided a way of salvation for us. To be a peacemaker is to be like God, and like the Son of God. He is called, you will remember, `the Prince of Peace', and you know what He did as the Prince of Peace. Though He counted it not robbery to be equal with God, He humbled Himself. There was no need for Him to come. He came deliberately because He is the Prince of Peace.

But beyond that, how has He made peace?. Paul, in writing to the Colossians, says `having made peace through the blood of his cross'. He gave Himself that you and I might be at peace with God, that we might have peace within and that we might have peace with one another. Take that glorious statement of the second chapter of Ephesians, `For he is our peace, who hath made both one, and hath broken down the middle wall of partition between us; having abolished in his flesh the enmity, even the law of commandments contained in ordinances; for to make in himself of twain one new man, so making peace.' It is all there, and that is why I kept that to the end, that we might remember, whatever else we may forget, that to be a peacemaker is to be like that. He did not clutch at His rights; He did not hold on to the prerogative of deity and of eternity. He humbled Himself; He came in the likeness of a man, He humbled Himself even to the death of the cross. Why? He was not thinking of Himself at all. `Let this mind be in you, which was also in Christ Jesus.' `Look not every man on his own things, but every man also on the things of others.' That is the New Testament teaching. You finish with self, and then you begin to follow Jesus Christ. You realize what He did for you in order that you might enjoy that blessed peace of God, and you begin to desire that everybody else should have it. So, forgetting self, and humbling self, you follow in His steps `who did no sin, neither was guile found in his mouth: who, when he was reviled, reviled not again; when he suffered, he threatened not; but committed himself to him that judgeth righteously.' That is it. God give us grace to see this blessed, glorious truth, and make us reflections, reproducers of the Prince of Peace, and truly children of `the God of peace'.

CHAPTER TWELVE

THE CHRISTIAN AND PERSECUTION

W E come in verse i o to the last of the Beatitudes, `Blessed are they which are persecuted for righteousness' sake.' It is generally agreed that verses i i and i 2 are a kind of elaboration of this Beatitude, and perhaps an application of its truth and message to the disciples in particular. In other words, our Lord has finished the general portrayal of the characteristics of the Christian man by the end of verse io, and He then applies this last statement in particular to the disciples.

At first, this Beatitude seems to be rather different from all the others in that it is not so much a positive description of the Christian as an account of what is likely to result because of what has gone before and because the Christian is what we have seen him to be. Yet ultimately it is not different because it is still an account and description of the Christian. He is persecuted because he is a certain type of person and because he behaves in a certain manner. The best way of putting it, therefore, would be to say that, whereas all the others have been a direct description, this one is indirect. `This is what is going to happen to you because you are a Christian', says Christ.

Nov it is interesting to observe that this particular Beatitude follows immediately the reference to the peacemakers. In a sense it is because the Christian is a peacemaker that he is persecuted. What a wealth of insight and understanding that gives us into the nature and character of the Christian life ! I do not think you will ever find the biblical doctrines of sin and the world put more perfectly or precisely anywhere in Scripture than in just these two Beatitudes-'Blessed are the peacemakers', and `Blessed are they which are persecuted for righteousness' sake'. If a Christian man is a peacemaker this is what happens to him.

Another preliminary point of interest is that the promise attached to this Beatitude is the same as the promise attached to the first, `theirs is the kingdom of heaven'. That is, if you like, a further and additional proof of the fact that this is the last Beatitude. You start with the kingdom of heaven and you end with it. It is not, of course, that the various blessings which have been attached to the other Beatitudes do not belong to those who are in the kingdom of heaven, or that they do not get blessings. They all get blessings; but our Lord started and ended with this particular promise in order to impress upon His listeners that the important thing was membership of the kingdom of heaven. As we have seen, the Jews had a false notion about the kingdom. `But,' our Lord says in effect, `I am not talking of this kind of kingdom. The important thing is that you should realize what My kingdom is, and you should know how to become members of it.' So He starts and ends with it. Over and above all these particular blessings which we receive, and which we are to receive in greater measure and greater fullness, the great thing is that we are citizens of the kingdom of heaven and thus belong to that spiritual realm.

Here, again, I think we are entitled to say that we are confronted by one of the most searching tests that can ever face us. Let no-one imagine that this Beatitude is a kind of appendix to the others. In its way it is as positive a description as any that precede it, though it may be indirect; and it is one of the most searching of all. `Blessed are they which are persecuted for righteousness' sake.' What an amazing, astounding and unexpected statement. Yet remember that it is part of the description of the Christian quite as much as being pure in heart, quite as much as being peacemakers, quite as much as being merciful. This is one of the characteristics of the Christian, as I am going to remind you, and that is why it is one of the most searching tests that we can ever face. All these Beatitudes have been searching, but there are ways in which this is even more searching than the others. But let me hasten to add that perhaps there is no Beatitude where we have to be quite so careful, there is no Beatitude that is so liable to misconstruction and misunderstanding. There is certainly no Beatitude that has been so frequently misunderstood and mis-applied. Therefore we must approach it with great circumspection and care. It is a vital statement, an essential and integral part of the whole teaching of the New Testament. You will find it right through the Gospels and the Epistles. Indeed, we can go so far as to say that it is one of the great characteristic messages of the whole Bible, which carries its inevitable implication with it. I suggest, therefore, that the most important thing to emphasize is this phrase, `for righteousness' sake'. It does not merely say, `blessed are they which are persecuted', but `blessed are they which are persecuted for righteousness' sake'.

Now I need not, I am sure, take any time in pointing out what a relevant statement this is for Christian people in every country at this moment. There is more persecution of Christians today, some would say, than there has been since the first centuries of the Christian era; and I think a good case can be made out for that statement. There have been grievous periods of persecution at various epochs in the long history of the Church, but they have generally been more or less localized. Now, however, persecution has spread throughout the world. There are Christian people who are being actively and bitterly persecuted in many countries at this very moment, and there may well be a strong case for saying that this may be the most important verse in your life and mine. There are so many indications that the Church may indeed be facing that fiery trial of which the apostle Peter writes and speaks. He was thinking primarily, of course, of one that was coming in his own day. But it may well be that we in this country, in apparent safety and ease, may know and experience something of the fiery trial and furnace of affliction and of persecution. Let us be clear, then, that we understand this verse and know exactly what it does say.

To that end let us start with a few negatives. It does not say, `Blessed are those who are persecuted because they are objectionable.' It does not say, `Blessed are those who are having a hard time in their Christian life because they are being difficult.' It does not say, `Blessed are those who are being persecuted as Christians because they are seriously lacking in wisdom and are really foolish and unwise in what they regard as being their testimony.' It is not that. There is no need for one to elaborate this, but so often one has known Christian people who are suffering mild persecution entirely because of their own folly, because of something either in themselves or in what they are doing. But the promise does not apply to such people. It is for righteousness' sake. Let us be very clear about that. We can bring endless suffering upon ourselves, we can create difficulties for ourselves which are quite unnecessary, because we have some rather foolish notion of witnessing and testifying, or because, in a spirit of self-righteousness, we really do call it down on our own heads. We are often so foolish in these matters. We are slow to realize the difference between prejudice and principle; and we are so slow to understand the difference between being offensive, in a natural sense, because of our particular make-up and temperament, and causing offence because we are righteous.

So let me put another negative. We are not told, `Blessed are the persecuted because they are fanatical.' Neither does it say, `Blessed are the persecuted because they are over-zealous.' Fanaticism can lead to persecution; but fanaticism is never commended in the New Testament. There are so many temptations that tend to come to us in the spiritual and Christian life. Some people, even in worship, seem to think that they must say their `Amen' in a particular way, or must say it often. Thinking that this is a sign of spirituality, they make themselves a nuisance at times to others and so get into trouble about that. That is not commended in Scripture; it is a false notion of worship. The spirit of fanaticism has also very often led people into grievous difficulties. I once remember a poor man who not only brought suffering upon himself, but also upon his wife on account of his zeal. He was over-zealous, and he was not facing some of the injunctions given by our Lord Himself, because he was so anxious to be testifying. Now let us be careful that we do not bring unnecessary suffering upon ourselves. We are to be `wise as serpents, and harmless as doves'. God forbid that any of us should suffer because we fail to remember that. In other words we are not told, 'Blessed are they who are persecuted because they are doing something wrong,' or because they themselves are wrong in some respect. You remember how Peter put it in his wisdom, `let none of you suffer as a murderer, or as a thief, or as an evildoer'. Let us notice, also, what he put into the same category as murderers, evildoers, thieves and so on-busybodies in other men's matters (see i Pet. iv. 15).

Let me now add another negative from a different category. This text surely does not even mean 'blessed are they that are persecuted for a cause'. This is a little subtle and we must be careful. I say that there is a difference between being persecuted for righteousness' sake and being persecuted for a cause. I know that the two things often become one, and many of the great martyrs and confessors were at one and the same time suffering for righteousness' sake and for a cause. But it does not follow by any means that the two are always identical. Now I think that this is one of the most vital points for us to bear in mind just at this present moment. I think that in the last twenty years there have been men, some of them very well known, who have suffered, and have even been put into prisons and concentration camps, for religion. But they have not been suffering for righteousness' sake. We have to be careful about that very distinction. There is always this danger of our developing the martyr spirit. There are some people who seem anxious for martyrdom; they almost court it. That is not the thing about which our Lord is talking.

We must also realize that it does not mean suffering persecution for religio-political reasons. Now it is the simple truth to say that there were Christian people in Nazi Germany who were not only ready to practise and live the Christian faith but who preached it in the open air and yet were not molested. But we know of certain others who were put into prisons and concentration camps, and we should be careful to see why this happened to them. And I think if you draw that distinction you will find it was generally something political. I need not point out that I am not attempting to excuse Hitlerism; but I am trying to remind every Christian person of this vital distinction. If you and I begin to mix our religion and politics, then we must not be surprised if we receive persecution. But I suggest that it will not of necessity be persecution for righteousness' sake. This is something very distinct and particular, and one of the greatest dangers confronting us is that of not discriminating between these two things. There are Christian people in China and on the Continent at the present time to whom this is the most acute problem of all. Are they standing for righteousness' sake, or for a cause? After all, they have their political views and ideas. They are citizens of that particular country. I am not saying that a man should not stand for his political principles; I am simply reminding you that the promise attached to this Beatitude does not apply to that. If you choose to suffer politically, go on and do so. But do not have a grudge against God if you find that this Beatitude, this promise, is not verified in your life. The Beatitude and the promise refer specifically to suffering for righteousness' sake. May God give us grace and wisdom and understanding to discriminate between our political prejudices and our spiritual principles.

There is much confusion on this very matter at the present time. Much talk which appears to be, and is said to be, Christian, in its denunciation of certain things that are happening in the world, is, I believe, nothing but the expression of political prejudices. My desire is that we might all be saved from this serious and sad misinterpretation of Scripture, which may lead to such needless and unnecessary suffering. Another great danger in these days is that this pure Christian faith should be thought of by those who are outside in terms of certain political and social views. They are eternally distinct and have nothing to do with one another. Let me illustrate this; the Christian faith as such is not anti-communism, and I trust that none of us will be foolish enough and ignorant enough to allow the Roman Catholic Church, or any other interest, to delude and mislead us. As Christians we are to be concerned for the souls of communists, and their salvation, in exactly the same way as we are concerned about all other people. And if once we give them the impression that Christianity is just anti-communism we are ourselves shutting and barring the doors, and almost preventing them from listening to our gospel message of salvation. Let us be very careful, Christian people, and take the words of Scripture as they are.

I.et us look at one final negative; this Beatitude does not even say, Blessed are they that are persecuted for being good, or noble, or self-sacrificing. There again, of course, is another vital and, it seems to some people, subtle distinction. The Beatitude does not say we are blessed if we suffer for being good or noble, for the excellent reason that you will probably not be persecuted for being good. I doubt very much also if you will ever be persecuted for being noble. The world, as a matter of fact, generally praises and admires and loves the good and the noble; it only persecutes the righteous. There are people who have made great sacrifices, those who have given up careers, prospects and wealth and who sometimes have even sacrificed their lives; and the world has thought of them as great heroes and has praised them. So we should suspect immediately that that is not true righteousness. There are certain men today who are acclaimed as very great Christians by the world simply because they have made such sacrifices. That, I suggest, should raise at once a query in our minds as to whether they are really practising the Christian faith, or whether it is not just something else-perhaps a general nobility of character.

What, then, does this Beatitude mean? Let me put it like this. Being righteous, practising righteousness, really means being like the Lord Jesus Christ. Therefore they are blessed who are persecuted for being like Him. What is more, those who are like Him always will be persecuted. Let me show this first of all from the teaching of the Bible. Listen to the way in which our Lord Himself puts it. `If the world hate you, ye know that it hated me before it hated you. If ye were of the world, the world would love his own : but because ye are not of the world, but I have chosen you out of the world, therefore the world hateth you. Remember the word that I said unto you, The servant is not greater than his lord. If they have persecuted me, they will also persecute you' (Jn. xv. 18-20). Now there is no qualification, it is a categorical statement. Listen to His servant Paul putting it in this way, `Yea', says Paul, writing to Timothy, who did not understand this teaching and was therefore unhappy because he was being persecuted, `Yea, and all that will live godly in Christ Jesus shall suffer persecution' (2 Tim. iii. 12). It is again a categorical statement. That is why I said at the beginning that I sometimes think this is the most searching of all the Beatitudes. Are you suffering persecution?

That is the teaching. Let us look at its out-working right through the Bible. For instance, Abel was persecuted by his brother Cain. Moses received grievous persecution. Look at the way in which David was persecuted by Saul, and at the terrible persecution that Elijah and Jeremiah had to endure. Do you remember the story of Daniel, and how he was persecuted? These are some of the most outstanding righteous men of the Old Testament, and every one of them verifies the biblical teaching. They were persecuted, not because they were difficult, or over-zealous, but simply because they were righteous. In the New Testament we find exactly the same thing. Think of the apostles, and the persecution they had to endure. I wonder whether any man has ever suffered more than the apostle Paul, in spite of his gentleness and kindness and righteousness. Read his occasional descriptions of the sufferings that he had to endure. It is not surprising that he said that `all that will live godly in Christ Jesus shall suffer persecution'. He had known and experienced it. But, of course, the supreme example is our Lord Himself. Here He is in all His utter, absolute perfection, and His gentleness and meekness, of whom it can be said that `a bruised reed shall he not break, and smoking flax shall he not quench'. Never was anyone so gentle and so kind. But look at what happened to Him and at what the world did to Him. Read also the long history of the Christian Church and you will find that this statement has been verified endlessly. Read the lives of the martyrs, of John Huss, or the Covenanters, or the Protestant Fathers. Read about it also in more modern times and observe the persecution endured by the leaders of the Evangelical Awakening in the eighteenth century. Not many men have known what it is to suffer as did Hudson Taylor, who lived into our century. He knew what it was to undergo at times grievous persecution. It is just a verification of the statement of this Beatitude.

By whom are the righteous persecuted? You will find as you go through the Scriptures, and as you study the history of the Church, that the persecution is not confined to the world. Some of the most grievous persecution has been suffered by the righteous at the hands of the Church herself, and at the hands of religious people. It has often come from nominal Christians. Take our Lord Himself. Who were His chief persecutors? The Pharisees and scribes and the doctors of the Law! The first Christians, too, were persecuted most bitterly of all by the Jews. Then read the history of the Church, and watch it in the Roman Catholic persecution of some of those men in the Middle Ages who had seen the pure truth and were trying to live it out quietly. How they were persecuted by nominal, religious people ! That was also the story of the Puritan Fathers. This is the teaching of the Bible, and it has been substantiated by the history of the Church, that the persecution may come, not from the outside but from within. There are ideas of Christianity far removed from the New Testament which are held by many and which cause them to persecute those who are trying in sincerity and truth to follow the Lord Jesus Christ along the narrow way. You may well find it in your own personal experience. I have often been told by converts that they get much more opposition from supposedly Christian people than they do from the man of the world outside, who is often glad to see them changed and wants to know something about it. Formal Christianity is often the greatest enemy of the pure faith.

But let me ask another question. Why are the righteous thus persecuted? And, especially, why is it that the righteous are persecuted rather than the good and noble? The answer, I think, is quite simple. The good and noble are very rarely persecuted because we all have the feeling that they are just like ourselves at our best. We think, `I am capable of that myself if I only put my mind to it,' and we admire them because it is a way of paying a compliment to ourselves. But the righteous are persecuted because they are different. That was why the Pharisees and the scribes hated our Lord. It was not because He was good; it was because He was different. There was something about Him that condemned them. They felt all their righteousness was being made to look very tawdry. That was what they disliked. The righteous may not say anything; they do not condemn us in words. But just because they are what they are, they do in fact condemn us, they make us feel unhappy, and we shrivel into nothing. So we hate them for it and try to find fault with them. `You know,' people say, `I believe in being a Christian; but that is much too much, that is going too far.' That was the explanation of Daniel's persecution. He suffered all he did because he was righteous. He did not make a show of it, he did it quietly in his own way. But they said, `This man condemns us by what he is doing; we shall have to catch him.' That is always the trouble, and that was the explanation in the case of our Lord Himself. The Pharisees and others hated Him just because of His utter, absolute holiness and righteousness and truth. And that is why you find gentle, loving, lovable people like Hudson Taylor, to whom I have already referred, suffering terrible and bitter persecution sometimes at the hands of ostensible Christians.

Obviously, then, we can draw certain conclusions from all this. For one thing, it tells us a great deal about our ideas concerning the Person of the Lord Jesus Christ. If our conception of Him is such that He can be admired and applauded by the nonChristian, we have a wrong view of Him. The effect of Jesus Christ upon His contemporaries was that many threw stones at Him. They hated Him; and finally, choosing a murderer instead of Him, they put Him to death. This is the effect Jesus Christ always has upon the world. But you see there are other ideas about Him. There are worldly people who tell us they admire Jesus Christ, but that is because they have never seen Him. If they saw Him, they would hate Him as His contemporaries did. He does not change; man does not change. So let us be careful that our ideas about Christ are such that the natural man cannot easily admire or applaud.

That leads to the second conclusion. This Beatitude tests our ideas as to what the Christian is. The Christian is like his Lord, and this is what our Lord said about him. `Woe unto you, when all men shall speak well of you ! for so did their fathers to the false prophets' (Lk. Vi. 26). And yet is not our idea of what we call the perfect Christian nearly always that he is a nice, popular man who never offends anybody, and is so easy to get on with? But if this Beatitude is true, that is not the real Christian, because the real Christian is a man who is not praised by everybody. They did not praise our Lord, and they will never praise the man who is like Him. `Woe unto you, when all men shall speak well of you!' That is what they did to the false prophets; they did not do that to Christ Himself.

So I draw my next deduction. It concerns the natural, unregenerate man, and it is this. The natural mind, as Paul says, `is enmity against God'. Though he talks about God, he really hates God. And when the Son of God came on earth he hated and crucified Him. And that is the attitude of the world towards Him now.

This leads to the last deduction, which is that the new birth is an absolute necessity before anybody can become a Christian. To be Christian, ultimately, is to be like Christ; and one can never be like Christ without being entirely changed. We must get rid of the old nature that hates Christ and hates righteousness; we need a new nature that will love these things and love Him and thus become like Him. If you try to imitate Christ the world will praise you; if you become Christlike it will hate you.

Finally, let us ask ourselves this question : Do we know what it is to be persecuted for righteousness' sake? To become like Him we have to become light; light always exposes darkness, and the darkness therefore always hates the light. We are not to be offensive; we are not to be foolish; we are not to be unwise; we are not even to parade the Christian faith. We are not to do anything that calls for persecution. But by just being like Christ persecution becomes inevitable. But that is the glorious thing. Rejoice in this, say Peter and James. And our Lord Him- selfsays, `Blessed are ye, happy are ye, ifyou are like that.' Because if ever you find yourself persecuted for Christ and for righteousness' sake, you have in a sense got the final proof of the fact that you are a Christian, that you are a citizen of the kingdom of heaven. `Unto you,' says Paul to the Philippians, `unto you it is given in the behalf of Christ, not only to believe on him, but also to suffer for his sake' (Phil. i. 29). And I look at those first Christians persecuted by the authorities and I hear them thanking God that at last they had been accounted worthy to suffer for the Name's sake.

May God through His Holy Spirit give us great wisdom, discrimination, knowledge and understanding in these things, so that if ever we are called upon to suffer, we may know for certain that it is for righteousness' sake, and may have the full comfort and consolation of this glorious Beatitude.

CHAPTER THIRTEEN

REJOICING IN TRIBULATION

As we suggested in the last chapter, verses i i and r 2 are an extension of the statement in verse io. They extend - - and apply that Beatitude to the particular condition of the disciples whom our Lord was addressing at that time, and through them, of course, to all other Christians in every subsequent age of the Church. Yet there is a sense, also, in which we can say that this amplification of the Beatitude adds somewhat to its meaning and thereby brings out certain further truths about the Christian.

As we have seen, all these Beatitudes when taken together are meant to be a delineation of the Christian man. They present a composite picture, so that each one of them should show a part of the Christian character. The Christian is a difficult man to describe, and undoubtedly the best way of doing so is to depict the various qualities that he manifests.

In this amplification of the last Beatitude our Lord again throws much light upon the character of the Christian. As we have seen repeatedly, there are two main ways of looking at him. You can look at him as he is, in and of himself, and you can also look at him in his reaction to the various things that happen to him in this life and world. There are certain positive statements you can always make about the Christian. But you learn still more. about him when you look at him in his contact with people and in his behaviour with respect to them. The two verses we are now considering belong to that second class, for we see the Christian's reactions to this matter of persecution. There are three principles with regard to the Christian which emerge very clearly from what our Lord tells us here. They are quite obvious; and yet I think that often we must all plead guilty to the fact that we forget them.

The first is once again that he is unlike everybody who is not a Christian. We have repeated that many times already because it is surely the principle that our Lord wished to stress above everything else. He Himself said, you remember, `Think not that I am come to send peace on earth : I came not to send peace, but a sword' (Mt. x. 34). In other words, `The effect of My ministry is going to be a division, a division even between the father and the son, and the mother and the daughter; and a man's foes may very well be those of his own household.' The gospel of Jesus Christ creates a clear-cut division and distinction between the Christian and the non-Christian. The non-Christian himself proves that by persecuting the Christian. The way in which he persecutes him does not matter; the fact is, that in some shape or form, he is almost certain to do so. There is an antagonism in the non-Christian towards the true Christian. That is why, as we saw in our last chapter, the last Beatitude is such a subtle and profound test of the Christian. There is something, as we saw, about the Christian character, due to its being like the character of our Lord Himself, which always calls forth this persecution. No-one was ever so persecuted in this world as the Son of God Himself, and `the servant is not greater than his lord'. So he experiences the same fate. That, then, can be seen here as a very clear and striking principle. The non-Christian tends to revile, to persecute, and to speak all manner of evil falsely against the Christian. Why? Because he is fundamentally different, and the rion-Christian recognizes this. The Christian is not just like everybody else with a slight difference. He is essentially different; he has a different nature and he is a different man.

The second principle is that the Christian's life is controlled and dominated by Jesus Christ, by his loyalty to Christ, and by his concern to do everything for Christ's sake. `Blessed are ye, when men shall revile you, and persecute you, and shall say all manner of evil against you falsely, for my sake.' Why are they persecuted? Because they are living for Christ's sake. From this I deduce that the whole object of the Christian should be to live for Christ's sake and no longer to live for his own. People are unpleasant to one another and may persecute one another, even when they are not Christian, but that is not for Christ's sake. The peculiar thing about the persecution of the Christian is that it is `for Christ's sake'. The Christian's life should always be controlled and dominated by the Lord Jesus Christ, and by considerations of what will be well-pleasing in

His sight. That is something which you find everywhere in the New Testament. The Christian, being a new man, having received new life from Christ, realizing that he owes everything to Christ and His perfect work, and particularly to His death upon the cross, says to himself, `I am not my own; I have been bought with a price'. He therefore wants to live his whole life to the glory of Him who has thus died for him, and bought him, and risen'again. So he desires to present himself, `body, soul and spirit', everything to Christ. This, you will agree, is something that was not only taught by our Lord; it is emphasized everywhere in all the New Testament Epistles. `For Christ's sake' is the motive, the great controlling motive in the life of the Christian. Here is something that differentiates us from everybody else and provides a thorough test of our profession of the Christian faith. If we are truly Christian, our desire must be, however much we may fail in practice, to live for Christ, to glory in His name and to live to glorify Him.

The third general characteristic of the Christian is that his life should be controlled by thoughts of heaven and of the world to come. `Rejoice, and be exceeding glad: for great is your reward in heaven: for so persecuted they the prophets which were before you.' This again is something that is all a part of the warp and woof of the New Testament teaching. It is vital and is, indeed, to be found everywhere. Look at that marvellous summary of the Old Testament in Hebrews xi. Consider these men, the author is saying, these heroes of the faith. What was their secret? It was just that they said, `Here we have no continuing city, but we seek one to come.' They were all men who were looking `for a city which hath foundations, whose builder and maker is God'. That is the secret. It must therefore be an essential part of the differentia of the Christian man, as we are reminded here. Again you see this obvious difference between the Christian and the non-Christian. The non-Christian does everything he can not to think of the world beyond. That is the whole meaning of the pleasure mania of today. It is just a great conspiracy and effort to stop thinking, and especially to avoid thinking of death and the world to come. That is typical of the non-Christian; there is nothing he so hates as talking about death and eternity. But the Christian, on the other hand, is a man who thinks a great deal about these things, and dwells upon them; they are great controlling principles and factors in the whole of his life and outlook.

Let us now see how all these three principles are illustrated in terms of the way in which the Christian faces persecution. That is how our Lord presents it. In showing how the Christian faces persecution He makes three specific statements. As we look at them together, let us remind ourselves again that these verses apply only to those who are really being persecuted falsely for Christ's sake and for no other reason. Our Lord was so concerned about it that He repeats it. The blessings of the Christian life are promised only to those who obey the conditions, and there is always a condition attached to every promise. The condition that is attached here is that the persecution must not in any sense be because of what we are as natural men; it is because of what we are as new men in Christ Jesus.

Let us look first of all at the way in which the Christian should face persecution. Again we need not waste any time in considering the form the persecution may take. We are all familiar with that. It may be violent; it may mean being arrested and thrown into prison or concentration camp. That is happening to thousands of our fellow Christians in this world today. It can take the form of men actually being shot, or murdered in some other way. It may take the form of a man losing his post. It may manifest itself just by sneering and jeering and laughter as he enters the room. It may take the form of a kind ofwhispering campaign. There is no end to the ways in which the persecuted may suffer. But that is not what matters. What really matters is the way in which the Christian faces these things. Our Lord tells us here how we are to do so.

We can put it first of all negatively. The Christian must not retaliate. It is very difficult not to do so, and more difficult for some of us than for others. But our Lord did not do so, and we who are His followers are to be like Him. So we must `stay the angry word'; we must not reply. To retaliate is just to be like the natural man who always does reply; by nature he has the instinct of self-preservation and the desire to get his own back. But the Christian is different, different in nature; so he must not do that.

Furthermore, not only must he not retaliate; he must also not feel resentment. That is much more difficult. The first thing you do is to control your actions, the actual reply. But our Lord is not content with that, because to be truly Christian is not simply to live in a state of repression. You have to go beyond that; you have to get into the state in which you do not even resent persecution. I think you will all know from experience the difference between these two things. We may have come to see long ago that to lose our temper over a thing, or to manifest annoyance, is dishonouring to our Lord. But we still may feel it, and feel it intensely, and be hurt about it and resent it bitterly. Now the Christian teaching is that we must get beyond that. We see in Philippians i how the apostle Paul had done so. He was a very sensitive man-his Epistles make that plain-and he could be grievously hurt and wounded. His feelings had been hurt, as he shows quite clearly, by the Corinthians, the Galatians and others; and yet he has now come to the state in which he really is no longer affected by these things. He says he does not even judge his own self; he has committed the judgment to God.

We must therefore not even resent what is done to us. But we must go further, because these things are very subtle. If we know the psychology of our own souls, and the psychology of the Christian life-using the term `psychology' in its real sense and not in its modern, perverted sense-we must realize that we must go a step beyond that. The third negative is that we must never be depressed by persecution. After you have done the first two, you may still find that the thing is casting you down and making you feel generally unhappy. Not the thing itself, perhaps; but somehow a sense of depression or oppression covers your soul and spirit. It is not that you feel any resentment to a particular person; but you say to yourself, `Why should it be like this? Why am I being treated thus?' So a feeling of depression in your spiritual life seems to settle down upon you, and you tend to lose control of your Christian living. That again is something which our Lord denounces. He puts it positively by saying explicitly, `Rejoice, and be exceeding glad.' We have seen frequently in our consideration of these Beatitudes, that they do show more clearly than anything else perhaps in the New Testament the utter fallacy and futility of imagining that men can make themselves Christian by their own e6orts. This is what it means to be a Christian. When you are persecuted and people are saying all manner of evil against you falsely, you `rejoice' and are `exceeding glad'. Now that to the natural man is an utter impossibility. He cannot even control his spirit of retaliation. Still less can he rid himself of a sense of resentment. But to `rejoice and be exceeding glad' in such circumstances is something he will never do. That, however, is the position to which the Christian is called. Our Lord says we must become like Him in these matters. The author of the Epistle to the Hebrews puts it in one verse. `Who for the joy that was set before him endured the cross, despising the shame.'

That, then, is our first proposition. We have looked at the way in which the Christian, in actual practice, faces persecution. Now let us ask a second question. Why is the Christian to rejoice like this, and how is it possible for him to do so? Here we come to the heart of the matter. Obviously the Christian is not to rejoice at the mere fact of persecution. That is always something which is to be regretted. Yet you will find as you read Christian biographies that certain saints have faced that temptation very definitely. They have rejoiced wrongly in their persecution for its own sake. Now that, surely, was the spirit of the Pharisees, and is something which we should never do. If we rejoice in the persecution in and of itself, if we say, 'Ali, well; I rejoice and am exceeding glad that I am so much better than those other people, and that is why they are persecuting me', immediately we become Pharisees. Persecution is something that the Christian should always regret; it should be to him a source of great grief that men and women, because of sin, and because they, are so dominated by Satan, should behave in such an inhuman and devilish manner. The Christian is, in a sense, one who must feel his heart breaking at the effect of sin in others that makes them do this. So he never rejoices in the fact of persecution as such.

Why then does he rejoice in it? Why should he be exceeding glad? Here are our Lord's answers. The first is that this persecution which he is receiving for Christ's sake is proof to the Christian of who he is and what he is. `Rejoice, and be exceeding glad: for great is your reward in heaven: for so persecuted they the prophets which were before you.' So if you find you are being persecuted and maligned falsely for Christ's sake, you know you are like the prophets, who were God's chosen servants, and who are now with God, rejoicing in glory. Now that is something to rejoice about. This is one of the ways in which our Lord turns everything into a victory. In a sense He makes even the devil a cause of blessing. The devil through his agencies persecutes the Christian and makes him unhappy. But if you look at it in the right way, you will find a cause for rejoicing, and will turn to Satan and say, `Thank you; you are giving me proof that I am a child of God, otherwise I should never be persecuted like this for Christ's sake.' James, in his Epistle, argues likewise that this is proof of your calling and sonship; it is something which makes you know for certain you are a child of God.

Or, take the second argument to prove this. It means, of course, that we have become identified with Christ. If we are thus being maligned falsely and persecuted for His sake, it must mean that our lives have become like His. We are being treated as our Lord was treated, and therefore we have proof positive that we do indeed belong to Him. As we saw, He Himself prophesied'before His going that this was going to happen and this teaching is found everywhere in the New Testament. The apostle Paul, for example, says, `Unto you it is given in the behalf of Christ, not only to believe on him, but also to suffer for his sake.' So that, as the Christian receives this kind of persecution, he finds that second proof of the fact that he has indeed become a child of God. It has established who he is and what he is, and in that he rejoices.

The second cause of rejoicing and of joy is, of course, that this persecution is proof also of where we are going. `Rejoice, and be exceeding glad.' Why? `For great is your reward in heaven.' Here is one of these great central principles that you find running all the way through the Bible. It is this consideration of the end, our final destiny. If this happens to you, says Christ in effect, it is just the hall-mark of the fact that you are destined for heaven. It means you have a label on; it means your ultimate destiny is fixed. By thus persecuting you the world is just telling you that you do not belong to it, that you are a man apart; you belong to another realm, thus proving the fact that you are going to heaven. And that, according to Christ, is something which causes us always to rejoice and be exceeding glad. Here another great test of the Christian life and profession emerges. As I have already pointed out, the question we ask ourselves is whether that is a cause of rejoicing, whether this proof, given by the world, that we are going to heaven and to God, is something that does truly fill us with this sense ofjoyful anticipation. Let me put it like this. Do you believe the cause of the gladness and the rejoicing should be our consciousness of the reward that awaits us? `Rejoice, and be exceeding glad: for great is your reward in heaven.'

Let us look at it in this way. According to this argument, my whole outlook upon everything that happens to me should be governed by these three things: my realization of who I am, my consciousness of where I am going, and my knowledge of what awaits me when I get there. You will find this argument in many places in the Scriptures. The apostle Paul once put it like this, `Our light affliction, which is but for a moment, worketh for us a far more exceeding and eternal weight of glory; while we look not at the things which are seen, but at the things which are not seen: for the things which are seen are temporal; but the things which are not seen are eternal' (2 Cor. iv. 17, i8). The Christian should always be looking at that.

But let me consider certain objections at this point. Someone may ask, Is this idea of a reward a right one for the Christian to entertain? Should a Christian ever be governed in his motives by a thought concerning the reward that remains for him in heaven? You know it was the tendency, particularly in the early part of this century (one does not hear it quite so often now), for people to say, `I do not like these ideas of seeking a reward and of fearing punishment. I believe that the Christian life should be lived for its own sake.' Such people say that they are not interested in heaven and hell; it is this wonderful life of Christianity itself that they are interested in. You remember they used to tell the story of the woman who was to be seen walking in an Eastern country carrying a bucket of water in one hand and a bucket of fuel with live coals of fire in the other hand. Somebody asked her what she was going to do, and she said she was going to drown hell with one and burn up heaven with the other. This idea, that you are not interested in reward or fear of punishment, but are just wonderful people who, with no ulterior motive, are enjoying a pure joy in Christian living, appeals to many.

Now these people consider themselves to be exceptional Christians. But the answer we give them is that their attitude is quite unscriptural, and any teaching that goes beyond the Scriptures is always wrong, however wonderful it may seem to be. Everything must be tested by the teaching of the Bible: and here it is in this one verse-`Rejoice, and be exceeding glad: for great is your reward in heaven.' Are we not even told by the author of the Epistle to the Hebrews, as I have already reminded you, that Christ endured the cross, and despised the shame `for the joy that was set before him'? It was by looking beyond it to what was coming that He endured.

We find this everywhere. The apostle Paul says in i Corinthians iii that what really controlled his whole life, and especially his ministry, was the fact that in the day that was coming every man's work would be tried `as by fire'. `I am very careful what I build on this one and only foundation,' he says, in effect; `whether I build wood, or hay, or stubble, or precious metal. The day is coming and will declare it. Every man's work shall be judged and every man shall be rewarded according to his work' (see t Cor. iii. 10-15). The reward counted a great deal in the life of this man. Again, in 2 Corinthians v, he writes, `We must all appear before the judgment seat of Christ; that every one may receive the things done in his body, according to that lie hath done, whether it be good or bad. Knowing therefore the terror of the Lord, we persuade men' (2 Cor. v. io, ii). And when, in his second Epistle to Timothy, he comes to look back across his life, he thinks about the crown that is laid up for him, that wonderful crown which the blessed Lord is going to put upon his brow. That is the scriptural teaching. Thank God for it. These things are written for our encouragement. The gospel is not impersonal, it is not inhuman. This whole idea of the reward is there, and we are meant to think about these things, and to meditate upon them. Let us be careful that we do not set up an idealistic philosophy in the place of the Scripture and its plain teaching.

But someone may ask a second question. 'How is this reward possible? I thought that all was of grace and man was saved by grace; why speak of reward?' The answer of Scripture seems to be that even the reward itself is of grace. It does not mean that we merit or deserve salvation. It just means that God treats us as a Father. The father tells the child that there are certain things he wants him to do, and that it is his duty to do them. He also tells him that if he does them he will give him a reward. It is not that the child merits a reward. It is given of grace, and it is the expression of the father's love. So God, of His infinite grace, 'throws these things into the bargain' as it were, and encourages us, and fills us with a sense of love and of gratitude. It is not that any man will ever deserve or merit heaven; but the teaching is, I say, that God does reward His people. We can even go further and say that there are differences in the reward. Take that reference in Luke xii where we read of the servants who are beaten with many and with few stripes. It is a great mystery, but it is clear teaching to the effect that there are rewards. No-one will have a sense of loss or of lack and yet there is a difference. Let us never lose sight of 'the recompense of the reward'.

The Christian is a man who should always be thinking of the end. He does not look at the things which are seen, but at the things which are not seen. That was the secret of those men in the eleventh chapter of Hebrews. Why did Moses not continue as the child of Pharaoh's daughter? Because he chose 'rather to suffer affliction with the people of God, than to enjoy the pleasures of sin for a season'. He had his eye upon the end, 'the recompense of the reward'. He did not stop at thoughts of this life; he looked at death and eternity. He saw the things that abide, he saw 'him who is invisible'. That is how he went on. That is how they all went on. 'Set your affection on things above, not on things on the earth' writes Paul to the Colossians. Does not this word condemn us all? Does it not make foolish the way we look so much at this world and all it has? We know perfectly well that it is all vanishing and disappearing, yet how little we look at those other things. 'Rejoice,' says Christ, 'and be exceeding glad: for great is your reward in heaven.'

What is this reward? Well, the Bible does not tell us much about it, for a very good reason. It is so glorious and wonderful that our human language is of necessity almost bound to detract from its glory. You see even our very language is polluted. Take the word `love'. It has become debased, and we have a wrong impression of it. The same is true of many other expressions such as `glory', `brightness', and `joy'. So there is a sense in which even the Bible cannot tell us about heaven because we should misunderstand it. But it does tell us something like this. We shall see Him as He is, and worship in His glorious presence. Our very bodies will be changed, and glorified, with no sickness or disease. There will be no sorrow, no sighing; all tears shall be wiped away. All will be perpetual glory. No wars or rumours of wars; no separation, no unhappiness, nothing that drags a man down and makes him unhappy, even for a second!

Unmixed joy, and glory, and holiness, and purity and wonder! That is what is awaiting us. That is your destiny and mine in Christ as certainly as we are alive at this moment. How foolish we are that we do not spend our time in thinking about that. Oh, how we cling to this unhappy, wretched world, and fail to think on these things and to meditate upon them. We are all going on to that, if we are Christians, to that amazing glory and purity and happiness and joy. `Rejoice, and be exceeding glad.' And if people are unkind and cruel and spiteful, and if we are being persecuted, well then we must say to ourselves, Ah, unhappy people; they are doing this because they do not know Him, and they do not understand me. They are incidentally proving to me that I belong to Him, that I am going to be with Him and share in that joy with Him. Therefore, far from resenting it, and wanting to hit back, or being depressed by it, it makes me realize all the more what is awaiting me. I have a joy unspeakable and full of glory awaiting me. All this is but temporary and passing; it cannot affect that. I therefore must thank God for it, because, as Paul puts it, it `worketh for us a far more exceeding and eternal weight of glory'.

How often do you think of heaven and rejoice as you think of it? Does it give you a sense of strangeness and of fear, and a desire, as it were, to avoid it? If it does so to any degree, I fear we must plead guilty that we are living on too low a level. Thoughts of heaven ought to make us rejoice and be exceeding glad. True Christian living is to be like Paul and to say, `to me to live is Christ, and to die is gain.' Why? Because it means, `to be with Christ; which is far better,' to see Him and to be like Him. Let us think more about these things, realizing increasingly, and reminding ourselves constantly, that if we are in Christ these things are awaiting us. We should desire them above everything else. Therefore, `Rejoice, and be exceeding glad: for great is your reward in heaven.'

CHAPTER FOURTEEN

THE SALT OF THE EARTH

W "E now come to a new and fresh section in the Sermon on the Mount. In verses 3--12 our Lord and Saviour has been delineating the Christian character. Here at verse 13 He moves forward and applies His description. Having seen what the Christian is, we now come to consider how the Christian should manifest this. Or, if you prefer it, having realized what we are, we must now go on to consider what we must be.

The Christian is not someone who lives in isolation. He is in the world, though he is not of it; and he bears a relationship to that world. In the Scriptures you always find these two things going together. The Christian is told that he must be otherworldly in his mind and outlook; but that never means that he retires out of the world. That was the whole error of monasticism which taught that living the Christian life meant, of necessity, separating oneself from society and living a life of contemplation. Now that is something which is denied everywhere in the Scriptures, and nowhere more completely than in this verse which we are now studying, where our Lord draws out the implications of what He has already been saying. You notice that in the second chapter of his first Epistle, Peter does exactly the same thing. He says, `Ye are a chosen generation, a royal priesthood, an holy nation, a peculiar people; that ye should shew forth the praises of him who hath called you out of darkness into his marvellous light.'

It is exactly the same here. We are poor in spirit, and merciful, and meek, and hungering and thirsting after righteousness in order, in a sense, that we may be `the salt of the earth'. We pass, therefore, from the contemplation of the character of the Christian to a consideration of the function and purpose of the Christian in this world in the mind and the purpose of God. In other words, in these verses that immediately follow, we are told very clearly the relationship of the Christian to the world in general.

177

There are certain senses in which we can say that this question of the function of the Christian in the world as it is today is one of the most urgent matters confronting the Church and the individual Christian at this present time. It is obviously a very large subject, and in many ways an apparently difficult one. But it is dealt with very clearly in the Scriptures. In the verse we are now considering we have a very characteristic exposition of the typical biblical teaching with regard to it. I say it is important because of the world situation. As we saw in our consideration of verses io and i i, it may very well become the most urgent problem for many of us. We saw there that we are likely to experience persecution, that, as the sin that is in the world becomes aggravated, the persecution of the Church is likely to be increased. Indeed, as we know, there are many Christian people in the world today who are already experiencing this. Whatever our conditions may be here, therefore, it behoves us to think this matter through very carefully in order that we may be able to pray intelligently for our brethren, and to help them by means of advice and instruction. Quite apart from the fact of persecution, however, this really is a most urgent question, because it arises even here and now for us in this country. What is to be the relationship of Christian people to society and the world? We are in the world; we cannot contract out of it. But the vital question is, what are we to do about it, what are we called to do as Christians in such a situation? This surely is an essential subject for us to consider. In this verse we have the answer to the question. First of all we shall consider what our text says about the world, and then we can consider what it has to say about the Christian in the world.

`Ye are the salt of the earth.' Now that is not only a description of the Christian; it is a description by implication of the world in which he finds himself. It really stands here for humanity at large, for mankind which is not Christian. What, then, is the biblical attitude towards the world? There can really be no uncertainty with regard to the biblical teaching on this matter. Here we come to what is, in many ways, the crucial problem of this twentieth century, undoubtedly one of the most interesting periods that the world has ever known. I do not hesitate to claim that there has never been a century which has so proved the truth of the biblical teaching as this one. It is a tragic century, and it is tragic very largely because its own life has completely disproved and demolished its own favourite philosophy.

As you know, there never was a period of which so much was expected. It is indeed pathetic to read the prognostications of the thinkers (so-called), the philosophers and poets and leaders, towards the end of the last century. How sad to note that easy, confident optimism of theirs, the things they expected from the twentieth century, the golden era that was to come. It was all based upon the theory of evolution, not only in a biological sense, but still more in a philosophical sense. The controlling idea was that the whole of life was advancing, developing and going upwards. That was what we were told in a purely biological sense; man had risen out of the animal and had arrived at a certain stage of development. But still more was this advance emphasized in terms of the mind and the thought and the outlook of man. Wars were going to be abolished, diseases were being cured, suffering was going to be not only ameliorated but finally eradicated. It was to be an amazing century. Most of the problems were going to be solved, for man had at last really begun to think. The masses, through education, would cease giving themselves to drink and immorality and vice. And as all the nations were thus educated to think and to hold conferences instead of rushing to war, the whole world was very soon going to be Paradise. That is not caricaturing the situation; it was believed confidently. By Acts of Parliament, and by international conferences, all problems would be solved now that man had begun at last to use his mind.

There are not many people living in the world today, however, who believe that. You still find an element of this teaching occasionally appearing in certain places, but surely this question no longer needs to be argued. I remember many years ago when I first began to preach, and when I began to say this kind of thing in public, I was often regarded as an oddity, as a pessimist, and as one who believed in some outmoded theology. For liberal optimism was then very prevalent, in spite of the first world war. But that is no longer so. The fallacy of it all has by now been recognized by all serious thinkers, and book after book is coming out just to explode the whole confident idea of that inevitable progress.

Now theeBible has always:taught that, and it is put perfectly by our Lord when He says, `Ye are the salt of the earth.' What does that imply? It clearly implies rottenness in the earth; it implies a tendency to pollution and to becoming foul and offensive. That is what the Bible has to say about this world. It is fallen, sinful and bad. Its tendency is to evil and to wars. It is like meat which has a tendency to putrefy and to become polluted. It is like something which can only be kept wholesome by means of a preservative or antiseptic. As the result of sin and the fall, life in the world in general tends to get into a putrid state. That, according to the Bible, is the only sane and right view to take of humanity. Far from there being a tendency in life and the world to go upwards, it is the exact opposite. The world, left to itself, is something that tends to fester. There are these germs of evil, these microbes, these infective agents and organisms in the very body of humanity, and unless checked, they cause disease. This is something which is obviously primary and fundamental. Our outlook with regard to the future must be determined by it. And if you bear this in mind you will see very clearly what has been happening during the present century. There is a sense, therefore, in which no Christian should be in the least surprised at what has taken place. If this scriptural position is right, then the surprising thing is that the world is as good as it is now, because within its own very life and nature there is this tendency to putrefaction.

The Bible is full of endless illustrations of this. You see it manifesting itself in the very first book. Though God had made the world perfect, because sin entered, this evil, polluting element at once began to show itself. Read the sixth chapter of Genesis and you find God saying, `My Spirit shall not always strive with man'. The pollution has become so terrible that God has to send the flood. After that there is a new start; but this evil principle still manifests itself and you come to Sodom and Gomorrah with their almost unthinkable sinfulness. That is the story which the Bible is constantly putting before us. This persistent tendency to putrefaction is ever showing itself.

Now that, obviously, must control all our thinking and proposals with regard to life in this world, and with regard to the future. The question in the minds of so many people today is, What lies ahead of us? Clearly if we do not start by holding this biblical doctrine at the centre of our thinking, our prophecy must of necessity be false. The world is bad, sinful and evil; and any optimism with regard to it is not only thoroughly unscriptural but has actually been falsified by history itself.

Let us turn, however, to the second aspect of this statement which is still more important. What does this have to say about the Christian who is in the world, the kind of world at which we have been looking? It tells him he is to be as salt; `ye, and ye alone'-for that is the emphasis of the text-'are the salt of the earth'. What does this tell us? The first thing is that which we have been reminded of in considering the Beatitudes. We are to be unlike the world. There is no need to stress that, it is perfectly obvious. Salt is essentially different from the medium in which it is placed and in a sense it exercises all its qualities by being different. As our Lord puts it here-`If the salt have lost his savour, wherewith shall it be salted? it is thenceforth good for nothing, but to be cast out, and to be trodden under foot of men.' The very characteristic of saltness proclaims a difference, for a small amount of salt in a large medium is at once apparent. Unless we are clear about this we have not even begun to think correctly about the Christian life. The Christian is a man who is essentially different from everybody else. He is as different as the salt is from the meat into which it is rubbed. He is as different as the salt is from the wound into which it is put. This external difference still needs to be emphasized and stressed.

The Christian is not only to be different, he is to glory in this difference. He is to be as different from other people as the Lord Jesus Christ was clearly different from the world in which He lived. The Christian is a separate, unique, outstanding kind of individual; there is to be in him something which marks him out, and which is to be obvious and clearly recognized. Let every man, then, examine himself.

But let us go on to consider more directly the function of the Christian. This is where the matter becomes slightly difficult and often controversial. It seems to me that the first thing which is emphasized by our Lord is that one of the Christian's main functions with respect to society is a purely negative one. Now what is the function of salt? There are those who would say that it is to give health, that it is health- or life-giving. But that seems to me to be a serious misunderstanding of the function of salt. Its business is not to provide health; it is to prevent putrefaction. The principal function of salt is to preserve and to act as an antiseptic. Take, for instance, a piece of meat. There are certain germs on its surface, perhaps in its very substance, which have been derived from the animal, or from the atmosphere, and there is the danger of its becoming putrid. The business of the salt which is rubbed into that meat is to preserve it against those agencies that are tending to its putrefaction. Salt's main function, therefore, is surely negative rather than positive. Now clearly this is a very fundamental postulate. It is not the only function of the Christian in the world, because, as we shall see later, we are also to be the light of the world, but in the first instance this is to be our effect as Christians. I wonder how often we conceive of ourselves in this way, as agents in the world meant to prevent this particular process of putrefaction and decay?

Another subsidiary function of salt is to provide savour, or to prevent food from being insipid. That is undoubtedly a further function of salt (whether a right one or not it is not for me to argue) and it is very interesting to look at it. According to this statement, therefore, life without Christianity is insipid. Does not the world today prove that? Look at the pleasure mania. Clearly people are finding life dull and boring, so they must be rushing out to this entertainment or that. But the Christian does not need these entertainments because he has a savour in lifehis Christian faith. Take Christianity out of life and the world, and what an insipid thing life becomes, especially when one gets old or is on one's deathbed. It is utterly tasteless and men have to drug themselves in various ways because they feel their need of a savour.

The Christian, then, first and foremost, should function in that way. But how is he to do this? Here you find the great answer. Let me put it first in what I regard as the positive teaching of the New Testament. Then we can consider certain criticisms. Here, I think, the vital distinction is between the Church as such and the individual Christian. There are those who say that the Christian should act as salt in the earth by means of the Church's making pronouncements about the general situation of the world, about political, economic and international affairs and other such subjects. Undoubtedly in many churches, if not in the vast majority, that is how this text would be interpreted. People denounce communism, and talk about war, the international situation, and other similar problems. They say that the Christian functions as salt in the earth in this general way, by making these comments upon the world situation.

Now, as I see it, that is a most serious misunderstanding of scriptural teaching. I would challenge anybody to show me such teaching in the New Testament. 'Ali,' they say, `but you get it in the prophets of the Old Testament.' Yes; but the answer is that in the Old Testament the Church was the nation of Israel, and there was no distinction between Church and state. The prophets had therefore to address the whole nation and to speak about its entire life. But the Church in the New Testament is not identified with any nation or nations. The result is that you never find the apostle Paul or any other apostle commenting upon the government of the Roman Empire; you never find them sending up resolutions to the Imperial Court to do this or not to do that. No; that is never found in the Church as displayed in the New Testament.

I suggest to you, therefore, that the Christian is to function as the salt of the earth in a much more individual sense. He does so by his individual life and character, by just being the man that he is in every sphere in which he finds himself. For instance, a number of people may be talking together in a rather unworthy manner. Suddenly a Christian enters into the company, and immediately his presence has an effect. He does not say a word, but people begin to modify their language. He is already acting as salt, he is already controlling the tendency to putrefaction and pollution. Just by being a Christian man, because of his life and character and general deportment, he is already controlling that evil that was manifesting itself, and he does so in every sphere and in every situation. He can do this, not only in a private capacity in his home, his workshop or office, or wherever he may happen to be, but also as a citizen in the country in which he lives. This is where the distinction becomes really important, for we tend to swing from one extreme error to the other in these matters. There are those who say, `Yes, you are quite right, it is not the business of the Church as a Church to intervene in political, economic or social conditions. What I say is that the Christian should have nothing whatsoever to do with these things; the Christian must not register his vote, he must have nothing to do in the control of affairs and society.' That, it seems to me, is an equal fallacy; for the Christian as an individual, as a citizen in a state, is to be concerned about these things. Think of great men, like the Earl of Shaftesbury and others, who, as private Christians and as citizens, worked so hard in connection with the Factory Acts. Think also of William Wilberforce and all that he did with regard to the abolition of slavery. As Christians we are citizens of a country, and it is our business to play our part as citizens, and thereby act as salt indirectly in innumerable respects. But that is a very different thing from the Church's doing so.

Someone may ask, `Why do you draw this distinction?' Let me answer that question. The primary task of the Church is to evangelize and to preach the gospel. Look at it like this. If the Christian Church today spends most of her time in denouncing communism, it seems to me that the main result will be that communists will not be likely to listen to the preaching of the gospel. If the Church is always denouncing one particular section of society, she is shutting the evangelistic door upon that section. If we take the New Testament view of these matters we must believe that the communist has a soul to be saved in exactly the same way as everybody else. It is my business as a preacher of the gospel, and a representative of the Church, to evangelize all kinds and conditions and classes of men and women. The moment the Church begins to intervene in these political, social and economic matters, therefore, she is hampering and hindering herself in her God-appointed task of evangelism. She can no longer say that she `knows no man after the flesh', and thereby she is sinning. Let the individual play his part as a citizen, and belong to any political party that he may choose. That is something for the individual to decide. The Church is not concerned as a Church about these things. Our business is to preach the gospel and to bring this message of salvation to all. And, thank God, communists can be converted and can be saved. The Church is to be concerned about sin in all its manifestations, and sin can be as terrible in a capitalist as in a communist; it can be as terrible in a rich man as in a poor man; it can manifest itself in all classes and in all types and in all groups.

Another way in which this principle works is seen in the fact that, after every great awakening and reformation in the Church, the whole of society has reaped the benefit. Read the accounts of all the great revivals and you will find this. For example, in the revival which took place under Richard Baxter at Kidderminster, not only were the people of the Church revived, but many from the world outside were converted and came into the Church. Furthermore, the whole life of that town was affected, and evil and sin and vice were controlled. This happened not by the Church denouncing these things, not by the Church persuading the Government to pass Acts of Parliament, but by the sheer influence of Christian individuals. And it has always been like that. It happened in the same way in the seventeenth and eighteenth centuries and at the beginning of this century in the revival which took place in 1904-5- Christians, by being Christian, influence society almost automatically.

You find proof of this in the Bible and also in the history of the Church. In the Old Testament after every reformation and revival there was this general benefit to society. Look also at the Protestant Reformation and you will find at once that the whole of life was affected by it. The same is true of the Puritan Reformation. I am not referring to the Acts of Parliament which were passed by the Puritans, but to their general manner of life. Most competent historians are agreed in saying that what undoubtedly saved this country from a revolution such as was experienced in France at the end of the eighteenth century was nothing but the Evangelical Revival. This was not because anything was done directly, but because masses of individuals had become Christian, and were living this better life and had this higher outlook. The whole political situation was affected, and the great Acts of Parliament which were passed in the last century were mostly due to the fact that there were such large numbers of individual Christians to be found in this land.

Finally, is not the present state of society and of the world a perfect proof of this principle? I think it is true to say that during the last fifty years the Christian Church has paid more direct attention to politics and to social and economic questions than in the whole of the previous hundred years. We have had all this talk about the social application of Christianity. Pronouncements have been made and resolutions have been sent from Church Assemblies and the General Assemblies of the various denominations to the governments. We have all been so tremendously interested in the practical application. But what is the result? No-one can dispute it. The result is that we are living in a society which is much more immoral than it was fifty years ago, in which vice and law-breaking and lawlessness are rampant. Is it not clear that you cannot do these things except in the biblical way? Though we try to bring them about directly by applying principles, we find that we cannot do so. The main trouble is that there are far too few Christian people, and that those of us who are Christian are not sufficiently salt. By that I do not mean aggressive; I mean Christian in the true sense. Also, we must admit that it is not true of us that when we enter a room people are immediately controlled in their language and their general conversation because we have arrived. That is where we fail lamentably. One truly saintly man radiates his influence; it will permeate any group in which he happens to be. The trouble is that the salt has lost its saltness in so many instances; and we are not controlling our fellows by being `saints' in the way we should. Though the Church makes her great pronouncements about war and politics, and other major issues, the average man is not affected. But if you have a man working at a bench who is a true Christian, and whose life has been saved and transformed by the Holy Spirit, it does affect others all around him.

That is the way in which we can act as salt in the earth at a time like this. It is not something to be done by the Church in general; it is something to be done by the individual Christian. It is the principle of cellular infiltration. Just a little salt can affect the great mass. Because of its essential quality it somehow or another permeates everything. That, it seems to me, is the great call to us at a time like this. Look at life; look at society in this world. Is it not obviously rotten? Look at the decay that is setting in amongst all classes of people. Look at these horrible divorces and separations, this joking about the sanctities of life, this increase in drink and pilfering. There are your problems, and it is obvious that men by passing Acts of Parliament cannot deal with them. Newspaper articles do not seem to touch them. Indeed nothing ever will, save the presence of an increasing number of individual Christians who will control the putrefaction, and the pollution, and the rottenness, and the evil, and the vice. Every one of us in our circle has thus to control this process, and so the whole lump, the whole mass, will be preserved.

May God give us grace to examine ourselves in the light of this simple proposition. The great hope for society today is an increasing number of individual Christians. Let the Church of God concentrate on that and not waste her time and energy on matters outside her province. Let the individual Christian be certain that this essential quality of saltness is in him, that because he is what he is, he is a check, a control, an antiseptic in society, preserving it from unspeakable foulness, preserving it, perhaps, from a return to a dark age. Before the Methodist Revival, life in London, as you can see in books written at the time and since, was almost unthinkable with its drink and vice and immorality. Is there not a danger that we are going back to that? Is not our whole generation going down visibly? It is you and I and others like us, Christian people, who alone can prevent that. God give us grace to do so. God stir up the gift within us, and make us such that we shall indeed be like the Son of God Himself and influence all who come into contact with us.

CHAPTER FIFTEEN

THE LIGHT OF THE WORLD

I-N verse 1 4 we have, surely, one of the most astounding and extraordinary statements about the Christian that was ever -made, even by our Lord and Saviour Jesus Christ Himself. When you consider the setting, and remember the people to whom our Lord uttered these words, they do indeed become most remarkable. It is a statement full of significance and profound implications with regard to an understanding of the nature of the Christian life. It is a great characteristic of scriptural truth that it can compress, as it were, the whole content of our entire position into a pregnant verse such as this. `Ye', said our Lord, looking out upon those simple people, those entirely unimportant people from the standpoint of the world, `Ye are the light of the world.' It is one of those statements which should always have the effect upon us of making us lift up our heads, causing us to realize once more what a remarkable and glorious thing it is to be a Christian. And of course it thus becomes, as all such statements inevitably become, a very good and thorough test as to our position and our experience. All these statements that are thus made about the Christian always come back to us in that form, and we should always be careful to see that they do this for us. The `ye' referred to in this statement means simply ourselves. The danger always is that we may read a statement like this and think about somebody else, the first Christians, or Christian people in general. But it is ourselves to whom it refers if we truly claim to be Christian.

A statement such as this, then, obviously calls for a detailed analysis. Before attempting this, however, we shall consider it in general and try to draw out from it some of its most obvious implications.

First of all let us look at its negative import or claim. For the real force of the statement is this: `Ye, and ye alone, are the light of the world'; the `ye' is emphatic and it carries that suggestion. Now at once you see there are certain things implied. The first is that the world is in a state of

189

darkness. This, indeed, is always one of the first statements that the Christian gospel has to make. There is no point, perhaps, at which we see this striking contrast between the Christian view of life and all other views more clearly than in a verse such as this. The world is always talking about its enlightenment. That is one of its favourite phrases, particularly since the Renaissance of the fifteenth and sixteenth centuries when men began to take a new interest in knowledge. That is regarded by all thinkers as a great turning-point in history, a great watershed which divides the history of civilizations, and all are agreed that modern civilization, as you and I know it, really did begin then. There was a kind of rebirth of knowledge and learning. The Greek classics were rediscovered; and their teaching and knowledge, in a purely philosophical sense, and still more in a scientific sense, really emerged and began to control the outlook and the lives of many.

Then there was, as you know, a similar revival in the eighteenth century, which actually gave itself this very name of the `Enlightenment'. Any who are interested in the history of the Christian Church and of the Christian faith must reckon with that movement. It was the beginning, in a sense, of the attack upon the authority of the Bible, for it put philosophy and human thought in the position of the authoritative divine revelation and the declaration of God's truth to man. Now that has continued up to this present hour, and the point I am emphasizing is that it always represents itself in terms of light, and men who are interested in that kind of movement always refer to it as `enlightenment'. Knowledge, they say, is that which brings light, and, of course, in so many respects it does. It would be foolish to dispute that. The increase in knowledge about the processes of nature and about physical illnesses and diseases and many other subjects has been truly phenomenal. New knowledge has also thrown greater light upon the working of the whole cosmos, and has given greater understanding with regard to so many different aspects of life. That is why people commonly talk about being `enlightened' as the result of knowledge and of culture. And yet, in spite of all that, this is still the scriptural statement: `Ye, and ye alone, are the light of the world.'

Scripture still proclaims- that the world as such is in a state of gross darkness, and the moment you begin to look at things seriously you can easily prove that this is nothing but the simple truth. The tragedy of our century has been that we have concentrated solely upon one aspect of knowledge. Our knowledge has been a knowledge of things, mechanical things, scientific things, a knowledge of life in a more or less purely biological or mechanical sense. But our knowledge of the real factors that make life life, has not increased at all. That is why the world is in such a predicament today. For, as has often been pointed out, in spite of our having discovered all this great and new knowledge, we have failed to discover the most important thing of all, namely, what to do with our knowledge. That is the essence of the whole problem with regard to atomic power at this moment. There is nothing wrong in discovering atomic power. The tragedy is that we have not yet a sufficient knowledge of ourselves to be able to know what to do with this power now that we have discovered it.

That is the difficulty. Our knowledge has been mechanical and scientific in that pure sense. But when you come back to the great basic and fundamental problems of life and living, of being and existence, is it not obvious that our Lord's statement is still true, that the world is in a state of terrible darkness? Think of it in the realm of personal life and conduct and behaviour. There are many men with great knowledge in many departments of thought who are just tragic failures in their own personal lives. Look at it in the realm of relationships between person and person. At the very time when we have been boasting of our enlightenment and knowledge and understanding, there is this tragic breakdown in personal relationships. It is one of the major moral and social problems of society. Observe how we have multiplied our institutions and organizations. We have to give instruction now concerning things about which people were never instructed in the past. For instance, we now have to have Marriage Guidance classes. Up to this century men and women were married without this expert advice which now seems to be so essential. It all proclaims very eloquently that as regards the great momentous questions of how to live, how to avoid evil, and sin, and all that is base and unworthy, how to be clean, and straight, and pure, and chaste, and wholesome, there is gross darkness. Then, as you come up the scale and look at the relationships between group and group, there is obviously again the same condition and so we have these great industrial and economic problems. On a still higher level, look at the relationships between nation and nation. This century, of all centuries, when we talk so much about our knowledge and enlightenment, is proving that the world is in a state of unutterable darkness with regard to these vital and fundamental problems.

We must go even further than that, however. Our Lord not only pronounces that the world is in a state of darkness, He goes so far as to say that nobody but a Christian can give any helpful advice, knowledge or instruction with respect to it. That is our proud claim and boast as Christian people. The greatest thinkers and philosophers are completely baffled at this present time and I could easily give you many quotations from their writings to prove that. I care not where you look in the realm of pure science or philosophy with regard to these ultimate questions; the writers are completely at a loss to explain or understand their own century. This is because their controlling theory was that all man needed was more knowledge. They believed that if man had knowledge he would inevitably apply it to the solution of his difficulties. But, patently, man is not doing that. He has the knowledge, but he is not applying it; and that is exactly where the `thinkers' are baffled. They do not understand the real problem of man; they are not able to tell us what is responsible for the present state of the world, and still less, therefore, are they able to tell us what can be done about it.

I remember some years ago, reading a review by a wellknown teacher of philosophy in this country of a book which was meant to deal with these problems. He put it very significantly like this. `This book as regards analysis is very good, but it does not go beyond analysis and therefore it does not help. We can all analyse, but the vital question we want answered is, What is the ultimate source of the trouble? What can be done about it? There it has nothing to say,' he said, `though it bears the imposing title of The Condition of Alan.' Now that is very true. You can turn today to the greatest philosophers and thinkers and again and again you will find they will never take you beyond analysis. They are very good at laying out the problem and showing the various factors which operate. But when you ask them what is ultimately responsible for this, and what they propose to do, they just leave you unanswered. Clearly they have nothing to say. There is obviously no light at all in this world apart from the light that is provided by Christian people and the Christian faith. That is no exaggeration. I am suggesting that if we want to be realistic we just have to face that, and realize that when our Lord spoke, nearly two thousand years ago, He not only spoke the simple, startling truth about His own age, but He also spoke the truth with regard to every subsequent age. Let us never forget that Plato, Socrates, Aristotle, and the rest, had given their full teaching several centuries before these words were uttered. It was after that amazing flowering of the mind and the intellect that our Lord made this statement. He looked at this band of ordinary, insignificant people and said, `You and you alone are the light of the world.' Now this is a tremendous and most thrilling statement; and I would say again that there are many respects in which I thank God that I am preaching this gospel today and not a hundred years ago. If I had made that statement a hundred years ago people would have smiled, but they do not smile today. History itself is now proving, more and more, the truth of the gospel. The darkness of the world has never been more evident than it is now, and here comes this astonishing and startling statement. That, then, is the negative implication of our text.

Now let us consider its positive implications. It says `ye'. In other words its claim is that the ordinary Christian, though he may never have read any philosophy at all, knows and understands more about life than the greatest expert who is not a Christian. This is one of the great major themes of the New Testament. The apostle Paul in writing to the Corinthians puts it quite explicitly when he says, `the world by wisdom knew not God,' and therefore `it pleased God by the foolishness of preaching to save them that believe'. This thing that appears to be utterly ridiculous to the world is the pure wisdom of God. This is the extraordinary paradox with which we are confronted. Its implication must be quite obvious; it shows that we are called to do something positive. This is the second statement which our Lord makes with regard to the function of the Christian in this world. Having described the Christian in general in the Beatitudes, the first thing He then says is, `You are the salt of the earth.' Now He says, `You are the light of the world, and you alone.' But let us always remember that it is a statement concerning the ordinary, average Christian, not certain Christians only. It is applicable to all who rightly claim this name.

Immediately the question arises, How, then, is it to become true of us? Once again we are led immediately into the teaching concerning the nature of the Christian man. The best way to understand it, I think, is this. The Lord who said, `Ye are the light of the world,' also said, `I am the light of the world.' These two statements must always be taken together, since the Christian is only `the light of the world' because of his relationship to Him who is-Himself `the light of the world'. Our Lord's claim was that He had come to bring light. His promise is that `he that followeth me shall not walk in darkness, but shall have the light of life'. Here, however, He also says, `ye are the light of the world.' It comes to this, therefore, that He and He alone gives us this vital light with respect to life. But He does not stop at that; He also makes us `light'. You remember how the apostle Paul put it in Ephesians v, where he says, `For ye were sometimes darkness, but now are ye light in the Lord'. So not only have we received light, we have been made light; we become transmitters of light. In other words, it is this extraordinary teaching of the mystical union between the believer and his Lord. His nature enters into us so that we become, in a sense, what He Himself is. It is essential that we bear in mind both aspects of this matter. As those who believe the gospel we have received light and knowledge and instruction. But, in addition, it has become part of us. It has become our life, so that we thus become reflectors of it. The remarkable thing, therefore, of which we are reminded here is our intimate relationship with Him. The Christian is a man who has received and has become a partaker of the divine nature. The light that is Christ Himself, the light that is ultimately God, is the light that is in the Christian. `God is light, and in him is no darkness at all.' `I am the light of the world.' `Ye are the light of the world.' The way to understand this is to grasp our Lord's teaching concerning the Holy Spirit in John xiv-xvi where He says, in effect, `The result of His coming will be this: My Father and I will take up Our abode in you; We will be in you and you will be in Us.' God, who is `the Father of lights', is the light that is in us; He is in us, and we are in Him, and thus it can be said of the Christian, `Ye arc the light of the world.'

It is interesting to observe that, according to our Lord, this is the second great result of our being the kind of Christian man He has already described in the Beatitudes. We should consider also the order in which these statements are made. The first thing our Lord said of us was, `Ye are the salt of the earth'; and it is only after this that He says, `Ye are the light of the world'. Why does He put it in that order instead of the reverse? This is a very interesting and important practical point. The first effect of the Christian on the world is a general one; in other words, it is more or less negative. Here is a man who has become a Christian; he lives in society, in his office or workshop. Because he is a Christian he immediately has a certain effect, a controlling effect, which we considered together earlier. It is only after that, that he has this specific and particular function of acting as light. In other words Scripture, in dealing with the Christian, always emphasizes first what he is, before it begins to speak of what he does. As a Christian, I should always have this general effect upon men before I have this specific effect. Wherever I may find myself, immediately that `something different' about me should have its effect; and that in turn ought to lead men and women to look at me and to say, `There is something unusual about that man.' Then, as they watch my conduct and behaviour, they begin to ask me questions. Here, the element of `light' comes out; I am able to speak and to teach them. Far too often we Christians tend to reverse the order. We have spoken in a very enlightened manner, but we have not always lived as the salt of the earth. Whether we like it or not, our lives should always be the first thing to speak; and if our lips speak more than our lives it will avail very little. So often the tragedy has been that people proclaim the gospel in words, but their whole life and demeanour has been a denial of it. The world does not pay much attention to them. Let us never forget this order deliberately chosen by our Lord; `the salt of the earth' before `the light of the world'. We are something before we begin to act as something. The two things should always go together, but the order and sequence should be the one which He sets down here.

Bearing that in mind, let us now look at it practically. How is the Christian to show that he is indeed `the light of the world'? That resolves itself into a simple question: What is the effect of light? What does it really do? There can be no doubt that the first thing light does is to expose the darkness and the things that belong to darkness. Imagine a room in darkness, and then suddenly the light is switched on. Or think of the headlights of a motor-car coming along a dark country road. As the Scripture puts it, `Whatsoever doth make manifest is light'. There is a sense in which we are not truly aware of darkness until the light appears, and this is something that is fundamental. Speaking of the coming of the Lord into this world, Matthew says, `The people which sat in darkness saw great light'. The coming of Christ and the gospel is so fundamental that it can be put in that way; and the first eflcct of His coming into the world is that He has exposed the darkness of the life of the world. That is something that is always, and inevitably, done by any good or saintly person. We always need something to show us the difference, and the best way of revealing a thing is to provide a contrast. The gospel does that, and everyone who is a Christian does that. As the apostle Paul puts it, the light exposes `the hidden things of darkness', and so he says, `They that be drunken are drunken in the night.' The whole world is divided into `children of light' and `children of darkness'. So much of the life of the world is life under a kind of shroud of darkness. The worst things always happen under cover of darkness; even the natural man, degenerate and in a state of sin, would be ashamed of such things in the glare of light. Why? Because light exposes; `Whatsoever doth make manifest is light.'

Now the Christian is `the light of the world' in that way. It is quite inevitable, he cannot help it. Just by being Christian he shows a different type of life, and that immediately reveals the true character and nature of the other way of living. In the world, therefore, he is like a light being put on, and immediately people begin to think, and wonder, and feel ashamed. The more saintly the person, of course, the more obviously will this take place. He need not say a word; just by being what he is he makes people feel ashamed of what they are doing, and in that way he is truly functioning as light. He is providing a standard, he is showing that there is another kind of life which is possible to mankind. He therefore brings out the error and the failure of man's way of thinking and of living. As we saw in dealing with the Christian as `the salt of the earth', the same thing can be said of him as `the light of the world'. Every true revival has always had this effect. A number of Christian people in any district or society will tend to affect the life of the whole. Whether other people agree with their principles or not, they just make them feel that the Christian way is right after all, and the other way unworthy. The world has discovered that `honesty is the best policy'. As someone puts it, that is the kind of tribute that hypocrisy always pays to truth; it has to admit in its heart of hearts that truth is right. The influence the Christian has as light in the world is to show that these other things belong to darkness. They thrive in darkness, and somehow or other they cannot stand the light. This is stated explicitly in John iii, where the apostle says, `This is the condemnation, that light is come into the world, and men loved darkness rather than light, because their deeds were evil.' Our Lord goes on to say that such men do not come into the light because they know that, if they do, their deeds will be reproved, and they do not want that.

That, of course, was really the ultimate cause of the antagonism of the Pharisees and the scribes to our Lord and Saviour Jesus Christ. Here were these men, who were teachers of the law, these men who were experts, in a sense, on the religious life. Why did they so hate and persecute Him? The only adequate explanation is His utter purity, His utter holiness. Without His saying a word against them at the beginning-for He did not denounce them until the end-His purity made them see themselves as they really were, and they hated Him for it. Thus they persecuted Him, and finally crucified Him, just because He was `the light of the world'. It revealed and manifested the hidden things of darkness that were within them. Now you and I have to be like that in this world: by just living the Christian life we are to have that effect.

Let us now go a step further and say that light not only reveals the hidden things of darkness, it also explains the cause of the darkness. That is where it becomes so practical and important at the present time. I have already reminded you that the best and greatest academic thinkers in the world today are entirely baffled with regard to what is wrong with the world. Two lectures were broadcast some years ago on the wireless by men who were described as humanists, Dr. Julian Huxley and Professor Gilbert Murray. Both admitted quite frankly in their talks that they could not explain life as it is. Dr. Julian Huxley said he could not see any end or purpose in life. The whole thing to him was fortuitous. Professor Gilbert Murray, also, could not explain the second world war and the failure of the League of Nations. He had nothing to offer as a corrective but the `culture' that has been available for centuries, and which has already failed.

It is just here that we Christians have the light which explains the situation. The sole cause of the troubles of the world at this moment, from the personal to the international level, is nothing but man's estrangement from God. That is the light which only Christians have, and which they can give to the world. Man has been so made by God that he cannot truly live unless he is in the right relationship to God. He was made like that. He was made by God; he was made for God. And God has put certain rules in his nature and being and existence, and unless he conforms to them he is bound to go wrong. That is the whole cause of the trouble. Every difficulty in the world today can be traced back, in the last analysis, to sin, selfishness and self-seeking. All the quarrels, disputes and misunderstandings, all the jealousy, envy and malice, all these things come back to that and nothing else. So we are `the light of the world' in a very real sense at this present time; we alone have an adequate explanation of the cause of the state of the world. It can all be traced to the fall; the whole trouble arises from that. I want to quote again John iii. i 9: `This is the condemnation, that light is come into the world, and men loved darkness rather than light, because their deeds were evil.' `This is the condemnation' and nothing else. This is the cause of the trouble. What, then, is the matter? If light is come into the world in the face of Jesus Christ, what is wrong with the world in the middle of this twentieth century? The verse we have just quoted gives the answer. In spite of all the knowledge that has been amassed in the last two hundred years since the beginning of the enlightenment half-way through the eighteenth century, fallen man by nature still `loves darkness rather than light'. The result is that, though he knows what is right, he prefers and does what is evil. He has a conscience which warns him before he does anything he knows to be wrong. Nevertheless he does it. He may regret it, but he still does it. Why? Because he likes it. The trouble with man is not in his intellect, it is in his nature-the passions and the lusts. That is the dominating factor. And though you try to educate and control man it will avail nothing as long as his nature is sinful and fallen and he is a creature of passion and dishonour.

That, then, is the condemnation; and there is no-one to warn the modern world except the Christian. The philosopher not only does not speak; he resents such teaching. Such a man does not like to be told that he, with his wide knowledge, is still nothing but a lump of ordinary human clay like everybody else, and that he himself is a creature of passions and lusts and desires. But that is the simple truth concerning him. As was the case in the time of our Lord with many of those philosophers in that ancient world, who went out of life by that forbidden gate of suicide, so it is often the case today. Baffled, bewildered, feeling frustrated, having tried all their psychological and other treatments, but still going from bad to worse, men give up in despair. The gospel offends in that it makes a man face himself, and it always tells him that self-same thing, `The fault, dear Brutus, is not in our stars, but in ourselves, that we are underlings."Men love darkness rather than light', that is the trouble, and the gospel alone proclaims it. It stands as a light in the heavens and it should be revealing itself through all of us amidst the problems of this dark, miserable, unhappy world of men.

But thank God we do not stop at that. Light not only exposes the darkness; it shows and provides the only way out of the darkness. This is where every Christian should be jumping to the task. The problem of man is the problem of a fallen, sinful, polluted nature. Can nothing be done about it? We have tried knowledge, we have tried education, we have tried political enactments, we have tried international conferences, we have tried them all but nothing avails. Is there no hope? Yes, there is abundant and everlasting hope: `Ye must be born again'. What man needs is not more light; he needs a nature that will love the light and hate the darkness-the exact opposite of his loving the darkness and hating the light. Man needs to be taken hold of, and he needs to get back to God. It is not enough just to tell him that, because, if we do, we are leaving him in a still greater state of hopelessness. He will never find his way to God, try as he may. But the Christian is here to tell him that there is a way to God, a very simple one. It is to know one Person called Jesus Christ of Nazareth. He is the Son of God and He came from heaven to earth to `seek and to save that which was lost'. He came to illumine the darkness, to expose the cause of the darkness, and to make a new and living way out of it all back to God and to heaven. He has not only borne the guilt of this terrible sinfulness that has involved us in such trouble, He offers us new life and a new nature. He does not merely give us new teaching or a new understanding of the problem; He does not merely procure pardon for our past sins; He makes us new men with new desires, new aspirations, a new outlook and a new orientation. But above all He gives us that new life, the life that loves the light and hates the darkness, instead of loving the darkness and hating the light.

Christian people, you and I are living in the midst of men and women who are in a state of gross darkness. They will never have any light anywhere in this world except from you and from me and the gospel we believe and teach. They are watching us. Do they see something different about us? Are our lives a silent rebuke to them? Do we so live as to lead them to come and ask us, `Why do you always look so peaceful? How is it you are so balanced? How can you stand up to things as you do ? Why is it you are not dependent upon artificial aids and pleasures as we are? What is this thing that you have got?' If they do we can then tell them that wondrous, amazing, but tragically neglected news, that `Christ Jesus came into the world to save sinners', and to give men a new nature and a new life and to make them children of God. Christian people alone are the light of the world today. Let us live and function as children of the light.

CHAPTER SIXTEEN

LET YOUR LIGHT SO SHINE

I-N the last two chapters we have considered the two positive statements which our Lord made about the Christian: he is -the `salt of the earth' and the `light of the world'. But He was not content with making merely a positive statement. To Him, evidently, this matter was so important that He must emphasize it, as was customary with Him, by means of certain negatives. He was anxious that those people to whom He was actually speaking, and, indeed, all Christians in every age, should see clearly that we are what He has made us in order that we may become something. That is the great argument which you find running right through the Scriptures. It is seen perfectly in that statement of the apostle Peter, `Ye are a chosen generation, a royal priesthood, an holy nation, a peculiar people; that ye should shew forth the praises of him who hath called you out of darkness into his marvellous light' (i Pet. ii. 9). That is the argument, in a sense, in every New Testament Epistle, which again shows the utter folly of regarding this Sermon on the Mount as merely meant for some Christians who are yet to live in some future age or dispensation. For the teaching of the apostles, as we saw in our general introduction to the Sermon, is just an elaboration of what we have here. Their letters provide many examples of the working out of this very matter we are considering. In Philippians ii, the apostle Paul describes Christians as `luminaries' or `lights' in the world, and he exhorts them to `hold forth the word of life' for that reason. He makes constant use of the comparison of light and darkness in order to show how the Christian functions in society because he is a Christian. Our Lord seems very anxious to impress this upon us. We are to be the salt of the earth. Very well; but remember, `If the salt have lost his savour, wherewith shall it be salted? it is thenceforth good for nothing, but to be cast out, and to be trodden under foot of men.' We are `the light of the world'. Yes; but let us remember that `a city that is set on an hill cannot be hid. Neither do men light a candle, and put it under a bushel, but on a candlestick; and it giveth light unto all that are in the house.' Then we have this final summing up of it all again: `Let your light so shine before men, that they may see your good works, and glorify your Father which is in heaven.'

In view of the way in which our Lord emphasizes this it is obvious that we must consider it also. It is not enough just to remember that we are to act as salt in the earth or as the light of the world. We also have to grasp the fact that it must become the biggest thing in the whole of our life., for the reasons which we shall consider. Perhaps the best way of doing so is to put it in the form of a number of statements or propositions.

The first thing to consider is why we as Christians should be like salt and light, and why we should desire to be so. It seems to me that our Lord has three main arguments there. The first is that, by definition, we were meant to be such. His very comparisons convey that teaching. The business of salt is to be salt, just that. The characteristic of salt is saltness. It is exactly the same with light. The whole function and purpose of light is to give light. We must start there and realize that these things are self-evident and need no illustration. Yet the moment we put it like that, does it not tend to come as a rebuke to us all? How prone we are to forget these essential functions of salt and light. As we proceed with the argument, I think you will agree that this is something of which we need constantly to be reminded. A lamp, as our Lord puts it-and He is just appealing to ordinary, natural common sense-a lamp is lit in order that it may give light to all that are in the house. There is no other purpose in lighting a lamp but that. The whole object is that light may be disseminated and diffused in that particular area. That, therefore, is our first statement. We have to realize what a Christian is by definition, and this is our Lord's own definition of him. So that, at the very outset, when we start describing a Christian in our own terms, our definition must never be less than that. These are the essential things about him: `salt'; `light'.

But let us come to the second argument, which seems to me to be that our position becomes not only contradictory but even ridiculous if we do not act in this way. We are to be like `a city that is set on an hill', and `a city that is set on an hill cannot be hid'. In other words, if we are truly Christian we cannot be hid. Put in a different way, the contrast between us and others is something which is to be quite self-evident and perfectly obvious. But our Lord does not leave it at that; He presses it still further. He asks us, in effect, to imagine a man lighting a light and then putting it under a bushel instead of putting it on a candlestick. Now, in the past, commentators have spent a good deal of their time in defining what is meant by a `bushel', sometimes with amusing results. To me the important thing is that it covers the light, and it does not matter very much what it is as long as it does that. What our Lord is saying is that it is a ridiculous and contradictory procedure. The whole purpose of lighting a light is that it may give light. And for a foolish man to cover it with something which prevents that quality from manifesting itself is, we are all agreed, utterly ridiculous. Yes; but remember that our Lord is speaking about us. There is obviously a danger, or at least a temptation, that the Christian may behave in this completely ridiculous and futile manner, and that is why He emphasizes the matter in this way. He seems to be saying, `I have made you something that is meant to be like a light, like a city set upon a hill which cannot be hid. Are you deliberately concealing it? Well, if you are, apart from anything else, it is something which is completely ridiculous and foolish.'

But come to the last step in His argument here. To do this, according to our Lord, is to render ourselves utterly useless. Now this is very striking, and there is no doubt that He uses these two comparisons in order to bring out this particular point. Salt without its savour is quite useless. In other words, as I said at the beginning, there is only one essential quality of salt and that is saltness. And when salt has lost its saltness it is of no use at all. Now that is not true of everything. Take flowers, for example; when they are alive they are very beautiful and they may have an aroma; but when the flower dies it does not become quite useless. You can throw it on to the compost heap and it may be useful as compost. So with many other things; they do not become useless when their primary function ceases to operate. You can still make some secondary or subsidiary use of them. But the extraordinary thing about salt is that the moment it loses its saltness it is really no use at all: `it is thenceforth good for nothing, but to be cast out, and to be trodden under foot of men.' It is very difficult to know what to do with it; you cannot throw it on a compost heap, it does harm there. It just has no function or value at all, and the only thing to do is to get rid of it. Nothing is left once it loses the essential quality and purpose for which it has been made. The same is true of light. The essential characteristic of light is that it is light, and gives light, and it really has no other function whatsoever. In other words, the moment it ceases to act as light it has no value. Its essential quality is its only quality, and once it loses that, it becomes entirely useless.

According to our Lord's argument that is the truth concerning the Christian. As I understand it, and it seems to me to be an inevitable piece of logic and interpretation, there is nothing in God's universe that is so utterly useless as a merely formal Christian. I mean by that, one who has the name but not the quality of a Christian. The apostle Paul describes this when he speaks of certain people `having a form of godliness, but denying the power thereof'. They appear to be Christian but they are not. They want to appear as Christians, but they are not functioning as Christians. They are salt without savour, light without light, if you can imagine such a thing. You can do so most easily, perhaps, when you think of the illustration of the light being hid by the bushel. If you test this by observation and experience you will have to agree that it is the simple truth. The formal Christian is a man who knows enough about Christianity to spoil the world for him; but he does not know enough about it for it to be of any positive value. He does not go with the world because he knows just enough about it to be afraid of certain things; and the people who live right in the world know that he is trying to be different and that he cannot be whole-heartedly with them. On the other hand he has no real fellowship with the Christian. He has enough `Christianity' to spoil everything else, but not enough to give him real happiness, peace and joy and abundance of life. I think such people are the most pathetic people in the world. Our Lord certainly says they are the most useless people in the world. They do not function as worldlings or as Christians. They are nothing, neither salt nor light, neither one thing nor the other. And as a matter of actual fact, they are cast out; cast out, as it were, by the world and cast out by the Church. They refuse to regard themselves as of the world, while on the other hand they do not enter truly into the life of the Church. They feel it themselves, and others feel it. There is always this barrier. They are finally outsiders. They are more outside, in a sense, than the man who is entirely worldly and makes no claim or profession, because he at least has his own society.

Of all people, then, these are the most pathetic and the most tragic, and the solemn warning which we have in this verse is the warning of our Lord against getting into such a state and condition. It is reinforced by those parables in Matthew xxv where we are told again of this final shutting out of such people, like salt that is thrown out. To their amazement they will eventually find themselves shut outside the door, trodden under foot of men. This has been proved historically. There have been certain Churches which, having lost their savour, or having ceased to give out the true light, have just been trodden under foot. There was once a powerful Christian Church in North Africa, a flourishing Church that produced many of those early giants, including the great St. Augustine. But it lost its savour and its true light, and because of that it was literally trodden under foot and has ceased to be. It has happened in other countries. God give us grace to take this solemn warning unto ourselves. A mere formal profession of Christianity is something that will ultimately always suffer that fate.

Perhaps we can sum it all up in this way. The true Christian cannot be hid, he cannot escape notice. A man truly living and functioning as a Christian will stand out. He will be like salt; he will be like a city set upon a hill, a candle set upon a candlestick. But we can also add this further word. The true Christian does not even desire to hide his light. He sees how ridiculous it is to claim to be a Christian and yet deliberately to try to hide the fact. A man who truly realizes what it means to be a Christian, who realizes all that the grace of God has meant to him and done for him, and understands that, ultimately, God has done this in order that he may influence others, is a man who cannot conceal it. Not only that; he does not desire to conceal it, because he argues thus, `Ultimately the object and purpose of it all is that I might be functioning in this way.'

These comparisons and illustrations, then, are meant by our Lord to show us that any desire which we may find in ourselves to hide the fact that we are Christian is not only to be regarded as ridiculous and contradictory, it is, if we indulge it and persist in it, something which (though I do not understand the doctrine at this point) may lead to a final casting out. Let me put it in this way. If we find in ourselves a tendency to put the light under a bushel, we must begin to examine ourselves and make sure that it really is 'light'. It seems to be a fact about salt and light that they want to manifest their essential quality, so if there is any uncertainty about this, we should examine ourselves and discover again the cause of this illogical and contradictory position. Let us put it, therefore, in this simple form. The next time I find myself with any sort of tendency to cover over the fact that I am a Christian, in order, maybe, to ingratiate myself with somebody else or to avoid persecution, I am just to think of the man lighting his candle and then covering it with a bushel. The moment I think of it like that and see how ridiculous it is, I shall recognize that the subtle thing which offered me that bushel is the hand of the devil. I shall therefore reject it, and shine still more brightly.

That is the first statement. Let us now come to the second, which is a very practical one. How are we to ensure that we really do function as salt and as light? In a sense both illustrations put this point, but the second is perhaps the simpler of the two. Our Lord talks about the difficulty, the impossibility, of a man ever restoring the quality of saltness to salt. Again the commentators are most interested in that and give an illustration of a man who had once, on a journey, found some sort of salt which had lost its saltness. How foolish we can become when we begin to study Scripture in terms of words instead of doctrine! We need not go to the East to try to find salt without saltness; our Lord's sole purpose here is to show how ridiculous the whole thing is.

The second of the two illustrations is the more definite. Two things only are necessary to the lamp-the oil and the wickand the two things always go together. You will find, of course, that some people talk only about the oil, others only about the wick. But without the oil and the wick you will never have a light. The two are absolutely essential, and so we are to pay attention to them both. The parable of the ten virgins again helps us to remember that. The oil is absolutely essential and vital; we can do nothing without it and the whole point of the Beatitudes, in a sense, is just to emphasize that fact. We have to receive this life, this divine life. We cannot function as light without it. We are only 'the light of the world' as He who is 'the light of the world' works in and through us. The first thing, then, which we must ask ourselves is, Have I received this life divine? Do I know that Christ is dwelling in me? Paul prays for the Ephesians that Christ may dwell in their hearts richly by faith, that they may be filled with all the fullness of God. The whole doctrine concerning the work of the Holy Spirit is essentially that. It is not to give particular gifts, such as tongues or the various other things about which people get so excited. His purpose is to give life and the graces of the Spirit, which is `a more excellent way'. Am I sure that I have the oil, the life, that which the Holy Spirit of God alone can give to me?

The first exhortation, then, must be that we must seek this constantly. That means, of course, prayer, which is the action of going to receive it. We so often tend to think that these gracious invitations of our Lord are something which are given once and for ever. He says, `Come unto me' if you want the water of life, `Come unto me' if you want the bread of life. But we tend to think that once and for ever we come to Christ and thereafter we have this permanent supply. Not at all. It is a supply that we have to renew; we have to go back and receive it constantly. We are to live in contact with Him, and it is only as we constantly receive this life from Him that we shall function as salt and as light.

But, of course, it not only means constant prayer, it means what our Lord Himself describes as `hungering and thirsting after righteousness'. You will remember we interpreted that as being something that goes on continuously. We are filled, yes; but we always want more. We are never static, we never rest upon our oars, we never say, `Once and for ever.' Not at all. We go on hungering and thirsting; we go on realizing our perpetual need of Him and of this supply of life and of everything He has to give. So we continue to read the Word of God where we can learn about Him and this life which He offers us. The supply of oil is essential. Read the biographies of the men who have obviously been like cities set upon a hill which cannot be hid. You will find that they did not say, `I have come to Christ once and for all; here is the one great climactic experience of life that will last for ever afterwards.' Not at all; they tell us that they found it an absolute necessity to spend hours in prayer and Bible study and meditation. They never ceased drawing the oil and receiving the supply.

The second essential is the wick. We must attend to this also. To keep that lamp burning brightly the oil is not enough, you must keep on trimming the wick. That is our Lord's illustration. Many of us today have never known anything other than this modern world of electricity. But some of us remember how the wick had to be given special attention. Once it began to smoke, it did not give the light, so the wick had to be trimmed. And a very delicate process it was. What does this mean in practice for us? I think it means that we constantly have to remind ourselves of the Beatitudes. We should read them every day. I ought to remind myself daily that I am to be poor in spirit, merciful, meek, a peacemaker, pure in heart, and so on. There is nothing that is better calculated to keep the wick in order and trimmed than just to remind myself of what I am by the grace of God, and of what I am meant to be. That, I suggest, is something for us to do in the morning before we start our day. In everything I do and say, I am to be like that man I see in the Beatitudes. Let us start with that and concentrate on it.

But not only are we to remind ourselves of the Beatitudes, we are to live accordingly. What does this mean? It means that we are to avoid everything that is opposed to this character, we are to be entirely unlike the world. It is a tragic thing to me that so many Christians, because they do not want to be different or to suffer persecution, seem to be living as near as they can to the world. But this is again a contradiction in terms. There is no mean between light and darkness; it is either one or the other, and there is no communion between them. Either it is light or it is not. And the Christian is to be like that in the earth. Far from being like the world, we should concentrate on being as different as we can.

Positively, however, it means that we should show this difference in our lives, and that, of course, can be done in a thousand and one ways. I cannot attempt to give a complete list; all I do know is that it means, at the very minimum, living a separated life. The world is becoming more and more rude; rougher, uglier, louder. I think all will agree with that. As the Christian influence is diminishing in this country the whole tone of society is becoming more gross; the decencies, yes, even the little politenesses, are less and less in evidence. The Christian is not to live in that way. We are far too prone these days just to say, `I am a Christian', or `Isn't it wonderful to be a Christian?' and then sometimes to be rude and inconsiderate. Let us remember that these are the things which proclaim what we are-'the manner doth proclaim the man'. We are to be humble, peaceable, peacemaking in all our talk and behaviour, and especially in our reactions to the behaviour of other persons. I believe that the individual Christian is having a greater opportunity today than lie has had for many a century, owing to the whole state of the world and of society. I believe that people are watching us very closely because we claim to be Christian; and they are watching our reactions to people and to the things they say and do to us. Do we flare up? The nonChristian does; the Christian should not. He is like the man in the Beatitudes, so he reacts differently. And when confronted with world events, with wars and rumours of wars, with calamities, pestilences and all these other things, he is not over-anxious, troubled and irritable. The world is; the Christian is not. He is essentially different.

The last principle is the supreme importance of doing all this in the right way. We have considered why we are to be like salt; we have considered why we are to be like light. We have considered how to be so, how to ensure that we are. But it must be done in the right way. `Let your light so shine before men',the great word there is `so'-`that they may see your good works, and glorify your Father which is in heaven.' You see, there is to be a complete absence of ostentation and display. It is a little difficult in practice, is it not, to draw the line between truly functioning as salt and light, and still not to be guilty of display or ostentation? Yet that is what we are told to do. We are so to live that men may see our good works, but glorify our Father which is in heaven. How difficult to function truly as an active Christian, and yet not to have any showmanship. This is true even in our listening to the gospel, quite apart from our preaching of it! As we produce and reveal it in our daily lives, we must remember that the Christian does not call attention to himself. Self has been forgotten in this poverty of spirit, in the meekness and all the other things. In other words, we are to do everything for God's sake, and for His glory. Self is to be absent, and must be utterly crushed in all its subtlety, for His sake, for His glory.

211

It follows from this that we are to do these things in such a way as to lead other men to glorify Him, and glory in Him, and give themselves to Him. `Let your light so shine before men, that they may see your good works.' Yes; and so see them that they will themselves glorify your Father which is in heaven. Not only are you to glorify your Father; you are to do so in order that these other people may glorify Him also.

That in turn leads to the fact that, because we are truly Christian, we are to have great sorrow in our hearts for those other people. We are to realize that they are in darkness, and in a state of pollution. In other words, the more we draw our life from Him, the more we shall become like Him; and He had a great compassion for the people. He saw them as sheep without a shepherd. He had great sorrow for them in His heart, and it was that which determined His conduct and behaviour. He was not concerned about Himself; He had compassion for the multitude. And that is the way in which you and I are to live and to regard these matters. In other words, in all our work and Christian living these three things should always be uppermost. We shall always do it for His sake and His glory. We shall lead men to Him and to glorify Him. And all will be based upon a love for them and a compassion for them in their lost condition.

That, then, is the way in which our Lord exhorts us to show what He has made of us. We must function as men and women who have received from Him life divine. He ridicules the opposite. He puts before us this wondrous picture of becoming like Himself in this world. It was as men and women saw Him that they were led to think of God. Have you noticed how often, after His miracles, we read that the people `gave glory unto God'? They said, `We have never seen things like this before'; and they glorified the Father. You and I are to live like that. In other words, we are to live in such a way that, as men and women look at us, we shall become a problem to them. They will ask, `What is it? Why are these people so different in every way, different in their conduct and behaviour, different in their reactions? There is something about them which we do not understand; we cannot explain it.' And they will be driven to the only real explanation, which is that we are the people of God, children of God, `heirs of God, and joint-heirs with Christ'. We have become reflectors of

Christ, re-producers of Christ. As He is `the light of the world' so we have become `the light of the world'.

CHAPTER SEVENTEEN

CHRIST AND THE OLD TESTAMENT

'THINK not that I am come to destroy the law, or the prophets: I am not come to destroy, but to fulfil. For verily I say unto you, Till heaven and earth pass, one jot or one tittle shall in no wise pass from the law, till all be fulfilled.' These verses, although they are a continuation of what has gone before, nevertheless mark the beginning of a new section in the Sermon. Hitherto we have seen that our Lord has been concerned to describe the Christian. First we have been reminded of what we arc; then we have been told that, this being so, we must ever remember it and let our life be such that it will always be a manifestation of this essential being of ours. It is like the parent saying to the child who is going away from home to a party, `Now remember who you are. You must behave in such a way that you reflect glory and honour upon your family and your parents.' Or the same appeal is made to children in the name of the school or to its citizens by a country.

That is what our Lord has been saying. We are children of God and citizens of the kingdom of heaven. Because of that, we have to manifest the characteristics of such people. We do this in order to manifest His glory, and so that others may be brought to glorify Him.

The question then arises as to how this is to be done. That is the subject which now confronts us. The answer, in a word, can be put like this: we are to live a life of righteousness. That is the one word that sums up Christian living, `righteousness'. And the theme of the remainder of the Sermon on the Mount is in many ways just that, the kind of life of righteousness which the Christian is to live. Until you come to vii. 14 that is the great theme which is expounded in various ways.

What is this righteousness which we have to manifest, what is its character? Verses 17 to 20 in this fifth chapter are a kind of general introduction to that subject. Here our Lord introduces this whole question of the righteousness and the righteous life which are to characterize the Christian. You observe His method. Before He comes to the details, He lays down certain general principles. He has an introduction before He really begins to explain and expound His subject. Some people, I gather, do not like introductions. In that case they do not like our Lord's method ! It is always vital to start with principles. The people who go wrong in practice are always those who are not sure of their principles. It seems to me that this is most vital today. We live in an age of specialists, and the specialist is almost invariably a man who is so lost in details that he often forgets principles. Most of the breakdown in life today is due to the fact that certain basic principles have been forgotten. In other words if only everybody lived a godly life we should have no need for this multiplicity of conferences and organizations.

The method of starting with basic principles is something we see here as our Lord goes on to deal with this question of righteousness. He does so by laying down in this paragraph two categorical propositions. In the first, in verses 17 and 18, He says that everything He is going to teach is in absolute harmony with the entire teaching of the Old Testament Scriptures. There is nothing in this teaching which in any way contradicts them.

The second proposition, which He lays down in verses 19 and 20, is that this teaching of His which is in such harmony with the Old Testament is in complete disharmony with, and an utter contradiction of, the teaching of the Pharisees and scribes.

Those are two great pronouncements and they are important, because we shall never understand the record of our Lord's life which we have in the four Gospels, unless we grasp these two principles. Here we have an explanation of all the antagonism towards Him which was displayed by the Pharisees, the scribes, the doctors of the law and various other people. Here is the explanation of all the troubles that He had to endure, and the misunderstanding to which He was so constantly subjected.

Another general observation is that our Lord was not content with making positive statements only; He made negative ones also. He was not content with just stating His doctrine. He also criticized other doctrines. I am emphasizing that again in passing because, as I have pointed out repeatedly in dealing with this Sermon, for some extraordinary reason a peculiar flabbiness-intellectual and moral-seems to have entered into many people, Evangelicals included. Many, alas, seem to object in these days to negative teaching. `Let us have positive teaching', they say. `You need not criticize other views.' But our Lord definitely did criticize the teaching of the Pharisees and scribes. He exposed and denounced it frequently. And it is essential, of course, that we should do the same. We are all talking about c cumenicity, and the argument is put forward that, because of a certain common danger, it is not the time to be arguing about points of doctrine; rather we should all be friendly and pull together. Not at all, according to our Lord. The fact that the Roman Catholic and Greek Orthodox Churches are called Christian is no reason why we should not expose the corruptness and the dangerous errors of their systems.

Our Lord, then, does not stop with the positive; and that, in turn, leads to another question. Why did He do this? Why this kind of introduction to the detailed part of the Sermon? I think the answer is very plain. As we read the four Gospels we see clearly that there was much confusion with regard to our Lord's teaching. He was undoubtedly a great problem to His contemporaries. There were so many unusual things about Him. He Himself, for instance, was unusual. He was not a Pharisee and He had not been trained as a Pharisee. He had not been to the customary schools, so they looked at Him and said, `Who is this fellow, this man who teaches and makes these dogmatic pronouncements? What is this?' He did not come into His position as a teacher along the usual lines or through the customary channels, and that at once created a problem. The leaders and the people were rather perplexed about it. But not only that. As I have been reminding you, He deliberately criticized the Pharisees and the scribes, and their teaching. Now they were the acknowledged leaders and religious teachers, and everyone was prepared to do what they said. They were quite outstanding in the nation. But, suddenly, here was a Man who did not belong to their schools, who not only taught, but also denounced their authoritative teaching. Then, over and above that, He did not spend all His time in expounding the law. He preached an extraordinary doctrine of grace and of the love of God which introduced such things as the parable of the Prodigal Son. But, even worse, He mixed with publicans and sinners, sitting down and eating with them. Not only did he not seem to observe all the rules and regulations; He actually seemed to be deliberately breaking them. In His words He criticized their official teaching, and in practice He did the same.

So questions began to arise at once because of His theory and because of His practice. `Does this new Teacher not believe the Holy Writings? The Pharisees and the scribes claim to be the exponents and the expounders of the Holy Scripture; does this Jesus of Nazareth, therefore, not believe it? Has He come to do away with it? Is His teaching absolutely new? Is it denouncing the law and the prophets? Is He teaching that there is some new way to God, some new way of pleasing God? Is He turning His back resolutely upon the whole of the past?' Now those were the questions which our Lord well knew were bound to arise because of His personal character and because of what He taught. So, here, at the very introduction to the detailed teaching, He met the criticism beforehand. In particular He warned His disciples lest they should be confounded and influenced by the talk and criticism which they were so likely to hear. He prepared their mind and outlook by laying down these two fundamental postulates.

Our Lord had already told them in general what they were to be like and the kind of righteousness they were to manifest. Now, as He came to detailed and specific questions, He wanted them to understand the whole setting. I am calling attention to this not out of a theoretical interest and not merely because it is a fresh section of this Sermon which we must expound. I am doing so because it is a very urgent and practical question for every one of us who is in any way concerned about the Christian life. For this is not merely an old problem; it is also a very modern one. It is not something theoretical, for there are large numbers of people who are still in trouble on this very question.There are those who stumble at Christ and His salvation because of this very point of His relationship to the law; and therefore I say that it is vital we should look at it. Indeed there are some who say that this verse we are considering actually increases their problem instead of diminishing it.

There are two main difficulties which are raised with regard to this. There is one school which believes that all our Lord Himself did was to continue the teaching of the law. You know the school, although it is not quite as popular now as it was some thirty years ago or more. Its followers say that they see a great difference between the four Gospels and the New Testament Epistles. The Gospels are nothing but a very wonderful exposition of the ancient law, and Jesus of Nazareth was only a Teacher of the Law. The real founder of so-called Christianity, they continue, was the man we know as the apostle Paul with all his doctrine and legalism. The four Gospels are nothing but law, ethical teaching and moral instruction; and there is nothing in them about the doctrine of justification by faith, sanctification and such things. That is the work of the apostle Paul with his theology. The real tragedy, they say, is that the simple, glorious gospel ofJesus was turned by this other man into what has become Christianity, which is entirely different from the religion of Jesus. Those who are old enough will remember that towards the turn of the century and after there were several books written along that line, The Religion of Jesus and the Faith of Paul, and so on, which tried to show the great contrast between Jesus and Paul. That is one difficulty.

The second main difficulty is the exact opposite to that; and it is interesting to observe how heresies almost invariably cancel one another out. For the second view is that Christ abolished the law completely, and that He introduced grace in place of it. `The law was given by Moses,' they quote, `grace and truth came by Jesus Christ.' The Christian, therefore, has nothing to do with the law. They argue that the Bible says we are under grace, so we must never even mention the law. You remember we dealt with this argument in chapter one. We considered there the view which said that the Sermon on the Mount had nothing to do with us today, that it had reference to the people to whom it was preached, and will have reference to the Jews in the future kingdom age. It is interesting to note how these old troubles still persist.

Our Lord answers both at one and the same time in this vital statement in verses 17 and 18 which deals with this specific matter of His relationship to the law and to the prophets. What has He to say about it? Perhaps the best thing to do at this point is to define our terms, and to be perfectly clear that we understand their meaning. What is meant by `the law' and `the prophets'? The answer is, the whole of the Old Testament. You can turn up passages for yourself and you will find that wherever this expression is used it includes the entire Old Testament canon.

What, then, is meant by `the law' in particular, at this point? It seems to me we must agree that the word, as used here, means the entire law. This, as given to the children of Israel, consisted of three parts, the moral, the judicial and the ceremonial. If you read again the books of Exodus, Leviticus and Numbers, you will find that this was how God gave it. The moral law consisted of the Ten Commandments and the great moral principles that were laid down once and for ever. Then there was the judicial law, which means the legislative law given for the nation of Israel in its peculiar circumstances at that time, which indicated how men were to order their behaviour in relationship to others and the various things they were and were not to do. Finally there was the ceremonial law concerning burnt offerings and sacrifices and all the ritual and ceremonial in connection with their worship in the temple and elsewhere. At this point we must assert that `the law' includes all that; so that our Lord is here referring to everything that it teaches directly about life, conduct and behaviour.

We must remember also, however, that the law includes everything that is taught by the various types, the different offerings and all the details that are given concerning them in the Old Testament. Many Christian people say that they find the books of Exodus and Leviticus so boring. `Why all this detail', they ask, `about the meal and the salt and all these various other things?' Well, all these are just types, and they are all prophecy, in their way, of what was done perfectly once and for ever by our Lord and Saviour Jesus Christ. I say, therefore, that when we talk of the law we must remember that all this is included. Not only the positive, direct teaching of these books and their injunctions on how life should be lived; but also all that they suggest and foretell with regard to what was to come. The law, then, must be taken in its entirety. Actually, we shall find that, from verse 21 onwards, when our Lord speaks of the law He is speaking only of the moral section. But in this general statement here He is talking about it all.

What is meant by `the prophets'? The term clearly means all that we have in the prophetic books of the Old Testament. There again we must never forget that there are two main aspects. The prophets actually taught the law, and they applied and interpreted it. They went to the nation and told them that the trouble with them was that they were not keeping God's law, their main endeavour being to call the people back to a true understanding of it. To this end they caused it to be read again and expounded. But, in addition, they did foretell the coming of the Messiah. They were `forth-tellers', but at the same time they were foretellers. Both aspects are included in the prophetic message.

That leaves us with one final term, the term `fulfil'. There has been a great deal of confusion with regard to its meaning, so we must point out at once that it does not mean to complete, to finish; it does not mean to add to something that has already been begun. This popular interpretation is an entire misunderstanding of the word. It has been said that the Old Testament began a certain teaching and that it carried on so far and up to a point. Then our Lord came and carried it a stage further, rounding it off and fulfilling it, as it were. That is not the true interpretation. The real meaning of the word `fulfil' is to carry out, to fulfil in the sense of giving full obedience to it, literally carrying out everything that has been said and stated in the law and in the prophets.

Having defined our terms, let us now consider what our Lord is really saying to us. What is His actual teaching? I am going to put it in the form of two principles and, in order to do so, I am going to take verse 18 before verse 17. The two statements come together, and are connected by the word `for'. `Think not that I am come to destroy the law, or the prophets: I am not come to destroy, but to fulfil.' And here is the reason why. `For verily I say unto you, Till heaven and earth pass, one jot or one tittle shall in no wise pass from the law, till all be fulfilled.'

The first proposition is that God's law is absolute; it can never be changed, not even modified to the slightest extent. It is absolute and eternal. Its demands are permanent, and can never be abrogated or reduced `till heaven and earth pass'. That last expression means the end of the age. Heaven and earth are signs of permanence. While they are there, says our Lord, nothing shall pass away, not even a jot or a tittle. There is nothing smaller than these, the smallest letter in the Hebrew alphabet and the smallest point in the smallest letter. Heaven and earth shall not pass away until every minute detail shall be absolutely and entirely fulfilled. Now that is the pronouncement, and it is, of course, one of the most momentous and important pronouncements that has ever been made. Our Lord emphasizes it by the word `for', which always calls attention to something and denotes seriousness and importance. Then He adds to the importance by saying, `Verily I say unto you.' He is impressing the statement with all the authority He possesses. The law that God has laid down, and which you can read in the Old Testament, and everything that has been said by the prophets, is going to be fulfilled down to the minutest detail, and it will hold and stand until this absolute fulfilment has been entirely carried out. I do not think I need emphasize the vital importance of that any further.

Then, in the light of that, our Lord makes His second statement to the effect that obviously, therefore, He has not come to destroy, or indeed to modify even to the slightest extent, the teaching of the law or the prophets. He has come, He tells us, rather to fulfil and to carry them out, and to give them a perfect obedience. There, we see the central claim which is made by our Lord. It is, in other words, that all the law and all the prophets point to Him and will be fulfilled in Him down to the smallest detail. Everything that is in the law and the prophets culminates in Christ, and He is the fulfilment of them. It is the most stupendous claim that He ever made.

This is a theme which we must elaborate, but here, first, is the immediate deduction. Our Lord Jesus Christ in these two verses confirms the whole of the Old Testament. He puts His seal of authority, His imprimatur, upon the whole of the Old Testament canon, the whole of the law and the prophets. Read these four Gospels, and watch His quotations from the Old Testament. You can come to one conclusion only, namely, that He believed it all and not only certain parts of it! He quoted almost every part of it. To the Lord Jesus Christ the Old Testament was the Word of God; it was Scripture; it was something absolutely unique and apart; it had authority which nothing else has ever possessed nor can possess. Here, then, is a vital statement with regard to this whole matter of the authority of the Old Testament.

You will find so many people today who seem to think they can believe on the Lord Jesus Christ fully and yet more or less reject the Old Testament. It must be said, however, that the question of our attitude to the Old Testament inevitably raises the question of our attitude towards the Lord Jesus Christ. If we say that we do not believe in the account of the creation, or in Abraham as a person; if we do not believe that the law was given by God to Moses, but think that it was a very clever bit of Jewish legislation produced by a man who was a good leader, and who obviously had certain sound ideas about public health and hygiene-if we say that, we are in fact flatly contradicting everything our Lord and Saviour Jesus Christ said about Himself, the law, and the prophets. Everything in the Old Testament, according to Him, is the Word of God. Not only that, it is all going to stand until it has all been fulfilled. Every jot and tittle, everything has meaning. Everything is going to be carried out down to the smallest detail imaginable. It is God's law, it is God's enactment.

Nor were the words of the prophets words of men who were simply poets, and who, having this poetic insight, saw a little further into life than other people, and, thus inspired, made wonderful statements about life and how to live it. Not at all. These were men of God who were given their message by Him. What they said is all true, and all will be fulfilled down to the smallest detail. It was all given with reference to Christ. He is the fulfilment of all these things, and it is only as they are fully carried out in Him that they can in any sense come to an end.

Now this, of course, is also of vital significance. People have often wondered why it was that the early Church decided to incorporate the Old Testament with the New Testament. So many people who are Christians say that they like reading the Gospels, but that they are not interested in the Old Testament, and that they do not think those five books of Moses and their message have anything to do with them. The early Church did not take that view, and for this reason : the one casts light upon the other, and each in a sense can only be understood in the light of the other. These two Testaments must always go together. As the great St. Augustine once put it, `The New Testament is latent in the Old Testament and the Old Testament is patent in the New Testament.'

But, above all, here is this pronouncement by the Son of God Himself, in which He says that He has not come to supersede the Old Testament, the law and the prophets. `No,' He seems to say, `all this is of God, and I am come to carry it out and fulfil it.' He regarded it all as the Word of God and finally authoritative. And you and I, if we are to be true followers of Him and believers in Him, are to do the same. The moment you begin to question the authority of the Old Testament, you are of necessity questioning the authority of the Son of God Himself, and you will find yourself in endless trouble and difficulty. If you once begin to say that He was just a child of His age and was limited in certain respects because of that and liable to error, you are seriously qualifying the biblical doctrine as to His full, absolute and unique deity. You must be very careful, therefore, in what you say about the Scriptures. Watch His quotations from themthe quotations from the law and the prophets, the quotations from the Psalms. He quotes them everywhere. To Him they are always the Scripture which has been given, and which, He says, in John x. 35, `cannot be broken'. It is God's own Word that is going to be fulfilled to the minutest detail and which will last while heaven and earth are in existence.

CHAPTER EIGHTEEN

CHRIST FULFILLING THE LAW
AND THE PROPHETS

W E have laid down our two main principles with regard to the relationship between the Old Testament Scriptures and the gospel and now we must consider this subject again in greater detail. First of all, let us see how our Lord `fulfils' and carries out what has been written by the prophets in the Old Testament-a most important subject. You remember the use which the apostle Peter makes of that in his second Epistle. He is writing to comfort people who were living in very hard and difficult times and who were experiencing persecution. He is now an old man and realizes that he has not long to live. He wants, therefore, to give them some final comfort before he goes. He tells them various things; how, for instance, he and James and John had the privilege of seeing the transfiguration of our Lord and how they even heard that voice from the excellent glory which said, `This is my beloved Son, hear him.' `And yet', says Peter in effect, `I have something even better than that to tell you. You need not place your confidence on my testimony and experience. There is the "more sure word of prophecy". Go hack and read your Old Testament prophets. See their verification in Christ Jesus and you will have the strongest buttress of faith that man can ever obtain.' This, then, is something of vital importance. Our Lord claims that He is the fulfilment, in and of Himself, of that which was taught by the Old Testament prophets. The apostle Paul makes a great and comprehensive statement about this in 2 Corinthians i. 20 where he says, `All the promises of God in him are yea, and in him Amen.' Now that is finality. All the promises of God are, in this wonderful Person, yea and amen. That, in effect, is what our Lord is saying here.

We cannot go into this fully; I must leave you to work out the details for yourself. The fulfilment of the prophecies is truly one of the most astounding and remarkable things that one can ever encounter, as has often been pointed out. Think of the exact prophecies as to His birth, the place of His birth even- BethelehemJudah; all these were fulfilled exactly. The extra ordinary things that are foretold of His Person make it almost incredible that the Jews should ever have stumbled at Him. It was their own ideas which led them astray. They should not have thought of the Messiah as a worldly king, or a political personage, because they had been told the opposite by their prophets. They had had these prophets read to them, but they were blinded by prejudice, and instead of looking at the words, they were looking at their own superimposed ideas-a constant danger. But there we have the prophetic record down to the smallest detail. Think of the extraordinarily accurate description of the type of life He lived-'a bruised reed shall he not break, and smoking flax shall he not quench'-and that wonderful description of His Person and life in Isaiah liii. Think of the accounts of what He was going to do, the foretelling of His miracles, His physical miracles, the kind of thing He was likely to do and the teaching involved in that. It is all there, and that is why it is always such an easy and wonderful thing to preach the gospel out of the Old Testament. Some people are still foolish enough to be amazed at it, but in a sense you can preach the gospel as well out of the Old Testament as out of the New. It is full of gospel.

Above everything else, however, you have the prophecy of His death and even the mode of His death. Read Psalm xxii for instance, and you will find there a literal, accurate description in detail of what actually happened on Calvary's cross. Prophecy, you see, is found in the Psalms as well as in the prophets. He fulfilled literally and completely what is foretold of Him there. In the same way you find even the resurrection quite clearly foretold in the Old Testament together with much wonderful teaching about the kingdom which our Lord was going to establish. Still more amazing, in a sense, are the prophecies concerning the bringing in of the Gentiles. That is really remarkable when you remember that these oracles of God were written in particular for one nation, the Jews, and yet there are these clear prophecies regarding the spreading of the blessing to the Gentiles in this extraordinary manner. In the same way, you will find clear accounts of what happened on that great day of Pentecost at Jerusalem when the Holy Spirit descended upon the infant Christian

Church and people were baffled and amazed. You remember how the apostle Peter faced it all and said, `You should not be surprised at this. This is that which was said by the prophet Joel; it is nothing but a fulfilment of that.'

We could go on like this endlessly, just showing the extraordinary way in which our Lord, in His Person and works and actions, in what happened to Him, and in what resulted from these events, is in a sense doing nothing but fulfilling the law and the prophets. We must never drive a wedge between the Old Testament and the Nev. We must never feel that the New makes the Old unnecessary. I feel increasingly that it is very regrettable that the New Testament should ever have been printed alone, because we tend to fall into the serious error of thinking that, because we are Christians, we do not need the Old Testament. It was the Holy Spirit who led the early Church, which was mainly Gentile, to incorporate the Old Testament Scriptures with their New Scriptures and to regard them all as one. They are indissolubly bound together, and there are many senses in which it can be said that the New Testament cannot be truly understood except in the light that is provided by the Old. For example, it is almost impossible to make anything of the Epistle to the Hebrews unless we know our Old Testament Scriptures.

Let us also observe, very hurriedly, how Christ fulfils the law. This again is something so wonderful that it should lead us to worship and adoration. First, He was `made under the law'. `When the fulness of the time was come, God sent forth his Son, made of a woman, made under the law' (Gal. iv. 4). It is very difficult for our finite minds to grasp what that means, but it is one of the essential truths concerning the incarnation that the eternal Son of God was made under the law. Though He is eternally above it, as Son of God He came and was made under the law, as one who had to carry it out. At no time has God shown more clearly the inviolable and absolute character of His own holy law than when He placed His own Son under it. It is an astounding conception; and yet, as you read the Gospels, you will find how perfectly true it is. Notice how very careful our Lord was to observe the law; He obeyed it down to the minutest detail. Not only that; He taught others to love the law and explained it to them, confirming it constantly and asserting the absolute necessity of obedience to it. That was why He could say at the end of His life that no-one could find any wrong in Him, no-one could bring any charge against Him. He defied them to do so. No-one could arraign Him before the law. He had lived it fully and obeyed it perfectly. There was nothing, not a jot or a tittle, in connection with it which He had to the slightest extent broken or failed to fulfil. You see that in His life, as well as in His birth, He was made subject to the law.

Once more, however, we come to what is to us the centre of our whole faith-the cross on Calvary's hill. What is the meaning of that? Well, I suggest again that if we are not clear in our understanding of the law, we shall never understand the meaning of the cross. The essence of evangelism is not merely to talk about the cross but to proclaim the true doctrine of the cross. There are people who talk about it, but they do so in a purely sentimental manner. They are like the daughters of Jerusalem, whom our Lord Himself rebuked, weeping as they thought of what they called the tragedy of the cross. That is not the right way to view it. There are those who regard the cross as something which exercises a kind of moral influence upon us. They say that its whole purpose is to break down our hard hearts. But that is not the biblical teaching as to its meaning. The purpose of the cross is not to arouse pity in us, neither is it merely some general display of the love of God. Not at all! It is finally understood only in terms of the law. What was happening upon the cross was that our Lord and Saviour Jesus Christ, the Son of God, was enduring in His own holy body the penalty prescribed by the holy law of God for the sin of man. The law condemns sin, and the condemnation that it pronounces is death. `The wages of sin is death.' The law pronounces that death must pass upon all who have sinned against God and broken His holy law. Christ says, `Think not that I am come to destroy the law, or the prophets; I am not come to destroy, but to fulfil.' One of the ways in which the law has to be fulfilled is that its punishment of sin must be carried out. This punishment is death, and that was why He died. The law must be fulfilled. God cannot put it on one side in any respect, and the punishment cannot be put on one side. God in forgiving us-let us say so clearly-does not do so by deciding not to exact the punishment that He has decreed. That would imply a contradiction of His holy nature. Whatever God says must be brought to pass. He does not go back upon Himself and upon what He says. He has said that sin has to be punished by death, and you and I can be forgiven only because the punishment has been thus exacted. In respect of its punishment of sin God's law has been fulfilled absolutely, because He has punished sin in the holy, spotless, blameless body of His own Son there upon the cross on Calvary's hill. Christ is fulfilling the law on the cross, and unless you interpret the cross, and Christ's death upon it, in strict terms of the fulfilling of the law you have not the scriptural view of the death upon the cross.

We see also that, in a most extraordinary and wonderful manner, by so dying upon the cross and bearing in Himself and upon Himself the punishment due to sin, He has fulfilled all the Old Testament types. Go back again and read the books of Leviticus and Numbers; read all about the burnt offerings and sacrifices; read all about the tabernacle, and the temple ceremonial, all about the altar and the laver of washing and so on. Go back to those details and ask yourself, `What do all these things mean? What are they for, the shewbread, and the high priest, and the vessels, and all these other things? What are they meant to do?' They are nothing but shadows, types, prophecies of what is going to be done fully and finally by the Lord Jesus Christ. He indeed has literally fulfilled and carried out and brought to pass every single one of those types. Some may be interested in this subject and there are certain books in which you may find out all the details'. But the principle, the great truth, is just this: Jesus Christ, by His death and all He has done, is an absolute fulfilment of all these types and shadows. He is the high priest, He is the offering, He is the sacrifice, and He has presented His blood in heaven so that the whole of the ceremonial law has been fulfilled in Him. `Think not that I am come to destroy the law, or the prophets: I am not come to destroy, but to fulfil.' By His death and resurrection, and the presentation of Himself in heaven, He has done all this.

But we go a step beyond this and say that He fulfils the law also in us and through us by means of the Holy Spirit. That is the argument of the apostle Paul in Romans viii. 2-4. He tells us quite clearly that this is one of the explanations of why our Lord died. `For the law of the Spirit of life in Christ Jesus hath made me free from the law of sin and death. For what the law could not do, in that it was weak through the flesh, God sending his own Son in the likeness of sinful flesh, and for sin, condemned sin in the flesh: that the righteousness of the law might be fulfilled in us, who walk not after the flesh, but after the Spirit.' This is most important and significant, for the apostle here links together two things: the way in which our Lord fulfilled the law Himself and the way in which He fulfils the law in us. That is precisely what our Lord is saying at this point in Matthew v. He fulfils the righteousness of the law, and we are to do the same. The two go together. He does this in us by giving us the Holy Spirit, and the Holy Spirit gives us a love of the law and the power to live by it. `The carnal mind is enmity against God: for it is not subject to the law of God, neither indeed can be', says the apostle Paul in that same eighth chapter of Romans. But we who have received the Spirit are not like that. We are not at enmity with God, and therefore we are also subject to the law. The natural man hates God and is not subject to His law; but the man who has received the Spirit loves God and is subject to the law. He wants to be so and is given power to be so: `that the righteousness of the law might be fulfilled in us, who walk not after the flesh, but after the Spirit.' Look at it in this way. Through the prophet Jeremiah, God gave a great promise. He said, in effect, `I am going to make a new covenant, and the difference between the new and the old will be this, that I am going to write My law in your minds and on your hearts. No longer will it be on tables of stone outside you, but on the fleshly tables of the heart.' The author of the Epistle to the Hebrews takes that up in the eighth chapter where he glories in the new covenant, the new relationship, because under it the law is within us, not outside us. It is because the law has been written in our minds and our hearts that we are anxious to fulfil it, and are enabled to do so.

Let me summarize all this by asking a question. What, then, is the position with regard to the law and the prophets? I have already tried to show you how the prophets have been fulfilled in and through our Lord Jesus Christ; and yet there still remains something to be fulfilled. What about the law? We can say with regard to the ceremonial law, as I have shown, that it has been already completely fulfilled. Our Lord observed it in His life while here on earth, and He exhorted the disciples to do the same. In His death, resurrection and ascension the whole of the ceremonial law has been entirely fulfilled. In confirmation of that, as it were, the temple was later destroyed. The veil of the temple had already been rent in twain at His death, and finally the temple and all that belonged to it were destroyed. So that, unless I see that the Lord Jesus Christ is the altar and the sacrifice and the laver of washing and the incense and everything else, I am still bound to that levitical order. Unless I see all this fulfilled in Christ, unless He is my burnt offering, my sacrifice, my everything, all this ceremonial law still applies to me, and I shall be held responsible unless I perform it. But seeing it all fulfilled and carried out in Him, I say I am fulfilling it all by believing in Him and by subjecting myself to Him. That is the position with regard to the ceremonial law.

What of the judicial law? This was primarily and especially for the nation of Israel, as God's theocracy, in its then special circumstances. But Israel is no longer the theocratic nation. You remember that at the end of His ministry our Lord turned to the Jews and said, `Therefore say I unto you, The kingdom of God shall be taken from you, and given to a nation bringing forth the fruits thereof.' That is Matthew xxi. 43, one of the most crucial and important statements in the whole of Scripture with regard to prophecy. And the apostle Peter, in i Peter ii. 9, 1 o, makes it abundantly clear that the new nation is the Church. There is then no longer a theocratic nation, so the judicial law has likewise been fulfilled.

That leaves us with the moral law. The position with regard to this is different, because here God is laying down something which is permanent and perpetual, the relationship which must always subsist between Himself and man. It is all to be found, of course, in what our Lord calls the first and greatest commandment. `Thou shalt love the Lord thy God with all thy heart, and with all thy soul, and with all thy strength, and with all thy mind.' That is permanent. That is not for the theocratic nation only; it is for the whole of mankind. The second commandment, He says, `is like unto it, Thou shalt love thy neighbour as thyself.' That again was not only for the theocratic nation of Israel; that was not merely the old ceremonial law. It is a permanent condition and part of our perpetual relationship to God. Thus the moral law, as interpreted by the New Testament, stands now as much as it has ever done, and will do so until the end of time and until we are perfected. In i John iii the apostle is very careful to remind his readers that sin in Christian people is still `a transgression of the law'. `We still see our relationship to the law', says John in effect, `for sin is a transgression of the law.' The law is still there, and when I sin I am breaking that law, though I am a Christian and though I have never been a Jew, and am a Gentile. So the moral law still applies to us. That, it seems to me, is the present position.

With regard to the future, I have simply two statements to make. The first is that the kingdom will eventually cover the whole earth. The stone that is spoken of in the second chapter of Daniel is going to fill the whole world; the kingdoms of this world shall become `the kingdoms of our Lord, and of his Christ'. The process is going on, it will finally be completed. Every tittle of the law and the prophets will thus be completely carried out. The law breakers will finally be punished. Let us make no mistake about this. Those who die finally impenitent, and unbelieving in the Lord Jesus Christ, are under the condemnation of the law. And at the very end the pronouncement delivered upon them will be, `Depart from me, ye cursed, into everlasting fire.' And it is the law that will condemn them to that. So that the law of God is going to be carried out fully in every respect. Those who do not avail themselves of what is offered in the Lord Jesus Christ will abide under the condemnation of the law which is the expression of the justice and righteousness of God.

The last question must be this. What then is the relationship of the Christian to the law? We can put our answer in this form. The Christian is no longer under the law in the sense that the law is a covenant of works. That is the whole argument in Galatians iii. The Christian is not under the law in that respect; his salvation does not depend upon his keeping of it. He has been delivered from the curse of the law; he is no longer under the law as a covenant relationship between himself and God. But that does not release him from it as a rule of life. Now I think the whole trouble tends to arise because we become confused in our minds as to the relationship between law and grace. Let me put it like this. We tend to have a wrong view of law and to think of it as something that is opposed to grace. But it is not. Law is only opposed to grace in the sense that there was once a covenant of law, and we are now under the covenant of grace. Nor must the law be thought of as being identical with grace. It was never meant to be something in and of itself. The law was never meant to save man, because it could not. Some people tend to think that God said to the nation, `I am now giving you a law; you keep that law and it will save you.' But that is ridiculous because no man can save himself by keeping the law. No! the law was `added because of transgressions'. It came in 430 years after the promise was given to Abraham and his seed in order that it might show the true character of God's demands, and that it might show `the exceeding sinfulness of sin'. The law was given, in a sense, in order to show men that they could never justify themselves before God, and in order that we might be brought to Christ. In Paul's words it was meant to be `our schoolmaster to bring us unto Christ'.

You see, therefore, that the law has a great deal of prophecy in it, and a great deal of the gospel. It is full of grace, leading me to Christ. We have already seen that all the sacrifices and the ceremonial in connection with the law were also designed to do the same thing. That is where the critics of the Old Testament, who say they are not interested in the burnt offerings and the ceremonial, who argue that these are but pagan rites which the Jews and others employed and which can therefore be explained away in terms of comparative religion, that is where such people are really denying the New Testament gospel of the grace of God in Christ. All the rites and ceremonial were given to Israel in detail by God. He called Moses up into the mount and said, `See . . . that thou make all things according to the pattern showed to thee in the mount.'

We must realize, therefore, that all these aspects of the law are but our schoolmaster to bring us to Christ, and we must beware lest we fall into a false view of the law. In the same way, people have a false view of grace. They think that grace is apart from law and has nothing to do with it. That is what is called antinomianism, the attitude of people who abuse the doctrine of grace in order to live a sinful, slack or indolent type of spiritual life. They say, `I am not under the law, but under grace, and therefore it does not matter what I do.' Paul wrote his sixth chapter of Romans to deal with that: `Shall we continue in sin, that grace may abound? God forbid', says Paul. That is an absolutely wrong and false view of grace. The whole purpose of grace, in a sense, is just to enable us to keep the law. Let me put it in this way. The trouble with us is that we so often have a wrong view of holiness at this point. There is nothing more fatal than to regard holiness and sanctification as experiences to be received. No; holiness means being righteous, and being righteous means keeping the law. Therefore if your so-called grace (which you say you have received) does not make you keep the law, you have not received grace. You may have received a psychological experience, but you have never received the grace of God. What is grace? It is that marvellous gift of God which, having delivered a man from the curse of the law, enables him to keep it and to be righteous as Christ was righteous, for He kept the law perfectly. Grace is that which brings me to love God; and if I love God, I long to keep His commandments. `He that hath my commandments, and keepeth them,' Christ said, `he it is that loveth me.'

We must never separate these two things. Grace is not sentimental; holiness is not an experience. We must have this new mind and disposition which leads us to love the law and to desire to keep it; and by His power He enables us to fulfil the law. That is why our Lord goes on to say in verse 19, `Whosoever therefore shall break one of these least commandments, and shall teach men so, he shall be called the least in the kingdom of heaven: but whosoever shall do and teach them, the same shall be called great in the kingdom of heaven.' That was not spoken only to the disciples for the three short years they were to be with Christ until He died; it is permanent and everlasting. He enforces it again in Matthew vii, where He says, `Not every one that saith unto me, Lord, Lord, shall enter into the kingdom of heaven; but he that doeth the will of my Father which is in heaven.' What is the will of the Father? The ten commandments and the moral law. They have never been abrogated. He `gave himself for us,' says Paul to Titus, `that he might ... purify unto himself a peculiar people, zealous of good works.' `Yea', says our Lord, as we hope to consider later, `except your righteousness shall exceed the righteousness of the scribes and Pharisees, ye shall in no case enter into the kingdom of heaven.'

This study has been in some ways a difficult one but, at the same time, it has been concerned with a glorious truth. Looking at the law and the prophets and seeing them all fulfilled in Him, have you not seen an aspect of the grace of Christ that has given you a deeper view of it? Do you not see that it was the law of God that was being enacted upon the cross and that God has punished your sin there in the body of Christ? The substitutionary doctrine of the atonement emphasizes that He has carried out the law fully. He has submitted Himself to it absolutely, actively and passively, negatively and positively. All the types have been fulfilled in Him. And what yet remains of the prophecy will certainly be carried out. The effect of this glorious, redeeming work is not only to give forgiveness to us miserable, law-breaking rebels against God, but to make us sons of God-those who delight in the law of God, those indeed who `hunger and thirst after righteousness' and who long to be holy, not in the sense of having a wonderful feeling or experience, but who long to live like Christ and to be like Him in every respect.

CHAPTER NINETEEN

RIGHTEOUSNESS EXCEEDING THAT
OF THE SCRIBES AND PHARISEES

W "E turn now to deal particularly with the statement of verse 20 in which our Lord defines His attitude to the law and the prophets, and especially perhaps to the law. We have seen how vital this short paragraph, running from verses 17 to 20, is in His ministry, and how it must influence our whole outlook upon the Christian gospel. Nothing was more important than that He should state very clearly and explicitly, at the outset, the characteristics of His ministry. There were many reasons why men should harbour various misapprehensions with regard to that. He Himself was unusual; He did not belong to the order of the scribes and Pharisees; He was not an official doctor of the law. Yet here He was standing before them as a Teacher. Not only that, He was a Teacher who did not hesitate to criticize, as He did here, the teaching of the recognized, and, in a sense, authorized teachers of the people. Moreover, His conduct was strange at certain points. Far from avoiding the company of sinners, He went out of His way to choose it. He was known as `the friend of publicans and sinners'. There was also an element in His teaching which emphasized the doctrine called `grace'. All these things seemed to differentiate what He said from everything that the people had ever heard, so they were obviously liable to certain grave misunderstandings with regard to His message and its general import.

We have seen, therefore, that He defines it here by laying down two main principles. First, His teaching is in no way inconsistent with that of the law and the prophets; but, secondly, it is very different from the teaching of the scribes and Pharisees.

We have seen, too, that our attitude towards the law, therefore, is most important. Our Lord has not come to make it easier for us or to make it in any sense less stringent in its demands upon us. His purpose in coming was to enable us to keep the law, not to abrogate it. So He emphasizes here that we must know what the law is, and then must keep it: `Whosoever therefore shall break one of these least commandments, and shall teach men so, he shall be called the least in the kingdom of heaven: but whosoever shall do and teach them, the same shall be called great in the kingdom of heaven.' Now we need not spend any time in considering what is meant by `the least' and `greatest' of the commandments. There is obviously a distinction in some sense between them. They are all the commandments of God, and, as He emphasizes here, even the least commandment is therefore of the most vital importance. Furthermore, as James reminds us, anyone who fails in one point of the law has failed in it all.

But all the same there is a kind of division of the law into two sections. The first section concerns our relationship to God; the second concerns our relationship to man. There is a relative difference in the importance therefore; our relationship to God is obviously of greater importance than our relationship to man. You remember when the scribe came to our Lord and asked Him which was the greatest commandment, our Lord did not turn to him and say, `You must not talk about greater and lesser, you must not talk about first and second.' He said, `The first commandment is this; Thou shalt love the Lord thy God with all thy heart, and with all thy soul, and with all thy mind, and with all thy strength. And the second is like, namely this, Thou shalt love thy neighbour as thyself.' Very well; as you read the law you can see there is a meaning in this distinction between the least and the greatest of the commandments. What our Lord says, therefore, is that we must keep every part and portion of the law, that we must do and teach it all.

It is at that point that He turns our thoughts to the teaching of the Pharisees and scribes, because if the law is thus vitally important to us, and if, in the last analysis, the whole purpose of the grace of God in Jesus Christ is to enable us to fulfil and to keep the righteousness of the law, then we must obviously be clear in our minds as to what the law is, and what it demands of us. We have seen that that is the biblical doctrine of holiness. Holiness is not an experience that we have; it means keeping and fulfilling the law of God. Experiences may help us to do that, but we cannot receive holiness and sanctification as experiences. Holiness is something we practise in our daily life. It is the honouring and the keeping of the law, as the Son of God Himself kept it while He was here on earth. It is being like Him. That is holiness. So you see it is intimately related to the law, and must always be thought of in terms of keeping the law. It is at that point that the Pharisees and the scribes come in, because they appeared to be most holy people. But our Lord is able to show very clearly that they were lacking in righteousness and holiness. That was true of them very largely because of their tragic misunderstanding and misinterpretation of the law. In the two verses which we are now considering, our Lord enforces His teaching by means of a negative, and the words in verse 20 must have come as a most surprising and almost shocking statement to the men and women to whom they were uttered. `Do not imagine', says our Lord in effect, `that I have come to make things easier by reducing the demands of the law. Far from doing that, I am here to tell you that unless your righteousness shall exceed that of the scribes and Pharisees, you have no hope of entering the kingdom of heaven at all, let alone being the least in it.'

Now what does this mean? We must remember that the scribes and Pharisees were in many senses the most outstanding people of the nation. The scribes were men who spent their time in teaching and expounding the law; they were the great authorities on the law of God. They gave their whole life to the study and illustration of it. They, more than anyone else, therefore, could claim to be concerned about it. They were the men who made copies of it, exercising great care as they did so. Their whole life was lived with the law, and everyone looked up to them for that reason.

The Pharisees were the men who were quite outstanding and famous for their sanctity, so-called. The very word `Pharisee' means `separatist'. They were people who set themselves apart, and they did so because they had formed a code of the ceremonial acts connected with the law which was more rigid than the law of Moses itself. They had drawn up rules and regulations for life and conduct which in their stringency went far beyond anything we find demanded in the Old Testament Scriptures. For example, in our Lord's picture of the Pharisee and the publican who went up to the temple to pray, the Pharisee said that he fasted twice in the week. Now there is no demand in the Old Testament that men should fast twice in the week. Indeed the Old Testament asked for only one fast in the year. But gradually these men had elaborated the system and had actually brought it to the point at which they exhorted and commanded the people to fast twice in the week, instead of only once in the year. It was in such ways that they formed their excessively stringent code of morals and behaviour and, as a result of that, everybody thought of the scribes and Pharisees as paragons of virtue. The average man said to himself, 'Ali, there is very little hope of my ever being as good as the scribes or the Pharisees. They are outstanding; they just live to be sanctified and holy. That is their profession; that is their whole aim and object in a religious, moral and spiritual sense.' But here comes our Lord; and He announces to these people that unless their righteousness shall exceed that of the scribes and Pharisees they shall in no wise enter into the kingdom of heaven.

This, then, is surely one of the most vital things we can ever consider. What is our conception of true holiness and sanctification? What is our idea of being religious? What is our conception of a Christian? Our Lord sets it down here as a postulate, that the righteousness of the Christian, the very least Christian, must exceed that of the scribes and Pharisees. Let us therefore examine our profession of the Christian faith in the light of this analysis of His. You must often have been struck by the fact that in the four Gospels a great deal of space is given to what our Lord had to say about the scribes and Pharisees. He was always, as it were, referring to them and dealing with them. That was not only because they criticized Him; it was chiefly because He knew that the common people depended upon these men and their teaching. In a sense, the one thing our Lord had to do was to show the hollowness of their teaching, and then present the people with the true teaching. That is what He does in these words.

Let us, then, glance at the religion of the Pharisees in oraer that we may see its defects, and in order that we may see what is demanded of us. One of the most convenient ways of doing this is to look at that picture which our Lord Himself drew of the Pharisee and the publican going up together to the temple to pray. The Pharisee, you remember, stood forward in a very prominent place, and thanked God he was not as other men, especially not as that publican. Then he began to say certain things about himself: he was not an extortioner, not unjust, not an adulterer, and not as that publican. Now those statements were true. Our Lord accepted them; that was why He repeated them. These men had that kind of external righteousness. Not only that, they fasted twice in the week, as I have reminded you. They also gave a tithe, a tenth, of all they possessed to God and to His cause. They tithed everything they had even down to their herbs, the mint and anise and cummin. But in addition to that they were highly religious, and most punctilious in their observance of certain religious services and ceremonials. All that was true of the Pharisees. They did not merely say it, they did it. Yet no-one can read the four Gospels, even in a casual or cursory manner, without seeing that there was nothing that called forth such wrath from our blessed Lord as that very religion of the scribes and the Pharisees. Take the twenty-third chapter of Matthew's Gospel with its terrible pronouncement of woes upon the scribes and the Pharisees, and there you see in its essence our Lord's exposure of these people and His criticism of their whole attitude towards God and towards religion. It is because of all this that He says, `except your righteousness shall exceed the righteousness of the scribes and Pharisees, ye shall in no case enter into the kingdom of heaven.'

We must realize that this is one of the most serious and important matters we can ever consider together. There is a real and terrible possibility of our deluding and fooling ourselves. The Pharisees and the scribes were denounced by our Lord as being hypocrites. Yes; but they were unconscious hypocrites. They did not realize it, they really thought all was well. You cannot read your Bible without constantly being reminded of that terrible danger. There is the possibility of our relying upon the wrong thing, of resting upon things that appertain to true worship rather than being in the position of true worship. And let me remind you tenderly, in passing, that it is something of which those of us who not only claim to be evangelical, but are proud to call ourselves such, may very easily be guilty.

Let us, then, follow our Lord's analysis of the religion of the scribes and Pharisees. I have- tried to extract certain principles which I put to you in this form. The first and, in a sense, the basic charge against them is that their religion was entirely external and formal instead of being a religion of the heart. He turned to them one day and said, `Ye are they which justify yourselves before men; but God knoweth your hearts: for that which is highly esteemed among men is abomination in the sight of God' (Lk. xvi. i5). Now let us remember that all these statements which are thus made about the Pharisees by our Lord are judicial condemnations. There is no contradiction between the love of God and the wrath of God. The Lord Jesus Christ was so full of love that He never complained of anything done to Himself. But He denounced judicially the people who misrepresented God and religion. That does not imply any contradiction in His character. Holiness and love must go together; and it is a part of holy love to unmask the false and the spurious and to denounce the hypocritical.

On another occasion our Lord said something like this to them. Some of the Pharisees were rather surprised at the actions of His disciples who came in from the market place and immediately sat down at the table and began to eat without first washing their hands. 'Ali', He said in effect, `how careful you Pharisees are about the outside, but how negligent you are about the inside. It is not that which goes into man which defiles him, but that which comes out. It is the heart that matters, for it is out of the heart that come evil thoughts, murders, adulteries, fornications, thefts, false witness and all these other things.' But you remember how the record puts it later in Matthew xxiii. Our Lord tells the Pharisees that they are like whited sepulchres; the outside seems to be all right, but look at the inside! It is possible for us to be highly regular in our attendance at the house of God and yet to be envious and spiteful. That is the thing our Lord denounces in the Pharisees. And unless our righteousness exceeds these external religious demands we do not belong to the kingdom of God. The kingdom of God is concerned about the heart; it is not my external actions, but what I am inside that is important. A man once said that the best definition of religion was this: `Religion is that which a man does with his own solitude.' In other words, if you want to know what you really are, you can find the answer when you are alone with your thoughts and desires and imaginations. It is what you say to yourself that matters. How careful we are in what we say to others; but what do we say to ourselves? What a man does with his own solitude is what ultimately counts. The things that are within, which we hide from the outside world because we are ashamed of them, these proclaim finally whatwereallyare.

The second charge which our Lord brought against the scribes and Pharisees was that they were obviously more concerned with the ceremonial than with the moral; and that, of course, always follows upon the first. These people were careful externally; they were most punctilious with the washing of hands and with the ceremonial aspects of the law. But they were not as careful with regard to the moral aspects of the law. Need I remind you that this is still a terrible danger? There is a type of religionand, alas, it seems to me that it is becoming more commonwhich does not hesitate to teach that as long as you go to the house of God on Sunday morning it does not matter very much what you do with the rest of the day. I am not thinking only of those who say that all you need to do is to go to holy communion in the morning and then you are free to keep Sunday as you like. I wonder whether we are all perfectly happy in our consciences about this? There is, it seems to me, this increasing tendency to say, `Of course it is the morning service that matters; I need the teaching and instruction. But the evening service is purely evangelistic, so I will spend the rest of my time writing my letters and reading.' That, I say, is to be guilty of the error of the Pharisees. The Lord's day is a day that is meant to be given as much as possible to God. We ought on this day to put everything aside as far as we can, that God may be honoured and glorified and that His cause may prosper and flourish. The Pharisee was quite content so long as he had done his external duty. Yes, he had been to the service and that for him was sufficient.

Another characteristic of the Pharisees' religion was that it was one of man-made rules and regulations which were based upon certain dispensations they had decided to grant to one another, and which really violated the law they pretended to keep. Some of them were even guilty of neglecting their duties as children. They said, `Now, we have devoted that particular sum of money to the Lord, so we cannot very well give it to our parents to help to look after them and their needs.''Hypocrites', says our Lord in effect, `that is just the way you have of avoiding the demands of the law that you should honour your father and your mother.' They worked by traditions, and most of these traditions were really nothing but very clever and subtle ways of evading the demands of the law. You avoided these demands by saying that you did it in this special way, which meant that you really did not do it at all. I think we all know something about that. We Protestants are highly critical of the Roman Catholics and especially its teachers in the Middle Ages who were called casuists. These men were experts in making fine and subtle distinctions, especially with regard to matters relating to the conscience and behaviour. They often appeared to be able to reconcile things that seemed hopelessly contradictory. You have probably observed it in the newspapers. You see that a Roman Catholic who does not believe in divorce has obtained one. How has it happened? It has probably been done by means of casuistry-some kind of explanation on paper that seems to satisfy the letter of the law. But, again, I am not simply concerned to denounce that Catholic type of religion. God knows we are all experts at this. We can all rationalize our own sins and explain them away, and excuse ourselves for the things we do and do not do. That was typical of the Pharisees.

The next charge which our Lord brings against them, however, is that they were clearly primarily concerned about themselves and their own righteousness, with the result that they were almost invariably self-satisfied. In other words the ultimate object of the Pharisee was to glorify not God, but himself. When he went about his religious duties he was really considering himself and his performance of the duty, not the glory and the honour of God. Our Lord shows, in that picture of the Pharisee and the publican praying in the temple, that the Pharisee did and said all without worshipping God at all. He said, `I thank thee, that I am not as other men are.' It was an insult to God; there was no worship there. The man was full of his own activity, his own religious life and of what he was doing. Of course if you set out like that and you have your own standard, you select the things you think ought to be done. And as long as you conform to that particular list you are all right, you are satisfied. Now the Pharisees were self-satisfied and concentrated always upon their own achievements rather than on their relationship to God. I wonder whether we are not sometimes guilty of the same attitude? Is it not one of the besetting sins of those of us who are called Evangelicals? We see other men obviously denying the faith and living godless lives. How easy it is to become self-satisfied because we are better than such people-'I thank God I am not as other men and especially as that modernist.' The trouble with us is that we never look at ourselves in the sight of God: we never remind ourselves of the character and the being and the nature of God. Our religion consists of a certain number of things we have decided to do; and having done them we think all is well. Smugness, glibness, self-satisfaction are surely far too much in evidence among us.

That leads us in turn to consider the Pharisee's regrettable and tragic attitude towards others. The ultimate condemnation of the Pharisee is that there is in his life a complete absence of the spirit delineated in the Beatitudes. That is the difference between him and the Christian. The Christian is a man who exemplifies the Beatitudes. He is `poor in spirit', he is `meek', he is `merciful'. He is not satisfied because he has performed one prescribed task. No; he is `hungering and thirsting after righteousness'. He longs to be like Christ. There is a profound lack of satisfaction within him. That is the test by which we must judge ourselves. In the last analysis our Lord condemns these Pharisees for completely failing to keep the law. The Pharisees, He says, tithe mint and anise and cummin, but they forget and ignore the weightier matters of the law, which are love of God and love of man. But that is the whole centre of religion and the whole purpose of our worship. May I remind you once more that what God demands of us is that we should love Him with all our heart, and with all our soul, and with all our strength, and with all our mind, and our neighbour as ourselves. The fact that you are tithing mint and anise and cummin, that you are pressing these matters of your tithe even down to the smallest detail, that is not sanctity. The test of sanctity is your relationship to God, your attitude to Him and your love for Him. How do you stand up to that particular test? To be holy does not just mean the mere avoidance of certain things, or even not thinking certain things; it means the ultimate attitude of the heart of man towards that holy, loving God, and, secondly, our attitude towards our fellow men and women.

The trouble with the Pharisees was that they were interested in details rather than principles, that they were interested in actions rather than in motives, and that they were interested in doing rather than in being. The remainder of this Sermon on the Mount is just an exposition of that. Our Lord said to them in effect, `You are pleased with yourselves because you do not commit adultery; but if you even look with lust in your eyes, that is adultery.' It is the principle, not the action only, that matters; it is what you think and desire, it is the state of your heart that is important. You do not become Christian by just refraining from some actions and doing others; the Christian is a man who is in a particular relationship to God and whose supreme desire is to know Him better and to love Him more truly. That is not a part-time job, if I may so put it, it is not achieved by the religious observance of a part of Sunday; it demands all the time and attention we have. Read the lives of the great men of God and you will find that that is the principle that always emerges.

Now let me ask the question that is probably in your mind at this point. What then is our Lord teaching? Is He teaching salvation by works? Is He saying that we have to live a life better than that of the Pharisees in order to enter the kingdom? Patently not, because `there is none righteous, no, not one'. The law of God given to Moses condemned the whole world; `every mouth has been stopped'; all are `guilty before God' and have `come short of the glory of God'. Our Lord did not come to teach justification or salvation by works, or by our own righteousness. `Very well,' says the opposite school; `is He not teaching that salvation is by means of the righteousness of Christ alone, so that it does not matter at all what we may do? He has done it all and therefore we have nothing to do.' Now that is the other extreme, and the other error. That, I argue, is an impossible exposition of this verse because of the little word `for' at the beginning of verse twenty. It links up with verse nineteen where He said, `Whosoever therefore shall break one of these least commandments, and shall teach men so, he shall be called the least in the kingdom of heaven: but whosoever shall do and teach them, the same shall be called great in the kingdom of heaven.' He is emphasizing the practical carrying out of the law. That is the whole purpose of the paragraph. It is not to make it easy for us or to enable us to say, `Christ has done it all for us and therefore it matters not what we do.' We always tend in our folly to consider things as antitheses which are meant to be complementary. Our Lord is teaching that the proof of our having truly received the grace of God in Jesus Christ is that we are living a righteous life. You know the old argument, of course, about faith and works. Some say the one is all important, some say the other. The Bible teaches that both these views are wrong: it is faith showing itself by works which is the mark of a true Christian.

Now lest you may think this is my doctrine, let me quote the apostle Paul, who of all others is the apostle of faith, and of grace. `Be not deceived', he says-not to the world, but to church members at Corinth-'be not deceived: neither fornicators, nor idolaters, nor adulterers ... nor extortioners, shall inherit the kingdom of God.' `It is no use saying, "Lord, Lord," unless you do the things that I command you', says Christ. It comes to this, that unless my life is a righteous life, I must be very careful before I claim that I am covered by the grace of God in Jesus Christ. For to receive the grace of God in Jesus Christ means not only that my sins are forgiven because of His death for me on the cross on Calvary's hill, but also that I have been given a new life and a new nature. It means that Christ is being formed in me, that I have become a partaker of the divine nature, that old things have passed away and all things have become new. It means that Christ is dwelling in me, and that the Spirit of God is in me. The man who has been born again, and who has the divine nature within him, is a man who is righteous and his righteousness does exceed that of the scribes and Pharisees. He is no longer living for self and his own attainments, he is no longer self-righteous and self-satisfied. He has become poor in spirit, meek, and merciful; he hungers and thirsts after righteousness; he has become a peacemaker. His heart is being purified. He loves God, yes unworthily, alas, but he loves Him and longs for His honour and glory. His desire is to glorify God and to keep and honour and fulfil His law. The commandments of God to such a man `are not grievous'. He wants to keep them, for He loves them. He is no longer at enmity against God; but he now sees the holiness of the law and nothing so appeals to him as the living of this law and the exemplifying of it in his daily life. It is a righteousness that far exceeds the righteousness of the scribes and Pharisees.

Some of the most vital questions that can be asked, then, are these. Do you know God? Do you love God? Can you say honestly that the biggest and the first thing in your life is to glorify Him and that you so want to do this that you do not care what it may cost you in any sense? Do you feel that this must come first, not that you may be better than somebody else, but that you may honour and glorify and love that God who, though you have sinned against Him grievously, has sent His only begotten Son to the cross on Calvary's hill to die for you, that you might be forgiven and that He might restore you unto Himself? Let every man examine himself.

.

CHAPTER TWENTY

THE LETTER AND THE SPIRIT

W E come now to the beginning of another new section. To understand the real import of this Sermon, it is essential that we should understand the precise connection between what our Lord begins to say at verse 2 t and what has gone before. And of course it is a very direct connection. The danger in dealing with a part of Scripture such as this is that we shall become so immersed in a consideration of the details that we miss the essential teaching and the great principles which our Lord was enunciating. It will be good for us, therefore, to remind ourselves again of the general outline of the Sermon so that every part will be seen in relationship to the whole.

Our Lord is concerned to describe the citizens of the kingdom, the kingdom of God or the kingdom of heaven. First and foremost, He gives us in the Beatitudes a general description of the essential nature of the Christian man. Then He goes on to tell us about the function and the purpose of the Christian in this life and world. Then we have seen that that brings Him immediately to this whole question of the relationship of such a person to the law. It was essential that He should do that because the people to whom He was preaching were Jews who had been taught the law, and obviously they would evaluate any new teaching in terms of the law. So He had to show them the relationship of Himself and His teaching to the law, and He does that in verses i 7-20, summing it up in the vital statement which we have just been studying.

Now here, at verse 2 i, He proceeds to expand that statement. He expounds the relationship of the Christian to the law in two respects. He gives us His own positive exposition of the law, and He also contrasts it with the false teaching of the scribes and Pharisees. Indeed, there is a sense in which it can be said that the whole of the remainder of this Sermon, from verse 21 right through to the end of chapter vii, is nothing but an elaboration of that fundamental proposition, that our righteousness must exceed that of the scribes and Pharisees if we are indeed to be citizens of the kingdom of heaven. This is something which our Lord does in a most interesting manner. Looking at it broadly we can say that in the remainder of chapter v He is concerned to do this in terms of a true exposition of the law over against the false exposition of the Pharisees and the scribes. His main concern in chapter vi is to show the true nature of fellowship with God, again in contra-distinction to the Pharisaical teaching and practice. Then in chapter vii He is concerned to show true righteousness as it views itself and others, once more contrasted with what was taught and practised by the Pharisees and the scribes. That is the essential analysis of the teaching which we must try to hold in our minds.

In V.'21-48, then, our Lord is concerned mainly to give a true account of the law. He does this by putting forward a series of six particular statements and we should look at these very carefully. The first is in verse 21: `Ye have heard that it was said by them of old time, Thou shalt not kill.' The next comes in verse 27 where He says again: `Ye have heard that it was said by them of old time, Thou shalt not commit adultery.' Then in verse 31 we read: `It hath been said, Whosoever shall put away his wife, let him give her a writing of divorcement.' The next is in verse 33: `Again, ye have heard that it hath been said by them of old time, Thou shalt not forswear thyself, but shalt perform unto the Lord thine oaths.' Then in verse 38 we read: `Ye have heard that it hath been said, An eye for an eye, and a tooth for a tooth.' And the last is in verse 43: `Ye have heard that it bath been said, Thou shalt love thy neighbour, and hate thine enemy.'

It is most important, before we come to deal with each of these statements separately and in particular, that we should consider them together as a whole, because, if you look at them, you will see at once that there are certain principles which are common to all six. Indeed, I do not hesitate to suggest that our Lord was really more concerned about these common principles than He was about the particulars. In other words, He lays down certain principles and then illustrates them.

Obviously, therefore, we must make certain that we really grasp the principles first.

The first thing we must consider is the formula which He uses: `Ye have heard that it was said by them of old time'. There is a slight variation in the form here and there, but that, essentially, is the way in which He introduces these six statements. We must be perfectly clear about this. You will find that certain translations put it like this: `Ye have heard it was said to them of old time.' On purely linguistic grounds no-one can tell whether it was `by' or `to' for, as usual, when you come to matters of linguistics, you find the authorities are divided, and you cannot be sure. Only a consideration of the context, therefore, can help us to determine exactly what our Lord meant to convey by this. Is He referring simply to the law of Moses, or is He referring to the teaching of the Pharisees and scribes? Those who would say it should read `to them of old time' obviously must say that He is referring to the law of Moses given to the fathers; whereas those who would emphasize the `by', as we have it in the Authorized Version, would say that it has reference to what was taught by the scribes and Pharisees.

It seems to me that certain considerations make it almost essential for us to take the second view, and to hold that what our Lord is really doing here is showing the true teaching of the law over against the false representations of it made by the Pharisees and the scribes. You remember that one of the great characteristics of their teaching was the significance which they attached to tradition. They were always quoting the fathers. That is what made the scribe a scribe; he was an authority on the pronouncements which had been made by the fathers. These had become the tradition. I suggest, therefore, that the verses must be interpreted in that way. Indeed, the wording used by our Lord more or less clinches the matter. He says: `Ye have heard that it was said by them of old time.' He does not say `You have read in the law of Moses', or `It was written and you have read'. That is significant in this way. Perhaps we can best show it by means of an illustration. The condition of the Jews in our Lord's day was remarkably like that of people in this country before the Protestant Reformation. You remember that in those days the

Scriptures were not translated into English, but were read Sunday by Sunday in Latin to people who did not understand Latin. The result was that the people were entirely dependent for their knowledge of the Scriptures upon the priests who read the Bible to them and who claimed to be expounding it. They were unable to read the Scriptures for themselves and to verify and confirm that which they were hearing from the various pulpits on Sundays and weekdays. What the Protestant Reformation did, in a sense, was to give the Bible to the people. It enabled them to read the Scriptures for themselves, and to see the false teaching and the false representations of the gospel which had been given to them.

Now the position when our Lord was speaking here was very similar to that. The children of Israel during their captivity in Babylon had ceased to know the Hebrew language. Their language when they came back, and at this time, was Aramaic. They were not familiar with Hebrew so they could not read the law of Moses as they had it in their own Hebrew Scriptures. The result was that they were dependent for any knowledge of the law upon the teaching of the Pharisees and the scribes. Our Lord, therefore, very rightly said, 'Ye have heard', or `That is what you have been hearing; that is what has been said to you; that is the preaching that has been given to you as you have gone to your synagogues and listened to the instruction.' The result was that what these people thought of as the law was in reality not the law itself, but a representation of it given by the scribes and Pharisees. In particular it consisted of the various interpretations and traditions which had been added to the law during the centuries, and thus it was essential that these people should be given a true account of what the law really did say and teach. The Pharisees and scribes had added their own interpretations to it, and it was almost impossible at this time to tell which was law and which was interpretation. Again the analogy of what happened in this country before the Reformation will help us to see the exact position. The Roman Catholic teaching before the Protestant Reformation was a false representation of the gospel of Jesus Christ. It said you had to believe in the sacraments to be saved, and that apart from the Church and priesthood there was no salvation. That was how salvation was being taught.

Tradition and various additions had beclouded the simple gospel. Our Lord's object, as I think we shall see as we work through these examples, was to show exactly what had been happening to the law of Moses as the result of the teaching of the scribes and Pharisees. So He is concerned to make clear to them exactly what the law has to say. That is the first principle which we must hold in mind.

Then we must also consider this other extraordinary statement: 'I say unto you'. This is, of course, one of the most crucial statements with regard to the doctrine of the Person of the Lord Jesus Christ. You see, He does not hesitate here to set Himself up as the authority. Obviously, also, it has real significance with regard to the previous statement. If you take the view that 'by them of old time' means just the law of Moses, then you are more or less forced into the position of believing that our Lord was saying: 'The law of Moses said ... but I say . . .', which suggests that He was correcting the law of Moses. But that is not so. He is saying, rather, `I am interpreting to you the law of Moses, and it is My interpretation that is true and not that of the Pharisees and scribes.' Indeed there is even more than that in it. There is a suggestion that He is saying something like this: `I who am speaking to you am the very One who was responsible for the law of Moses; it was I who gave it to Moses, and it is I alone, therefore, who can truly interpret it.' You see, He does not hesitate here to claim for Himself a unique authority; He claims to speak as God. Regarding the law of Moses, as He does, as something which shall not pass away until every jot and tittle has been fulfilled, He does not hesitate, nevertheless, to say, `But I say unto you.' He claims the authority of God; and that, of course, is the claim which is made for Him everywhere in the four Gospels and in the entire New Testament. It is vitally important, therefore, that we should realize the authority with which these words come to us. He was not a mere teacher, He was not a mere man; He was not a mere expounder of the law or just another scribe or Pharisee, or prophet. He was infinitely more than that, He was God the Son in the flesh presenting the truth of God. We might very well spend much time considering this great phrase, but I trust that we are all clear and all agreed about that. Everything we have in this Sermon on the Mount must be accepted as coming from the Son of God Himself. So we are confronted with this stupendous fact that here in this world of time the very Son of God has been amongst us; and though He came in the likeness of sinful flesh, He still speaks with this divine authority and His every word is of crucial importance to us.

That leads us on to the consideration of what He actually said. Here it is important that we should consider the statement as a whole before looking at the particular injunctions in detail. Let us once and for all get rid of the idea that our Lord came to set up a new law, or to announce a new code of ethics. As we consider the detailed statements we shall find that many people have dropped into that error. There are those who do not believe in the unique deity of the Lord Jesus Christ or in His atonement, and who do not worship Him as the Lord of glory, but who say that they are great believers in the Sermon on the Mount because they find there a code of ethics for this life and world. That, they say, is how life should be lived. I am, therefore, emphasizing the principles in order that we may see that to look at the Sermon in that way is to nullify its real purpose. It is not meant to be a detailed code of ethics; it is not a new kind of moral law which was given by Him. It was probably thought of in that way in His own day, so He constantly said something like this: `I have come to found a new kingdom. I am the first of a new race of people, the first-born among many brethren; and the people of whom I am Head will be of a certain type and character, people who, because they conform to that description, are going to behave in a certain manner. Now I want to give you some illustrations of how they are going to behave.'

That is what our Lord is saying, and that is why He is concerned about the principles rather than the detailed examples. So if we take the illustrations and turn them into a law we are denying the very thing He was setting out to do. Now it is characteristic of human nature that we always prefer to have things cut and dried rather than have them in the form of principles. That is why certain forms of religion are always popular. The natural man likes to be given a definite list; then he feels that, as long as he conforms to the things stated in the list, all will be well. But that is not possible with the gospel; that is not possible at all in the kingdom of God. That was partly the position under the Old

Dispensation, and even there it was carried too far by the Pharisees and scribes. But it is not at all like that under the New Testament dispensation. However, we still tend to like this sort of thing. It is very much easier, is it not, to think of holiness in terms of observing Lent for six weeks or so during the year, rather than to be living with a principle which demands and insists upon application day by day. We always like to have a set of routine rules and regulations. That is why I am pressing this point. If you take the Sermon on the Mount with these six detailed statements and say, `As long as I do not commit adultery-and so on-I am all right', you have entirely missed our Lord's point. It is not a code of ethics. He is out to delineate a certain order and quality of life, and He says in effect: `Look, I am illustrating this kind of life. It means this type of behaviour.' So we must hold on to the principle without turning the particular illustration into a law.

Let me put it again in this form. Any man in the ministry has to spend a good deal of his time answering the questions of people who come and want him to make particular pronouncements upon particular questions. There are certain problems which face us all in life, and there are people who always seem to want some kind of detailed statement so that when they are confronted by any particular problem, all they have to do is to turn up their textbook and there they find the answer. The Catholic types of religion are prepared to meet such people. The casuists of the Middle Ages, whom we have already mentioned, those so-called doctors of the Church, had thought out and discussed together the various moral and ethical problems likely to confront Christian people in this world, and they codified them and drew up their rules and regulations. When you were faced with a difficulty you immediately turned up your authority and found the appropriate answer. There are people who are always anxious for something like that in the spiritual realm. The final answer to them in terms of this Sermon can be put in this form. The gospel of Jesus Christ does not treat us like that. It does not treat us as children. It is not another law, but something which gives us life. It lays down certain principles and asks us to apply them. Its essential teaching is that we are given a new outlook and understanding which we must apply with respect to every detail of our lives. That is why the Christian, in a sense, is a man who is always walking on a kind of knife edge. He has no set regulations; instead he applies this central principle to every situation that may arise.

All this must be said in order to emphasize this point. If we take these six statements made by our Lord in terms of the formula `Ye have heard' and `I say unto you', we shall find that the principle He uses is exactly the same in each case. In one He is dealing with sex-morality, in the next with murder and in the next with divorce. But every single time the principle is the same. Our Lord as a great Teacher knew the importance of illustrating a principle, so here He gives six illustrations of the one truth. Let us now deal with this common principle which is to be found in the six, so that when we come to work each one out we shall always be holding this central principle in our minds. Our Lord's chief desire was to show the true meaning and intent of the law, and to correct the erroneous conclusions which had been drawn from it by the Pharisees and scribes and all the false notions which they had founded upon it. These, I suggest, are the principles.

First, it is the spirit of the law that matters primarily, not the letter only. The law was not meant to be mechanical, but living. The whole trouble with the Pharisees and the scribes was that they concentrated only on the letter, and they did so to the exclusion of the spirit. It is a great subjectthis relationship between form and content. Spirit is always something that must be embodied in form, and that is where the difficulty arises. Man will ever concentrate on the form rather than on the content; upon the letter rather than upon the spirit. You remember that the apostle Paul stresses this in 2 Corinthians where he says: `The letter killeth, but the spirit giveth life', and his whole emphasis in that chapter is that Israel was so constantly thinking of the letter that they lost the spirit. The whole purpose of the letter is to give body to the spirit; and the spirit is the thing that really matters, not the mere letter. Take, for example, this question of murder. As long as the Pharisees and scribes did not actually murder a man they thought they had kept the law perfectly. But they were missing the whole point and spirit of the law, which is not merely that I should literally not commit murder, but that my attitude towards my fellow men should be a right and loving one. Likewise with all these other illustrations. The mere fact that you do not commit adultery in an actual physical sense does not mean that you have kept the law. What is your spirit? What is your desire as you look, and so on? It is the spirit, not the letter, that counts.

It is clear, then, that if we rely only upon the letter we shall completely misunderstand the law. Let me emphasize that this applies not only to the law of Moses, but still more, in a sense, to this very Sermon on the Mount. There are people today who so look at the letter of the Sermon on the Mount as to miss its spirit. When we come to details we shall see that in practice. Take for instance the attitude of the Quakers with regard to taking the oath. They have taken the letter here literally, and, it seems to me, have not only denied the spirit, but have even made our Lord's statement almost ridiculous. There are people who do exactly the same with turning the other cheek, and giving to those who ask gifts of us, bringing the whole teaching into ridicule because they are constantly living on the letter, whereas our Lord's whole emphasis was upon the primary importance of the spirit. That does not mean of course that the letter does not matter; but it does mean that we must put the spirit before it and interpret the letter according to the spirit.

Now take a second principle, which is really another way of putting the first. Conformity to the law must not be thought of in terms of actions only. Thoughts, motives and desires are equally important. The law of God is concerned as much with what leads to the action as it is with the action itself. Again it does not mean that the action does not matter; but it does mean very definitely that it is not the action only that is important. This should be an obvious principle. The scribes and Pharisees were concerned only about the act of adultery or the act of murder. But our Lord was at pains to emphasize to them that it is the desire in man's heart and mind to do these things that is really and ultimately reprehensible in the sight of God. How often He said in this connection that it is out of the heart that evil thoughts and actions come. It is the heart of man that matters. So we must not think of this law of God and of pleasing God merely in terms of what we do or do not do; it is the inward condition and attitude that God is always observing. `Ye are they which justify yourselves before men; but God knoweth your hearts: for that which is highly esteemed among men is abomination in the sight of God' (Lk. xvi. 15).

The next principle we can put in this form. The law must be thought of not only in a negative manner, but also positively. The ultimate purpose of the law is not merely to prevent our doing certain things that are wrong; its real object is to lead us positively, not only to do that which is right, but also to love it. Here again is something which comes out clearly in these six illustrations. The whole Jewish conception of the law was a negative one. I must not commit adultery, I must not commit murder, and so on. But our Lord emphasizes all along that what God is really concerned about is that we should be lovers of righteousness. We should be hungering and thirsting after righteousness, not merely negatively avoiding that which is evil.

It is surely unnecessary that I should turn aside to show the practical relevance of each one of these points to our present condition. Alas, there are still people who seem to think of holiness and sanctification in this purely mechanical manner. They think that, as long as they are not guilty of drinking, gambling or going to theatres and cinemas, all is well. Their attitude is purely negative. It does not seem to matter if you are jealous, envious and spiteful. The fact that you are full of the pride of life seems to be of no account as long as you do not do certain things. That was the whole trouble with the scribes and Pharisees who perverted the law of God by regarding it purely in a negative manner.

The fourth principle is that the purpose of the law as expounded by Christ is not to keep us in a state of obedience to oppressive rules, but to promote the free development of our spiritual character. This is vitally important. We must not think of the holy life, the way of sanctification, as something hard and grievous which puts us into a state of servitude. Not at all. The glorious possibility that is offered us by the gospel of Christ is development as children of God and growing `unto the measure of the stature of the fulness of Christ'. `His commandments', says John in his first Epistle, `are not grievous.' So if you and I regard the ethical teaching of the New Testament as something that cramps us, if we think of it as something narrow and restrictive, it means we have never understood it. The whole purpose of the gospel is to bring us into `the glorious liberty of the children of God', and these special injunctions are simply particular illustrations of how we may arrive at that and enjoy it.

That, in turn, brings us to the fifth principle which is that the law of God, and all these ethical instructions of the Bible, must never be regarded as an end in themselves. We must never think of them as something to which we just have to try to conform. The ultimate objective of all this teaching is that you and I might come to know God. Now these Pharisees and scribes (and the apostle Paul said it was true of him too before he was truly converted) put, as it were, the Ten Commandments and the moral law on the wall, and having viewed them in this negative, restricted manner said: `Well, now; I am not guilty of these various things, therefore I am all right. I am righteous, and all is well between me and God.' You see they viewed the law as something in and of itself. They codified it in this way, and as long as they kept to that code they said all was well. According to our Lord that is an utterly fallacious view of the law. The one test which you must always apply to yourself is this, `What is my relationship to God? Do I know Him? Am I pleasing Him?' In other words, as you examine yourself before you go to bed, you do not just ask yourself if you have committed murder or adultery, or whether you have been guilty of this or that, and if you have not, thank God that all is well. No. You ask yourself rather, `Has God been supreme in my life today? Have I lived to the glory and the honour of God? Do I know Him better? Have I a zeal for His honour and glory? Has there been anything in me that has been unlike Christ-thoughts, imaginations, desires, impulses?' That is the way. In other words, you examine yourself in the light of a living Person and not merely in terms of a mechanical code of rules and regulations. And as the law must not be thought of as an end in itself, neither must the Sermon on the Mount. These are simply agencies which are meant to bring us into that true and living relationship with God. We must always be very careful, therefore, lest we do with the Sermon on the Mount what the Pharisees and the scribes had been doing with the old moral law. These six examples chosen by our Lord arc nothing but illustrations of principles. It is the spirit not the letter that matters; it is the intent, object and purpose that are important. The one thing we have to avoid above everything else in our Christian lives is this fatal tendency to live the Christian life apart from a direct, living, and true relationship to God.

Finally, we can illustrate it like this. Discipline in the Christian life is a good and essential thing. But if your main object and intent is to conform to the discipline that you have set for yourself it may very well be the greatest danger to your soul. Fasting and prayer are good things; but if you fast twice a week or pray at a particular hour every day merely in order to carry out your discipline, then you have missed the whole object of fasting and praying. There is no point in either of them, or in observing Lent, or in anything else that is meant to be an aid to the spiritual life, unless they bring us into a deeper relationship to God. I may stop smoking, I may stop drinking or gambling during these six weeks or at any other period. But if during that time my poverty of spirit is not greater, my sense of weakness is not deepened, my hunger and thirst after God and righteousness is not greatly increased, then I might just as well not have done it at all. Indeed I would say it would be very much better for me if I had not done it. All this is the fatal danger of making these things ends in themselves. We can be guilty of the same thing with public worship. If public worship becomes an end in itself, if my sole object in a pulpit is to preach a sermon and not to try to explain the blessed gospel of God that you and I, and all of us, may come to know and love Him better, my preaching is vain and it may be the thing that will damn my soul. These things are meant to be aids to help us, and illustrations of the Word. God forbid that we should turn them into a religion. `The letter killeth, but the spirit giveth life.'

CHAPTER TWENTY-ONE

THOU SHALT NOT KILL

I"N the paragraph comprising verses 2I-26 we have the first of this series of six examples which our Lord gives of His interpretation of the law of God over and against that of the scribes and Pharisees. I would remind you that that is the way in which we interpret the remainder of this chapter, and indeed most of the remainder of this Sermon on the Mount. It is all, in a sense, an exposition of that amazing statement: `Except your righteousness shall exceed the righteousness of the scribes and Pharisees, ye shall in no case enter into the kingdom of heaven.' The contrast, therefore, is not between the law given through Moses and the teaching of the Lord Jesus Christ; it is a contrast, rather, between the false interpretation of the law of Moses, and the true presentation of the law given by our Lord Himself. This distinction is made by the apostle Paul in Romans vii, where he says that once he thought he was keeping the law perfectly. Then he suddenly understood that the law said `Thou shalt not covet', and at once he was convicted. `When the commandment came, sin revived, and I died.' He had not realized that it was the spirit of the law that mattered, and that coveting is as reprehensible under the law as the actual doing of the deed itself. That is the kind of thing we have in principle running through the exposition of the law which is given here by our Lord.

Having thus defined His attitude towards the law, and announced that He has come to fulfil it, and having told His hearers that they must realize exactly what that means, our Lord proceeds now to give these practical illustrations. He presents us with six contrasts, each of which is introduced by the formula: `Ye have heard it was said by them of old time ... but I say unto you.' We now consider the first example.

The Pharisees and scribes were always guilty of reducing the meaning and even the demands of the law, and there is a perfect illustration of that here. He said: `Ye have heard that it was said by them of old time, Thou shalt not kill; and whosoever shall kill shall be in danger of the judgment.' It is very important that we should approach that in the right way. `Thou shalt not kill' is in the Ten Commandments, and if the Pharisees taught `thou shalt not kill', surely they were teaching the law? What conceivable criticism can there be even of the Pharisees and scribes at that particular point? So we are tempted to speak and to ask. The answer is that they had added something to that: `Thou shalt not kill; and whosoever shall kill shall be in danger of the judgment.' But, says someone again, does it not say in the law, `whosoever shall kill shall be in danger of the judgment'? The answer is that the law did say so, and you will find it in Numbers xxxv. 30, 31. What then is wrong with this? It is that the Pharisees, by putting these two things together in juxtaposition, had reduced the import of this commandment `Thou shalt not kill' to just a question of committing actual murder. By immediately adding the second to the first they had weakened the whole injunction.

The second thing they did was to reduce and confine the sanctions with which this prohibition was associated, to mere punishment at the hands of the civil magistrates. `Whosoever shall kill shall be in danger of the judgment.' The `judgment' there means the local court. The result was that they were merely teaching, `You must not do murder because if you do you will be in danger of being punished by the civil magistrate.' That was their full and complete interpretation of the great commandment which says: Thou shalt not kill. In other words they had evacuated it of its truly great content and had reduced it merely to a question of murder. Furthermore, they did not mention the judgment of God at all. It is only the judgment of the local court that seems to matter. They had made of it something purely legal, just a matter of the letter of a law which said: `Ifyou commit murder, certain consequences will follow.' The effect of this was that the Pharisees and scribes felt perfectly happy about the law on this point, so long as they were not guilty of murder. For a man to commit murder was, of course, a terrible thing to them, and if he did do so he should be arraigned before the court, and the judgment suitable to such a crime should be meted out to him. But, as long as one did not actually commit murder, all was well, and he could face the commandment, `Thou shalt not kill', with equanimity and say to himself, `I have kept and fulfilled the law.'

`No, no', says the Lord Jesus Christ in effect. `It is just here that you see how the whole conception of righteousness and law which has characterized the teaching of these scribes and Pharisees has become an utter travesty. They have so reduced the law, and confined it, that it is no longer in fact the law of God. It does not convey the real injunction which God had in His mind when He promulgated this particular law. They have simply and very conveniently reduced it within bounds and measures designed to render them perfectly happy. And therefore they say that they have completely kept the law.'

We have seen earlier that we have here one of the guiding principles which enables us to understand this false interpretation of the law of which the Pharisees and scribes were guilty. We tried to point out also that it is something of which we still tend to be guilty ourselves. It is possible for us to face the law of God as we find it in the Bible, but so to interpret and define it, as to make it something which we can keep very easily because we only keep it negatively. So we may persuade ourselves that all is well. The apostle Paul, as we have already seen, as the result of that very process, thought before his conversion that he had kept the law perfectly. The rich young ruler thought lie had kept the law because he likewise had been taught in this way and believed the same false interpretation. And as long as you and I accept the letter, and forget the whole spirit, content and meaning, we may persuade ourselves that we are perfectly righteous face to face with the law.

Now let us see how our Lord exposes that fallacy and shows us that to look at it like that is completely to misunderstand the meaning of God's holy law. He states His view and His exposition under three clear headings which we shall now consider.

The first principle is that what natters is not merely the letter of the law bnt the spirit. The law says: `Thou shalt not kill'; but that does not just mean: `Thou shalt not commit murder'. To interpret it like that is merely to define the law in a way which enables us to imagine that we escape it. Yet we may be guilty in a most grievous manner of breaking this very law. Our Lord proceeds to explain that. This commandment, He says, includes not only actual physical murder, but also causeless anger in our heart against a brother. The true way of understanding `Thou shalt not kill' is this: `Whosoever is angry with his brother without a cause shall be in danger of the judgment.' `Do not listen', He says in effect, `to these Pharisees and scribes who say you are only in danger of the judgment when you actually murder a man; I say unto you that if you are angry in your heart with a brother without a cause you are exposed to precisely the same demand and the same punishment of the law.' It is at this point we begin to see something of the real spiritual content of the law. It is at this point also that we must see, surely, the meaning of His words when He said that the law must be `fulfilled'. In that ancient law given through Moses there was all this spiritual content. It was the tragedy of Israel that they missed it. Let us not imagine, therefore, that as Christians we have finished with the law of Moses. No, the old law asks a man not to feel a causeless anger in his heart against his brother. For us as Christians to feel enmity in our hearts is, according to our Lord Jesus Christ, to be guilty of something which, in the sight of God, is murder. To hate, to feel bitter, to have this unpleasant, unkind feeling of resentment towards a person without a cause is murder. Indeed, let me remind you that there are some authorities who say that this qualifying phrase `without a cause' should not be there. In some of the manuscripts it is omitted. It is impossible to decide exactly on grounds of textual criticism whether it should be included or not. But even taking it as it is, it is a tremendous demand; and if we leave out the qualifying phrase it is still more so. You should not be angry with your brother. Anger in the heart towards any human being, and especially to those who belong to the household of faith, is, according to our Lord, something that is as reprehensible in the sight of God as murder.

But that is not all. Not only must we not feel this causeless anger; we must never even be guilty of expressions of contempt. `Whosoever shall say to his brother, Raca, shall be in danger of the council.' `Raca' means `worthless fellow'. It is an attitude of contempt, that tendency which, alas, we are all aware of, within our hearts and spirits. To dismiss the brother, saying `Raca', `worthless fellow', is, according to our Lord, something which, in the sight of God, is terrible. And of course it is. Our Lord frequently pointed out this very thing. Have you ever noticed some of those lists of sins which He uses? Take that statement: `Out of the heart proceed evil thoughts, murders, adulteries,' and so on. You see we are remarkably like these Pharisees and scribes in the way we talk about murder, and robbery, and drunkenness and certain particular sins. But our Lord always includes evil thoughts with murders, and such things as strife, enmity, deceit and many other things which we do not regard as being such terrible, foul sins. And, obviously, the moment we stop to think about it, and to analyse the position, we see how perfectly true it is. Contempt, a feeling of scorn and derision, is the very spirit that ultimately leads to murder. We may have various reasons for not allowing it to be expressed in actual committal of murder. But, alas, we have often murdered one another in mind and heart and thought, have we not? We have nursed thoughts against people which are as foul as murder. There has been this disturbance in the realm of the spirit and we have said of another, `Raca'. Oh, yes, there are ways in which men can be destroyed short of murder. We can destroy a man's reputation, we can shake somebody else's confidence in him by whispering criticism or by deliberate fault finding. That is the kind of thing which our Lord is here indicating, and His whole purpose is to show that all that is included in this commandment: `Thou shalt not kill.' Killing does not only mean destroying life physically, it means still more trying to destroy the spirit and the soul, destroying the person in any shape or form.

Our Lord then moves to the third point: `But whosoever shall say, Thou fool, shall be in danger of hell fire.' This means an expression of abuse, the vilifying of a person. It means this bitterness and hatred in the heart finding its expression in words. I think that, as we follow this analysis, we can see, as was pointed out in chapter one, what a terrible and dangerous error it is for us as Christian people to feel that, because we are Christians, the Sermon on the Mount has nothing to do with us, or to feel that this is something which does not apply to present-day Christians. It speaks to us today; it searches us to the depths of our being. Here we are confronted not only with actual murder, but with all this within our hearts, feelings and sensibilities, and ultimately our spirit, that is regarded by God as murder.

Now this, obviously, is a very important statement. `Does it mean', asks someone, `that anger is always wrong? That anger is always prohibited?' `Arc there not illustrations', asks another, `in the New Testament itself where our Lord spoke of these Pharisees in strong terms; when, for example, He referred to them as "blind" and as "hypocrites", and when He turned to the people and said, "0 fools, and slow of heart to believe", and "Ye fools and blind"? How can He issue these prohibitions at this point, and then use such language Himself? How do you reconcile this teaching with Matthew xxiii where He pronounces His woes upon the Pharisees?' Surely there is no real difficulty in that question. When our Lord pronounced those woes, He did so in a judicial manner. He did so as one given authority by God. Our Lord is pronouncing final judgment upon the Pharisees and the scribes. He, as the Messiah, is authorized to do so. He had offered the gospel to them; every opportunity had been given to them. But they had rejected it. Not only that, we must remember that He always utters these statements against false religion and hypocrisy. What He is really denouncing is the self-righteousness that rejects the grace of God and would even justify itself before God and reject Him. It is judicial, and if you and I can always claim that any such expression we may use is uttered in a similar sense, then we are free from this particular charge.

It is exactly the same with the so-called imprecatory Psalms which trouble so many people. The Psalmist, under the inspiration of the Holy Spirit, is pronouncing judgment against not only his own enemies, but the enemies of God and those who are abusing the Church and the kingdom of God as it is represented in him and in the nation. Let me put it like this. Our anger must only be against sin; we must never feel angry with the sinner, but only full of sorrow and compassion for him. `Ye that love the Lord, hate evil', says the Psalmist. We should feel a sense of anger as we view sin, hypocrisy, unrighteousness, and everything that is evil. That is the way, of course, in which we fulfil the injunction of the apostle Paul to the Ephesians: `Be ye angry, and sin not.' The two things are not incompatible at all. Our Lord's anger was always a righteous indignation, it was a holy anger, an expression of the wrath of God Himself. Let us remember that `The wrath of God is revealed from heaven against all ungodliness and unrighteousness of men' (Rom. i. 18). `Our God', against sin, `is a consuming fire.' There is no question about this. God hates evil. God's anger is displayed against it, and His wrath will be poured out upon it. That is essentially a part of the biblical teaching.

The holier we become, the more anger we shall feel against sin. But we must never, I repeat, feel anger against the sinner. We must never feel angry with a person as such; we must draw a distinction between the person himself and what he does. We must never be guilty of a feeling of contempt or abhorrence, or of this expression of vilification. Thus I think we are enabled to draw lines of distinction between these things. `Do not imagine you are clear with regard to this injunction,' says Christ in effect, `simply because you have not committed murder.' What is the state of your heart? How do you react to things that happen? Do you find yourself flaring into a raging temper when a person has done something to you? Or do you sometimes feel anger against a person who really has done nothing to you at all? These are the things that matter. It is that which God meant when He said, `Thou shalt not kill'. `God seeth the heart', and is not concerned only with the external action. God forbid that we should produce a kind of self-righteousness by reducing the law of God to something which we know we have already kept, or which we feel sure we are not likely to transgress. `Let every man examine himself.'

Let us now go on to the second statement. Our attitude is meant to be not negative, but positive. Our Lord puts it in these words. Having emphasized the negative He goes on to put it positively like this: `Therefore if thou bring thy gift to the altar, and there rememberest that thy brother hath ought against thee; leave there thy gift before the altar, and go thy way; first be reconciled to thy brother, and then come and offer thy gift.' This is a most significant and important statement. Not only are we not to harbour murder and evil thoughts in our heart against another; but the commandment not to kill really means we should take positive steps to put ourselves right with our brother. The danger is that we may stop at the negative, and feel that, as long as we have not actually committed murder, all is well. But there is a second stage which we have forgotten. `All right', we say, `I must not actually commit murder, and I must not say these unkind things against people. I must put a guard upon my lips; though the thought is there I must not say it.' And there we tend to stop and say: `As long as I do not say these things all is well.' But our Lord tells us that we must not stop even there, we must not even harbour the thought and the feeling in our heart. That is the point at which so many stop. The moment these ugly, unworthy thoughts tend to come into their hearts they switch their minds to something positive and beautiful. That is quite all right as long as we do not stop at that. We must not only repress these unkind and unworthy thoughts, says Christ; we have to do more than that. We must actually take steps to remove the cause of the trouble; we must aim at a positive goal. We have to reach the stage in which there shall be nothing wrong even in spirit between our brother and ourselves.

Our Lord enforces that by reminding us in verses 23 and 24 of a very subtle danger in the spiritual life, the terrible danger of trying to atone for moral failure by balancing evil with good. I think we know something about this; we must all plead guilty to it. The danger is that of making certain ceremonial sacrifices to cover up moral failure. The Pharisees were expert at that. They went to the temple regularly; they were always punctilious in these matters of the details and minutiae of the law. But the whole time they were judging and condemning their fellows with contempt. They avoided every twinge of conscience by saying, `After all I am worshipping God; I am taking my gift to the altar.' I think I can say again that we all know something about this tendency not to face directly the conviction which the Holy Spirit produces in our heart, but to say to ourselves: `Well, now; I am doing this and that; I am making great sacrifices at this point; I am being helpful in that matter; I am busily engaged in that piece of Christian work.' The whole time we are not facing the jealousy we may feel against another Christian worker, or something in our personal, private life. We are balancing one thing with another, thinking that this good will make up for that evil. No, no, says our Lord. God is not like that: We are they which justify yourselves before men; but God knoweth your hearts: for that which is highly esteemed among men is abomination in the sight of God' (Luke xvi. 15). This matter, He tells us, is so important, that, even if I find myself at the altar with a gift I am going to offer to God, and there suddenly remember something I have said or done, something which is causing another person to stumble or go wrong somehow; if I find that I am harbouring unkind and unworthy thoughts about him or in any way hindering his life, then our Lord tells us (may I put it thus with reverence), we should, in a sense, even keep God waiting rather than stay. We must get right with our brother and then come back and offer the gift. In the sight of God there is no value whatsoever in an act of worship if we harbour a known sin.

The Psalmist puts it like this, 'If I regard iniquity in my heart, the Lord will not hear me.' If I, in the presence of God, and while trying to worship God actively, know there is sin in my heart which I have not dealt with and confessed, my worship is useless. There is no value in it at all. If you are in a state of conscious enmity against another, if you are not speaking to another person, or if you are harbouring these unkind thoughts and are a hindrance and an obstacle to that other, God's Word assures you that there is no value in your attempted act of worship. It will avail you nothing, the Lord will not hear you. Or take that statement which we read in i John iii. 20, 'If our heart condemn us, God is greater than our heart, and knoweth all things.' There is no value or purpose in praying to God if you know in your own heart that you are not right with your brother. It is impossible for God to have any dealings with sin and iniquity. He is of such a pure countenance that He cannot even look upon it. According to our Lord the matter is so vital that you must even interrupt your prayer, you must, as it were, even keep God waiting. Go and put it right, He says; you cannot be right with God until you put yourself right with man.

Let me sum it all up by reminding you of the great illustration of all this which is found in the Old Testament in i Samuel xv. God has given His commandments and He means us to keep them. You remember on one occasion Saul was told by God to destroy the Amalekites entirely. But Saul thought to himself that he need not go as far as that and said, 'I will spare some of the people, and some of the beasts and cattle to sacrifice to God.' He thought all was well, and began to worship and to praise God. But suddenly Samuel the prophet arrived and asked: `What have you been doing?' Saul replied, saying: `I have just been carrying out the commandments of God.' `If you have been carrying out the commandments of God', said Samuel, `what is the meaning of the bleating of the sheep and the lowing of the cattle which I am hearing? What have you done?' `I decided I would spare some of them', said Saul. Then Samuel uttered those momentous and terrifying words: `Rath the Lord as great delight in burnt offerings and sacrifices, as in obeying the voice of the Lord? Behold, to obey is better than sacrifice, and to hearken than the fat of rams.' I always feel sorry for king Saul because I understand him so well. You see, we do not do what God tells us; and when we thus put our limits upon the commandment, we somehow feel that to perform a great act ofworship will cover it, and all will be well, thinking that the Lord has as great delight in burnt offerings and sacrifices as in obeying the voice of the Lord. Of course He has not ! `Behold, to obey is better than sacrifice.' Leave thy gift; run away and put it right with thy brother; get rid of the obstacle. Then come back; and then, and only then, is it of any value. `To obey is better than sacrifice, and to hearken than the fat of rams.'

Just a word on the last principle. Let me impress upon you the urgency of all this because of our relationship to God. `Agree with thine adversary quickly, whiles thou art in the way with him; lest at any time the adversary deliver thee to the judge, and the judge deliver thee to the officer, and thou be cast into prison. Verily I say unto thee, Thou shalt by no means come out thence, till thou hast paid the uttermost farthing.' Yes, says Christ, it is as urgent and as desperate as that. You must do it at once; delay not a moment, for that is your position. This is just His way of saying that we must always remember our relationship to God. We must not only think in terms of our brother whom we are offending, or with whom there is something wrong, we must always think of ourselves before God. God is the judge, God is the Justifier. He is always making these demands upon us, and He has power over all the courts of heaven and earth. He is the judge, and His laws are absolute; and He has a right to demand the uttermost farthing. What then are we to do? Come to an agreement as quickly as we can with God. Christ says here that we are `in the way'. We are in this world, we are in life, walking, as it were, along the road. But suddenly our adversary comes and says: `What of that which you owe?' Well, says Christ, make an agreement with him at once or the processes of the law will be set going, and the uttermost farthing will be demanded of you. That is nothing but a picture. You and I are travelling through this world, and the law is there making its demands. It is the law of God. It says: `What about that relationship between you and your brother, what about those things that are in your heart? You have not attended to them.' Settle it at once, says Christ. You may not be here tomorrow morning and you are going to eternity like that. `Agree with thine adversary quickly, whiles thou art in the way with him.'

How do we feel at this point? As we have seen our Lord's exposition of this holy law, do we feel the demands of the law? Are we aware of the condemnation? What of the things we have said and thought, the things we have done? Are we aware of all this, the utter condemnation of it all? It is God making demands through His law. I thank God for the injunction that tells us to act as quickly as we can while we are in the way. Thank God, His terms are very easy. They are just this, that I face and acknowledge this sin and confess it utterly and absolutely, that I stop any self-defence or self-justification, though there was provocation from this other person. I must just confess and admit it without any reservation to God. If there is something in actual practice that I can do about it I must do it at once. I must humble myself, make a fool of myself as it were, and let the other person gloat over me if necessary, as long as I have done everything I can to remove the barrier and the obstacle. Then He will tell me that all is right. `I will settle with you', He will say, `indeed I will forgive it all because, though you are a guilty and foul sinner before Me, and the bill you owe Me is one you can never pay, I have sent My Son into your world and He has paid it for you. He has cancelled it. He did not do it because you are loving and kind and good, He did not do it for you because you have done nothing against Me. It was while you were an enemy, hateful in yourself, hating Me and hating others. It was in spite of all your foulness and your unworthiness that I sent Him. And He came deliberately and gave Himself even unto death. It is because of all this that I forgive you utterly and freely and absolutely.' Thank God for such terms, such terms for bankrupt, foul sinners. Those are the terms, utter, absolute confession and repentance; everything we can do byway of restitution; and an acknowledgment that we are forgiven only as the result of the grace of God manifested perfectly in the loving, self-giving, self-sacrifice of the Son of God upon the cross. Come to a quick agreement. Do not delay. Whatever you may be convicted of at this moment, come, leave your gift, run away, put it right. `Agree with thine adversary quickly, whiles thou art in the way with him.'

CHAPTER TWENTY-TWO

THE EXCEEDING SINFULNESS OF SIN

W E come now to verses 27-30, our Lord's second illustration of His teaching with respect to the law. `Ye have heard that it was said by them of old time, Thou shalt not commit adultery: but I say unto you, That whosoever looketh on a woman to lust after her hath committed adultery with her already in his heart.' The Pharisees and scribes had reduced the commandment which prohibits adultery to the mere physical act of adultery; and again they imagined that, as long as they were not actually guilty of the act itself, the commandment had nothing to say to them and they were perfectly innocent as far as it was concerned. It is the same thing again. Once more they had taken the letter of the law and reduced it to one particular matter, and thereby had nullified it. In particular, they had forgotten the whole spirit of the law. As we have seen, this is something that is fundamentally vital to a true understanding of the New Testament gospel: `the letter killeth, but the spirit giveth life.'

There is a very simple way of looking at this. The real trouble with the Pharisees and scribes was that they had never even read the Ten Commandments properly. If they had truly considered and studied them, they would have seen that you cannot take each one in isolation. For example, the tenth says that we must never covet our neighbour's wife, and that, obviously, should be taken in conjunction with this command not to commit adultery. The apostle Paul, in that striking statement of his in Romans vii, confesses that he himself had been guilty of that very error. He says that it was when he realized that the law said, `Thou shalt not covet', that he began to understand the meaning of lust. Before that he had been thinking of the law in terms of action only; but the law of God does not stop at mere action, it says `Thou shalt not covet'. The law had always stressed the importance of the heart, and these people, with their mechanical notions of worshipping God and their purely mechanical conception of obedience, had entirely forgotten that. Our Lord, therefore, is anxious to stress that important truth and to impress it upon His followers. Those who think they can worship God and obtain salvation in terms of their own actions are always guilty of this error. That is why they never truly understand the Christian way of salvation. They have never seen that ultimately it is a question of the heart, but think that, as long as they do not do certain things and as long as they try to do certain good works, they can put themselves right in the sight of God. To that, as we have seen already, our Lord replies always, `Ye are they which justify yourselves before men; but God knoweth your hearts: for that which is highly esteemed among men is abomination in the sight of God.' Our Lord is concerned here to bring out that principle once more. They said in effect, `As long as you do not commit adultery you have kept this law.' He says: `Whosoever looketh on a woman to lust after her hath committed adultery with her already in his heart.'

Here again we have our Lord's teaching with regard to the nature of sin. The whole purpose of the law, as Paul reminds us, was to show the exceeding sinfulness of sin. But by misunderstanding it in this way the Pharisees had nullified it. Nowhere, perhaps, do we have such a terrible exposure of sin as it really is as in the words of our Lord at this particular point.

I know, of course, that the doctrine of sin is not popular today. People dislike the whole idea, and try to explain it away psychologically, in terms of development and temperament. Man has evolved out of the animal, they say, and he is just sloughing off very slowly these relics and remnants of his animal past and his animal nature. Thus the whole doctrine of sin is entirely denied and avoided. But, obviously, if that is our view and position, the Scriptures must be quite meaningless to us, because everywhere in the New Testament, as in the Old Testament also, this is something which is central. That is why we must consider it, for there is nothing at the present time which is more urgently necessary than that we should truly grasp the biblical doctrine with respect to sin. I assert that most of our failures and troubles in the Church, as well as in the world, are due to the fact that we have not really understood this doctrine. We have all been influenced by the idealism that has been controlling thought for the past hundred years, this idea that man was evolving towards perfection, and that education and culture were going to put us right. Thus we have never taken seriously this tremendous teaching which is found from beginning to end in the Bible; and most of our troubles arise from this source.

Let me illustrate what I mean. I suggest that unless we are clear about the doctrine of sin we shall never truly understand the New Testament way of salvation. Take, for instance, the death of our Lord Jesus Christ upon the cross. Look at all the misunderstanding with regard to that. The great question one has to face is; Why did He die upon the cross? Why did He set His face steadfastly to go to Jerusalem and refuse to allow His followers to defend Him? Why did He say that, if He desired, He could command twelve legions of angels to protect Him, but that if He did so He could not fulfil all righteousness? What is the meaning of the death upon the cross? Now I maintain that if we do not understand the doctrine of sin, we shall never really know the answers to these questions. There is only one way to understand the death upon the cross and it is this:

> There was no other good enough To pay
> the price of sin; He only could unlock the
> gate Of heaven, and let us in.

It is the problem of sin that accounts for it. Indeed the incarnation would never have been necessary were it not for sin. The problem of sin is as profound as that. To tell mankind what to do is not enough. God had done that in the law given through Moses, but no-one had kept it. `There is none righteous, no, not one.' All the exhortations to men and women to live a better life had failed before ever Christ came. The Greek philosophers had all lived and taught before His birth. Knowledge and information and all these things are not enough. Why? Because of sin in the human heart. Thus the only way to understand the New Testament doctrine of salvation is to start with the doctrine of sin. Whatever else sin may be, it is at least something that could be dealt with only by the coming of the eternal Son of God from heaven into this world and by His actually going to the death of the cross. That had to happen; there was no other way. God, I say with reverence, would never have allowed

His only-begotten, beloved Son to suffer in the way He did unless it was absolutely essential: and it was essential because of sin.

But the same is true of the New Testament doctrine of regeneration. Consider all the teaching about being born again, and the new creation, which is to be found right through the Gospels and Epistles. That is meaningless unless you understand the New Testament doctrine of sin. But if you do understand it, then you can see quite clearly that unless a man is born again, and given a new nature and a new heart, he cannot possibly be saved. But regeneration is meaningless to people who have a negative view of sin and do not realize its profundity. This, then, is the point at which we must start. So if you dislike the New Testament doctrine of sin, it simply means that you are not a Christian. For you cannot be one without believing that you must be born again and without realizing that nothing but the death of Christ upon the cross saves you and reconciles you to God. All who are trusting to their own efforts are denying the gospel, and the reason for that is always that they have never seen themselves as sinners or understood the New Testament doctrine of sin. This is a crucial matter.

This doctrine, therefore, is absolutely vital in determining our conception of true evangelism. There is no true evangelism without the doctrine of sin, and without an understanding of what sin is. I do not want to be unfair, but I say that a gospel which merely says `Come to Jesus', and offers Him as a Friend, and offers a marvellous new life, without convicting of sin, is not New Testament evangelism. The essence of evangelism is to start by preaching the law; and it is because the law has not been preached that we have had so much superficial evangelism. Go through the ministry of our Lord Himself and you cannot but get the impression that at times, far from pressing people to follow Him and to decide for Him, He put great obstacles in their way. He said in effect: `Do you realize what you are doing? Have you counted the cost? Do you realize where it may lead you? Do you know that it means denying yourself, taking up your cross daily and following Me?' True evangelism, I say, because of this doctrine of sin, must always start by preaching the law. This means that we must explain that mankind is confronted by the holiness of God, by His demands, and also by the consequences of sin. It is the Son of God Himself who speaks about being cast into hell. If you do not like the doctrine of hell you are just disagreeing with Jesus Christ. He, the Son of God, believed in hell; and it is in His exposure of the true nature of sin that He teaches that sin ultimately lands men in hell. So evangelism must start with the holiness of God, the sinfulness of man, the demands of the law, the punishment meted out by the law and the eternal consequences of evil and wrong-doing. It is only the man who is brought to see his guilt in this way who flies to Christ for deliverance and redemption. Any belief in the Lord Jesus Christ which is not based on that is not a true belief in Him. You can have a psychological belief even in the Lord Jesus Christ; but a true belief sees in Him one who delivers us from the curse of the law. True evangelism starts like that, and obviously is primarily a call to repentance, 'repentance toward God, and faith toward our Lord Jesus Christ.'

In exactly the same way this doctrine of sin is also vital to a true conception of holiness; and here again I think we see its urgent relevance at the present time. Not only has our evangelism been superficial, our conception of holiness has been superficial also. Far too often there have been people who have been smug and glibly satisfied with themselves because they are not guilty of certain things-adultery, for example-and therefore think that they are all right. But they have never examined their heart. Self-satisfaction, smugness and glibness are the very antithesis of the New Testament doctrine of holiness. Here we see holiness as a matter of the heart, and not merely a matter of conduct; it is not only a man's deeds that count but his desires; not only must we not commit, we must not even covet. It penetrates to the very depths, and thus this conception of holiness leads to constant watchfulness and self-examination. `Watch ye', says the apostle Paul to the Corinthians. `Examine yourselves, whether ye be in the faith; prove your own selves.' Search your own heart and discover whether there is any evil there. That is New Testament holiness. How much more disconcerting it is than that superficial conception of holiness which thinks only in terms of action.

Above all, this doctrine of sin leads us to see the absolute need of a power greater than ourselves to deliver us. It is a doctrine that makes a man run to Christ and rely upon Him; it makes him realize that without Him he can do nothing. So again. I would say that the New Testament way of presenting holiness is not just to say, `Would you like to live life with a capital "L"? Would you like to be permanently happy?' No, it is to preach this doctrine of sin, it is to reveal man to himself so that, having seen himself, he will abhor himself and become poor in spirit and meek, he will mourn, he will hunger and thirst after righteousness, he will fly to Christ and abide in Him. It is not an experience to be received so much as a life to be lived and a Christ to be followed.

Finally, it is surely only a true grasp of the New Testament doctrine of sin that enables us to realize the greatness of God's love to us. Do you feel that your love to God is weak and faint and that you do not love Him as much as you should? Let me remind you again that this is the ultimate test of our profession. We are meant to love God, not only to believe certain things about Him. These men of the New Testament loved Him and they loved the Lord Jesus Christ. Read the biographies of the saints and you will find that they had a love for God which became greater and greater. Why do not we love God as we should? It is because we have never realized what He has done for us in Christ, and this itself is because we have not realized the nature and the problem of sin. It is only as we see what sin really is in the sight of God, and realize that, nevertheless, He did not spare His only Son, that we begin to understand and to measure His love. So if you want to love God more, grasp this doctrine of sin, and as you realize what it meant to Him, and what He has done about it, you will see that His love is indeed `so amazing, so divine'.

There, then, are the reasons for concentrating upon this doctrine of sin. But now let us look at what our Lord actually says about it. There is no true understanding of the gospel of salvation, no true evangelism, no true holiness, no true knowledge of the love of God unless we realize what sin is. Well, what is it? Let us first attempt just a brief analysis of what our Lord says about it, and then we can go on to state what He says in these same verses about how we can be delivered from it. It is no use talking about deliverance from sin until we know what sin is. There must be a radical diagnosis before we can begin to think of treatment. Here is the diagnosis.

The first thing our Lord emphasizes is what we may call the depth or the power of sin. `Thou shalt not commit adultery.' He does not say `As long as you do not do the act all is well'; rather `I say unto you, That whosoever looketh on a woman to lust after her hath committed adultery with her already in his heart.' Sin is not merely a matter of actions and of deeds; it is something within the heart that leads to the action. In other words the teaching here is the characteristic teaching of the Bible everywhere about this subject, namely, that what we must really concentrate upon is not so much sins as sin. Sins are nothing but the symptoms of a disease called sin and it is not the symptoms that matter but the disease, for it is the disease that kills and not the symptoms. Symptoms can vary tremendously. I may see one person propped up in bed, breathing painfully, and in acute distress; and I say that person is desperately ill suffering from pneumonia or something like that. But I may see another person lying flat on his back in bed, no distress, no acute symptoms, no pain, no difficult breathing, lying apparently at ease and in comfort. And yet there may be some foul disease, some foul growth in that person's constitution eating away at the vitals, a disease which will kill him as certainly and as surely as the other. It is not the mode but the fact of death that matters. It is not the symptoms that finally count, but the disease.

That is the truth which our Lord here impresses upon us. The fact that you have not committed the act of adultery does not mean you are guiltless. What about your heart? Is there disease there? And His teaching is that what matters is this fell and foul power that is in human nature as the result of sin and the fall. Man was not always like that, for God made him perfect. If you believe in the evolutionary theory, you are really saying that God never made man perfect, but is bringing him to perfection. Therefore there is no true sin. But the Bible teaching is that man was made perfect and that he fell from that perfection, with the result that this power, this canker, has entered human nature and is there as an evil force within. The consequence is that man desires and covets. Quite apart from what is happening round and about him, this thing is within him. I quote again, as I have quoted so often in this connection, that our Lord said it is `out of the heart' that `proceed evil thoughts, murders, adulteries, . . .' Now sin must be understood like this, as a terrible power. It is not so much that I do a thing, it is what makes me do it, what urges me to do it, that matters. There it is in all of usand we must face it-the depth and the power of sin.

But let me say a word about the subtlety of sin. Sin is this terrible thing which so deludes and fools us as to make us feel quite happy and contented so long as we have not committed the act. `Yes', I say, `I was tempted, but thank God I did not fall.' That is all right up to a point, so long as I am not too content with that. If I am merely satisfied with the fact that I did not do the thing, I am all wrong. I ought to go on and ask: `But why did I want to do it?' That is where the subtlety of sin comes in. It affects the whole constitution of man. It is not merely something in the animal part of our nature; it is in our mind and outlook, and it makes us think corruptly in that manner. Then think of the clever way in which it insinuates itself into the mind, and the terrible way in which we arc guilty of sinning with the mind. There are highly respectable men and women who would never dream of committing an act of adultery, but look at the way in which they enjoy sinning in the mind and in the imagination. We are dealing with practical matters, we are dealing with life as it is. This is what I mean. You have never been guilty of adultery? All right. Would you then answer me this simple question. Why do you read all the details of divorce cases in the newspapers? Why do you do it? Why is it essential that you should read right through these reports? What is your interest? It is not a legal interest, is it? or a social one? What is it? There is only one answer: you are enjoying it. You would not dream of doing these things yourself, but you are doing them by proxy. You are sinning in your heart and mind and in your imagination, and you are therefore guilty of adultery. That is what Christ says. How subtle this awful, terrible thing is! How often do men sin by reading novels and biographies. You read the reviews of a book and find that it contains something about a man's misconduct or behaviour, and you buy it. We pretend we have a general philosophical interest in life, and that we are sociologists reading out of pure interest. No, no; it is because we love the thing; we like it. It is sin in the heart; sin in the mind!

A further illustration of this state of sin is found in the way in which we always try to explain away our failures in this respect in terms of eye and hand. We say: `I was born like that. Look at that other man, he is not like that.' You do not know the other man; and in any case it is the subtlety of sin that would have you explain yourself away in terms of your particular nature-the hand, the foot, the eye or something like that. No, the trouble is in your heart. All else is but the expression. It is that which leads to the sin that matters.

Then there is the perverting nature and effect of sin. Sin is something that perverts. Wherefore, says our Lord, `if thy right hand offend thee, cut it off, and cast it from thee.' How true that is of what sin does. It is such a devastating, perverting thing that it turns the very instruments that God has given me, and which were meant to minister to my good, into my enemies. There is nothing wrong with the instincts of human nature. They are all God-given; they are excellent. But these very instincts, because of sin, have become our enemies. The things which God put into man to make him man, and to enable him to function, have become the cause of his downfall. Why? Because sin twists everything, so that precious gifts such as the hand or the eye may become a nuisance to me, and I have, metaphorically, to cut them off and pluck them out. I have to get rid of them. Sin has perverted man, turning good itself into evil. Read again the way in which Paul expounded that. This, he says, is what sin has done to man; it has made the law of God, which is holy and just and good, into something that actually leads a man to sin (Rom. vii). The very fact that the law tells me not to do a thing makes me think of that thing. That then brings it to my imagination, and I end by doing it. But if the law had not forbidden me to do it, I would not have done so. `Unto the pure all things are pure.' Yes, but if you are not pure, some things which are good in themselves may be harmful. That is why I never believe in giving sex-morality teaching to children in schools. You are introducing them to sin. You are telling them about things they never knew before, and they are not `pure'. Therefore you cannot act on the assumption that such teaching will lead to good. That is the whole tragedy of modern education; it is based entirely on a psychological theory that does not recognize sin, instead of on New Testament teaching. There is that within us that drives us to sin. The law is right and good and pure. The trouble is in us and in our perverted natures.

Finally, sin is something which is destructive. `If thy right eye offend thee, pluck it out, and cast it from thee.' Why? `It is profitable for thee that one of thy members should perish, and not that thy whole body should be cast into hell.' Sin destroys man; it introduced death into the life of man and death into the world. It always leads to death, and ultimately to hell, suffering and punishment. It is hateful to God, it is abhorrent to Him. And I say with reverence that because God is God sin must lead to hell. `The wages of sin is death.' God and sin are utterly incompatible, and therefore sin, of necessity, leads to hell. He is of such pure countenance that He cannot look upon sinit is so utterly hateful to Him.

That is the biblical, the New Testament doctrine of sin. `Thou shalt not commit adultery.' Of course not! But is it in our hearts? Is it in our imagination? Do we like it? God forbid that any of us should be able to look at this holy law of God and feel satisfied. If we do not feel unclean at this moment, God have mercy upon us. If we can conceivably be satisfied with our lives because we have never committed an act of adultery or of murder or any one of these things, I say that we do not know ourselves nor the blackness and the foulness of our own hearts. We must listen to the teaching of the blessed Son of God and examine ourselves, examine our thoughts, our desires, and our imagination. And unless we feel that we are vile and foul, and need to be washed and cleansed, unless we feel utterly helpless with a terrible poverty of spirit, and unless we are hungering and thirsting after righteousness, I say, God have mercy upon us.

I thank God that I have a gospel which tells me that Another who is spotless and pure and utterly holy has taken my sin and my guilt upon Himself. I am washed in His precious blood, and He has given me His own nature. When I realized that I needed a new heart, I found, thank God, that He had come to give it me, and He has given it.

> Thy nature, gracious Lord, impart;
>   Come quickly from above;
> Write Thy new name upon my heart,
>   Thy new, best name of Love.

Let that be our prayer.

CHAPTER TWENTY-THREE

THE MORTIFICATION OF SIN

W-E have already considered verses 27-3o as a whole, in order that we might understand our Lord's view of sin over against the teaching of the Pharisees and scribes. Now let us look at verses 29 and 30 in particular. Our Lord, having dealt with the whole nature of sin, did not leave it at that point, for in thus describing it He also, in a sense, indicated the way in which we are to deal with it. He wants us to see the character of sin in such a way that we shall abhor and forsake it. It is this second aspect of the matter that we must now consider.

We must start first at the point of pure interpretation. What exactly is meant by the words: `And if thy right eye offend thee, pluck it out, and cast it from thee: for it is profitable for thee that one of thy members should perish, and not that thy whole body should be cast into hell'? There are many who think that these extraordinary and startling statements should be interpreted like this. Our Lord, they maintain, has been emphasizing the importance of a clean heart; He says that it is not enough that you do not commit an act of adultery-it is the heart that matters. They imagine that at that point there was a kind of objection, perhaps expressed, or perhaps our Lord sensed it. Or perhaps He anticipated an objection which would be put like this: `We are so constituted that our very faculties inevitably lead us to sin. We have eyes and we see, and as long as we have them it is no use telling us that we must have a clean heart. If I see with my right eye and that leads to certain consequences, what is the use of telling me to improve and clean it? It is an impossible demand. The trouble with me, really, is the fact that I have a right eye and a right hand.' Then they interpret this statement as meaning that our Lord replies to such an objection: `Well, if you tell Me it is your right eye that leads to sin, pluck it out, and if you tell Me it is your right hand, cut it off.' In other words, they assert, He met the objectors on their own level. `The Pharisees', they say, `try to evade the issue by saying that the trouble is not so much in their own desires and hearts, as in the very fact that they can see. That, inevitably, leads to temptation, and temptation leads to sin. It is an attempt again at an avoidance of His teach ing. So He, as it were, turns back and says: "Very well, if you say your whole trouble is due to your right eye and hand, get rid of them".'

Furthermore, they would have us understand that by saying that, of course, our Lord is ridiculing that whole position because He only refers to the right eye and hand; whereas if a man plucks out his right eye he still has his left, and he sees the same thing with the left as with the right; and if he chops off the right hand he has not solved his problem because his left hand is still there. `Thus', they say, `our Lord ridicules this whole conception of holiness and the sanctified life which would regard it as a matter of our physical being, and shows that if a man is ever to have a clean and pure heart along that line, well, to put it absolutely plainly, both eyes must be plucked out, both hands, both feet must be cut off. He must mutilate himself in a sense until he is no longer a man.'

Now I do not want to reject that exposition entirely. There is undoubtedly true teaching in it. But whether or not it is an exact explanation of what our Lord says at this point I am not so certain. It seems to me that a better interpretation of this statement is that our Lord was anxious to teach at one and the same time the real and horrible nature of sin, the terrible danger in which sin involves us, and the importance of dealing with sin and getting rid of it. So He deliberately puts it in this way. He talks about the precious things, the eye and the hand, and He singles out in particular the right eye and the right hand. Why? At that time people held the view that the right eye and hand were more important than the left. It is not difficult to see why they believed that. We all know the importance of the right hand and the similar relative importance of the right eye. Now our Lord takes up that common, popular belief, and what He says in effect is this: `If the most precious thing you have, in a sense, is the cause of sin, get rid of it.' Sin is as important as that in life; and its importance can be put in that way. It seems to me that that is a much more natural interpretation of this statement than the other. He is saying that, however valuable a thing may be to you in and of itself, if it is going to trap you and cause you to stumble, get rid of it, throw it away. Such is His way of emphasizing the importance of holiness, and the terrible danger which confronts us as the result of sin.

How, then, are we to deal with this problem of sin? I would remind you again that it is not merely a question of not committing certain acts; it is a question of dealing with the pollution of sin in the heart, this force that is within us, these powers which are resident in our very natures as the result of the fall. These are the problems, and merely to deal with them in a negative manner is not enough. We are concerned about the state of our hearts. How are we to face these problems? Here our Lord indicates a number of points, which we must observe and grasp.

The first, obviously, is that we must realize the nature of sin, and also its consequences. We have already been looking at that and He Himself starts with it once more. There is no doubt whatever that an inadequate view of sin is the chief cause of a lack of holiness and sanctification, and indeed of most of the false teaching with respect to sanctification. All your antinomianisms throughout the centuries, all the tragedies that have ever followed the perfectionist movements, have really arisen because of false notions concerning sin, and a failure to see that not only is sin a power and something which leads to guilt, but that there is such a thing as the pollution of sin. Though a man does not do anything wrong he is still sinful. His nature is sinful. We must grasp the idea of `sin' as distinct from `sins'. We must see it as something that leads to the actions and that exists apart from them.

Perhaps the most convenient way of putting all this is to remind ourselves of Palm Sunday, a day which brings us right back to all the details of the earthly life of the Son of God. There He is going up to Jerusalem for the last time. What is the meaning of all this? Why is He going to that cross and to that death? There is only one answer to that question. Sin is the cause; and sin is something that can be dealt with in that way only, and in no other. Sin is something, let me say it with reverence, that has created a problem even in heaven. It is as profound a problem as that, and we must start by realizing this. Sin in you and in me is something that caused the Son of God to sweat drops of blood in the

Garden of Gethsemane. It caused Him to endure all the agony and the suffering to which He was subjected. And finally it caused Him to die upon the cross. That is sin. We can never remind ourselves of that too frequently. Is it not our danger-I think we all must admit it-to think of sin merely in terms of ideas of morality, to catalogue sins and to divide them into great and small, and various other classifications? There is a sense, no doubt, in which there is some truth in these ideas; but there is another sense in which such classifications are all wrong and indeed dangerous. For sin is sin, and always sin; that is what our Lord is emphasizing. It is not, for example, only the act of adultery; it is the thought, and the desire also which is sinful.

That is the fact on which we must concentrate. We must realize what a terrible thing sin is. So let us cease to be so interested in our moral classifications, and let us cease to think even of actions in terms of moral catalogues. But let us think of everything in terms of the Son of God and what it meant for Him, and what it led to in His life and in His ministry. That is the way to think of sin. Of course, as long as we think of it only in these moral terms we may feel smug and contented because we have not done certain things. But that is an utterly false conception, and what we have to realize is that, because we are what we are, the Son of God had to come from heaven and go through all that, and even die that cruel death upon the cross. You and I are such that all that became necessary. Such is this pollution of sin that is in us. We can never look too often at the nature of sin and its consequences. One of the most direct roads to holiness, always, is to consider Him and His suffering and agony. Nowhere is the nature of sin displayed in such terrible and awful colours as in the death of the blessed Son of God.

The second thing we must realize is the importance of the soul and its destiny. `It is profitable for thee that one of thy members should perish, and not that thy whole body should be cast into hell.' Notice that our Lord says this twice in order to emphasize it. The soul, He says, is so important that ifyour right eye is the cause of your being trapped by sin, you should pluck it out and get rid of it. Not, as I am going to show you, in a physical sense. There are many things in this life and world which, in and of themselves, are very good, right and profitable. But our Lord tells us here that if even those things trap us, we must put them on one side. He put it still more strongly on one occasion when He said, `If any man ... hate not his father, and mother, and wife, and children, and brethren, and sisters, yea, and his own life also, he cannot be my disciple' (Lk. xiv. 26). This means that it does not matter who or what it is that comes between us and Him, if it is harmful to the soul, it must be hated and put on one side. It does not mean that a man who is a Christian has, of necessity, to hate his loved ones. Obviously not, for our Lord told us to love even our enemies. It simply means that anything which militates against the soul and its salvation is an enemy at that point, and must be dealt with as such. It is our misuse of these things, our putting them in the wrong position, that is wrong; and that is the point which He stresses here. If my faculties, propensities and abilities do lead me to sin, then I must forsake them and get rid of them. I must put even those on one side. If you examine your own experience, I think you will see at once what this means. The trouble is that because of sin we tend to pervert everything. `Unto the pure all things are pure.' Yes; but, as we said earlier, we are not pure; and the result is that even pure things at times become impure. Our Lord here shows us that the importance of the soul and its destiny is such that everything must be subservient to it. Everything else must be secondary where this is concerned, and we must examine the whole of our life and see to it that this is ever in the forefront of our considerations. That is His message, and He puts it in this striking and emphatic manner. Your most important possession-your right eye, even-if it is trapping you, must be plucked out. Nothing must be allowed to come between you and your soul's eternal destiny.

That, then, is the second great principle. I wonder whether it is ever in the forefront in our considerations. Do we all realize that the most important thing we have to do in this world is to prepare ourselves for eternity? There is no question at all about that. This is not in any way to detract from the importance of life in this world. It is important. It is God's world, and we are to live a full life here. Yes; but only as those who are preparing themselves for eternity and for the glory that awaits us. `It is profitable for thee that one of thy members should perish', that we should, as it were, be cripples while we are here, in order to make certain that when we get there we shall stand in His presence with joy and with glory. Oh, how sadly we neglect the culture of the soul, how negligent we are about our eternal destiny! We are all so very concerned about this life. But are we equally concerned about our soul and spirit and our eternal destiny? That is the question our Lord is asking us. It is tragic that we are so negligent about the eternal and are so concerned about that which must inevitably come to an end. It is better to be a cripple in this life, says our Lord, than to lose everything in the next. Put your soul and its eternal destiny before everything else. It may mean that you will not get promotion in your work or that you will not do as well as somebody else. Well, `what shall it profit a man, if he shall gain the whole world, and lose his own soul?' That is the calculation. `It is profitable for thee that one of thy members should perish, and not that thy whole body should be cast into hell.' `Fear not them which kill the body, but are not able to kill the soul: but rather fear him which is able to destroy both soul and body in hell' (Mt. X. 28).

The third principle is that we must hate sin, and do all we can to destroy it at all costs within ourselves. You remember how the Psalmist puts it, `Ye that love the Lord, hate evil.' We must train ourselves to hate sin. In other words we must study it and understand its working. I think we have been very negligent in this respect; and here we are in very striking and pathetic contrast to those great men whom we call the Puritans. They used to analyse sin and expose it, with the result that they were laughed at and were called specialists in sin. Let the world laugh if it likes; but that is the way to become holy. Look at it; read the biblical description of it; analyse it; and the more we do so the more we shall hate it and do all we can to get rid of it at all costs, and to destroy it out of our lives.

The next principle is that we must realize that the ideal in this matter is to have a clean and pure heart, a heart that is free from lusts. The idea is not simply that we be free from certain actions, but that our hearts should become pure. So we come back again to the Beatitudes: `Blessed arc the pure in heart: for they shall see God.' Our standard must always be a positive one. We must never think of holiness merely in terms of not doing certain things. Every type of holiness teaching which simply ends at that, and which tells us not to do certain things for a certain period in the year, is always negative. The true teaching, however, is always positive. Of course we must not do certain things. But the Pharisees were expert at that, and they stopped there. No, says our Lord; you must aim at a heart that is clean and pure:

> A heart in every thought renewed
> And filled with love divine,
> Perfect and right and pure and good;
> A copy, Lord, of Thine.

In other words, our ambition should be to have a heart which never knows bitterness, envy, jealousy, hate or spite, but is ever full of love. That is the standard; and again I think it is quite obvious that this is the point at which we often fail. We have only a negative conception of holiness, and therefore we feel selfsatisfied. If we examined our heart, if we came to know what the Puritans always called `the plague of our own heart', it would promote holiness. But we do not like examining our hearts. Far too often those of us who rejoice in the name of `Evangelical' are perfectly happy because we are orthodox and because we are unlike those liberals or modernists and various other sections of the Church, which are obviously wrong. So we sit down complacent and satisfied, feeling that we have arrived, and that we have only to maintain our position. But that means that we do not know our own hearts, and our Lord calls for a pure heart. You can commit sin in your heart, He says, without anybody knowing it; and you may still look perfectly respectable, and nobody would guess what is going on in your imagination. But God sees it, and in the sight of God it is awful, foul, ugly, filthy. Sin in the heart!

The last principle is the importance of the mortification of sin. `If thy right hand offend thee, cut it off, and cast it from thee.' Now mortification is a great subject. If you are interested in it you should read a book, The Mortification of Sin, by that great Puritan, Dr. John Owen. What does the term mean? There are two views on this subject. There is a false conception of mortification which says that we must literally cut off our hands and throw them away. It is the view which regards sin as being resident in the physical frame, and which therefore deals severely with the physical body as such. There were many in the early days of Christianity who literally cut off their hands, and thought they were carrying out the injunctions of the Sermon on the Mount by so doing. They interpreted our Lord's word here exactly as do others, whom we shall consider later, who have taken the teaching about `turning the other cheek' in that literal, unintelligent manner. They say: `It is the Word; there it is, and we must carry it out as it is.' But they were still left with the left eye and hand, and they still sinned. In the same way the idea that celibacy is essential to sanctification and holiness belongs to the same category. Any teaching that makes us live an unnatural life is not New Testament holiness. To argue thus is the negative view of mortification, and it is false.

What is the true view? It is to be found in many places in the New Testament. Take, for instance, Romans viii. 13 where Paul says: `For if ye live after the flesh, ye shall die: but if ye through the Spirit do mortify the deeds of the body, ye shall live.' And in i Corinthians ix. 27 he expresses it thus: `I keep under my body, and bring it into subjection: lest that by any means, when I have preached to others, I myself should be a castaway.' What does he mean? Well, this is what the authorities on the Greek words tell us. He punches his body and knocks it about until it is black and blue in order to keep it down. That is the mortification of the body. In Romans xiii. 14, he says: `Make not provision for the flesh, to fulfil the lusts thereof.' Now these are things which we must do. Instead of, `Let go and let God', or `Receive this marvellous experience and then you will have nothing to do', we are rather told, `Mortify therefore your members which are upon the earth' (Col. iii. 5). That is the apostle's teaching. Mortify through the Spirit the deeds of the body. Keep under the body. And our Lord says: `If thy right hand offend thee, cut it off.' It is the same principle everywhere.

These are things which we must do. What does it mean? Again, I am merely going to give some indication of the principles. First, we must never feed the flesh'. `Make not provision for the flesh,' says Paul, `to fulfil the lusts thereof.' There is a fire within you; never bring any oil anywhere near it, because if you do there will be a flame, and there will be trouble. Do not give it too much food; which being interpreted means this, among other things: never read anything that you know will do you harm. I referred to that earlier and I repeat it again, for these matters are very practical. Do not read those reports in the newspapers which are suggestive and insinuating and which you know always do you harm. Don't read them; `pluck out your eye.' They are of no value to anybody; but alas, there they are in the paper and they pander to the public taste. The majority like that sort of thing, and you and I by nature like it. Well, then; don't read it, `pluck out your eye.' The same is true of books, especially novels, radio programmes, television and also the cinema. We must come down to these details. These things are generally a source of temptation, and when you give time and attention to them you are making provision for the flesh, you are adding a little fuel to the flame, you are feeding the thing you know is wrong. And we must not do so. `But', you say, `it is educational. Some of those books are written by marvellous people, and if I do not know these things I shall be considered an ignoramus.' Our Lord's reply is that, for the sake of your soul, you had better be an ignoramus, if you know it does harm to know these things. Even the most valued thing must be sacrificed.

It also means avoidance of what the Bible calls `foolish talking arid jesting'-stories and jokes thought to be clever but which are insinuating and polluting. You will often get that kind of thing with its cleverness, subtlety and wit, from highly intelligent men. The natural man admit cs it all; but it leaves a nasty taste in the mouth. Reject it; say you do not want it, that you are not interested. You may offend people by saying so. Well, offend them if that is their mentality and morality. Offend them, I say, for the sake of your soul. Again, we must be careful in the company that we keep. Let me put it like this. We must avoid everything that tends to tarnish and hinder our holiness. `Abstain from all appearance of evil', which means, `avoid every form of evil'. It does not matter what form it takes. Anything that I know does me harm, anything that arouses, and disturbs, and shakes my composure, no matter what it is, I must avoid it. I must `keep under my body', I must `mortify my members'. That is what it means; and we must be strictly honest with ourselves.

But someone may ask at this point: `Are you not teaching a kind of morbid scrupulosity? Is not life going to be rather wretched and miserable?' Well, there are people who become morbid. But if you want to know the difference between them and what I am teaching, think of it in this way. Morbid scrupulosity is always concerned about itself, its state and condition, and its own achievements. True holiness, on the other hand, is always concerned about pleasing God, glorifying Him and ministering to the glory of Jesus Christ. If you and I keep that ever in the foreground of our minds we need not be very worried about becoming morbid. All that will be at once avoided if we do it for His sake, instead of spending the whole of our time feeling our spiritual pulse and taking our spiritual temperature.

The next principle I would lay down would he this, that the must deliberately restrain the flesh and deal with every suggestion and insinuation of evil. In other words, we must `watch and pray'. We must all be concerned to do as the apostle Paul says, `I keep under my body.' If Paul needed to do it, how much more so the rest of us.

Those are things that you and I have to do ourselves. They will not be done for us. I do not care what experience you have or may have had, nor how much you have been filled with the Spirit, if you read suggestive matter in the newspaper, you will probably be guilty of sin, you will sin in your heart. We are not machines; we are told that we ourselves must put these things into practice.

That, in turn, leads me to the last great principle, which I put in this form: We must realize once more the Brice, that had to be paid to deliver us from sin. To the true Christian there is no greater stimulus and incentive in the fight to `mortify the deeds of the body' than this. How frequently we are reminded that our Lord's object in coming into the world and enduring all the shame and the suffering of death upon the cross was `to deliver us from this present evil world', to `redeem us from all iniquity', and to separate `unto himself a peculiar people, zealous of good works'. It was all designed in order that `we should be holy and without blame before him in love'. If His love and His sufferings mean anything to us, they will inevitably lead us to agree with Isaac Watts that such love `demands my soul, my life, my all'.

Finally, these considerations must have brought us to see our absolute need of the Holy Spirit. You and I have to do these things. Yes, but we need the power and the help that the Holy Spirit alone can give us. Paul put it like this: `If ye through the Spirit do mortify the deeds of the body'. The Holy Spirit's power will be given to you. He has been given if you are a Christian. He is in you, He is working in you `both to will and to do of his good pleasure'. If we realize the task we have to do, and long to do it, and are concerned about this purification; if we start with this process of mortification, He will empower us. That is the promise. So we must not do those things which we know to be wrong: we act as empowered by Him. Here it is all in one phrase: `Work out your own salvation with fear and trembling. For it is God which worketh in you both to will and to do of his good pleasure.' The two sides are absolutely essential. If we try to mortify the flesh alone, in our own strength and power, we shall produce an utterly false type of sanctification which is not really sanctification at all. But if we realize the power and the true nature of sin; if we realize the awful grip it has on man, and its polluting effect; then we shall realize that we are poor in spirit and utterly feeble, and we shall plead constantly for that power which the Holy Spirit alone can give us. And with this power we shall proceed to `pluck out the eye' and `cut off the hand', `mortify the flesh', and thus deal with the problem. In the meantime He is still working in us and we shall go on until finally we shall see Him face to face, and stand in His presence faultless and blameless, without spot and without rebuke.

CHAPTER TWENTY-FOUR

CHRIST'S TEACHING ON DIVORCE

WE now come to consider our Lord's statement in verses 31 and 32 on the subject of divorce. Let me begin by pointing out that, when we come to a subject and passage like this, we see the value of a systematic study of the teaching of Scripture. How often do we hear an address on a text such as this? Is it not true to say that this is the kind of subject that preachers tend to avoid? And thereby, of course, we are guilty of sin. Is it not for us to study some parts of the Word of God and to ignore others; it is not for us to shy at difficulties. These verses that we are now considering are as much the Word of God as anything else which is to be found in the Scriptures. But because of our failure to expound the Bible systematically, because of our tendency to take texts out of their context and to choose what interests and pleases us, and to ignore and forget the rest, we become guilty of an unbalanced Christian life. That in turn leads, of course, to failure in actual practice. It is a very good thing, therefore, that we should work our way through the Sermon on the Mount in this manner, and so find ourselves face to face with this statement.

For some reason or another many commentators, even though they may have set out to write a commentary on the Sermon on the Mount, slide over this and do not deal with it. One can easily understand why people tend to avoid a subject like this; but that is no excuse for them. The gospel of Jesus Christ concerns every part and portion of our life, and we have no right to say that any part of our life is outside its scope. Everything that we need is here provided for us and we have clear teaching and instruction upon every aspect of our life and being. But at the same time, anyone who has ever troubled to read up this subject and the various interpretations will realize that it is a matter that is surrounded by many difficulties. Most of these difficulties, however, are man-made, and can be traced ultimately to the particular teaching of the Roman' Catholic Church about marriage as a sacrament. Having started by taking up that position she manipulates statements in Scripture to suit her theory.

We should thank God, however, that we are not left to ourselves and our own ideas, but have this clear instruction and teaching. It is our business to face it honestly.

As we approach these verses, let us once more remind ourselves of their background or context. This statement is one of six statements made by our Lord in which He introduces the subject by the formula `Ye have heard ... but I say unto you'. It comes in the section of the Sermon on the Mount in which our Lord is showing the relationship of His kingdom and teaching to the law of God that was given through Moses to the children of Israel. He began by saying that He has not come to destroy but to fulfil; indeed He says, till heaven and earth pass, one jot or one tittle shall in no wise pass from the law till all be fulfilled. Then comes the following: `Whosoever therefore shall break one of these least commandments, and shall teach men so, he shall be called the least in the kingdom of heaven: but whosoever shall do and teach them, the same shall be called great in the kingdom of heaven. For I say unto you, That except your righteousness shall exceed the righteousness of the scribes and Pharisees, ye shall in no case enter into the kingdom of heaven.' He then proceeds to display His teaching in the light of this background.

Bearing all that in mind, let us also remember that in these six contrasts which our Lord draws, he is comparing not the law of Moses, as such, with His own teaching, but rather the false interpretation of this law by the Pharisces and scribes. Our Lord obviously does not say that He had come to correct the law of Moses, because it was God's law, given by God Himself to Moses. No; our Lord's purpose was to correct the perversion, the false interpretation of the law which was being taught to the people by the Pharisees and scribes. He is therefore honouring the law of Moses and displaying it in its great fullness and glory. That, of course, is precisely what He does with regard to the question of divorce. He is especially concerned to expose the false teaching of the Pharisees and scribes with regard to this important matter.

The best way to approach the subject is to consider it under three headings. First of all we must be clear in our minds as to what the law of

Moses really did teach about this matter. Then we must be clear as to what the Pharisees and scribes taught. Lastly we must consider what our Lord Himself teaches.

First, then, what did the law of Moses really teach concerning this problem? The answer is to be found in Deuteronomy xxiv, especially verses 1-4. In Matthew xix our Lord again refers to that teaching and in a sense gives us a perfect summary of it, but it is important that we should look at the original statements. There is often a good deal of confusion about this. The first thing to notice is that in the old Mosaic dispensation the word adultery is not mentioned in the matter of divorce, for the good reason that under the law of Moses the punishment for adultery was death. Anybody under that old law who was found guilty of adultery was stoned to death, so there was no need to mention it. The marriage had come to an end; but it was not brought to an end by divorce but by punishment by death. That is a very important principle to have clearly in our minds.

What then was the object and purpose of the Mosaic legislation with regard to divorce? You see the answer at once, not only as you read Deuteronomy xxiv, but especially when you read our Lord's pronouncement upon, and exposition of, that legislation. The whole object of the Mosaic legislation in this matter was simply to control divorce. The position had become entirely chaotic. This is what was happening. In those days, you remember, the men generally held a very low and poor view of women, and they had come to believe that they had a right to divorce their wives for almost any and every kind of frivolous and unworthy reason. If a man, for any reason whatsoever, was anxious to get rid of his wife, he did so. He brought forward some trumpery excuse and on the basis of that he divorced her. Of course the ultimate cause of it all was nothing but lust and passion. It is interesting to observe how, in this Sermon on the Mount, our Lord introduces this subject in immediate connection with the subject that went before it, namely, the whole question of lust. In the Authorized Version of the Bible, these two things are put together in one paragraph. That may not be right, but it does remind us of the intimate connection between the two. The Mosaic legislation, therefore, was introduced in order to regularize and control a situation that had not only become chaotic, but was grossly unfair to the women, and which, in addition, led to untold and endless suffering on the part of both the women and the children.

In the main, it laid down three great principles. The first was that it limited divorce to certain causes. It was only to be permitted henceforth when there was some natural, moral or physical defect discovered in the wife. All the various excuses which men had been using and bringing forward were now prohibited. Before he could obtain a divorce a man had to establish that there was some very special cause, described under the title of uncleanness. He not only had to prove that, he had also to establish it in the sight of two witnesses. Therefore the Mosaic legislation, far from giving a number of excuses for divorce, greatly limited it. It dismissed all the frivolous, superficial and unjust reasons, restricting it to one particular matter.

The second thing it enforced was that any man who thus divorced his wife must give her a bill of divorcement. Before the Mosaic law, a man could say he no longer wanted his wife, and could turn her out of the house; and there she was, at the mercy of the whole world. She might be charged with unfaithfulness or adultery and so be liable to being stoned to death. Therefore, in order to protect the woman, this legislation provided that she should be given a bill of divorcement in which a statement was made that she had been dismissed, not because of unfaithfulness, but because of one of these reasons which had been discovered. It was to protect her, and the bill of divorcement was handed to her in the presence of two witnesses whom she could always call in any case of need and necessity. Divorce was made something formal, something serious, the idea being to impress upon the minds of those people that it was a solemn step and not something to be undertaken lightly in a moment of passion when a man suddenly felt he disliked his wife and wanted to get rid of her. In this way the seriousness of marriage was emphasized.

Then the third step in the Mosaic legislation was a very significant one, namely, that a man who divorces his wife and gives her a bill of divorcement is not allowed to marry her again. The case was put like this. Here is a man who has divorced his wife, and given her a bill of divorcement. With that in her hand she is entitled to marry somebody else. Now the second husband may also give her a bill of divorcement. Yes, says the law of Moses, but if that does happen and she is free to get married once more, she must not marry the first husband. The whole force of that enactment is again exactly the same; it is to make these people see that marriage is not something you can walk in and out of at will. It tells the first husband that, if he gives his wife a bill of divorcement, it is a permanent enactment.

When we examine it like that, we can see at once that the old Mosaic legislation is very far indeed from being what we thought it was, and especially what the Pharisees and scribes thought it to be. Its object was to reduce to a certain amount of order a situation that had become utterly chaotic. You will find that this was the characteristic of all the details of the Mosaic legislation. Take for example the matter of `an eye for an eye, and a tooth for a tooth'. The Mosaic legislation enacted that. Yes, but what was the object of it? It was not to tell the people that if a man knocked out another man's eye, the victim must retaliate in the same way. No; its purpose was to say this: You are not entitled to kill a man for that offence; it is only an eye for an eye, or if a man knocks out another's tooth, all you are entitled to is a tooth. It is restoring order in a state of chaos, limiting the consequences and legislating for a particular condition. Now the law concerning divorce was exactly the same as that.

Next we must consider the teaching of the Pharisees and scribes because, as we have seen, it was to this especially that our Lord was referring. They said that the law of Moses commanded, indeed urged, a man to divorce his wife under certain conditions. Now, of course, it never said anything of the kind. The law of Moses never commanded anybody to divorce his wife; all it did was to say to a man: If you do want to divorce your wife you should do so only under these conditions. But the Pharisees and scribes, as our Lord makes particularly plain in Matthew xix when He was speaking on this same subject, were teaching that Moses commanded divorce. And, of course, the next step was that they were again demanding divorce and insisting upon their right to it, for all kinds of inadequate reasons. They took that old Mosaic legislation with regard to this question of uncleanness and had their own interpretation as to what was meant by it. They actually taught that, if a man ceased to like his wife, or for any reason found her to be unsatisfactory to him, that, in a sense, was `uncleanness'. How typical this is of the teaching of the Pharisees and scribes, and their method of interpreting the law! But in reality they were avoiding the law in principle as well as in letter. The result was that at the time of our Lord terrible injustices were again being done to many women who were being divorced for most unworthy and frivolous reasons. There was only one factor that really mattered to these men, and that was the legal one of giving a bill of divorcement. They were very punctilious about that, as they were careful about other legal details. They did not, however, state why they were divorcing her. That was unimportant. But what did matter supremely was that she be given a writing of divorcement! Our Lord puts it like this: `It hath been said'- that is the sort of thing you have been hearing from the Pharisees and scribes. What is the important thing for `whosoever shall put away his wife'? `Let him give her a writing of divorcement.' Well, of course, that is important, and the law of Moses had enacted it. But you see that is not the main thing, or the thing to be stressed and emphasized. But it was in the centre of the picture as far as the Pharisees and scribes were concerned and, in emphasizing this, they had been failing to see the real meaning of marriage. They had failed to consider this whole question of divorce, and the reason for it, in a true, just and righteous manner. Such was the perversion by the Pharisees and scribes of the Mosaic teaching. They were avoiding it and circumventing it with their clever interpretations and traditions which they added to the law. The result was that the ultimate object of the Mosaic legislation had really been entirely concealed and nullified.

That brings us to our third and last main heading. What does our Lord say about this? `But I say unto you, That whosoever shall put away his wife, saving for the cause of fornication, causeth her to commit adultery: and whosoever shall marry her that is divorced committeth adultery.' Now the statement in Matthew xix. 3-9 is most important and helpful in interpreting this teaching, because it is a fuller explication of what our Lord puts here in a summarized form. The Pharisees and scribes said to Him-they were trying to trap Him-'Is it lawful for a man to put away his wife for every cause?' They were really giving themselves away in asking such a question for they themselves were actually sanctioning this. And here is our Lord's answer. The first principle He emphasizes is that of the sanctity of marriage. 'Whosoever shall put away his wife, saving for the cause of fornication.' You notice that He goes back beyond the law of Moses to the law that was given by God at the very beginning. When God created woman to be a help meet for man He made that great pronouncement. He said, 'They twain shall be one flesh.' 'What therefore God hath joined together, let not man put asunder.' Marriage is not a civil contract, or a sacrament; marriage is something in which these two persons become one flesh. There is an indissolubility about it, and our Lord goes right back to that great principle. When God made woman for man that was His intention, that was what He indicated, and that was what He ordained. The law which God laid down was that a man should leave father and mother and be joined to his wife and that they should become one flesh. Something new and distinct has taken place, certain other ties are broken and this new one is formed. This aspect of 'one flesh' is all-important. You will find that it is a principle running right through Scripture whenever this subject is dealt with. It is seen in r Corinthians vi, where Paul says that the terrible thing about fornication is that a man becomes one flesh with a harlot-a most solemn and important teaching. Our Lord starts there. He goes back to the beginning, to God's own original view of marriage.

'If that is so', asks someone, 'how do you explain the law of Moses? If that is God's own view of marriage why did He allow divorce to take place on the conditions which we have just considered?' Our Lord again answered that question by saying that, because of the hardness of their hearts, God made a concession, as it were. He did not abrogate His original law with regard to marriage. No, He introduced a temporary legislation because of the conditions then prevailing. God controlled it. It was exactly the same as we have seen with regard to 'an eye for an eye, and a tooth for a tooth'. It was a tremendous innovation at that time; but in reality it was God leading the people back in the direction of His original pronouncement. `Because of the hardness of your hearts', says our Lord, `Moses gave you this concession.' It was not God advocating divorce, or commanding anybody to divorce his wife; it was God just reducing the chaos to a certain amount of order, regularizing what had become utterly irregular. We must keep in the forefront of our minds in these matters God's original object and intention with regard to this whole estate of marriage: the one flesh, the indissolubility, and the coming together in that way.

The first principle leads us to the second, which is that God has never anywhere commanded anybody to divorce. The Pharisees and scribes were suggesting that this was so with Moses' law. Yes; he certainly commanded them to write that bill of divorcement if there was to be a divorce. But that is not the same thing as commanding them to divorce. The idea taught by God's Word is not only that of the indissolubility of marriage, but that of the law of love and forgiveness. We must get rid of this legalistic approach which makes a man say, `She has spoiled my life, therefore I must divorce her.' As unworthy and undeserving sinners we have all been forgiven by the grace of God, and that must enter into and control our view of everything that happens to us with respect to all other persons, and especially in the relationship of marriage.

The next principle is one which is of the utmost importance. There is only one legitimate cause and reason for divorce-that which is here called `fornication'. Now I need not emphasize the urgent relevance of all this teaching. We are living in a country in which conditions have become chaotic in this matter of divorce, and there are still further bills proposed which are designed to make divorce easier and which would aggravate the position still further. Here is our Lord's teaching with regard to the subject. There is only one cause for divorce. There is one; but there is only one. And that is unfaithfulness by one party. This term `fornication' is inclusive, and it really means unfaithfulness on the part of one party to a marriage. `Whosoever shall put away his wife, saving for the cause of fornication, causeth her to commit adultery.' We must realize the importance of this principle. It was particularly important in the days of the early Church. If you read r Corinthians vii you will find there that this matter is referred to again. In those early days the problem presented itself to many Christians in this form. Imagine a husband and wife. The husband is suddenly converted, the wife is not. Here is a man who has become a new creature in Christ Jesus, but his wife still remains a pagan. These people had been taught the doctrine about separation from the world and sin. They, therefore, immediately jumped to the conclusion which forced them to say, `It is impossible for me to go on living with a woman like that who is a pagan. Surely, if I am to live the Christian life, I must divorce her because she is not a Christian.' And many a wife who had been converted and whose husband was not, was saying the same thing. But the apostle Paul taught these people that the husband was not to leave his wife because he was converted and she was not. You see, even that is not a ground for divorce. Take all this modern talk of incompatibility of temperament. Can you imagine anything more incompatible than a Christian and a non-Christian? And according to modern ideas, if ever there was cause for divorce surely there it is. But the plain teaching of Scripture is that even that is not a ground for divorce. Do not leave the unconverted one, says Paul. The wife who has been converted having an unbelieving husband sanctifies that husband. You need not worry about your children; if one party is Christian they are covered and have the privilege of Christian nurture within the life of the Church.

Now that is a most important and vital argument. It is the way of impressing upon us this great principle which is laid down by our Lord Himself. Nothing is a cause for divorce save fornica tion. It does not matter how difficult it may be, it does not matter what the stress or the strain, or whatever can be said about the incompatibility of temperament. Nothing is to dissolve this indissoluble bond save this one thing. But I emphasize again that this one thing does. Our Lord Himself says that this is a cause and a legitimate one for divorce. He says Moses granted certain concessions `because of the hardness of your hearts'. But this is now laid down as a principle, not as a concession to weakness. He Himself tells us that unfaithfulness is a cause for divorce and the reason for this is surely obvious. It is this question of the `one flesh' again; and the person who is guilty of adultery has broken the bond and has become united to another. The link has gone, the one flesh no longer obtains, and therefore divorce is legitimate. Let me emphasize again, it is not a commandment. But it is a ground for divorce, and a man who finds himself in that position is entitled to divorce his wife, and the wife is entitled to divorce the husband.

The next step makes this even clearer. Our Lord says that if you divorce your wife for any other reason you cause her to commit adultery. `Whosoever shall put away his wife, saving for the cause of fornication, causeth her to commit adultery.' The argument is this: There is only one thing that can break this bond. Therefore, if you put away your wife for any other reason you are putting her away without breaking the bond. In this way you are making her break the bond if she should marry again; and she is therefore committing adultery. So that a man who divorces his wife for any reason but for this is thereby causing her to commit adultery. He is the cause, and the man who marries her is in like manner an adulterer. Thus our Lord enforces this great principle in this positive and clear manner. There is only one cause for divorce, and no other.

What, then, is the effect of this teaching? We can summarize it in this way. Our Lord here shows Himself to us as the great Law-giver. All law comes from Him; everything appertaining to this life and world has come from Him. There was temporary legislation for the children of Israel because of their peculiar circumstances. The Mosaic penalty for adultery was death by stoning. Our Lord abrogated that temporary legislation. The next thing He has done is to make divorce for the case of adultery legitimate; He has established the law on this matter. These are two main results of His teaching. From that time onwards men and women are not stoned and put to death for adultery. If you want to do anything you are entitled to a divorce. Out of that we may legitimately draw one very important and serious deduction. We can say not only that a person who thus has divorced his wife because of her adultery is entitled to do so. We can go further and say that the divorce has ended the marriage, and that this man is now free and as a free man he is entitled to re-marriage. Divorce puts an end to this connection, our Lord Himself says so. His relationship to that woman is the same as if she were dead; and this innocent man is therefore entitled to re-marriage. Even more than this, if he is a Christian, he is entitled to Christian re-marriage. But he alone is in that position and she is not, or vice versa.

`Have you nothing to say about the others?' asks someone. All I would say about them is this, and I say it carefully and advisedly, and almost in fear lest I give even a semblance of a suggestion that I am saying anything that may encourage anyone to sin. But on the basis of the gospel and in the interest of truth I am compelled to say this: Even adultery is not the unforgivable sin. It is a terrible sin, but God forbid that there should be anyone who feels that he or she has sinned himself or herself outside the love of God or outside His kingdom because of adultery. No; if you truly repent and realize the enormity of your sin and cast yourself upon the boundless love and mercy and grace of God, you can be forgiven and I assure you of pardon. But hear the words of our blessed Lord: `Go, and sin no more.'

There, then, is our Lord's teaching on this important subject. You see the state of the world and of society round about us today. Is it surprising that our world is as it is while men and women play fast and loose with God's Word in this vital matter? What right have we to expect nations to stand to their bonds and keep their vows if men and women do not do it even in this most solemn and sacred union of marriage? We must start with ourselves; we must start at the beginning, we must observe the law of God in our own personal, individual lives. And then, and then only, will we be entitled to trust nations and peoples, and to expect a different type of conduct and behaviour from the world at large.

CHAPTER TWENTY-FIVE

THE CHRISTIAN
AND THE TAKING OF OATHS

W E consider now verses 33-37 containing the fourth of the six examples and illustrations which show what our Lord meant when He defined in verses i 7-20 of this chapter the relationship of His teaching and kingdom to the law of God. Having laid down the principle, He proceeds thus to demonstrate and to illustrate it. But of course He is concerned not only to illustrate His principle, but also to give specific and positive teaching. In other words, all these detailed matters are of great importance in the Christian life.

There may be those who ask: `Is it profitable for us, confronted as we are by vast problems in this modern world, to be considering this simple matter of our speech and how we should be speaking to one another?' The answer, according to the New Testament, is that everything that a Christian does is most important because of what he is, and because of his effect upon others. We must believe that if everybody in the world today were a Christian, then most of our major problems would simply vanish out of sight and there would be no need to fear war and such horrors. The question is, then, how are people to become Christian? One of the ways is that they observe Christian people. That is perhaps one of the most potent means of evangelism at the present time. We are all being watched and therefore everything we do is of tremendous importance.

Thus it comes to pass that in the various Epistles which are included in the New Testament canon (not only in those of the apostle Paul but in the others also) the writers invariably have laid down their doctrine with regard to the various details of life. In that great Epistle to the Ephesians, after Paul has risen to the heights and given us in the first chapters that amazing conception of God's ultimate purpose for the whole universe and has transported us into the heavenly places, suddenly he comes back to earth and looks at us and says to us in effect: `Lie not to one another; speak the truth always.' But there is no contradiction there. The gospel is, as Wordsworth says of the skylark, `true to the kindred points of heaven and home'. It always presents doctrine, and yet it is concerned about the smallest details of life and of living. In the words we are now going to consider we have an illustration of this.

As we have seen, this whole section of the Sermon on the Mount is framed by our Lord to expose the sham and the falseness of the Pharisees' and scribes' representation of the Mosaic law, and to contrast it with His own positive exposition. That is what we have here. He says: `Ye have heard that it hath been said by them of old time, Thou shalt not forswear thyself, but shalt perform unto the Lord thine oaths.' Those exact wprds are not to be found anywhere in the Old Testament, which again is a proof that He was not dealing with the Mosaic law as such but with the Pharisaical perversion of it. Nevertheless, as was generally true of the teaching of the Pharisees and scribes, it was indirectly dependent upon certain Old Testament statements. For instance, they clearly had in mind the third commandment which reads like this: `Thou shalt not take the name of the Lord thy God in vain'; also Deuteronomy vi. 13: `Thou shalt fear the Lord thy God, and serve him, and shalt swear by his name,' and also Leviticus xix. 12, which reads: `And ye shall not swear by my name falsely, neither shalt thou profane the name of thy God: I am the Lord.' The Pharisees and scribes were familiar with those Scriptures and out of them they had extracted this teaching: `Thou shalt not forswear thyself, but shalt perform unto the Lord thine oaths.' Our Lord is concerned here to correct that false teaching, and not only to correct it, but to replace it with the true teaching. In so doing He brings out, as He always does, the real intent and object of the law as given to Moses by God, the law that is therefore binding upon all of us who are Christian and who are concerned about the honour and glory of God.

Once again we can approach the subject under three main headings. First let us look at the Mosaic legislation. What was the purpose of these various statements, such as those I have just quoted, with regard to this matter of forswearing or taking of oaths? The answer is, undoubtedly, that its main intent was to place a bridle upon man's proneness, as the result of sin and the fall, to lying. One of the greatest problems with which Moses had to deal was the tendency of people to lie to one another and deliberately to say things that were not true. Life was becoming chaotic because men could not rely upon one another's words and statements. So one of the chief purposes of the law at this point was to check that, to control it, and, as it were, to make life possible. The same principle was true, as we saw, of the commandment with regard to divorce where, in addition to the specific object, there was a more general one also.

Another object of this Mosaic legislation was to restrict oathtaking to serious and important matters. There was the tendency on the part of the people to take an oath about any trivial kind of matter. On the slightest pretext they would take an oath in the name of God. The object of the legislation was, therefore, to put an end to this indiscriminate, glib oath-taking, and to show that to take an oath is a very solemn matter, something that must be reserved only for those causes and conditions where a matter of exceptional gravity and unusual concern for the individual or for the nation was involved. In other words this enactment was concerned to remind them of the seriousness of the whole of their life; to remind these children of Israel, especially, of their relationship to God, and to stress that everything they did was under the eye of God, that God was over all, and that every part and portion of their life must be lived as unto Him.

That is one of the great principles of the law which is illustrated in particular at this point. We must always bear in mind, as we consider all these Mosaic commandments, the statement: `I am the Lord your God:... ye shall be holy; for I am holy.' These people had to remember that everything they did was important. They were God's people and were reminded that even in their talk and conversation, and especially in the taking of oaths, everything must be done in such a way as to, realize that God was looking upon them. They must therefore recognize the great seriousness of all these matters because of their relationship to Him.

The teaching of the Pharisees and scribes, however, which our Lord desired to expose and correct, said: `Thou shalt not forswear thyself, but shalt perform unto the Lord thine oaths.' In our consideration of the general principle we saw that ultimately the trouble with the Pharisees and scribes was that their attitude was legalistic. They were more concerned about the letter of the law than the spirit. As long as they could persuade themselves that they were keeping the letter of the law they were perfectly happy. For example, as long as they were not guilty of physical adultery they were all right. And the same thing again applied to divorce. Now here it is once more. They had so construed the meaning and so turned and phrased it in a legal form that they allowed themselves ample scope to do many things that were utterly contradictory to the spirit of the law, yet they felt they were free because they had not actually broken the letter. In other words, they had confined the whole purpose of the enactment at this point to the one question of committing perjury. To commit perjury was to them a very serious and solemn matter; it was a terrible sin and they denounced it. You could, however, take all kinds of oaths, and do all sorts of things, but as long as you never committed perjury you were not guilty before the law.

You see the importance of all this. Legalism is still with us; all these matters are highly relevant to ourselves. It is not at all difficult to see this self-same legalistic attitude towards religion and the Christian faith in large numbers of people today. It is to be found in certain types of religion and it is obvious on the surface in nearly all creeds. To illustrate the case let me point out how obvious it all is in the typical Roman Catholic attitude towards this matter. Take their view of divorce. Their attitude is stated in their written principles. But suddenly in the newspaper you see that a certain prominent Roman Catholic has been granted a divorce. How does it happen? It is a matter of interpretation, and their claim is that they are able to prove that no real marriage had taken place. By subtle arguments they seem to be able to prove anything. You find the same thing in every other type of religion, even, at times, among those who are strongly evangelical. What we do is to isolate a certain thing and say: `To do that is sin, and as long as you are not doing it all is well.' How often have we indicated that this is the tragedy of the modern view of holiness. Holiness and worldliness are defined in a manner far removed from biblical usage. According to some people, to be worldly seems to mean going to a cinema, and that is the sum total of worldliness. As long as you do not do that you are not worldly. But they forget pride-the pride of life, the lust of the flesh, the lust of the eye; pride in ancestry and things like that. You isolate and confine the definition to one matter only. And as long as you are not guilty of that, all is well. That was the trouble with the Pharisees and scribes; they reduced the whole great question to one of perjury only. In other words, they thought there was no harm in a man taking an oath at any time as long as he did not forswear himself. As long as he did not do that he could take an oath by heaven, by Jerusalem and almost by anything. Thus they opened a door for men to multiply oaths at any time or with respect to any matter whatsoever.

The other characteristic of their false interpretation was that they drew a distinction between various oaths, saying that some were binding while others were not. If you took an oath by the temple, that was not binding; but if you took an oath by the gold of the temple, that was binding. If you took an oath by the altar you need not keep it; but if you took an oath by the gift that was on the altar then it was absolutely binding. You notice how in Matthew xxiii our Lord poured His scorn and ridicule, not only upon the perversion of the law therein displayed, but also upon the utter dishonesty of it all. And it is good for us to observe that our Lord did do this. There are certain things in connection with the Christian faith which must be treated in that way. We have all become so uncertain of principles in this loose, effeminate age, that we are afraid of denunciations such as we read here, and are almost ready to condemn our Lord for having spoken about the Pharisees as He did. Shame on us! This utter, rank dishonesty in connection with the things of God is to he exposed and denounced for the thing it is. The Pharisees were guilty of this in distinguishing between oath and oath, saying that some were binding and some not, and the result of all this teaching of theirs was that solemn oaths were being used commonly and lightly in conversation and with respect to almost everything.

Let us now consider our Lord's teaching. The same contrast is here again: `... I say unto you'. Here is the Legislator Himself speaking. Here is the Law-Giver; here is one standing absolutely as a Man among men, yet He speaks with the whole authority of the Godhead. He says in effect: `I who gave the old Law am saying this to you. I say, Swear not at all; neither by heaven; for it is God's throne: nor by the earth; for it is His footstool: neither by Jerusalem; for it is the city of the great King. Neither shalt thou swear by thy head, because thou canst not make one hair white or black. But let your communication be, Yea, yea; Nay, nay: for whatsoever is more than these cometh of evil.' What does this mean?

The first thing we must do, perhaps, is to deal with the situation as it confronts us in a concrete example. Members of the Society of Friends, commonly called the Quakers, have always had a great interest in this paragraph, and it is on the basis of this that they have always traditionally refused to take an oath even in a Court of Law. Their interpretation is that this is a complete and absolute ban upon the taking of an oath in every shape or form and under any circumstance whatsoever. They say that our Lord said: `Swear not at all', and our business is to take His words as they are. We must examine this position, but not because the matter of taking oaths in a Law Court is that which is dealt with here. Indeed I am not at all sure but that those who interpret the passage thus have not quite unwittingly and unconsciously placed themselves almost in the ancient legalistic position of the Pharisees and scribes. If we reduce this whole paragraph to taking an oath in a Court of Law, then we have concentrated on the `mint and anise and cummin' and have forgotten the `weightier matters of the law'. I cannot possibly accept their interpretation for the following reasons.

The first is the Old Testament injunction in which God laid down legislation as to how and when oaths should be taken. Is it conceivable that God could ever do that if it was His will that man should never take an oath at all? But not only that, there is the Old Testament practice. When Abraham sent his servant to find a wife for Isaac, he first of all extracted an oath from him -Abraham, the friend of God. That holy man Jacob extracted an oath from Joseph, Joseph extracted an oath from his brethren and Jonathan asked an oath from David. You cannot read the Old Testament without seeing that, on certain special occasions, these holiest of men had to take an oath in a most solemn and serious manner. Indeed we have higher authority for this in the passage which describes our Lord's own trial. In Matthew xxvi. 63, we are told that `Jesus held his peace'. He was being tried by the high priest. `And the high priest answered and said unto him, I adjure thee by the living God, that thou tell us whether thou be the Christ, the Son of God.' Our Lord did not say: `You must not speak like that.' Not at all. He did not condemn his using the name of God in this manner. He did not denounce it on such an occasion, but seemed to regard it as perfectly legitimate. Then, and only then, in response to this solemn charge, did He reply.

However, let us also consider the custom practised by the apostles, who had been taught these matters by our Lord. You will find they frequently took oaths. The apostle Paul says in Romans ix. i : 'I say the truth in Christ, I lie not, my conscience also bearing me witness in the Holy Ghost'; and again in 2 Corinthians i. 23: `I call God for a record upon my soul, that to spare you I came not as yet unto Corinth.' That was his practice and custom. But there is a very interesting argument based on this whole matter in Hebrews vi. i6. The author at that point is trying to give his readers assurance and strong consolation, and his argument is that God has taken an oath in this matter. `For men verily swear by the greater: and an oath for confirmation is to them an end of all strife.' God therefore `confirmed it by an oath'. In other words, in referring to the practice of men taking an oath he shows how an oath is a confirmation to man, and puts an end to all strife. He does not say it is wrong; he accepts it as something which is right and customary and taught of God. Then he proceeds to argue that even God Himself has taken an oath, `that by two immutable things, in which it was impossible for God to lie, we might have a strong consolation, who have fled for refuge to lay hold upon the hope set before us'. In the light of all this the case for not taking an oath in a Court of Law as based upon this Scripture is something which indeed seems unsatisfactory. The conclusion we can come to, based upon Scripture, is that, while oath-taking must be restricted, there are certain solemn, vital occasions when it is right, when it is not only legitimate, but actually adds a solemnity and an authority which nothing else can give.

That is the negative view of our Lord's teaching. But what does He teach positively? Clearly the first thing that our Lord wants to do is to forbid the use of the sacred title always in the matter of swearing or cursing. The name of God and of Christ must never be used in this way. You have only to walk the streets of a city or sit in its trains or buses to hear this being constantly done. It is utterly and absolutely condemned.

The second thing He absolutely forbids is swearing by any creature, because all belong to God. We must not swear by heaven or earth or by Jerusalem; we must not swear by our heads, or by anything but by the name of God Himself. So these discriminations and distinctions drawn by the Pharisees and scribes were utterly ridiculous. What is Jerusalem? It is the city of the great King. What is the earth? It is nothing but His footstool. You cannot even determine whether your hair be white or black. All these things are under God. Also the temple is the seat of God's presence, so you cannot differentiate between the temple and God in that way. His very presence is in that Shekinah glory. Those distinctions were quite false.

Furthermore, He forbids all oaths in ordinary conversation. There is no need to take an oath about an argument, and you must not do so. Indeed I go further and would remind you that He says no oaths or exaggerated avowals are ever necessary. It must either be 2 ea,yea; or Nay, nay. He calls for simple veracity, the speaking of truth always in all ordinary communications and cynversations and speech. `Let your communication be, Yea, yea; Nay, nay: for whatsoever is more than these cometh of evil.'

All this is a most solemn matter. We can see its relevance in this modern world and life of ours. Are not most of our troubles in life due to the fact that men and women are forgetting these things? What is the main trouble in the international sphere? Is it not just that we cannot believe what is being said-lying? Hitler based his whole policy upon it, and said it was the way to succeed in this world. If you want your nation to be great, you lie about it. And the more you lie the more likely you are to succeed. One country cannot believe another; the oaths, the solemn pledges no longer matter and no longer count.

But it is not only true in the international realm, it is equally true in our own country, and in some of the most sacred associations of life. One of the great scandals of life today is the appalling increase in divorce and infidelity. To what is it due? It is that men have forgotten the teaching of Christ with regard to vows and oaths, and common veracity and truth and honesty in speech. How like these Pharisees and scribes we are. Men on political platforms have waxed eloquent on the sanctity of international contracts. But, at the very time they were speaking, they were not loyal and true to their own marriage vows. When Hitler lied, we all held up our hands aghast; but we seem to think it is somehow different when we tell what we call a `white lie' in order to get out of a difficulty. It is terrible, we think, to lie on the international level, but not, apparently, when it comes to a matter between husband and wife, or parents and children. Is not that the position?

It is the old fallacy. The temple-nothing; the gold of the temple-everything. The altar-nothing; the gift on the altartremendous. No, we must realize that this is a universal law and principle which runs from top to bottom and covers the whole of life. It applies to us also; the message comes right home to each one of us. We must not lie. And we are all given to it, if not always in a bare-faced form. What a terrible thing perjury is to us. We should never dream of it. But surely to tell a lie is as bad as perjury, for, as Christians, we should always speak as in the presence of God. We are His people, and a lie which we may tell to a private individual may come between that individual's soul and its salvation in Christ Jesus. Everything we do is of tremendous importance. We must not exaggerate, or allow people to exaggerate for us, because exaggeration becomes a lie. It gives those who hear a false impression. All that is involved here. Once more: `Let every man examine himself.' God have mercy upon us in that we are so like these Pharisees and scribes, trying to distinguish between big sins and little sins, lies and things which are not exactly lies. There is but one way to deal with all these things. I am not exhorting you to indulge in morbidity or encouraging what might be called morbid scrupulosity, but we must realize that we are always in the presence of Gorl. We claim we are walking through this world in fellowship with Him and with His Son and that we are indwelt by the Holy Spirit. Very well, `grieve not the Holy Spirit of God', says Paul. He sees and hears everything-every exaggeration, every suggested lie. He hears it all and it hurts and offends. Why? Because He is the `Spirit of truth', and there is no lie anywhere near Him. Let us then listen to the command of our heavenly King, who is also our Lord and Saviour, who when He suffered, threatened not, and of whom we read, that `there was no guile found in his mouth'. Let us follow in His steps and desire to be like Him in all things. Let us remember that everything in our lives and conversation is in His presence, and may indeed be the thing which will determine what others will think of Him. `Swear not at all ... let your communication be, Yea, Yea; Nay, nay: for whatsoever is more than these cometh of evil.'

CHAPTER TWENTY-SIX

AN EYE FOR AN EYE,
AND A TOOTH FOR A TOOTH

I-'N verses 38-42 we have our Lord's fifth illustration of the way in which His interpretation of the Mosaic law is con-trasted with the perversion of it by the scribes and Pharisees. With that in mind, the best procedure is perhaps to adopt again the threefold division of the matter which we have used in our consideration of some of the previous illustrations. The first thing, therefore, is to look once more at the intent of the Mosaic enactment.

The Old Testament statement 'an eye for an eye, and a tooth for a tooth' is found in Exodus xxi. 24, Leviticus xxiv. 20 and Deuteronomy xix. 21. It was made to the children of Israel by Moses and the important thing now is to determine why this was so. The same principle obtains as in the matter of adultery and divorce, and in the taking of oaths. The main intent of the Mosaic legislation was to control excesses. In this case in particular, it was to control anger and violence and the desire for revenge. There is no need to elaborate this, because we are all unfortunately familiar with it. We are all guilty of it. If any harm is done to us, the immediate natural instinct is to hit back, and not only that, but to do more than hit back. That is what men and women were doing then, and it is what they still do. A slight injury, and the man injured will have his vengeance, including bodily injury to the other; he might even kill him. This whole tendency to wrath and anger, to retribution and retaliation is there at the very depths of human nature. Not only is nature 'red in tooth and claw', mankind is also. Look at children, for example. From our very earliest days we have this desire for revenge; it is one of the most hideous and ugly results of the fall of man, and of original sin.

Now this tendency was manifesting itself amongst the children of Israel and there are examples of it given in the Old Testament literature. The object, therefore, of this Mosaic legislation was to control and reduce this utterly chaotic condition to a certain amount of order. This, as we have seen, is a great funda mental principle. God, the Author of salvation, the Author of the way whereby mankind can be delivered from the bondage and the tyranny of sin, has also ordained that there shall be a check upon sin. The God of grace is also the God of law, and this is one of the illustrations of the law. God will not only ultimately destroy evil and sin and all its works entirely. He is also, in the meantime, controlling it and has set a bound upon it. We find this working out in the Book ofJob, where even the devil cannot do certain things until he is given permission. He is ultimately under the control of God, and one of the manifestations of that control is that God gives laws. He gave this particular law which insists that a certain principle of equality and equity must enter into these matters. So, if a man knocks out another man's eye, he must not be killed for that-'an eye for an eye'. Or if he knocks out the tooth of another, the victim is only entitled to knock out one of his teeth. The punishment must fit the crime and not be in excess of it.

That is the purpose of this Mosaic legislation. The principle of justice must come in, and justice is never excessive in its demands. There is a correspondence between the crime and the punishment, the thing done and what is to be done about it. The object of that law was not to urge men to take an eye for an eye and a tooth for a tooth, and to insist upon it every time; it was simply meant to avoid this horrible excess, this terrible spirit of revenge and demand for retribution, and to check it and hold it within bounds.

But perhaps the most important thing is that this enactment was not given to the individual, but rather to the judges who were responsible for law and order amongst the individuals. The system of judges was set up amongst the children of Israel, and when disputes and matters arose the people had to take them to these responsible authorities for judgment. It was the judges who were to see to it that it was an eye for an eye and a tooth for a tooth and no more. The legislation was for them, not for the private individuals-as in the law of our land at this moment. The law is carried out by the magistrate or the judge, by the one who is appointed in the nation to do this. That was the principle; and it is a true picture of the

Mosaic legislation itself. Its main object was to introduce this element of justice and of righteousness into a chaotic condition and to take from man the tendency to take the law into his own hands and to do anything he likes.

As far as the teaching of the Pharisees and scribes is concerned, their main trouble was that they tended to ignore entirely the fact that this teaching was for the judges only. They made it a matter for personal application. Not only that, they regarded it, in their typical legalistic manner, as a matter of right and duty to have `an eye for an eye, and a tooth for a tooth'. To them it was something to be insisted upon rather than something which should be restrained. It was a legalistic outlook which thought only of its rights-a kind of Shylock attitude. They were therefore guilty of two main errors at that point. They were turning a negative injunction into a positive one and, furthermore, were interpreting it and carrying it out themselves, and teaching others to do so, instead of seeing that it was something that was to be carried out only by the appointed judges who were responsible for law and order.

It is in the light of that background that our Lord's teaching is given, `I say unto you, That ye resist not evil', together with the further statements that follow.

Clearly, we are face to face here with a subject which has often been debated, which has been frequently misunderstood, and which has always been the cause of much confusion. There is possibly no passage in Scripture which has produced as much heat and disputation as this very teaching which tells us not to resist evil and to be loving and forgiving. Pacifism is the cause of much wordy warfare and it often leads to a spirit which is as far removed as possible from that which is taught and inculcated here by our blessed Lord. It is of course one of those passages to which people rush the moment the Sermon on the Mount is mentioned. Many people, no doubt, have been longing for us to arrive at this point and now at last we have reached it, yet nothing is more important than that we should have taken all this time to come to it, because, as we have seen in these expositions, this kind of injunction can only be understood truly if it is always kept in its context and setting.

We saw at the beginning that there are certain principles of interpretation which must be observed if we want to know the truth concerning these matters. We should remind ourselves of some of them now. First, we must never regard the Sermon on the Mount as a code of ethics, or a set of rules to cover our conduct in detail. We must not think of it as being a new kind of law to replace the old Mosaic law; it is rather a matter of emphasizing the spirit of the law. So that we must not, if we are in trouble as to what to do at a particular point, rush to the Sermon on the Mount and turn up a particular passage. You do not get that in the New Testament. Is it not rather tragic that those of us who are under grace always seem to want to be under law? We ask one another, `What is the exact teaching about this?' and if we cannot be given `yes' or `no' as an answer we say, `It is all so vague and indefinite'.

Secondly, these teachings are never to be applied mechanically or as a kind of rule of thumb. It is the spirit rather than the letter. Not that we depreciate the letter, but it is the spirit that we must emphasize.

'Thirdly, if our interpretation ever makes the teaching appear to be ridiculous or leads us to a ridiculous position, it is patently a wrong interpretation. And there are people who are guilty of this.

The next principle is this: If our interpretation makes the teaching appear to be impossible it also is wrong. Nothing our Lord teaches is ever impossible. There are people who do interpret certain things in the Sermon on the Mount in such a way and their interpretation must be false. Its teaching was meant for daily life.

Lastly, we must remember that if our interpretation of any one of these things contradicts the plain and obvious teaching of Scripture at another point, again it is obvious that our interpretation has gone astray. Scripture must be taken and compared with Scripture. There is no contradiction in biblical teaching.

Bearing all this in mind, let us consider what our Lord teaches. He says, `I say unto you, That ye resist not evil.' They say, `an eye for an eye, and a tooth for a tooth'. What does it mean? We must inevitably start with the negative which is that this statement is not to be taken literally. There are always people who say, `Now what I say is this, you must take the Scripture exactly as it is, and Scripture says resist not evil. There you are; there is no more to be said.' We cannot deal now with that whole attitude towards Scripture interpretation; but it would be a very simple thing to show that if that is carried out in every respect, we should arrive at an interpretation which is not only ridiculous but impossible. There are, however, certain famous people in the history of the Church and Christian thought who insisted on our interpreting this particular statement in this way. Perhaps no man has more influenced men's thinking concerning these matters than that great writer Count Tolstoy, and he did not hesitate to say that these words of our Lord are to be taken at their face value. He said that to have soldiers, or police, or even magistrates, is unchristian. Evil, he maintained, is not to be resisted; for Christ's way is not to resist evil in any sense. He said that the statement is not qualified, that it does not say that this is true only under certain special conditions. It says, `resist not evil'. Now policemen resist evil; therefore you must not have them. The same is true of soldiers, magistrates, judges and law courts. There should be no punishment for crime. `Resist not evil.'

There are others who do not go quite so far as Tolstoy. These people say that we must have magistrates and courts and so on; but they do not believe in soldiers, in wars, or in capital punishment. They do not believe in killing in any sense, whether judicial or otherwise.

You are familiar with that kind of teaching and outlook; and it is part of the business of preaching and of interpreting the Scriptures to meet such an attitude when it is put forward honestly and sincerely. It seems to me that the answer to it is that we must remember once more the whole context and connection of these statements. This can never be emphasized too often. The Sermon on the Mount must be taken in the order in which it was preached and in which it is presented to us. We start not with this injunction, but with the Beatitudes. We start with those fundamental definitions and advance from them. We shall see the relevance of this later; but first we must deal with the paragraph in general.

The first main principle is that this teaching is not for nations or for the world. Indeed we can go further and say that this teaching has nothing whatever to do with a man who is not a Christian. Here we see the importance of the right order. `This is the sort of way in which you must live', says our Lord to these people. To whom is He speaking? They are the people whom He has already described in the Beatitudes. The first thing He said about them was that they are `poor in spirit'. In other words they are perfectly aware of their own utter inability. They are aware of the fact that they are sinners, and are absolutely helpless in the sight of God. They are those who are mourning because of their sins. They have come to understand sin as a principle within them that is vitiating the whole of their lives, and they mourn because of it. They are meek; they have a spirit in them that is the very antithesis of the spirit of the world. They are hungering and thirsting after righteousness, and so on. Now these particular injunctions which we are studying are meant only for such people.

We need not stress this point further. This teaching is utterly impossible for anyone who lacks such qualities. Our Lord never asks a man who is but a natural man, the dupe of sin and Satan, and under the dominion of hell, to live a life like this, for he cannot. We must be new men and born again before we can live such a life. Therefore to advocate this teaching as a policy for a country or a nation is no less than heresy. It is heretical in this way: if we ask a man who has not been born again, and who has not received the Holy Spirit, to live the Christian life, we are really saying that a man can justify himself by works, and that is heresy. We are suggesting that a man by his own efforts, and by putting his mind to it, can live this life. That is an absolute contradiction of the whole of the New Testament. Our Lord established that once and for ever in His interview with Nicodemus. Nicodemus was clearly on the point of asking, `What have I to do in order that I may be like you?' `My dear friend,' said our Lord to him in effect, `Do not think of it in terms of what you can do;

you cannot do anything; you must be born again.' Therefore to ask for Christian conduct from an individual who is not born again, let alone a nation or a group of nations or a world of nations, is both impossible and wrong.

For the world, and for a nation, and for non-Christians the law still applies, and it is the law which says `an eye for an eye, and a tooth for a tooth'. These people are still under that justice which restrains and holds man back, preserving law and order and controlling excesses. In other words, that is why a Christian must believe in law and order, and why he must never be negligent of his duties as a citizen of a State. He knows that `the powers that be are ordained of God', that lawlessness must be controlled, and vice and crime kept within bounds-'an eye for an eye, and a tooth for a tooth,' justice and equity. In other words the New Testament teaches that, until a man comes under grace, he must be kept under the law. It is at this point that all this modern muddle and confusion has entered in. People who are not Christian talk vaguely about Christ's teaching concerning life, and interpret it as meaning that you must not punish a child when it does wrong, that there must be no law and order, and that we must first love everybody and make them nice. And now we are seeing the results ! But this is heresy. It is `an eye for an eye, and a tooth for a tooth' until the spirit of Christ enters into us. Then, something higher is expected of us, but not until then. The law exposes evil and keeps it within bounds and it is God Himself who has ordained this, and all `the powers that be' that are to enforce it.

That is our first principle. This has nothing to do with nations or so-called Christian pacifism, Christian socialism and things like that. They cannot be based on this teaching; indeed they are a denial of it. That was the whole tragedy of Tolstov, and alas, poor rnan, he himself hccan.~, a tragedy at the end when he faced the utter uselessness of it all. That was quite inevitable from the beginning, as he would have seen had he truly understood the teaching.

Secondly, this teaching, which concerns the Christian individual and nobody else, applies to him only in his personal relationships and not in his relationships as a citizen of his country. This is the whole crux of the teaching. We all of us live in different realms. Here am I, a citizen of Great Britain with my relationship to the State, to the Government and to other such organizations. Yes, but there are also certain more personal relationships, my relationship to my wife and children, my relationship as an individual to other people, my friendships, my membership of the Church and so on. All these are quite apart from my general relationship to the country to which I belong. Now here, I would repeat, our Lord's teaching concerns the behaviour of the Christian in his personal relationships only; indeed, in this saying, the Christian's relationship to the State is not even considered or mentioned. Here we have nothing but the reaction of the Christian as an individual to the things that are done to him personally. With regard to the Christian's relationship to the State and his general relationships, there is ample teaching in the Scriptures. If you are anxious about your relationship to the State or your attitude as a citizen do not stay with the Sermon on the Mount. Rather go on to other chapters that deal specifically with that subject, such as Romans xiii and i Peter ii. So that if I, as a young man, am considering my duty to the State in the matter of going into the Forces, I do not find the answer here. I must loot; for it elsewhere. This is only concerned about my personal relationships. And yet how often, when a man's duty towards the State is being considered, this passage is quoted. I suggest it has nothing whatsoever to do with it.

The third principle which controls the interpretation of this subject is, clearly, that the question of killing and taking of life is not considered as such in this teaching, whether it be regarded as capital punishment, or killing in war, or any other form of killing. Our Lord is considering this law of the Christian's personal reaction to the things that happen to him. Ultimately, of course, it will cover the whole question of killing, but that is not the principle that He puts in the forefront. Therefore, to interpret this paragraph in terms of pacifism and nothing else is to reduce this great and wonderful Christian teaching to a mere matter of legalism. And those who base their pacifism upon this paragraph-whether pacifism is right or wrong I am not concerned to say-are guilty of a kind of heresy. They have dropped back into the legalism of the Pharisees and scribes; and that is an utterly false interpretation.

What, then, is taught here? Surely there is but one principle in this teaching, and that is a man's attitude towards himself. We could discuss the Christian in terms of the State and war and all these things. But that is something very much easier than that which the Lord Jesus Christ asks us to face here. What He asks you to face is yourself, and it is very much easier to discuss pacifism than to face His clear teaching at this point. What is it? I suggest that the key to it is to be found in verse 42: 'Give to him that asketh thee, and from him that would borrow of thee turn not thou away.' That is most important. As you read this paragraph, your first feeling when you come to verse 42 is that it should not be there at all. 'Ye have heard that it hath been said, An eye for an eye, and a tooth for a tooth: But I say unto you, That ye resist not evil.' That is the theme, resisting evil, and therefore these questions of war and killing and capital punishment seem to arise. But then He goes on to say: 'but whosoever shall smite thee on thy right cheek, turn to him the other also. And if any man will sue thee at the law, and take away thy coat, let him have thy cloke also. And whosoever shall compel thee to go a mile, go with him twain.' Then suddenly: 'Give to him that asketh thee, and from him that would borrow of thee turn not thou away.' And at once we feel like asking, What has this question of borrowing to do with resisting evil and not hitting back, or with fighting and killing? How does this come in? There, we are given a clue to the understanding-of the principles our Lord is here inculcating. He is concerned the whole time about this question of the 'self' and of our attitude towards our selves. He is saying in effect that if we are to be truly Christian we must become dead to self. It is not a question of whether we should go into the Army or anything else; it is a question of what I think of myself, and of my attitude towards myself.

It is very spiritual teaching, and it works out in the following respects. First, I must be right in my attitude towards myself and the spirit of self-defence that immediately rises when any wrong is done to me. I must also deal with the desire for revenge and the spirit of retaliation that is so characteristic of the natural self. Then there is the attitude of self towards injustices that are done to it and towards the demands that are made upon it by the community or by the State. And finally there is the attitude of self to personal possessions. Our Lord here is unveiling and exposing this horrible thing that controls the natural man-self; that terrible legacy that has come down from the fall of man and which makes man glorify himself and set himself up as a god. He protects this self all along and in every way. But he does it not only when he is attacked or -,%,hen something is taken from him; he does it also in the matter of his possessions. If another wants to borrow from him, his instinctive response is: `Why should I part with my goods and impoverish myself?' It is self the whole time.

The moment we see that, there is no contradiction between verse 42 and the others. It is not only a connection, it is an essential part of it. The tragedy of the Pharisees and scribes was that they interpreted `An eye for an eye, and a tooth for a tooth' in a purely legal manner or as something physical and material. Men still do that. They reduce this amazing teaching just to the question of capital punishment or whether we should take part in war. `No,' says Christ in effect, `it is a matter of the spirit, it is a matter of your whole attitude, especially your attitude towards yourself; and I would have you see that if you are to be truly My disciples you must become dead to yourself.' He is saying, if you like: `If any man would be My disciple, let him deny himself (and all his rights to himself and all the rights of self), and take up the cross, and follow Me.'

CHAPTER TWENTY-SEVEN

THE CLOAK AND THE SECOND MILE

W "E have already dealt with verses 38-42 in general, and laid down certain great principles that it is essential to consider before we can even hope to understand the meaning of this challenging paragraph. How often do we tend to forget that the most important factor when we come to Scripture, and especially to a difficult statement like this, is the preparation of the spirit. It is not enough to come to Scripture with a mind, however clear, powerful or intellectual. In the understanding and the elucidation of Scripture, the spirit is very much more important even than the mind. Therefore it is fatal to rush at a statement like this in an argumentative or debating mood. That is why we have taken some time in painting in the background or, if you like, in preparing our spirits and making sure that our whole attitude is one which is set and prepared to receive the message.

We come now to deal with it in detail. It is not that our Lord is giving us here a complete list of what we have to do in every circumstance and condition which we are likely to meet in life. He tells us first that we have to die to self. What does this mean? This paragraph shows us how we can do that; it shows us some ways in which we can test ourselves as to whether we are dying to self or not. These are just three illustrations that He takes, as it were, almost at random, in order to illustrate the principle. It is not an exhaustive list. The New Testament does not provide us with detailed instructions of that kind. Rather, it says: `You are called; remember you are God's men. Here are the principles; go and apply them.' Of course it is a good thing that we should discuss these things together. But let us be careful that we do not put ourselves back under the law. This needs to be stressed because there are many people who, though they object to Roman Catholicism and its casuistry, are very Catholic in their ideas and doctrine at this point. They think that it is the business of the Church to give them a detailed answer to every little question, and they are always worried about these things. We must get right out of that atmosphere into the realm of great principles.

The first principle is this whole question which we generallyrefer to as `turning the other cheek'. `I say unto you, That ye resist not evil: but whosoever shall smite thee on thy right cheek, turn to him the other also.' What does this mean in the light of the general principles we have enunciated earlier? It means that we must rid ourselves of the spirit of retaliation, of the desire to defend ourselves and to revenge ourselves for any injury or wrong that is done to us. Our Lord starts on the physical level. He imagines a man coming along and, without any provocation, striking us on the right check. Immediately the instinct is to hit back and punish him and to have vengeance. The moment I am hit I want to retaliate. That is what our Lord is concerned about, and He just says simply and categorically that we are not to do it. `Vengeance is mine; I will repay, saith the Lord.'

Let me give you two illustrations of men who, we must all agree, put this teaching into practice. The first is about the famous Cornish evangelist, Billy Bray, who before his conversion was a pugilist, and a very good one. Billy Bray was converted; but one day, down in the mine, another man who used to live in mortal dread and terror of Billy Bray before Bray's conversion, knowing he was converted, thought he had at last found his opportunity. Without any provocation at all he struck Billy Bray, who could very easily have revenged himself upon him and laid him down unconscious on the ground. But instead of doing that Billy Bray looked at him and said, `May God forgive you, even as I forgive you', and no more. The result was that that man endured for several days an agony of mind and spirit which led directly to his conversion. He knew what Billy Bray could do, and he knew what the natural man in Billy Bray wanted to do. But Billy Bray did not do it; and that is how God used him.

The other is a story of a very different man. Hudson Taylor, standing on a river bank in China one evening, hailed a boat to take him across a river. Just as the boat was drawing near, a wealthy Chinese came along who did not recognize Hudson Taylor as a foreigner because he had affected native dress. So when the boat came he struck and thrust Hudson Taylor aside with such force that the latter fell into the mud. Hudson Taylor, however, said nothing; but the boatman refused to take his fellow-countryman, saying, `No, that foreigner called me, and the boat is his, and he must go first.' The Chinese traveller was amazed and astounded when he realized he had blundered. Hudson Taylor did not complain but invited the man into the boat with him and began to tell him what it was in him that made him behave in such a manner. As a foreigner he could have resented such treatment; but he did not do so because of the grace of God in him. A conversation followed which Hudson Taylor had every reason to believe made a deep impression upon that man and upon his soul.

These are but two instances of men trying to implement and, indeed, succeeding in implementing, this particular injunction. What it means is this: we should not be concerned about personal injuries and insults, whether of a physical kind or any other. To be struck on the face is humiliating and insulting. But an insult can be given in many ways. It can be done with the tongue or by a look. Our Lord desires to produce in us a spirit that does not take offence easily at such things, that does not seek immediate means of retaliation. He wants us to reach a state in which we are indifferent to self and self-esteem. The apostle Paul, for instance, puts this perfectly in i Corinthians iv. 3. He is writing to those Corinthians who have been saying some very unkind things about him. He had been the means of establishing the church, but rival factions had arisen within her. Some were boasting about Apollos and his wonderful preaching, while others were saying they were followers of Cephas. Many had been criticizing the great apostle in a most insulting manner. Notice what he says: With me it is a very small thing that I should be judged of you, or of man's judgment: yea, I judge not mine own self.' He means that he has become indifferent to personal criticism, insult and abuse, and to anything that men may do to him.

That is the broad principle which our Lord lays down. But let us be careful that we do not violate one of the principles of interpretation to which we drew attention earlier. This is not so much a qualification, as an elaboration of the teaching. Our Lord's teaching here does not mean that we should be unconcerned about the defence of law and order. To turn the other cheek does not mean that it does not matter at all what happens in national affairs, whether there is order or chaos. Not at all. That, as we saw, was the error of Tolstoy, who said that there should be no policemen, soldiers or magistrates. That is a complete travesty of the teaching. What our Lord says is that I am not to be concerned about myself, my own personal honour and so on. But that is a very different thing from being unconcerned about the maintenance of law and order, or about the defence of the weak and unprotected. While I must and should be prepared to suffer any personal insult or indignity that man can ever inflict upon me, I should at the same time believe in law and order. I assert on biblical authority that `the powers that be are ordained of God', that the magistrate is a necessary power, that evil and sin must be restrained and restricted, and that I, as a citizen, am to be concerned about that. Therefore I must not construe our Lord's teaching at this point in that general way; it is a personal word to me. For example, it makes our Lord's teaching ridiculous to say that if a drunken man, or a violent lunatic, should happen to come along and strike me on the right cheek, I am immediately to turn the other cheek to him. For if a man in that intoxicated condition, or a lunatic, should so deal with me, what is happening is really not any personal insult or injury. This man who is not in control of his faculties is behaving like an animal and does not know what he is doing. What our Lord is concerned about is my spirit and my attitude towards such a man. Because of the alcohol, this poor man is not aware of what he is doing; he is not really concerned to insult me, he is a man who is doing harm to himself as well as to me and to others. He is, therefore, a man who is to be restrained. And, in the full spirit of this injunction, I should restrain him. Or if I see a man ill-treating or abusing a child I should do precisely the same thing. The teaching has reference to my concern about myself. `I have been insulted, I have been struck; therefore I must defend myself, and my honour.' That is the spirit our Lord is anxious to banish from our lives.

The second illustration our Lord uses is this matter of the cloak and the coat. `If any man will sue thee at the law, and take away thy coat, let him have thy cloke also.' Now what does this mean? It can be put as a principle in this way. Our Lord is concerned here with the tendency to insist upon our rights, our legal rights. He gives this example of a man coming and suing me in a Court of Law for my inner garment. Now according to Jewish law a. man could never be sued for his outer garment, though it was legitimate to sue for an inner one. Yet our Lord says, `If a man comes and sues thee for thy coat, instead of resisting him let him have thy cloak also.'

Here again is a very difficult matter, and the only way of dealing with the problem is to pay close attention to the principle, which is this tendency of men always to demand and insist upon their legal rights. We are all familiar with this at the present time. There are people who are never tired of telling us that the real problem in the world today is that everybody is talking about his rights instead of his duties. It is with this tendency that our Lord is dealing here. Men are always thinking of their rights and saying, `I must have them.' That is the spirit of the world and of the natural man who must have his pound of flesh, and insists upon it. That, our Lord is concerned to show, is not the Christian spirit. He says we must not insist upon our legal rights even though we may at times suffer injustice as the result.

That is the bald statement of the principle, but once more we must elaborate it. There are passages of Scripture which are most important in this connection. Here we see most clearly the importance of taking Scripture with Scripture and of never interpreting it at one point in such a way that it contradicts the teaching at another point. Our Lord says here, `If any man will sue thee at the law, and take away thy coat, let him have thy cloke also.' But He also said, `Moreover if thy brother shall trespass against thee, go and tell him his fault between thee and him alone: if he shall hear thee, thou hast gained thy brother.' He also goes on to say, `If he will not hear thee, then take with thee one or two more ... And if he shall neglect to hear them, tell it unto the church: but if he neglect to hear the church, let him be unto thee as an heathen man and a publican' (Mt. xviii. 15-17). In other words, He does not seem to be telling us there to turn the other cheek or to throw in the cloak in addition to the coat.

Then again in John xviii. 22, 23 we read, `And when he had thus spoken, one of the officers which stood by struck Jesus with the palm of his hand, saying, Answerest thou the high priest so? Jesus answered him, If I have spoken evil, bear witness of the evil: but if well, why smitest thou me?' He protests, you see, against the action of the officer.

Let me remind you, too, of what we are told of the apostle Paul in Acts xvi. 37. Paul and Silas had been thrown into prison at Philippi and their feet were made fast in the stocks. Then, next morning, after the earthquake and all the other events of that memorable night, the magistrates realized they had made a mistake and sent down an order that Paul and Silas should be set at liberty. But see the reply Paul gave: `They have beaten us openly uncondemned, being Romans, and have cast us into prison; and now do they thrust us out privily? nay verily; but let them come themselves and fetch us out.' And the magistrate had to come down into the prison in order to release them.

How do we reconcile these things? Our Lord here in the Sermon on the Mount seems to be saying that invariably you must turn the other check, or if ever you are sued for your coat you must throw in your cloak as well. But He Himself, when He is smitten on the face, does not turn the other cheek, but registers a protest. And the apostle Paul insisted upon the magistrate coming down to release him. If we accept the original principle, there is no difficulty at all in reconciling the two sets of statements. It can be done in this way. These instances are not examples and illustrations of either our Lord or the apostle insisting upon personal rights. What our Lord did was to rebuke the breaking of the law and His protest was made in order to uphold the law. He said to these men, in effect: `You know by striking me like this you are breaking the law.' He did not say: `Why do you insult me?' He did not lose His temper or take it as a personal affront. He did not become angry, or show concern about Himself. But He was concerned to remind these men of the dignity and honour of the law. And the apostle Paul did exactly the same thing. He did not make a great protest about having been thrown into prison. His concern was that the magistrates should see that by throwing him into prison like that they were doing something that was illegal and were violating the law that they had been appointed to carry out. So he reminded them of the dignity and honour of that law.

The Christian is not to be concerned about personal insults. and personal defence. But when it is a matter of honour and justice, righteousness and truth, he must be concerned and thus he makes his protest. When the law is not honoured, when it is flagrantly broken, not in any personal interest, not in any way to protect himself, he acts as a believer in God, as one who believes that all law ultimately derives from God. That was the tragic heresy of Tolstoy and others, though they did not realize they were being heretical. Law and laws ultimately come from God. It is He who has appointed the bounds of every nation; it is He who has appointed kings and governments and magistrates and those who are meant to maintain law and order. The Christian, therefore, must believe in observing the law. Thus, while he is prepared for anything to happen to himself personally, he must protest when injustices are being done.

It is obvious that these questions are all tremendously significant and important in the lives of large numbers of Christian people today in many countries. There are many Christians in China and in the countries behind the so-called `iron curtain' who are facing these things. It may well be that we ourselves may have to face them also, so let us try to keep these principles clearly in our minds.

The next principle involves the question of going the second mile. `And whosoever shall compel thee to go a mile, go with him twain.' That is to be explained in this way. This compelling to go a mile is a reference to a custom which was very common in the ancient world, by means of which a government had a right to commandeer a man in a matter of porterage or transport. A certain amount of baggage had to be moved from one place to another, so the authorities had the right to commandeer a man at any place and they would make him carry the baggage from that stage to the next. Then they took hold of someone else and made him take it to the next stage, and so on. This, of course, was a power that was especially exercised by any country that had conquered another, and at this time Palestine had been conquered by the Romans. The Roman army was in control of the life of the Jews, and they very frequently did this sort of thing. A man might be doing his own work when suddenly a band of soldiers would come and say to him, `You must carry this baggage from here to the next stage. You must carry it for a mile.' That is the kind of thing our Lord had in mind and He says: `When they come to you like that and compel you to go a mile, go with them the second mile.' Go beyond what they have demanded, `go with them twain'.

Here again is a most important and a most practical matter. The principle is that, not only are we to do what is demanded of us, we are to go beyond it in the spirit of our Lord's teaching here. This passage is concerned with a man's natural resentment at the demands of government upon him. It has reference to our dislike and hatred of legislation of which we do not approve, to Acts of Parliament, for example, which we do not like and which we have opposed. `Yes', we tend to say; `they are passed by Parliament. But why should I obey? How can I get out of' this?' That is the attitude our Lord is condemning. Let us be perfectly practical. Take the question of the payment of taxes. We may dislike and resent them, but the principle involved is exactly the same as in being willing to go a second mile. Our Lord says that not only must we not resent these things, we must do them willingly; and we must even be prepared to go beyond what is demanded of us. Any resentment that we may feel against the legitimate, authoritative government ofour land is something which our Lord condemns. The government that is in power has a right to do these things, and it is our business to carry out the law. Even further, we must do so though we may entirely disagree with what is being done, and though we may regard it as unjust. If it has legal authority and sanction it is for us to do it.

Peter in his Epistle (i Peter ii) says, `Servants, be subject to your masters . . .' and goes on to show the spirit of our Lord's teaching-'not only to the good and gentle, but also to the froward.' Christian people are often heard quoting that about servants: `Ah', they say, `the trouble is that servants are always talking about their rights, never about their duties. They are all rebellious and do not do things in a good spirit. They do everything grudgingly and reluctantly. Men no longer believe in work', and so on. Yes; but the very same people speak about the Government and about Acts of Parliament in exactly the same spirit which they condemn in servants. Their attitude towards income tax or the law at certain points is just the one they condemn. That has never occurred to them. But let us remember, if we are employers, that what Peter and our Lord say about the servant applies to all of us. For we are all servants of the State. The principle, therefore, can be put in this way. If we become excited about these matters, or lose our temper about them, if we are always talking about them and if they interfere with our loyalty to Christ or our devotion to Him, if these things are monopolizing the centre of our lives, we are living the Christian life, to put it mildly, at the very lowest level. No, says our Lord, if you are doing that job and this soldier comes along and says you have to carry his baggage for a mile, not only do it cheerfully, but go the second mile. The result will be that when you arrive this soldier will say: `Who is this person? What is it about him that makes him act like this? He is doing it cheerfully, and is going beyond his duty.' And they will be driven to this conclusion: `This man is different, he seems to be unconcerned about his own interests.' As Christians, our state of mind and spiritual condition should be such that no power can insult us.

There are thousands of Christian people who are in this position today in occupied countries, and we know not what may be coming to us. It may be that we shall be subjected ourselves some day to a tyrannous power which we naturally hate and which will compel us to do things we dislike. This is the way in which you are to behave in such circumstances, says Christ. You do not stand up for your rights; you do not show the bitterness of the natural man. You have another spirit. We must get into that spiritual state and condition in which we are invulnerable to these attacks which come upon us in different ways.

There is one qualification which must be added. This injunc tion does not say that we are not entitled to a change of government. But this must always be done by lawful means. Let us change the law if we can, as long as we do it constitutionally and in a lawful manner. It does not say that we must take no interest in politics and in the reform of law. Certainly, if reform seems necessary, let us seek to achieve it, but only within the framework of the law. If we believe that a particular law includes injustices, then in the name of justice, not for our own personal feelings, nor for our own private gain, let us try to change the law. Let us be certain however that our interest in the change is never personal and selfish, but that it is always done in the interest of government and justice and truth and righteousness.

The last point, which we can only touch upon, is the whole question of giving and lending. `Give to him that asketh thee, and from him that would borrow of thee turn not thou away.' Of course, this again could be interpreted in a mechanical and literal manner so as to make it ridiculous. But what it really means can be put in this form. It is this denial of self once more. It is just our Lord's way of saying that the spirit which says, `What I have I hold, and what is mine is mine; and I cannot listen to the request of those other people because ultimately I may suffer', is completely wrong. He is rebuking the wrong spirit of those who are always considering themselves, whether they are being struck on the face, or whether their coat is being taken, or whether they are compelled to carry the baggage or to give of their own goods and wealth to help someone in need.

Let us now go immediately to the qualification, realizing that that is the principle. Our Lord does not encourage us here to help frauds or professional beggars or drunkards. I put it like this plainly because we all have these experiences. A man comes to you under the influence of drink and asks you to give him some money. Although he says he wants it for a night's lodging you know he will go immediately and spend it upon drink. Our Lord does not tell us to encourage or help such a man. He is not even considering that. What He is considering is the tendency of a man because of self, and a self-centred spirit, not to help those who are in real need. It is this holding on to what is mine that He is concerned about. We can therefore put it like this. We must always be ready to listen and to give a man the benefit of the doubt. It is not something we do mechanically or thoughtlessly. We must think, and say: `If this man is in need, it is my business to help him if I am in a position to do so. I may be taking a risk, but if he is in need I will help him.' The apostle John gives us a perfect exposition of this. `But whoso hath this world's good, and seeth his brother have need, and shutteth up his bowels of compassion from him, how dwelleth the love of God in him? My little children, let us not love in word, neither in tongue; but in deed and in truth' (i Jn. iii. 17, 18). That is the way we are to follow. `Whoso hath this world's good, and seeth his brother have need.' The man under the influence of drink who asks us for money is not in need, neither is the man who lives by this sort of thing and is too lazy to work. Paul says of such: `If any would not work, neither should he eat.' So your professional beggar is not in need and I do not give to him. But if I see that my brother is in need and I have this world's goods and am in a position to help him, I must not shut up the bowels of my compassion from hiin, because, if I do, the love of God is not in me. The love of God is a love that gives of itself in order to help and strengthen those who are in need.

Finally then, having simply studied these injunctions one by one and step by step, and having considered this teaching, we should see clearly that it takes a new man to live this kind of life. This is no theory for the world or for the non-Christian. No man can hope to live like this unless he is born again, unless he has received the Holy Spirit. Such people alone are Christian, and it is to such that our Lord addresses this noble, exalted and divine teaching. It is not comfortable teaching to consider and I can assure you that it is not an easy thing to spend a week with a text like this. But this is the Word of God, and this is what Christ would have us be. It deals with our whole personality, down to the little practical details of life. Holiness is not something to be received in a meeting; it is a life to be lived and to be lived in detail. We may be truly interested and moved as we listen to wonderful addresses about giving ourselves, and so on. But we must not forget our attitude towards legislation which we do not like, and the rates and taxes and the ordinary pin-pricks of life. It is all a question of this attitude towards self. God have mercy upon us and fill us with His Spirit.

CHAPTER TWENTY-EIGHT

DENYING SELF AND FOLLOWING CHRIST

I-N this chapter I want again to consider verses 38-42. We have already studied them twice. First, we looked at them in -general, reminding ourselves of certain principles which govern the interpretation. Then we considered the statements one by one in detail, and saw that our Lord's concern is that we should be set free from all desire for personal revenge. There is nothing which is so tragic as the way in which many people, when they come to this paragraph, become so immersed in details, and are so ready to argue about the rightness or wrongness of doing this or that, that they completely lose sight of the great principle here expressed, which is the Christian's attitude towards himself. These illustrations are used by our Lord simply to bring out His teaching concerning that great central principle. `You', He says in effect, `must have a right view of yourselves. Your troubles arise because you tend to go wrong at that particular point.' In other words, our Lord's primary concern here is with what we are, rather than with what we do. What we do is important, because it is indicative of what we are. He illustrates that here, and says: `If you are what you claim to be, this is how you will behave.' So we must concentrate not so much upon the action as upon the spirit that leads to the action. That is why, let us repeat it again, it is so essential that we should take the teaching of the Sermon on the Mount in the order in which it is given. We have no right to consider these particular injunctions unless we have already grasped, and mastered, and have submitted ourselves to, the teaching of the Beatitudes.

In this paragraph we have our attitude towards ourselves presented in a negative manner; in the paragraph that follows it is presented positively. There our Lord goes on to say: `Ye have heard that it hath been said, Thou shalt love thy neighbour, and hate thine enemy. But I say unto you, Love your enemies, bless them that curse you, do good to them that hate you, and pray for them which despitefully use you, and persecute you.'

But here we are concerned with the negative, and this teaching is of such central importance in the New Testament that we must consider it once more.

We have already found more than once that the Sermon on the Mount is full of doctrine. There is nothing quite so pathetic as the way in which people used to say some thirty or forty years ago (and some still say it) that the only part of the New Testamerit they really believed in and liked was the Sermon on the Mount, and that because it contained no theology or doctrine. It was practical, they said; just an ethical manifesto, which contained no doctrine or dogma. There is nothing quite so sad as that, because this Sermon on the Mount is full of doctrine. We have it here in this paragraph. The important thing is not so much that I turn the other cheek, as that I should be in a state in which I am ready to do so. The doctrine involves my whole view of myself.

No man can practise what our Lord illustrates here unless he has finished with himself, with his right to himself, his right to determine what he shall do, and especially must he finish with what we commonly call the `rights of the self'. In other words we must not be concerned about ourselves at all. The whole trouble in life, as we have seen, is ultimately this concern about self, and what our Lord is inculcating here is that it is something of which we must rid ourselves entirely. We must rid ourselves of this constant tendency to be watching the interests of self, to be always on the look-out for insults or attacks or injuries, always in this defensive attitude. That is the kind of thing He has in mind. All that must disappear, and that of course means that we must cease to be sensitive about self. This morbid sensitiveness, this whole condition in which self is `on edge' and so delicately and sensitively poised and balanced that the slightest disturbance can upset its equilibrium, must be got rid of. The condition which our Lord is here describing is one in which a man simply cannot be hurt. Perhaps that is the most radical form in which one can put that statement. I reminded you in the last chapter of what the apostle Paul says about himself in i Corinthians iv. 3. He writes: `With me it is a very small thing that I should be judged of you, or of man's judgment: yea, I judge not mine own self.'He has committed the whole question of his judgment to God, and thus he has entered into a state and condition in which he just cannot be hurt. That is the ideal at which we should be aiming-this indifference to self and its interests.

A statement which the great George Muller once made about himself seems to illustrate this very clearly. He writes like this: `There was a day when I died, utterly died, died to George Muller and his opinions, preferences, tastes and will; died to the world, its approval or censure; died to the approval or blame of even my brethren and friends; and since then I have studied only to show myself approved unto God.' That is a statement to be pondered deeply. I cannot imagine a more perfect or adequate summary of our Lord's teaching in this paragraph than that. Muller was enabled to die to the world and its approval or censure, to die even to the approval or censure of his friends and most intimate companions. And we should notice the order in which he put it. First, it was the approval or censure of the world; then the approval or censure of his intimates and friends. But he said he had succeeded in doing both, and the secret of it, according to Muller, was that he had died to himself, to George Muller. There is no doubt that there is a very definite sequence in this matter. The furthest removed is the world, then come his friends and associates. But the most difficult thing is for a man to die to himself, to his own approval or censure of himself. There are many great artists who treat with disdain the opinion of the world. The world does not approve of their work? `So much the worse for the world', says the great artist. `Men are so ignorant they do not understand.' You can become immune to the opinion of the mass and the mob, to the world. But then there is the approval or censure of those who are near and dear to you, those who are intimately associated with you. You value their opinion more highly, and you are therefore more sensitive to it. But the Christian must reach the stage in which he surmounts even that and realizes that he must not be controlled by it. And then he goes on to the last, the ultimate stage which concerns what a man thinks of himself-his own assessment, his own approval of himself and his own judgment of himself'. You will find, in many a biography, stories of men who have delivered themselves from sensitivity to the world and to intimates, but who have found that it means a terrible battle, an almost impossible fight not to be concerned about one's self, and one's own judgment of one's self. And as long as we are concerned about that we are not really safe even from the other two. So the key to it all, as George Muller reminds us, is that we must die to ourselves. George Muller had died to himself, to his opinion, his preferences, his likes and dislikes, his tastes, his will. His one concern, his one idea, was to be approved unto God.

Now that is our Lord's teaching here, that the Christian is to get into such a state and condition that he can say that.

V The next point is obviously that only the Christian can do this. That is where we find doctrine in this paragraph. No man can possibly attain to this except a Christian. It is the very opposite and antithesis of what is true of the natural man. It is difficult to imagine anything further removed from what the world generally describes as a gentleman. A gentleman, according to the world, is one who fights for his honour and his name. Although he no longer challenges to a duel the moment he is insulted because it is prohibited by law, this is what he would do if he could. That is the world's idea of a gentleman and of honour; and it always means self-defence. It applies not only to man individually but to his country and to everything that belongs to him. It is surely true to say that the world despises a man who does not do that, and it admires the aggressive kind of person, the person who asserts himself and is always most ready to defend himself and his so-called honour. We say, therefore, plainly and without apology, that no man can implement this teaching who is not a Christian. A man must be born again and be a new creature before he can live like this. No man can die to himself except the man who can say, `I live; yet not I, but Christ liveth in me.' It is the doctrine of the rebirth. In other words our Lord says: `You have to live like that, but you can do so only when you have received the Holy Spirit and there is a new life in you. You have to become utterly different; you have to become entirely changed; you have to become a new being.' The world dislikes this teaching and would have us believe that in various ways man can approximate to it unaided. We used to hear a great deal about the `word of a sportsman', about being `a sport' and so on. We do not hear quite so much about that these days, for the obvious reason that we have found men who are famous as `sportsmen' and who, when they arc playing games, are full of a sense of honour and ready to stand aside and not consider themselves, figuring in Divorce Court cases, and displaying there a complete lack of honour, even a lack of ordinary decency, truthfulness, and the sense of right and fair play. Oh no, by being a `sportsman' you cannot live like this. This is something utterly removed from the world and its sport even at its very highest and best. It is something that is only possible for one who is regenerate, who has received the Spirit of the Lord Jesus Christ.

Having thus stated the doctrine, we must now ask a practical question. How am I to live like that? Someone may say: `You have confronted us with teaching; but I find it difficult, I tend to fail in practice. How can one live that kind of life?'

Let us, first of all, approach the matter on a purely practical level. The first thing we must do is to face this whole problem of the self in an honest manner. We must cease to make excuses, cease trying to evade and circumvent it. It is to be faced honestly and squarely. We must hold all this teaching before us and examine ourselves in the light of it. But it is not enough that we should do that in general only; we must do it in particular also. Whenever I notice in myself a reaction of self-defence, or a sense of annoyance or a grievance, or a feeling that I have been hurt and wronged and am suffering an injustice-the moment I feel this defensive mechanism coming into play, I must just quietly face myself and ask the following questions. `Why exactly does this thing upset me? Why am I grieved by it? What is my real concern at this point? Am I really concerned for some general principle of justice and righteousness? Am I really moved and disturbed because I have sonic true cause at heart or, let me face it honestly, is it just myself? Is it just this horrible, foul selfcentredness and self-concern, this morbid condition into which I have got? Is it nothing but an unhealthy and unpleasant pride?' Such self-examination is essential if we are to conquer in this matter. We all know this by experience. How easy it is to explain it in some other way. We must listen to the voice that speaks within us, and if it says: `Now you know perfectly well it is just yourself, that horrid pride, that concern about yourself and your reputation and your own greatness'-if it is that, we must admit and confess it. It will be extremely painful, of course; and yet, if we want to rise to our Lord's teaching, we have to pass through such a process. It is the denial of self.

Another thing on the practical level which is of the very greatest importance is to realize the extent to which self controls your life. Have you ever tried doing that? Examine yourself and your life, your ordinary work, the things you do, the contacts you have to make with people. Reflect for a moment upon the extent to which self comes into all that. It is an amazing and terrible discovery to note the extent to which self-interest and self-concern are involved, even in the preaching of the gospel. It is a horrible discovery. We are concerned about doing it well. Why? For the glory of God, or f or our own glory ? All the things we do and say, the impression we make even when we meet people casually-what are we really concerned about? If you analyse the whole of your life, not only your actions and conduct, but your dress, your appearance, everything, it will amaze you to discover the extent to which this unhealthy attitude towards self comes in.

But let us go one step further. I wonder whether we have ever realized the extent to which the misery and the unhappiness and the failure and the trouble in our lives is due to one thing only, namely self. Go back across last week, consider in your mind and recall to your conscience the moments or the periods of unhappiness and strain, your irritability, your bad temper, the things you have said and done of which you are now ashamed, the things that have really disturbed you and put you off your balance. Look at them one by one, and it will be surprising to discover how almost every one of them will come back to this question of self, this self sensitivity, this watching of self. There is no question about it. Self is the main cause of unhappiness in life. 'Ali', you say, `but it is not my fault; it is what somebody else has done.' All right; analyse yourself and the other person, and you will find the other person probably acted as he did because of self, and you are really feeling it for the same reason. If only you had a right attitude towards the other person, as our Lord goes on to teach in the next paragraph, you would be sorry for him and would be praying for him. So ultimately it is you who are to blame. Now it is a very good thing on the practical level just to look at it honestly and squarely. Most of the unhappiness and sorrow, and most of our troubles in life and in experience, arise from this ultimate origin and source, this self.

Let us come to a higher level, however, and look at it doctrinally. It is a very good thing to look at self in a doctrinal and theological manner. According to the teaching of Scripture, self was responsible for the fall. But for it, sin would never have entered into the world. The devil was subtle enough to know its power, so he put it in terms of self. He said: `God is not being fair to you; you have a legitimate grudge and a grievance.' And man agreed, and that was the whole cause of the fall. There would be no need of International Conferences to try to solve the problems of the nations at the present time if it were not for the fall. And the whole trouble is just self and self-assertion. That is self regarded doctrinally. But self always means defiance of God; it always means that I put myself on the throne instead of God, and therefore it is always something that separates me from Him.

All moments of unhappiness in life are ultimately due to this separation. A person who is in real communion with God and with the Lord Jesus Christ is happy. It does not matter whether he is in a dungeon, or whether he has his feet fast in the stocks, or whether he is burning at the stake; he is still happy if he is in communion with God. Is not that the experience of the saints down the centuries? So the ultimate cause of any misery or lack of joy is separation from God, and the one cause of separation from Him is self. Whenever we are unhappy it means that in some way or other we are looking at ourselves and thinking about ourselves, instead of communing with God. Man, according to the Scriptures, was meant to live entirely to the glory of God. He was meant to love the Lord God with all his heart, with all his soul, with all his mind and with all his strength. The whole of man was meant to glorify God. Therefore, any desire to glorify self or safeguard the interests of self is of necessity a sin, because I am looking at myself instead of looking at God and seeking His honour and glory. And it is that very thing in man which God has condemned. It is that which is under the curse of God and the wrath of God. And as I understand the teaching of the Scriptures, holiness eventually means this, deliverance from this self-centred life. Holiness, in other words, must not be thought of primarily in terms of actions, but in terms of an attitude towards self. It does not mean essentially that I do not do certain things and try to do others. There are people who never do certain things that are regarded as sinful; but they are full of pride of self. So we must look at it in terms of self and our relationship to ourselves, and we must realize again that the essence of holiness is that we should be able to say with George Muller that we have died, died completely, to this self that has caused so much ruin in our lives and experience.

Now, lastly, let us come to the highest level and look at the problem of self in the light of Christ. Why did the Lord Jesus Christ the Son of God ever come into this world? He came ultimately in order to deliver mankind from self. We see this selfless life so perfectly in Him. Look at His coming from the glory of heaven to the stable in Bethlehem. Why did He come? There is only one answer to that question. He did not consider Himself. That is the essence of the statement that Paul makes in Philippians ii. He was eternally the Son of God and was `equal with God' from eternity, but He did not consider that; He did not hold on to that and to His right to the manifestation of that glory. He humbled Himself and denied Himself. There would never have been the incarnation had it not been that the Son of God put self, as it were, aside.

Then look at His selfless life here upon earth. He often said that the words He spake He did not speak of Himself, and the actions He performed He said `are not mine; they have been given to me of the Father'. That is how I understand Paul's teaching of the self-humiliation of the cross. It means that, coming in the likeness of man, He deliberately made Himself dependent upon God; He did not consider Himself at all. He said: `I have come to do thy will, 0 God,' and He was wholly dependent upon God for everything, for the words He spoke and for everything He did. The very Son of God humbled Himself to that extent. He did not live for Himself or by Himself in any measure. And the apostle's argument is, `Let this mind be in you, which was also in Christ Jesus.'

We see it supremely of course in His death upon the cross. He was innocent and guiltless, He had never sinned or done anyone any harm, yet `when he was reviled, (he) reviled not again; when he suffered, he threatened not; but committed himself to him that judgeth righteously' (I Pet. ii. 23). That is it. The cross of Christ is the supreme illustration, and the argument of the New Testament is this, that if we say we believe in the Lord Jesus Christ and believe that He has died for our sins, it means that our greatest desire should be to die to self. That is the final purpose of His dying, not merely that we might be forgiven, or that we might be saved from hell. Rather it was that a new people might be formed, a new humanity, a new creation, and that a new kingdom be set up, consisting of people like Himself. He is `the firstborn among many brethren', He is the pattern. God has made us, says Paul to the Ephesians: `We are his workmanship, created in Christ Jesus.' We are `to be conformed to the image of his Son'. That is the language of Scripture. So that we may say that the reason for His death on the cross is that you and I might be saved and separated from that life of self. `He died for all', says the apostle again in 2 Corinthians v. We believe `that if one died for all, then were all dead; and that he died for all.' Why? For this reason, says Paul: `that they which live should not henceforth live unto themselves, but unto him which died for them, and rose again.' That is the life to which we are called. Not the life of self-defence or selfsensitivity, but such a life that, even if we are insulted, we do not retaliate; if we receive a blow on the right cheek we are ready to turn the other also; if a man sues us at the law and takes away our coat we are ready to give our cloak also; if we are compelled to go a mile, we go twain; if a man comes and asks something of me I do not say, `This is mine'; I say rather, `If this man is in need and I can help him, I will'. I have finished with self, I have died to myself, and my one concern now is the glory and lion our of God.

That is the life to which the Lord Jesus Christ calls us and He died in order that you and I might live it. Thank God the gospel also goes on to tell us that He rose again and that He has sent into the Church, and into every one who believes on Him, the Holy Spirit with all His renovating and energizing power. If we are trying to live this kind of life in and of ourselves, we are doomed; we are damned before we start. But with the blessed promise and offer of the Spirit of God to come and dwell in us and work in us, there is hope for us. God has made this life possible. If George Muller could die to George Muller, why should not every one of us who is a Christian die in the same way to that self that is so sinful, that leads to so much misery and wretchedness and unhappiness, and which finally is such a denial of the blessed work of the Son of God upon the cross on Calvary's hill.

CHAPTER TWENTY-NINE

LOVE YOUR ENEMIES

W E come now to verses 43-48 in which we have the last of the six illustrations which our Lord has used to explain and display His teaching with regard to the meaning of God's holy law for man, as contrasted with the perversion of it by the Pharisees and scribes. There is just one textual point which we must dismiss first. You will notice that in the Revised Version there is a slight difference in verse 44. In the Authorized Version we read: `But I say unto you, Love your enemies, bless them that curse you, do good to them that hate you, and pray for them which despitefully use you, and persecute you.' In the Revised Version it is just: `Love your enemies, and pray for them that persecute you.' The Authorized Version is therefore fuller than the Revised Version and contains a number of clauses which the latter lacks. The explanation of course is simply a matter of textual criticism. There are many ancient manuscripts containing the Gospels, and there are slight variations in them here and there, not with regard to any vital matter of doctrine, but with regard to certain details such as this. Now many of the recognized best manuscripts do not contain this fullness which is to be found in the Authorized Version, and that is why these statements are absent from the Revised. However, as the same teaching is certainly to be found elsewhere, I think it is best for us to take the teaching as given in the Authorized Version.

Once more, the way to approach this statement is to start with the teaching of the Pharisees and scribes. They said: `Thou shalt love thy neighbour, and hate thine enemy.' That was actually what they taught. The question at once arises in one's mind, where did they find this in the Old Testament? Is there anywhere there a statement to that effect? And the answer is, of course, `No'. But that was the teaching of the Pharisees and scribes and they interpreted it like this. They said that the `neighbour' meant only an Israelite; so they taught the Jews to love the Jews, but they told them at the same time to regard everybody else not only as an alien but as an enemy. Indeed they went so far as to suggest that it was their business, almost their right and their duty, to hate all such people. We know from secular history of the hatred and the bitterness which divided the ancient world. The Jews regarded all others as dogs and many Gentiles despised the Jews. There was this terrible `middle wall of partition' dividing the world and causing intense animosity in that way. Thus there were many amongst the zealous Pharisees and scribes who thought they were honouring God by despising everybody who was not a Jew. They thought it was their business to hate their enemies. But these two statements are not found in juxtaposition anywhere in the Old Testament.

Nevertheless, there does seem to be a certain amount to be said for the teaching of the Pharisees and scribes. It is not surprising in a sense that they taught what they did and tried to claim justification for it from the Scriptures. We must say this, not by any means because we are anxious to mitigate the crimes of the Pharisees and scribes, but because this point has often caused, and still causes, considerable difficulty in the minds of many Christian people. Nowhere in the Old Testament, I repeat, do we find `Love your neighbour and hate your enemy'; but we do find many statements that may have encouraged people to hate their enemies. Let us consider some of them.

When the Jews entered the Promised Land of Canaan, they were commanded by God, you will remember, to exterminate the Canaanites. They were literally told to exterminate them, and though they did not in fact do this, they should have done so. Then they were told that the Amorites, the Moabites and the Midianites were not to be treated with kindness. That was a specific command from God. Later we read that the memory of the Amalekites was to be blotted out from under heaven because of certain things they had done. Not only that, it was part of God's law that if any man murdered another, the relative of the murdered man was allowed to kill the murderer if he could catch him before he had entered one of the cities of refuge. That was part of the law. But perhaps the main difficulty which people encounter as they face this subject is the whole problem of the so-called imprecatory Psalms in which curses are called down upon certain people. Perhaps one of the most famous examples of this is Psalm lxix in which the Psalmist says: `Let their eyes be darkened, that they see not; and make their loins continually to shake. Pour out thine indignation upon them, and let thy wrathful anger take hold of them. Let their habitation be desolate; and let none dwell in their tents,' and so on. There can be little question but that it was Old Testament teaching of that type and order that seemed to the Pharisees and scribes to justify their injunction to the people that, while they were to love their neighbours, they must hate their enemies.

What is the answer to this problem? Surely there is only one way of facing it and that is to regard all these various injunctions, including the imprecatory Psalms, as always being judicial and never something individual. In writing his Psalms, the Psalmist is not so much writing about himself as about the Church; and his Psalms, you will find, are concerned in every single instance, in every imprecatory Psalm, with the glory of God. As he talks about the things that are being done to him, he is speaking of things that are being done to God's people and to God's Church. It is the honour of God that he is concerned about, it is his zeal for the house of God and for the Church of God that moves him to write these things.

But perhaps it can best be put like this. If you do not accept that principle which says that all these imprecations are always judicial in character, then at once you are involved in an insoluble problem with regard to the Lord Jesus Christ Himself. Here He is telling us we are to love our enemies. Turn then to Matthew xxiii and listen to Him thundering out woes upon the heads of the Pharisees. How do you reconcile the two things? How do you reconcile the exhortation to love your enemies with these woes pronounced upon the Pharisees, and all the other things that He said with respect to them? Or, indeed, let us look at it in this way. Here our Lord tells us to love our enemies, because, He says, that is exactly what God does: `That ye may be the children of your rather which is in heaven: for he maketh his sun to rise on the evil and on the good, and sendeth rain on the just and on the unjust.' There are people who have foolishly interpreted this to mean that the love of God is universal absolutely, and that it does not matter whether a man sins or not. Everybody is going to heaven because God is love; because God is love He can never punish. But that is to deny the teaching of Scripture from beginning to end. God punished Cain, and the ancient world in the flood; He punished the cities of Sodom and Gomorrah; and He punished the children of Israel when they were recalcitrant. Then the whole teaching of the New Testament from the lips of Christ Himself is that there is to be a final judgment, that, finally, all the impenitent are going to a lake of fire, to the place where `their worm dieth not, and the fire is not quenched'. If you do not accept this judicial principle, you must just say that there is a contradiction running right through not only the teaching of the Bible, but even through the teaching of the Lord Jesus Christ Himself; and that is an impossible position.

The way to resolve the problem, therefore, is this. We must recognize that, ultimately, there is this judicial element. While we are in this life and world, God does indeed cause His sun to rise on the evil and on the good, He blesses people who hate Him, and He does send rain upon those who defy Him. Yes, God goes on doing that. But at the same time He announces to them that, unless they repent, they shall finally be destroyed. Therefore there is no ultimate contradiction. People like the Moabites and the Amorites and the Midianites had deliberately rejected the things of God, and God, as God and as the righteous judge Eternal, pronounced judgment upon them. It is the prerogative of God to do that. But the difficulty with the Pharisees and scribes was that they did not draw that distinction. They took this judicial principle and put it into operation in their ordinary affairs and in their daily lives. They regarded this as ajustifica- tion, on their own part, for hating their enemies, hating anybody they disliked, or anybody who was offensive to them. Thus they deliberately destroyed the principle of God's law, which is this great principle of love.

Let us now consider this positively and perhaps it will throw still further light upon the matter. Our Lord, again contrasting the perverted teaching of the Pharisees and the scribes with His own teaching, says: `But I say unto you, Love your enemies.' Then, as an illustration: `Bless them that curse you, do good to them that hate you, and pray for them which despitefully use you, and persecute you.' Once more we are dealing with exactly the same principle as we had in verses 38-42. It is a definition of what the attitude of the Christian should be towards other people. In the previous paragraph we had that in a negative form, here we have it positively. There the position was that of a Christian man subjected to insults by others. They come and strike him a blow, and inflict other kinds of injury upon him. And all our Lord says in the previous paragraph is that you must not hit back. 'Ye have heard that it hath been said, An eye for an eye, and a tooth for a tooth: But I say unto you, That ye resist not evil.' That is the negative. Here, however, our Lord leaves that and goes on to the positive and it is, of course, the very climax of Christian living. Here He leads us on to one of the greatest and most glorious things that are to be found even in His own teaching. The principle that guides and governs our exposition, once more, is this simple and yet profound one of our attitude towards ourselves. It was the principle with which we expounded the previous paragraph. The only thing that enables a man not to hit back, to turn the other cheek and to go the second mile, to give his cloak as well as his coat when that is forcibly demanded, and to help others in desperate need, the vital thing is that a man should be dead to himself, dead to self-interest, dead to a concern about self. But our Lord goes very much further here. We are told we must positively love these people. We are even to love our enemies. It is not simply that we are not to strike back at them, but that we must be positive in our attitude towards them. Our Lord is at pains to have us see that our `neighbour' must of necessity include even our enemy.

The best way of facing this is to see it in the form of a number of principles. It is the most exalted teaching that we can find anywhere, for it ends on this note: `Be ye therefore perfect, even as your Father which is in heaven is perfect.' It all concerns this matter of love. What we are told, therefore, is that you and I in this world of time, faced as we are by problems and difficulties and people and many things that assail us, are to behave as God behaves, are to be like Him, and to treat others as He treats them. Do this, says Christ, `that ye may be the children of your Father which is in heaven: for he maketh his sun to rise on the evil and on the good, and sendeth rain on the just and on the unjust.' You are to be like that, He says, and to behave like that.

What does this mean? The first thing, of necessity, is that our treatment of others must never depend upon what they are, or upon what they do to us. It must be entirely controlled and governed by our view of them and of their condition. Clearly that is the principle which He enunciates. There are people who are evil, foul and unjust; nevertheless God sends rain upon them and causes the sun to shine upon them. Their crops are fructified like the crops of the good man; they have certain benefits in life, and experience what is called `common grace'. God does not bless only the efforts of the Christian farmer; no, at the same time He blesses the efforts of the unjust, the evil, the unrighteous farmer. That is a common experience. How does He do so? The answer must be that God is not dealing with them according to what they are or according to what they do to Him. What is it, if one may ask such a question with reverence, that governs God's attitude to them? The answer is that He is governed by His own love which is absolutely disinterested. In other words, it does not depend upon anything that is in us, it is in spite of us. `For God so loved the world, that he gave his only begotten Son, that whosoever believeth in him should not perish, but have everlasting life.' What made Him do it? Was it something loving, or lovely, or lovable in us or in the world? Was it something that stimulated the eternal heart of love? Nothing whatsoever. It was entirely and altogether in spite of us. What moved God was His own eternal heart of love unmoved by anything outside itself. It generates its own movement and activity-an utterly disinterested love.

This is a tremendously important principle, because according to our Lord that is the kind of love that we are to have, and the love that we are to manifest with respect to others. The whole secret of living this kind of life is that man should be utterly detached. He must be detached from others in the sense that his behaviour is not governed by what they do. But still more important, he should be detached from himself, for until a man is detached from himself he will never be detached from what others do to that self. As long as a man is living for himself, he is sensitive, watchful and jealous; he is envious and is therefore always reacting

363

immediately to what others do. He is in intimate contact with them. The only way to detach yourself from what others do to you is that you first of all detach yourself from yourself. That is the principle that governs not only this paragraph but the previous one also, as we have already seen. The Christian is a man who is taken out of this present evil world. He is placed in a position apart and lives on a higher level. He belongs to a different kingdom. He is a new man, a new creature, a new creation. Because of that, he sees everything differently, and therefore reacts in a different manner. He is no longer of the world, but outside it. He is in a position of detachment. `There', says Christ, `you can become like God in this respect, that you will no longer be governed exclusively by what other people do to you; you will have something within you that will determine your conduct and behaviour.'

We must not linger over this; but I think that, if we examine ourselves, we shall see at a glance that one of the most tragic things about us is that our lives are so much governed by other people and by what they do to us and think about us. Try to recall a single day in your own life. Think of the unkind and cruel thoughts that have come into your mind and heart. What produced them? Somebody else! How much of our thinking and acting and behaviour is entirely governed by other people. It is one of the things that make life so wretched. You see a particular person and your spirit is upset. If you had not seen that person you would not have felt like that. Other people are controlling you. `Now', says Christ in effect, `you must get out of that condition. Your love must become such that you will no longer be governed and controlled by what people say. Your life must be governed by a new principle in yourself, a new principle of love.'

The moment we have that, we are enabled to see people in a different way. God looks down upon this world and sees all the sin and shame, but He sees it as something that results from the activity of Satan. There is a sense in which He sees the unjust man in a different way. He is concerned about him and about his good and welfare, and He therefore causes the sun to shine upon him and sends the rain upon him. Now we must learn to do that. We must learn to look at other people and say: `Yes, they are doing this, that and the other to me. Why? They are doing it because they are dupes of Satan; because they are governed by the god of this world and are his helpless victims. I must not be annoyed. I see them as hell-bound sinners. I must do everything I can to save them.' That is God's way of doing it. God looked at this sinful, arrogant, foul world, and He sent His only begotten Son into it to save it because He saw its condition. What was the explanation of that? He did it for our good and our welfare. And we must learn to do this for other people. We must have a positive concern for their good. The moment we begin to think of it like this it is not so difficult to do what He asks us to do. If we know in our hearts something of this compassion for the lost and the sinful and those who are perishing, then we shall be able to do it.

Why should we do this? There is often a great deal of sentimentalizing about this. People say we should do it in order to turn them into friends. That is often the basis of pacifism. They say: `If you are nice to people they will become nice to you.' There were people who thought that could be done even with Hitler. They thought that you simply had to speak to him across a table and he would soon become nice if you were nice to him. There are people who still think that way; but let us be realists, not sentimentalists, because we know that that is not true and it does not work. No, our action is not aimed at turning them into friends.

Others say, `God regards and treats them not so much as they actually are, but in terms of what they are capable of becoming.' That is the modern psychological view of this matter. It governs the way in which some school-teachers handle children. They must not punish them or exercise discipline. They must not treat children as they are, but rather as they ought to be and as they are capable of becoming, in order that they may become that. Some would like to see the same principle put into operation more widely with regard to the treatment of prisoners in prison. We must not punish, we must just be nice. We must see in that man what he can become, and we must draw it out of him. But what of the results? No; it is not because our action will somehow change these people psychologically and turn them into what we want them to be, that we are to do these things. We must do them for one reason only, not that we can ever redeem or make anything of them, but that in this way we can display to them the love of God. It is not looking for that spark of divinity in the heart which would save it, and then fanning it into a flame. No, men are born in sin and shapen in iniquity, they are not capable, in and of themselves, of becoming anything that is right. But God has so ordained it that His wonderful gospel of redemption has sometimes been conveyed to men and women in the following manner. They look at a person and ask: `What has made that person different?' and that person says: `I am what I am by the grace of God. It is not because I am born different, it is because God has done something to me. And what the love of God has done to me, it can do for you.'

How then may we manifest this love of God in our contact with other people? Here it is: `Bless them that curse you', which, in more ordinary language, we put like this: reply to the bitter words with kind words. When people say harsh and unkind things we all tend to reply in kind-'I told him; I answered him; I gave it to him'. And so we put ourselves on their level. But our rule must be kind words instead of bitter words.

Secondly: `Do good to them that hate you', which means benevolent actions for spiteful actions. When somebody has been really spiteful and cruel to us we must not be the same to them. Rather we must respond with actions of benevolence. Though that farmer may hate God, and is unjust, and is a sinner, and has rebelled against Him, God causes His sun to shine upon hies and sends the rain that is going to fructify the crops. Benevolent actions for cruel ones.

Lastly: `Pray for them which despitefully use you, and persecute you.' In other words, when we are being cruelly persecuted by another person, we must pray for them. We must get on our knees, and talk to ourselves before we talk to God. Instead of being bitter and harsh, instead of reacting in these terms of self and in a desire to get our own back, we must remind ourselves that in everything we do we are under God, and before God. Then we must say: `Well now; why should this person be behaving like this? What is it? Is it something in me, perchance? Why do they do it? It is because of that horrible, sinful nature, a nature which is going to lead them to hell.' Then we should go on thinking, until we see them in such a way that we become sorry for them, until we see them as going to their terrible doom, and at last become so sorry for them that we have no time to be sorry for ourselves, until we are so sorry for them, indeed, that we begin to pray for them.

This is the way in which we should test ourselves. Do you pray for people who persecute you and who use you despitefully? Do you ask God to have mercy and pity upon them, and not to punish them? Do you ask God to save their souls and open their eyes before it is too late? Do you feel a great concern? It is that which brought Christ to earth and sent Him to the cross. He was so concerned about us that He did not think about Himself. And we are to treat other people like that.

In order that we may be quite clear as to what this means and involves we must understand the difference between loving and liking. Christ said: `Love your enemies,' not `Like your enemies'. Now liking is something which is more natural than loving. We are not called upon to like everybody. We cannot do so. But we can be commanded to love. It is ridiculous to command anyone to like another person. It depends upon the physical constitution, temperament and a thousand and one other things. That does not matter. What does matter is that we pray for the man whom we do not like. That is not liking but loving him.

Pcr.ple have stumbled at this. `Do you mean to say that it is right to love and not to like?' they ask. I do. What God commands is that we should love a man and treat him as if we do like him. Love is much more than feeling or sentiment. Love in the New Testament is very practical-'For this is the love of God, that we keep his commandments.' Love is active. If, therefore, we find we do not like certain people, we need not be worried by that, so long as we are treating them as if we did like them. That is loving, and it is the teaching of our Lord everywhere. We have some glorious examples of it in the New Testament. You remember the parable of the Good Samaritan told by our Lord in response to the question `who is my neighbour?' The Jews traditionally hated the Samaritans and were their bitter enemies. However our Lord tells us in the parable that when the Jew was attacked by thieves and robbers on the road between Jericho and Jerusalem, several Jews passed by and did not help him. But the Samaritan, the traditional enemy, went across the road and cared for him and did everything for him. That is loving our neighbour and our enemy. Who is my neighbour? Any man who is in need, any man who is down through sin or anything else. We must help him, whether he is a Jew or a Samaritan. Love your neighbour, even if it means loving your enemy. `Do good to them that hate you.' And our Lord, of course, not only taught it, but He did it. There we see Him dying upon the cross, and what has He to say about those men who condemned Him to that, and who drove in the cruel nails? These are the blessed words that come from His holy lips: `Father, forgive them; for they know not what they do.'

It also became the teaching and the practice of the apostles everywhere in the New Testament. How foolish to say that the Sermon on the Mount does not apply to Christians now but refers to the future, when the kingdom comes. No, it is for us now. Paul says: `If thine enemy hunger, feed him; if he thirst, give him drink', which is exactly the same teaching. It is everywhere. And the apostles not only taught it; they lived it. Look at that wonderful man, Stephen, being stoned to death by cruel, foolish enemies. These were his last words: `Lord, lay not this sin to their charge.' He has reached the level of his Master; he is loving, as God in heaven loves this sinful world. And, thank God, the saints throughout the centuries have done the same. They have manifested the same, glorious, wonderful spirit.

Are we like that? This teaching is for us. We are meant to love our enemies and to do good to them that hate us and to pray for those that despitefully use and malign us; we are meant to be like this. I go further; we can be like this. The Holy Spirit, the Spirit of love and joy and peace, is given to us, so that, if we are not like this, we are without excuse and we are doing great dishonour to our great and gracious Lord.

But I have a word of comfort for you. For unless I am greatly mistaken, every person confronted by these things feels at this moment condemned. God knows I feel condemned; but I have a word of comfort at this point. I believe in a God who `maketh his sun to rise on the evil and on the good, and sendeth rani on the just and on the unjust'. But the God whoiui I know has done more than that; He has sent His only begotten Son to the cruel cross of Calvary that I might be saved. I fail; we all fail. But, `It we confess our sins, lie is faithful and just to forgive us our sins, and to cleanse us from all unrightcousness.' Do not feel that you are not a Christian if you are not living this kind of life fully. But, above all, having received this comfort, do not presume upon it, but rather feel that it breaks your heart still more because you are not like Christ, and not as you ought to be. If only we all might begin to love like this, and every Christian in the world were loving in this way! If we (lid, revival would soon come, and who knows what might happen even in the whole world.

`Love your enemies, bless them that curse you, do good to them that hate you, and pray for them which despitefully use you, and persecute you,' and then you will be like your Father who is in heaven.

CHAPTER THIRTY

WHAT DO YE MORE THAN OTHERS?

I'N our study of this paragraph concerning our attitude towards our enemies, let us now concentrate in particular .upon one phrase, `What do ye more than others?', which is to be found in verse 47: `And if ye salute your brethren only, what do ye more than others? do not even the publicans so?' Having given His detailed exposition of how His people should treat and regard their enemies, our Lord, as it were, brings the entire section and the whole teaching to a grand and glorious climax. All along, as we have seen, He has not been concerned so much about the details of their behaviour; rather, His desire has been that they should understand and grasp who they are and how they are to live. And here He sums it all up in this amazing statement that comes right at the very end: `Be ye therefore perfect, even as your Father which is in heaven is perfect.' That is to be the quality of life we are to live.

There is no attitude with regard to the Sermon on the Mount which is quite so ridiculous as that which regards it as if it were but an ethical programme, a kind of social scheme. We have already considered that, but we must return to it, because it seems to me that this paragraph alone is enough to explode once and for ever any such false notion with respect to this great Sermon. This one paragraph contains what we might call the most essential characteristic of the New Testament gospel in its entirety, and that is the paradox which runs right through it. The gospel ofJesus Christ, though I object to much modern use of the term, is essentially paradoxical; there is an apparent contradiction in it from the beginning to the very end. We find that here, in the very essence of this message.

The paradoxical character of the gospel was first stated by that ancient man, Simeon, when he had the Infant Jesus in his arms. He said, `This child is set for the fall and rising again of many in Israel.' There is the paradox. At one and the same time He is set for the fall and for the rising again. The gospel always does these two things, and unless our view of it contains these two elements, it is not a true one. Here is a perfect illustration of it. Have we not felt that as we have been working our way through this Sermon? Is there anything known to us that is more discouraging than the Sermon on the Mount? Take this passage from verse 17 to the end of this fifth chapter-these detailed illustrations given by our Lord as to how we are to live. Is there anything more discouraging? We feel that the Ten Commandments, the ordinary moral standards of decency, are difficult enough; but look at these statements about not even looking with lust, about going the second mile and throwing in the cloak together with the coat, and so on. There is nothing more discouraging than the Sermon on the Mount; it seems to throw us right out, and to damn our every effort before we have started. It seems utterly impossible. But at the same time do we know of anything more encouraging than the Sermon on the Mount? Do we know of anything that pays us a greater compliment? The very fact that we are commanded to do these things carries with it an implicit assertion that it is possible. This is what we are supposed to be doing; and there is a suggestion, therefore, that this is what we can do. It is discouraging and encouraging at the same time; it is set for the fall and rising again. And nothing is more vital than that we should always be holding those two aspects firmly in our minds.

The trouble with that foolish, so-called materialistic view of the Sermon on the Mount was that it did not see either side of the Sermon clearly. It reduced both of them. In the first place it reduced the demands. Those who held it said: `The Sermon on the Mount is something practical, something that we can do.' Well, the answer to such people is that what we are asked to do is to be as perfect as God, as perfect in this matter of loving our enemies as He is. And the moment we face the actual demands, we see that they are quite impossible to the natural man. But these people have never seen that. What they have done, of course, is just to isolate certain statements and say: `This is all we have to do.' They do not believe in fighting under any circumstances. They say, `We are to love our enemies'; so they just become passive resisters. But that is not the whole of the Sermon on the Mount. The Sermon on the Mount includes this injunction: Be ye therefore perfect, even as your Father which is in heaven is perfect.' They have never faced the stringency of the demand.

At the same time they have never seen the other side, which is that we are children of God, and are unusual and exceptional. They have never seen the glory and grandeur and the uniqueness of the Christian position. They have always thought of the Christian as just a man who makes a greater moral effort than anyone else and disciplines himself. In other words, most of the trouble experienced by such people with this Sermon on the Mount, as indeed with the whole of the New Testament teaching, is that they never truly understand or grasp what it means to be a Christian. That is the fundamental trouble. People who are in difficulty about salvation in Christ are in this difficulty because they have never understood what a Christian really is.

In this phrase we have, once more, one of those perfect definitions as to what constitutes a Christian. The dual aspect is displayed; discouragement and encouragement; the fall and the rising again. Here it is: `What do ye more than others?' Now here there is real value in Dr. Moffatt's translation, `If you only salute your friends, what is special about that?' That is the key to it all. We find this thought not only here but also in verse 20. Our Lord started by saying: `I say unto you, That except your righteousness shall exceed the righteousness of the scribes and Pharisees. . . .' The Pharisees and scribes had a high and exalted standard, but the righteousness in view here is more than their righteousness; there is something special about it.

Let us consider this great principle in the form of three subsidiary principles. The Christian is essentially a unique and special kind of person. This is something which can never be emphasized sufficiently. There is nothing more tragic than the failure on the part of many professing Christians to realize the uniqueness and the special character of a Christian. He is a man who can never be explained in natural terms. The very essence of the Christian's position is that he is an enigma. There is something unusual, something inexplicable and something elusive about him from the standpoint of the natural man. He is something quite distinct and apart.

Now our Lord tells us here that this special characteristic, this uniqueness, is twofold. First of all it is a uniqueness that separates him from everybody who is not a Christian. `If ye love them which love you, what reward have ye? do not even the publicans the same?' They can do that, but you are different. `And if ye salute your brethren only, what do ye more than others? do not even the publicans so?' (So reads the Authorized Version; the Revised Version has `Do not even the Gentiles the same?') The Christian, you see, is a man who is different from others. He does what other people do, yes; but he does more than they do. That is what our Lord has been emphasizing all along. Anyone can go the first mile, but it is the Christian who goes the second. He is always doing more than anybody else. This is obviously tremendously important. The Christian at once, and by primary definition, is a man who stands out in society, and you cannot explain him in terms of the natural man.

However, we must go beyond that. The Christian, by our Lord's definition, and it is repeated elsewhere right through the New Testament, is not only a man who is doing more than others; lie does what others cannot do. That is not to detract from the capacity and ability of the natural man; but the Christian is a man who can do things which nobody else can do. We can emphasize that still more by putting it like this. The Christian is a man who is above, and goes beyond, the natural man at his very best and highest. Our Lord showed that here in His attitude towards the standard of morality and behaviour of the Pharisees and scribes. They were the teachers of the people, and they exhorted everybody else. He says to those who listened: `You must go beyond all that.' And we must go beyond it also. There are many people in the world who are not Christian but who are very moral and highly ethical, men whose word is their bond, and who are scrupulous and honest, just and upright. You never find them doing a shady thing to anybody; but they are not Christian, and they say so. They do not believe on the Lord Jesus Christ and may have rejected the whole of the New Testament teaching with scorn. But they are absolutely straightforward, honest and true. As

What about your thoughts?' That is the view of the Christian man. Not actions only, he goes beyond that to the heart.

What about the attitude of these two men towards themselves? The natural man is prepared to admit that perhaps he is not entirely perfect. He says: `You know I am not a complete saint, there are certain defects in my character.' But you will never find a man who is not a Christian feeling that he is all wrong, that he is vile. He is never `poor in spirit', he never `mourns' because of his sinfulness. He never sees himself as a hell-deserving sinner. He never says, `Were it not for the death of Christ on the cross, I would have no hope of seeing God.' He will never say with Charles Wesley, `Vile and full of sin I am'. He regards that as an insult, because he claims that he has always tried to live a good life. He therefore resents that and does not go as far as that in his self-condemnation.

Then what about the attitude of these two men towards other people? Your natural man may regard others with tolerance; he may bring himself to be sorry for them and say that we must not be too hard on others. But the Christian goes beyond that. He sees them as sinners, and as the dupes of Satan; he sees them as the terrible victims of sin. He does not merely see them as men for whom allowances are to be made; he sees them as dominated by `the god of this world' and held captive by Satan in all his various forms. He goes beyond the other.

The same is true of their respective views of God. The natural man thinks of God primarily as Someone who is to be obeyed, and Someone whom he fears. That is not the essential view of the Christian. The Christian loves God because he has come to know Him as Father. He does not think of God as One whose law is grievous and hard. He knows He is a holy yet loving God, and he enters into a new relationship with Him. He goes beyond everybody in his relationship to God, and desires to love Him with all his heart, and mind, and soul, and strength, and his neighbour as himself.

Then in the matter of living, the way in which the Christian does everything is different. The great motive to Christian living is love. Paul puts it in a remarkable way when he says: `Love is the fulfilling of the law.' The difference between your naturally good, moral man and the Christian is that the Christian has an element of grace in his actions; he is an artist, while the other man acts mechanically. What is the difference between the Christian and the natural man in doing good? Well, the natural man often does a great deal of good in this world, but I hope I am not being unfair to him when I say that he generally likes to keep a record of it. He is rather subtle sometimes in the indirect way in which he refers to it, but he is always conscious of it, and keeps an account of it. One hand always knows what the other hand is doing. Not only that, there is always a limit to what he does. He generally gives out of his superabundance. It is the Christian who gives without counting the cost, who gives sacrificially and in such a way that each hand does not know what the other is doing.

But look at these two men as they react to what happens to them in this life and world. What about the trials and tribulations that come, as they must come, such as sickness or war? The good, natural, moral man often faces these things with real dignity. He is always a gentleman. Yes; by exercising an iron will-power, he faces it with a stoical kind of resignation. I do not want to detract from his qualities, but he is always negative, he is just holding himself in check. He does not complain, he is just bottling it up as it were. Does he ever know what it is to rejoice in tribulation? The Christian does. The Christian rejoices in tribulations for he sees a hidden meaning in them. He knows that `all things work together for good to them that love God', and that God allows things to happen at times in order to perfect him. He can wrestle with the storm, he can rejoice in the midst of his tribulation. The other man never rises to that. There is something special about the Christian. The other man just maintains his calm and dignity. You see the difference?

Our Lord puts it here finally in the matter of injuries and injustice. How does your natural man behave when he suffers these? Again, he may face it with this calm and iron will. He just manages not to hit back and retaliate. He merely ignores it all, or cynically dismisses the person who misunderstands him. But the Christian deliberately takes up the cross, and holds to Christ's injunction which tells him to `deny himself, and take up his cross'. `He who will come after me', says Christ in effect, `is certain to get persecution, and to suffer injuries. But take up the cross.' And here He tells us how we are to do these things. He says: `Whosoever shall smite thee on thy right cheek, turn to him the other also. And if any man will sue thee at the law, and take away thy coat, let him have thy cloke also. And whosoever shall compel thee to go a mile, go with him twain. Give to him that asketh thee, and from him that would borrow of thee turn not thou away.' And he is to do it all gladly and willingly. That is the Christian. There is something special about him, he is always going further than anybody else.

The same is true of our attitude towards our neighbour, even if he is our enemy. The natural man can sometimes be passive. He can decide not to strike back and hit back, but not easily. Once more, there has never been a natural man who has been able to love his enemy, to do good to them that hate him, to bless them that curse him, and to pray for them that despitefully use him and persecute him. I do not want to be unfair in what I am saying. I have known men who call themselves pacifists and who would not hit back, or kill; but I have sometimes known bitterness in their hearts against men who have been in the Forces and against certain Prime Ministers, which was simply terrible. Loving your enemy does not just mean that you do not fight and kill. It means that you are positively loving that enemy and praying for him and for his salvation. I have known men who would not fight, but who do not love even their brethren. It is the Christian alone who can rise to this. Your natural ethics and morality can make a passive resister; but the Christian is a man who positively loves his enemy, and goes out of his way to do good to them that hate him, and to pray for them that use him despitefully and malign him.

But finally let us look at these two men as they die. The natural man, again, may die with dignity. He may die on his death-bed, or on the field of battle, without a grumble, or without complaining. He maintains the same general attitude to death as he had to life, and he goes out with stoical calm and resignation. That is not the Christian's way of facing death. The Christian is one who should be able to face death as Paul faced it, and he should be able to say: `To me to live is Christ, and to die is gain', and: `having a desire to depart, and to be with Christ; which is far better.' He is entering into his eternal home, going into the presence of' God. Even more, the Christian not only dies gloriously and triumphantly; he knows where he is going. He is not only not afraid; there is a sense of anticipation. There is always something special about him.

What is it that thus makes the Christian a special person? What is it that accounts for this uniqueness? What makes him do more than others? It is his whole outlook on sin. The Christian man has seen himself as utterly hopeless and condemned; he has seen himself as a man who is utterly guilty before God and who has no claim whatsoever on His love. He has seen himself as an enemy of God and an outsider. And then he has seen and understood something about the free grace of God in Jesus Christ. He has seen God sending His only begotten Son into the world, and not only that, sending Him even to the death of the cross for him, the rebel, the vile and guilty sinner. God did not turn His back on him, He went beyond that. The Christian knows that all this happened for him, and it has changed his whole attitude towards God and to his fellow men. He has been forgiven when he did not deserve it. What right then has he, not to forgive his enemy?

Not only that, he has an entirely new outlook towards life in this world. He comes to see that it is only an antechamber to real life and that he himself is a sojourner and a pilgrim. Like all the men of faith described in Hebrews xi he is seeking that `city which bath foundations'. He says: `Here have we no continuing city, but we seek one to come.' That is his whole view of life, and it changes everything. He has also a hope of glory. The Christian is a man who believes he is going to look into the face of Christ. And when that great morning comes, when he looks into the face of One who endured the cruel cross for him in spite of his vileness, he does not want to remember, as he looks into those eyes, that he refused to forgive someone while he was here on earth, or that he did not love that other person, but despised and hated him and did everything he could against him. He does not want to be reminded of things like that. So, knowing all this, he loves his enemies and does good to them that hate him, because he is conscious of what has been done for him, what is coming to him, and of the glory that remains. His whole outlook has been changed; and this has happened because he himself has been changed.

What is a Christian? A Christian is not a man who reads the Sermon on the Mount and says: `Now I am going to live like that, I am going to follow Christ and emulate His example. There is the life I am going to live and I shall do so by my great will-power.' Nothing of the kind. I will tell you what a Christian is. He is one who has become a child of God and is in a unique relationship to God. That is what makes him `special'. `What do ye more than others?' He should be special, you should be special, because you are a special person. You say breeding counts. If this is so, what is the breeding of a Christian? It is this, he has been born again, he has been born spiritually and he is a child of God. Did you notice the way our Lord puts it? `I say unto you, Love your enemies, bless them that curse you, do good to them that hate you, and pray for them which despitefully use you, and persecute you.' Why? `That you may be like God'? No: `That ye may be the children'-and not even of God-'ye may be the children of your Father which is in heaven'. God has become Father to the Christian. He is not the Father of the non-Christian; He is God to them and nothing else, the great Law-Giver. But to the Christian, God is Father. Then, again, our Lord does not say, Be ye therefore perfect, even as God in heaven is perfect.' No, thank God, but `Be ye therefore perfect, even as your Father which is in heaven is perfect.' If God is your Father you must be special, you cannot help it. If the divine nature is in you, and has entered into you through the Holy Spirit, you cannot be like anybody else; you must be different. And that is what we are told about the Christian everywhere in the Bible, that Christ dwells in his heart richly through the Holy Ghost. The Holy Spirit is in him, filling him, working His mighty power in the depths of his personality, teaching him His will. `It is God which worketh in you both to will and to do.' And, above all, the love of God has been shed abroad in his heart through and by the Holy Spirit. He is bound to be special, he must be unique, he cannot help it.

How can a man who has never had the love of God shed abroad in his heart love his enemy and do all these other things? It is impossible. He cannot do it; and furthermore he does not do it. "There never has been a man outside Christ who can do this. The Sermon is not an exorbitant demand of this kind. When you first read it, it discourages you and casts you down. But then it reminds you that you are a child of your Father in heaven, that you are not just left to yourself but that Christ has come to dwell in you and to take up His abode in you. You are but a branch of the Vine. Power and life and sustenance are there; you are simply to bear the fruit.

I end, then, with this searching question. It is the most profound question a man can ever face in this life and world. Is there anything special about you? I am not asking whether you are living a good, moral, upright life. I am not asking whether you say your prayers, or whether you go to church regularly. I am asking none of these things. There are people who do all that and still are not Christians. If that is all, what do ye more than others, what is there special about you? Is there anything of this special quality about you? Is there something of your Father about you? It is a fact that children sometimes do not resemble their parents very closely. People look at them and say: `Yes, there is something of his father there after all,' or `I see something of the mother; not very much, but there is something.' Is there just that much of God about you? That is the test. If God is your Father, somewhere or another, in some form or other, the family likeness will be there, the traces of your Parentage will inevitably appear. What is there special about you? God grant that as we examine ourselves we may discover something of the uniqueness and the separateness that not only divides us from others, but which proclaims that we are children of our Father which is in heaven.